Fundamentals of Arithmetic for Teachers

Fundamentals of Arithmetic for Teachers

Clifford Bell, *University of California, Los Angeles*

Clela D. Hammond, *El Camino College*

Robert B. Herrera, *Los Angeles City College*

John Wiley and Sons, Inc.

New York · London

SECOND PRINTING, MAY, 1963

Library of Congress Catalog Card Number: 62-10915
Printed in the United States of America

Preface

The material in this book includes the topics covered in a course in arithmetic presented by members of the Mathematics Department of the University of California, Los Angeles, for sophomore and upper division students in the elementary education curriculum. The course has been presented by the authors, at the university and elsewhere, for more than a decade, and by agreement with members of the education department of the university the emphasis has been on content and concepts of elementary arithmetic.

Content and concepts, as referred to here, are not mutually exclusive. Content includes (1) competence in work involving fundamental operations with natural numbers, fractions, decimal fractions, and per cent; (2) knowledge of prime numbers, divisibility, elementary algebra, and mensuration in geometry; (3) acquaintance with applications to consumer arithmetic, measurement, approximate numbers, and denominate numbers; and (4) appreciation of mathematical ideas. The concepts emphasized are (1) the nature of number and of number systems, place value, base ten and exponent notation, the use of other number bases, and operations with numbers in other bases; (2) understanding of the postulates of the rational number field and of the real number system; and (3) understanding the underlying meanings of operations with natural numbers and with fractions. One of the principal objectives of the book is to give students an appreciation of numbers, and of operations with them, as well as an understanding of the over-all structure of mathematics. Careful attention to problem solving is also a major concern of the book.

The first chapter of the book presents a survey of some of the main ideas to be explored in subsequent chapters. During a first reading this chapter serves as an overview; subsequently, it serves as a summary or as a review. Chapters 2 to 6 present a systematic development of number and its representation, number scales or bases, and operations with the natural numbers. Following this there are two chapters on work with natural numbers, Chapter 7 on the concepts of divisibility and Chapter 8 on applications to the measurement of area and volume. Meanings of fractions and operations with fractions are developed next, after which work with decimal fractions and operations with decimal fractions are discussed. Per cent and its applications are followed by a review of fundamental operations and of mental arithmetic. A study of approximate numbers and their applications to problems of measurement are taken up next, and the main body of elementary arithmetic is rounded out with a discussion of denominate numbers.

Additional topics which are desirable as supplementary material are covered in chapters on simple and compound interest, elementary algebra, square root and the Pythagorean theorem, and intuitive geometry.

Included in the appendix is a discussion of many visual aids useful in teaching arithmetic in the elementary school. We believe that this material should be brought to the attention of prospective teachers while they are taking a course in arithmetic content. These students should have an opportunity to observe the elementary classroom in session and should become familiar with some of the materials that have proved to be helpful. This work might be considered optional in a content course, but it is felt that there is no unnecessary duplication if it is given some attention. We have consistently used visual aids in teaching our sections of the course in arithmetic for teachers, and it has been our experience that students have found this work most valuable in actual application.

Los Angeles, California
January 1962

CLIFFORD BELL
CLELA D. HAMMOND
ROBERT B. HERRERA

Contents

1

Arithmetic and the Teacher

1.1 INTRODUCTION

The teacher in the elementary school is the person most directly responsible for acquainting growing children with a systematic account of the world of number, size, and form. With the complexity of modern-day science, business, and technology there goes an increasing responsibility for the systematic development of number concepts. As a result, there is a mounting need for teachers to have broad acquaintance with content and method in arithmetic, especially since points of view in both areas are changing. During the last decade considerable attention has been given to the development of pupils' understanding of arithmetic by the use of visual aids such as diagrams, charts, markers, and concrete materials. It is expected that this trend will continue and that added emphasis will be placed on concepts underlying the structure of number systems and the nature of fundamental operations in arithmetic. Studies in which experimental materials are used in the junior high school and the elementary school are making it clear that children can appreciate the general ideas of mathematics and work with them at an early age. There are indications that traditional topics of the fourth, fifth, and sixth grades may well be supplemented by new material on the structure of number systems and on the principles underlying mathematical operations. The teacher in the elementary school will thus find the opportunity to promote understanding and appreciation of mathematical ideas in work in arithmetic. Throughout this book an effort has been made to present the elementary teacher with a background of mathematical information and a variety of mathematical experience.

1.2 WHAT IS ARITHMETIC?

Arithmetic may be defined as the science that deals with numbers and with relations between numbers. Numbers, in turn, are abstractions arising from such concrete situations as counting, measuring, and ordering the various quantities and objects that we encounter in everyday life. As the science of numbers, arithmetic rests upon the fundamental notions of counting and one-to-one correspondence. Arithmetic, then, is a part of the broader science called mathematics, which treats of quantitative aspects of space, time, and matter. Mathematics also includes the study of abstract systems, which are made up of sets of objects and the relations between these objects. The concepts of "sets" and "relations" are discussed at various points in the book.

The branch of mathematics called *algebra* comprehends a more general treatment of numbers and number relations than does arithmetic. Arithmetic is concerned with such specific situations as the following facts:

$$3 + 5 = 8 \quad \text{and} \quad 3 \times 5 = 15;$$

it also deals with *principles* such as those illustrated by these statements:

$$\textit{if } 3 + 4 = 7, \textit{ then } 4 + 3 = 7, \quad \text{and} \quad \textit{if } 3 \times 4 = 12, \textit{ then } 4 \times 3 = 12.$$

Algebra is concerned with general statements about numerical situations; for example,

$$\textit{rate} \text{ times } \textit{time} \text{ equals } \textit{distance}, \quad \text{or} \quad R \times T = D.$$

It deals with general principles such as the following:

$$\textit{if } a + b = c, \textit{ then } b + a = c, \quad \text{and} \quad \textit{if } f \times g = h, \textit{ then } g \times f = h,$$

where a, b, c, f, g, and h are any numbers or quantities chosen from a given set or collection of quantities. Much of the work in algebra is based on the use of formulas and the solution of equations, both of which involve statements of relations among quantities. The elements used in these statements must satisfy certain basic assumptions. Arithmetic is a substructure of algebra in which the elements are the natural numbers, zero, common fractions, and decimal fractions. The operations in arithmetic are generally limited to those that will yield elements of these same kinds.

Mathematics also includes *geometry*, in which the relations of certain elements in the plane and in space are studied. The elements of geometry are points, lines, and planes, and the science of geometry is the study of the many possible relations among these elements which arise from a few basic assumptions about them. This study is carried on by means of logical reasoning and deductive proof. Some of the properties of plane figures and of the simpler solids are studied in arithmetic. Standard geometric constructions and the measurement of perimeters, areas, and volumes are also emphasized.

What has been said thus far about arithmetic does not indicate the wealth of application that it has in our everyday life. Arithmetic enters all of our ordinary business transactions and all of our record keeping. It has to do with the processing of measurements made in the shop, on the job, in all types of engineering, and in science. Arithmetic is used constantly in the production, distribution, and consumption of our commodities. Understanding its skills is important to everyone, from the clerk and the housewife to the project engineer, the scientist, and the director of every segment of industry. The same skills are basic to further work in mathematics and science. Understanding arithmetic, and thus working competently with numbers, is an achievement as indispensable to every person as the reading of a printed page and the writing of an acceptable paragraph.

1.3 TEACHING ARITHMETIC

The teacher of arithmetic has the privilege and responsibility of helping pupils to discover and to understand the principles of arithmetic. Many simple principles require detailed procedures for complete understanding but the results are rewarding. The mastery of skills also requires repeated practice, but it must be practice with and following understanding. There is a large body of factual material in arithmetic that must be applied in practical problems to be appreciated. Since most of the ideas are systematic and sequential, a considerable amount of planning of the course work is required. In developing ideas, it is important to know always how well pupils are doing in their work and to give repeated coverage of concepts and skills when there is need. Pupils must understand *why* the various concepts of arithmetic are correct as well as *how* the various procedures are performed. Since the attitudes of pupils are largely a reflection of that of the teacher, it is well for all concerned if the teacher can feel at ease with the material and can enjoy helping pupils to develop insight into number ideas.

It is not the purpose of this book to deal with techniques of teaching arithmetic. Such techniques are part of the usual methods courses. However, in much of the discussion of topics, in which content or fundamental concepts of arithmetic are being presented, incidental reference to methods will occur. Content as understood here includes the material usually taught in elementary schools, plus many of the underlying concepts of mathematics which the elementary-school teacher should understand.

The teaching of arithmetic has been influenced considerably by various theories which have been dominant at different periods of time.* Briefly, the principal theories are referred to as the drill theory, the incidental-learning theory, and the meaning theory. The *drill theory*, in effect, has

* W. A. Brownell, "Psychological Considerations in Learning and Teaching Arithmetic." National Council of Teachers of Mathematics, Tenth Yearbook, *The Teaching of Arithmetic*, New York, 1935.

held that repeated practice with basic facts of arithmetic is sufficient for mastery. Its thesis has been that practice is the main requisite for achievement. This theory has the advantage of ease of administration, but it has the disadvantage of lacking the challenge to do creative work in many circumstances. The drill theory has been found inadequate for mastery when it consists of rote practice without understanding.

The *incidental-learning theory* has held that proper motivation for learning fundamental facts can be achieved by presenting these facts as part of a more general learning situation (for example, the group activity of operating a model store). In the hands of a skilled teacher, proper motivation often can be induced by such activity. However, this method is generally unwieldy; the central activity, which is not arithmetic but a group project, often overshadows the other elements of the learning situation. Furthermore, since arithmetic is systematic and skills must be developed sequentially, it is not always possible to match the desired skills of the arithmetic program with those arising from the incidental program. The incidental program can, in fact, motivate problems for discussion beyond the level of skills intended as the outcome of a particular activity.

The *meaning theory* is in part a reaction to the inadequacies of the drill theory and the incidental-learning theory. However, the meaning theory implies more than either of the other theories, and it is not a compromise between them. The meaning theory holds that pupils will achieve mastery of ideas and skills in arithmetic if practice is given following understanding. As a theory of learning, it recognizes that practice or drill is required for mastery. It assumes that there is greater transfer and retention of ideas when the learner thoroughly understands what he is studying.* Likewise, in the matter of motivation it does not say that incidental-learning situations are useless, but it does hold that the development of mathematical concepts must be sequential and systematic. At the present time many authorities support the meaning theory or its general philosophy. It appears also that drill in the form of well-planned games and other activities is a valid part of the arithmetic learning program. Considerable implementation of the meaning program has been accomplished in recent years by the development of visual aids such as counting frames, place-value kits, fraction kits, markers, and charts. Similarly, in textbook discussions and in classroom procedures diagrams and charts are extensively used.

As indicated in the introduction, the teacher should be aware not only of changes in point of view in regard to methods in arithmetic but also in emphasis in regard to content. Concrete materials can be used to promote understanding of many concepts and semiconcrete presentations are very

* George Katona, *Organizing and Memorizing*, Columbia University Press, New York, 1940.

Arithmetic Content

Natural Numbers

1, 2, 3, 4, 5, ... 1000, 1001, 1002, ...

Rational Counting	Cardinal Numbers	Ordinal Numbers
10 little, 9 little, 8 little Indians	30 days hath September	The 4th of July The 30th of May

Number Systems	Number Names
$\mu\eta$ CCCXXXIII	forty-eight three hundred thirty-three

Operations with Numbers

Addition $$ and $$$ are $$$$$

Subtraction $$$$~~$$$~~ = $$$$

Multiplication (000)(000) = (00)(00)(00)

Division $6\overline{)6666}$ 1111

Fractions and Operations with Fractions

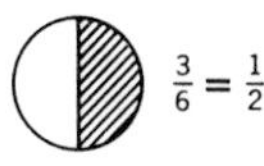

$\frac{3}{6} = \frac{1}{2}$

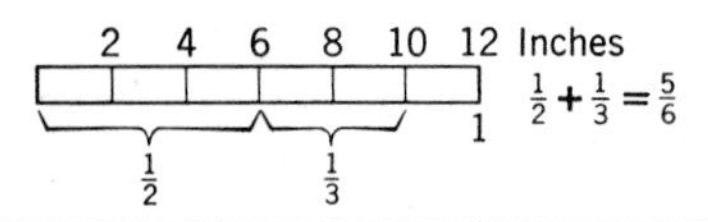

$\frac{1}{2} + \frac{1}{3} = \frac{5}{6}$

Decimal Fractions

$.5 = \frac{5}{10} = \frac{50}{100} = .50$

$.2 \times .4 = \frac{2}{10} \times \frac{4}{10} = \frac{8}{100} = .08$

Per Cent

parts in one hundred

$\frac{1}{5} = \frac{20}{100} = 20\%$

10 is 20% of 50

$15\% = \frac{15}{100} = \frac{3}{20}$

6% of $200 = $12

Denominate Numbers

1 mile = 5280 feet
1 kilometer = .62 miles

1 meter = 100 centimeters
1 meter = 39.37 inches

Mensuration

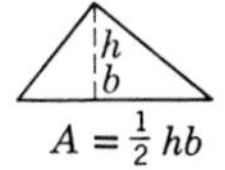

$A = \frac{1}{2} hb$

a c b

$c^2 = a^2 + b^2$

r

$c = 2\pi r$

$A = \pi r^2$

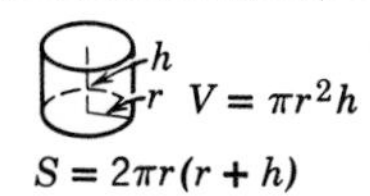

$V = \pi r^2 h$

$S = 2\pi r(r + h)$

The number six, for example, is represented by 110, since six consists of 1 of *two times two*, 1 of *two*, and no *ones*. Other bases such as eight and twelve can be worked with to illustrate place value. A careful study of operations with numbers in these various bases gives insight into the meaning of the operations in our own number system with base ten. In this book the study of numbers and operations in other bases is used to amplify the work with the conventional system; hence the treatment of other bases often follows—rather than precedes—the work with base ten.

In the remaining sections of this chapter a brief discussion of topics in arithmetic is given. The diagram Arithmetic Content indicates some of the topics to be covered.

1.5 OPERATIONS WITH NUMBERS

The fundamental operations of addition, subtraction, multiplication, and division for the natural numbers in a place-value number system constitute a major part of the work in arithmetic in the primary and intermediate grades. Not only must the principal facts and processes of these operations be presented, but their meanings, laws, and interrelations must be emphasized. *Addition* can be considered as the process used to obtain a single number of a given kind, called the *sum*, as the result of combining two or more numbers of the given kind, called the *addends*. (The numbers of a "given kind" may be thought of as belonging to a given set or collection of definite objects.) *Subtraction* can be thought of as an inverse of addition as well as a process for finding the remainder when one number is taken away from another. Here again the numbers considered must be of the same kind or belong to the same given set. *Multiplication* can first be considered as an operation in which several equal addends are combined. Later it can be considered as an operation on the elements of a set, with the operation satisfying certain basic laws. *Division* can be looked upon as the inverse of multiplication as well as a process of repeated subtraction in which the divisor is subtracted from the dividend. Two elementary views of division are *partition* and *measurement*. In partition the divisor indicates the number of equal shares or parts into which the dividend is to be separated. In measurement the divisor is a quantity that is measured or subtracted from the dividend.

Addition and multiplication are both said to be *commutative* operations, since the order of the numbers being combined does not affect the result. For example,

$$3 + 4 = 7 \quad \text{and} \quad 4 + 3 = 7; \qquad 3 \times 4 = 12 \quad \text{and} \quad 4 \times 3 = 12.$$

These operations are also said to be *associative*, since the grouping of the various elements will not affect the result. For example,

$$2 + (3 + 4) = (2 + 3) + 4 = 9$$

and

$$(3 \times 4) \times 2 = 3 \times (4 \times 2) = 24.$$

Addition and multiplication are connected by the distributive rule, which states that multiplication is *distributive* with respect to addition. Thus we find that

$$2 \times (3 + 4) = 2 \times 3 + 2 \times 4 = 14$$

and

$$(3 + 4) \times 2 = 3 \times 2 + 4 \times 2 = 14.$$

Subtraction as an inverse of addition is illustrated by

$$3 + 4 = 7 \quad \text{and} \quad 7 - 4 = 3.$$

If 3 plus 4 is 7, then 7 minus 4 is 3. In the same way, multiplication and division are seen to be inverses from the fact that

$$3 \times 4 = 12 \quad \text{and} \quad 12 \div 4 = 3.$$

If three fours are twelve, then twelve divided by four is three. In general, the facts of one operation can be used as a check against the facts of the inverse operation. Four related facts in addition and subtraction, such as

$$\begin{array}{r} 4 \\ +3 \\ \hline 7 \end{array} \qquad \begin{array}{r} 3 \\ +4 \\ \hline 7 \end{array} \qquad \begin{array}{r} 7 \\ -3 \\ \hline 4 \end{array} \qquad \begin{array}{r} 7 \\ -4 \\ \hline 3, \end{array}$$

are sometimes referred to as a unit of work in addition and subtraction. In a similar way, four related facts in multiplication and division are referred to as a unit of work:

$$\begin{array}{r} 4 \\ \times 3 \\ \hline 12 \end{array} \qquad \begin{array}{r} 3 \\ \times 4 \\ \hline 12 \end{array} \qquad 4\overline{)12}^{\,3} \qquad 3\overline{)12.}^{\,4}$$

1.6 RATIONAL NUMBERS

Pupils become familiar with some of the simpler ideas about fractions early in the primary grades. A child eats half of an apple, works half of an hour, or spends half of a dollar. Children begin to think in terms of a quarter of a dollar and a quarter of an hour. The purpose of the work in fractions is to help primary-grade pupils to clarify their understanding of them and to emphasize the less complicated aspects of their meaning. A fraction is first defined as the number obtained by comparing several of

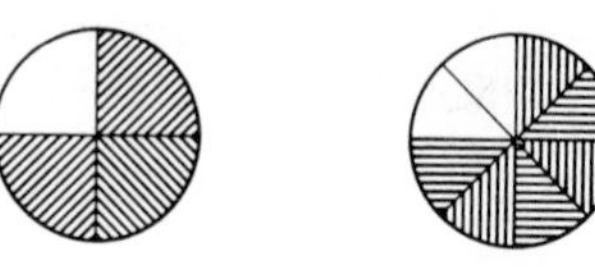

Fig. 1

the equal parts of one whole unit with all of the equal parts of the unit. This meaning of a fraction should emerge as a clear concept for the child, and in this connection diagrams and concrete illustrations are very important. The meaning of fourths as the relations of one or more "cubes" of a pound of butter to the set of four "cubes" in the pound and the meaning of sixths as illustrated by various collections of six equal pieces of a pie are examples. (The ordinary "cube" of butter does not fit the mathematical definition of a cube—a rectangular figure in three dimensions with all edges equal segments and all faces congruent squares.) Simple examples such as these should be pursued to the point at which notions of equivalence of fractions become quite familiar and commonplace. Thus the diagrams (Fig. 1) shown above indicate that three fourths are equal to six eighths, a notion that can be understood before the abstract equivalence $\frac{3}{4} = \frac{6}{8}$ is used.

Other meanings of fractions should be introduced in the development of the concepts of division and of ratios. The techniques for changing fractions to equivalent ones in higher or lower terms must be treated systematically. Pupils will gradually come to appreciate the steps in equivalences such as

$$\frac{3}{4} = \frac{3 \times 2}{4 \times 2} = \frac{6}{8} \quad \text{and} \quad \frac{6}{8} = \frac{6 \div 2}{8 \div 2} = \frac{3}{4}.$$

The definition of equivalence at this stage is that two fractions are equivalent if and only if they both represent the same portion of a whole quantity. Later, for the two fractions to be equal, the product of the numerator of one fraction times the denominator of a second must equal the product of the numerator of the second times the denominator of the first.

Operations with fractions parallel those with the natural numbers but require more extensive treatment because there is a greater variety in forms of numbers entering the operations as well as in forms of answers. There is also a greater variety in types of problems. In addition and subtraction of fractions problems are separated into groups according to the kinds of denominators involved. The notion of common denominator becomes important in this work. In multiplication and division of fractions problems of different types are considered, depending on whether the multiplier or divisor is a natural number or a fraction. In the early work of this kind problems are dealt with in the context of familiar situations, such as sharing, measuring, and counting. The notions of partition and measurement in division are used to advantage. For example in working out the problem $7\frac{1}{2} \div 3$, partition applies. Division by three is equivalent to finding $\frac{1}{3}$ of the dividend, hence $7\frac{1}{2} \div 3 = \frac{1}{3} \times 7\frac{1}{2} = 2\frac{1}{2}$. Measurement is used when $3 \div \frac{1}{4}$ is solved by determining how many quarter units are contained in three whole units. Since, by definition, there are four quarter units in one whole unit, it follows that there are three times four, or twelve, quarter units in three whole units.

Decimal fractions are in a special class in which the denominator is ten or *some higher power of ten.* Decimal fractions are thus a natural extension of a place-value number system to the case in which the value of a place is obtained by dividing by a power of ten instead of multiplying by a power of ten. A new notation is developed in connection with this work. We have, for example,

$$.3 = \frac{3}{10} = \text{three tenths}$$

$$.25 = \frac{25}{100} = \text{twenty-five hundredths}$$

$$.125 = \frac{125}{1000} = \text{one hundred twenty-five thousandths.}$$

One of the advantages of working with decimal fractions is that common denominators are very easily obtained. We find for example that

$$\frac{5}{10} = \frac{50}{100} = \frac{500}{1000}, \qquad \text{hence } .5 = .50 = .500, \text{ and so on.}$$

The comparison of decimals and the operations with decimal fractions rest on these properties. For example,

$$.56 \text{ is less than } .6 \quad \text{since} \quad \frac{56}{100} \text{ is less than } \frac{60}{100}.$$

Similarly, we find that

$$.2 + .3 = .5 \quad \text{since} \quad \frac{2}{10} + \frac{3}{10} = \frac{5}{10}$$

and

$$.2 \times .3 = .06 \quad \text{since} \quad \frac{2}{10} \times \frac{3}{10} = \frac{6}{100}.$$

1.7 APPLIED PROBLEMS

Throughout the work in elementary arithmetic stated or "word" problems should be used as illustrations and applications of numerical examples. One of the major difficulties that pupils meet in working problems is to decide what operations are required to set up and to solve a stated problem. It is important therefore for pupils to practice with stated problems at all levels. There should be emphasis upon careful reading and analysis of problems, and there should be practice in estimating the size of the answers. Answers to problems should be checked when they have been found.

In general, applied problems should be posed in contexts that will be of social significance to pupils. Early work should include problems related to their experiences and activities. Later work should emphasize parts of consumer arithmetic and semitechnical work, particularly that connected with measurement. Problems involving fractions, measurements, decimal fractions, and applications to per cents and business arithmetic should be made part of the work as pupils advance. Fundamental concepts and principles of mathematics should also be illustrated with suitable problems and applications. In this manner progress can be made toward achieving one of the principal goals of the arithmetic program: to develop in pupils the ability to analyze problems and to do quantitative thinking.

1.8 MEASUREMENT AND APPROXIMATE NUMBERS

Many of the numbers we use are obtained either from measurement or from counting. The numbers obtained from measurement are approximate and involve only a limited number of significant digits (see section 15.2). Thus a measurement of 22.5 inches has three significant digits, and a micrometer measurement of .0012 inch has two significant digits. Operations with approximate numbers cannot yield numbers as answers that are more accurate than the data in the measurements. Practice in making actual measurements and in working with approximate numbers should be part of the work in the intermediate grades. The use of areas and volumes as quantities to be computed from measurements can also be a part of this work.

Numbers expressing measurements in terms of various standard units of measure are known as *denominate numbers*. Three yards, 10 inches of cloth; 1 hour, 30 minutes of time; and 12 pounds, 3 ounces of food are examples of denominate numbers. In the *English system* of measurement some of the units of length are the inch, foot, yard, and mile; units of weight are the ounce, pound, and ton; units of time are the second, minute, hour, and day. The units of measure in this system are in general use in the United States.

In the *metric system* of measurement the units of length include the meter, centimeter (or .01 meter), kilometer (or 1000 meters), and the millimeter (or .001 meter). Base ten relates the various units of length and the units for other denominate numbers in the metric system. Units of mass include the gram, milligram (or .001 gram), and kilogram (or 1000 grams). Units of volume include the liter, milliliter (or .001 liter, which is also one cubic centimeter), and the kiloliter (or 1000 liters). This system of measurement, adopted by the French government in 1799, is standard in nearly all countries of the world. Although the metric system has been legal in the United States since 1866, it is little used for common measurement; neither has it much application in the countries of the United Kingdom except for work in science. The metric system has been almost exclusively adopted as the system of measurement in scientific work throughout the world.

One of the problems to be studied in arithmetic is that of converting measurements from the English to the metric system of measurement and vice versa. A few of the conversion factors have the following approximate values:

1 meter =	39.37 inches,	1 meter =	3.281 feet
1 liter =	1.06 quarts,	1 quart =	.943 liter
1 kilogram =	2.20 pounds,	1 pound =	454 grams

All pupils in elementary schools should become well acquainted with the English and the metric systems, since the first is needed in many everyday problems and the second is employed in general science in secondary schools.

To round out the work in arithmetic in the elementary school, there should be considerable study of simple formulas and equations of algebra and some study of the geometry of plane figures and simple solids. Work in geometry should include the measurement of areas, perimeters, and volumes, the classification of triangles and quadrilaterals, and applications of the Pythagorean theorem.

EXERCISE 1

1. Discuss briefly some of the different kinds of numbers that are studied in arithmetic.

2. What two meanings of division are mentioned in the text? Can you give an illustration of each one?

3. Discuss briefly the notion of a place-value number system. What is a base? What is place value?

4. Under what three headings can most of the theories of teaching arithmetic be classified?

5. What two principles are employed in constructing number systems such as the Roman number system and the Egyptian number system?

6. Explain why seven is represented by 111 in a place-value number system with base two.

7. The numbers one, two, three, and four are represented in base two by 1, 10, 11, and 100. Make a small square table showing the sums of these numbers taken two at a time, using a row of the numerals along the top and a column on the left and adding the number on the left to the number above to fill each position in the table.

8. Construct the numerals in base two that represent the base-ten numerals 9, 10, 11, 12, 15, 16, 31, 32.

9. Name the four fundamental operations of arithmetic and state which are inverse operations.

10. What are the principal laws that govern the operations of addition and multiplication? Illustrate each law.

11. Name the two systems of units employed in work with denominate numbers. What are the units of length, mass (weight), and time in each?

12. In Mexico the metric system of units is used. Suppose that you bought 4 liters of gasoline, 1 kilogram of cocoa, and 3 meters of cloth. Would you get more or would you get less than 1 gallon of gasoline, 2 pounds of cocoa, and 3 yards of cloth?

13. Mt. Whitney, in California, is about 14,495 feet high. Express this height in meters, assuming that 3.28 feet equal one meter. Mt. Kenya, in Kenya, Africa, is about 5200 meters high. Express this height in feet. How much higher is Mt. Kenya than Mt. Whitney (in feet)?

14. Use the fact that there are approximately 3.28 feet in one meter to determine the number of feet in one kilometer (1000 meters) and compare the result with 5280 feet (one mile) to obtain a decimal fraction equivalent of the kilometer in terms of the mile.

15. Arrange the following decimal fractions in order of increasing size:

.73, .4, .081, .129, .09, .567, .019, .8, .35.

16. A meter is equal to 39.37 inches, and a yard is equal to 36 inches. What is the difference between a distance of 200 meters and one of 220 yards?

17. Show by means of a diagram that the fractions $\frac{5}{6}$ and $\frac{10}{12}$ are equivalent. Could you use portions of a one-foot ruler, marked in inches, to show this fact?

18. A liter is about 1.06 quarts. Which tank will hold more liquid, one with a capacity of 4 gallons or one with a capacity of 15 liters? How would a 5-gallon tank compare with a 19-liter tank?

REFERENCES

At the end of each chapter a list of references is given to books and articles which treat of topics covered in the chapter. Only the names of the authors and the titles of the books or articles are contained in these short reference lists. Details concerning the publisher and the publication date may be found in the complete bibliography in Appendix C.

Banks, J. Houston, *Learning and Teaching Arithmetic*, pp. 1–31.
Boyer, L. E., *Introduction to Mathematics for Teachers*, pp. 1–48.
Brownell, W. A., *Arithmetic in Grades I and II.*
Brueckner, L. J., and F. E. Grossnickle, *How to Make Arithmetic Meaningful*, pp. 1–55.
Dantzig, Tobias, *Number, the Language of Science*, pp. 1–50.
Larsen, H. D., *Arithmetic for Colleges*, pp. 1–26, 121–141.
Layton, W. I., *College Arithmetic*, pp. 1–24, 71–94.
Morton, Robert L., *Teaching Arithmetic in the Elementary School*, Volume 2, pp. 1–70.
Mueller, Francis J., *Arithmetic, Its Structure and Concepts*, pp. 1–46.
National Council of Teachers of Mathematics, *Instruction in Arithmetic, Twenty-Fifth Yearbook*.

2

Number and Its Representation

2.1 COUNTING

As primitive tribes developed, they very soon found the need for keeping some account of their possessions. Thus a shepherd would count his sheep when they were moved to a new pasture by placing one stone in a bag or pile for each sheep as it passed by a certain place on its trip out. On arrival at the new pasture the sheep would again be checked against the stones in the bag. If some pebbles were left over, it would mean that a number of sheep had been lost in the move. In addition to matching with pebbles, other means were used, such as making notches on a stick or tying knots in a rope. This was the beginning of an important idea called *one-to-one correspondence*.

2.1.1. Sets and elements. A *set* in mathematics may be taken intuitively as any well-defined collection of distinct objects. The objects in a set are called its *elements*. We shall say that a set is well defined when it is known precisely what objects are in the set. Actually "set" and "element" are undefined basic concepts, much as the notions of "point," "line," and "plane" are undefined concepts in geometry. Sets may be specified in many ways. All that is required is that it may be said of a given object whether or not it belongs to a given set. Braces, { }, are used to inclose the elements of a set. A few examples of sets are cited in this section. Applications and further discussion of sets are contained in Chapter 19 in connection with the work in algebra. A set consisting of part or all of the elements of a given set is called a *subset* of the given set.

Example 1. The collection of the first four letters of the English alphabet is a set: $\{a, b, c, d\}$. This set might be designated by the single letter A. We note that the set A has four elements.

Example 2. The set $B = \{a, b, c, d, e, f, g, h\}$ contains eight elements. Since all elements of set A, Example 1, are elements of set B, A is called a subset of B.

Example 3. The set of all natural numbers, 1, 2, 3, · · · , or $I = \{1, 2, 3, \cdots\}$ is an example of a set with an infinite number of elements. The set $E = \{2, 4, 6, \cdots\}$, consisting of all of the even natural numbers, is an infinite set which is a subset of I.

Example 4. The collection C of all students in a given class is a set. $C =$ {students in a class}. The set $M =$ {men students in the class} is a subset of C; likewise, the set $W =$ {women students in the class} is a subset of C.

Example 5. A set containing no elements, called the *null set*, is designated by $\emptyset$. The null set is a subset of every set.

Example 6. A list of all subsets of set A in Example 1 is the following: $\emptyset$, A, $\{a\}$, $\{b\}$, $\{c\}$, $\{d\}$, $\{a, b\}$, $\{a, c\}$, $\{a, d\}$, $\{b, c\}$, $\{b, d\}$, $\{c, d\}$, $\{a, b, c\}$, $\{a, b, d\}$, $\{a, c, d\}$, $\{b, c, d\}$. Note that there are sixteen subsets in all.

Two notions to be explored later are those of the *union of two sets* and the *intersection of two sets.* The union of two sets is the set consisting of all elements occurring in one or the other or both sets. The intersection of two sets is the set of all elements occurring in both sets. These notions can be generalized for more than two sets.

Example 7. Find the union and the intersection of the sets $\{a, b\}$ and $\{c, d\}$; also for the sets $\{a, b\}$ and $\{b, c, d\}$ of Example 6.

Solution. $\{a, b\}$ union $\{c, d\} = \{a, b, c, d\} = A$.
$\{a, b\}$ intersection $\{c, d\} =$ the null set $= \emptyset$.
$\{a, b\}$ union $\{b, c, d\} = \{a, b, c, d\} = A$.
$\{a, b\}$ intersection $\{b, c, d\} = \{b\}$.

Project. Find all subsets of a set consisting of two elements. Next find all subsets of a set of three elements. Count the number of subsets in each case. Can you predict the number of subsets of a set consisting of five elements? Be sure to include the null set and the set itself in each count.

2.1.2. One-to-one correspondence. Two sets of objects can be put into one-to-one correspondence if every element of the first set corresponds to an element of the second set and, conversely, every element of the second set corresponds to an element of the first set. Suppose a classroom containing forty chairs is occupied by a class of forty students. The students in this class form a set that can be put into one-to-one correspondence with the set of forty chairs. If the class consisted of thirty students, even though each student would have a chair, the two sets could not be put into one-to-one correspondence. Likewise, if the class had forty-two students, a one-to-one correspondence could not be established.

As primitive man became more civilized, he developed better methods of counting his belongings. For example, scratches on clay tablets may very well have been the beginning of a notation for representing numbers; in fact, the Egyptian symbol for one was represented by a vertical staff or line. The symbol for two was two lines placed side by side; the symbol for three was three lines, and, in like manner, each of the symbols for the numbers that followed, up to and including nine, was made by the proper number of repetitions of the vertical line. The symbol for ten was supposed to have represented a heelbone and was made by a curved line written as ∩. In like manner, other civilizations developed various systems of notation to represent numbers. The symbols or groups of symbols in such a system are properly called *numerals.* With these numerals it was possible for the people of these cultures to make an inventory of their possessions by putting the objects to be counted into one-to-one correspondence with the numerals taken in order. The numeral corresponding to the last object in the set to be counted represented the *number* of objects in the set. Such a number is generally called a *natural number* in contrast to other types of numbers studied in mathematics.

EXERCISE 1

1. Is it possible to put a set of twenty IBM cards into one-to-one correspondence with a set of twenty students in a class?

2. Is it possible to set up a one-to-one correspondence between fifteen automobiles and the wheels on the automobiles? Is it possible to set up such a correspondence between the automobiles and the engines in the automobiles?

3. Primitive men oftentimes used their fingers for counting small sets of objects. If the tribe owned five camels how could this be recorded by the use of fingers?

4. A teacher has thirty pencils. She gives one to each pupil in her class and finds that she has three pencils remaining. How many pupils were in her class? Explain how the principle of one-to-one correspondence may be used in obtaining your answer.

5. How many numbers 1, 2, 3, · · ·, are needed following a single letter *A*, *B*, *C*, · · ·, or *Z* to number 260,000 tickets if no two tickets have the same letter and number?

6. Seventy-five copies of lecture notes were taken to a lecture and were issued one to each visitor. If eight copies were not issued, how many visitors attended the lecture? Explain.

7. In a hardware store each person served had to present a card taken from a stack arranged in order, 1 to 100. If the card next available read "85" after the last customer was served, how many customers were there?

8. If there are 100 farms in a county, each having one or more cows and none having more than 80 cows, why are there at least two farms with exactly the same number of cows?

9. If no head of hair has more than 80,000 hairs, why must there be at least one group of two or more persons with heads having the same number of hairs, at any given time, in a city with a quarter of a million people? Would there have to be at least one group of three people with identical numbers of hairs? A group of five people? Explain.

10. How many squared numbers, $1^2, 2^2, 3^2, \cdots$, are there up to 300^2? How many squared numbers up to 160,000?

2.2 CARDINAL AND ORDINAL NUMBERS

A set of dishes, a flock of birds, a herd of cattle, and other collections of objects may very well bring to mind the question, "How many?" This gives rise to what is called the cardinal meaning of number, so named because it is the principal or most important meaning. In order to determine the *cardinal number* of a set of objects, the numbers, in order, are put into one-to-one correspondence with the objects in the set taken in any order. The number used to designate the last object labeled is the cardinal number of the set. Hence numbers used to indicate the number of chairs in a room, the number of students in a class, and so on, are cardinal numbers.

Suppose that a small flock of birds is sitting on a fence. One person might say that there are seven birds on the fence. Seven would be a cardinal number. Another person might say that the third bird from left to right has a red spot on its head. In this case "third," which may be written 3rd, is an *ordinal number*, since it is bird number 3 in a series of birds arranged along a fence from left to right. It should be noted that it is not necessary to use the numbers in the form first, second, third, fourth, or the equivalents 1st, 2nd, 3rd, 4th, $\cdots$, respectively, to represent ordinal numbers. Thus we might say that an interesting story starts on page 27 of a magazine. This is an ordinal number, since it represents the twenty-seventh page in the magazine. Again in the statement that the magazine has 42 pages 42 is used in the cardinal sense.

EXERCISE 2

1. Indicate the cardinal and ordinal numbers in the following list:

(*a*) George VI
(*b*) 17 feet
(*c*) GR 30971
(*d*) February 13
(*e*) a dozen eggs
(*f*) page 87
(*g*) a gross of pencils
(*h*) Chapter 15
(*i*) a 90-day note
(*j*) 6200 Friar Street.

2. Indicate how a house number may be used as an ordinal number and as a cardinal number.

3. Give other examples in which numbers with either an ordinal or a cardinal meaning are used.

4. If you count the days in a week, what two sets have been put into one-to-one correspondence? In answering the question, "How many days are there in a week?," the answer is what kind of number? Describe Wednesday by an ordinal number.

5. The cardinal meaning of number is sometimes called the collection meaning of number. Why is this done?

6. The ordinal meaning of number is sometimes called the series meaning of number. Why is this done?

7. The princes of the Roman Catholic Church are called cardinals. What relation has this to cardinal numbers? Can you give other examples in which "cardinal" is used?

8. What is the cardinal number of the class of all sets of objects that can be put into one-to-one correspondence with the collection of months in a calendar year?

9. Suppose a clock strikes once at 1 o'clock, twice at 2 o'clock, and so on for twelve hours. What is the ordinal number of each hour struck? What are the successive cardinal numbers of all strikes made, each time an ordinal strike is completed?

10. Identify all cardinal and ordinal numbers in the statement: "The second-place car in the third race averaged 95 miles per hour in a 40-lap race on July 11, 1960. Only eight of twelve entries finished the race."

11. The set of all common fractions (with repetitions of some equivalent fractions) can be arranged as shown:

(*a*) How many fractions are there in each of the first four diagonals?

(*b*) What is the sum of the numerator and the denominator in each of the fractions in the first diagonal, the second diagonal, the third diagonal, and the fourth diagonal?

(*c*) Answer parts (*a*) and (*b*) for the seventh and for the tenth diagonal.

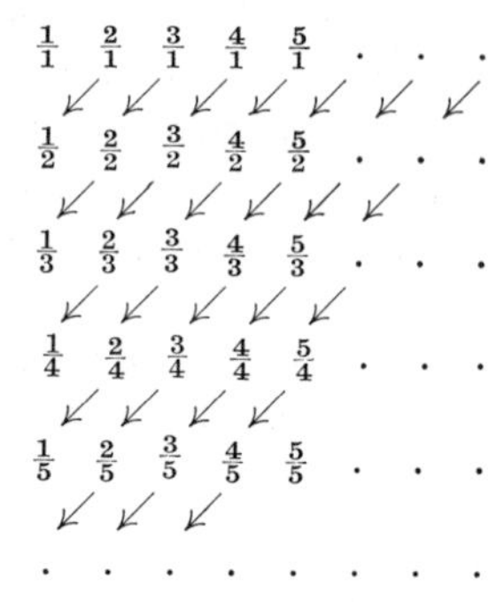

12. In the scheme for problem 11, what are the sixth, tenth, fifteenth, and twenty-first fractions? Would every possible simple fraction have an ordinal number in this scheme?

2.3 SYSTEMS OF NOTATION

In an election for the chairmanship of a club, Mr. Jones received 𝍸 𝍸 11 votes and Mr. White, the other candidate, received 𝍸 𝍸 𝍸 1 votes. Mr. White was declared elected because his vote totaled three 5's and one 1, whereas Mr. Jones received only two 5's and two 1's. Actually, in counting votes in this manner a *base five* is employed; that is, a larger unit is created by grouping five of the smaller units. Since a person has five fingers on one hand, five was a natural base for many early civilizations. However, since a person has ten fingers on two hands, it is not surprising that base ten ultimately replaced base five in most of the systems of notation used by early man. One exception to this has been found among the Mayas, in what is now South Mexico, where base twenty was used. Also, it is known that the Sumerians, who lived in the lower valley of the Tigris and Euphrates rivers, used a base sixty. The Sumerians had numerals for ten and for one hundred, but they did not use ten as a base in a place-value system of numeration; this earlier system of numeration was very similar to the Eygptian number system shown in Table 1.

Before developing a place-value system, the Sumerians used numerals with a base ten. The numerals consisted of cuneiform or wedge-shaped marks combined in a manner similar to that of the Egyptians. Thus $\triangledown = 1$, $\triangledown\triangledown = 2, \cdots$, $\triangleleft = 10$, $\triangleleft\triangledown = 11, \cdots$, $\triangleleft\triangleleft = 20$, $\triangleleft\triangleleft\triangleleft = 30, \cdots$, $\triangledown\triangleright = 100, \cdots$.

Table 1 displays some of the earlier systems of notation compared to the system now in use.

An examination of the Mayan and the Roman systems of notation in the table indicates an early tendency to use base five in both systems. Thus the Mayas used a dot to represent one, two dots to represent two, three dots for three, four dots for four, and then five was represented by a horizontal line. Furthermore the next symbol, representing six, consists of this horizontal line and a dot, and so on. The reader should note the similarity between this procedure and the method of tallying votes. The Roman system followed exactly the same principle of repetition, but in place of dots the Romans had the letter I. The symbol for two is the symbol for one repeated and so on.

It should be noted that later users of the Roman system of notation found it desirable to shorten some of the symbols formed by the principle of repetition. As mentioned in the second footnote to Table 1, the numeral IIII was changed to IV, VIIII to IX, and XVIIII to XIX. Here the *principle of subtraction* was employed to determine the value of the symbol. I before V meant V − I, or four; I before X meant X − I, or nine; and the I before the second X in XIX meant X + X − I, or nineteen. Similarly XL implied L − X, or forty.

Further observation of Table 1 shows a number of interesting facts. The Egyptians clearly used a base ten, since each of the numerals up to ten was formed by the repetition of the symbol for one (a vertical staff). For ten a new symbol, ∩ , was supposed to have represented a heelbone. Numbers beyond ten were formed both by the principle of repetition and the *principle of addition.* Thus twelve was represented by ∩||, which is

Table 1

Mayan	Egyptian	Roman	Greek	Present System
⊗				0
•	|	I	α	1
• •	||	II	β	2
• • •	|||	III	γ	3
• • • •	|| ||	IIII [2]	δ	4
—	||| ||	V	ϵ	5
• —	||| |||	VI	Ϝ [3]	6
• • —	|||| |||	VII	ζ	7
• • • —	|||| ||||	VIII	η	8
• • • • —	|||||||||	VIIII [2]	θ	9
═	∩	X	ι	10
• ═	∩|	XI	$\iota\alpha$	11
• • ═	∩||	XII	$\iota\beta$	12
≡	∩||| ||	XV	$\iota\epsilon$	15
• • • • ≡	∩|||||||||	XVIIII	$\iota\theta$	19
• ⊗ [1]	∩∩	XX	κ [4]	20
• • ═ [1]	∩∩∩∩∩	L	ν	50
— ⊗ [1]	𓍢	C	ρ	100
• — ⊗	𓍢𓍢𓍢𓍢𓍢	D	ϕ [4]	500
• • ═ ⊗	𓆼	M	α'	1,000
• — ⊗ ⊗	𓂭	$\overline{X}$	M	10,000

[1] These symbols for twenty and beyond are written in horizontal form for convenience. However, it is known that the Mayas usually wrote them in vertical form with the highest order at the top.

[2] The Roman symbols IIII, VIIII and XVIIII were later written as IV, IX and XIX, respectively.

[3] This symbol is the obsolete Greek letter *vau*. Two other obsolete letters used were ϙ (koppa) for 90, ϡ (sampi) for 900. A super-script or subscript multiplied the number by 1000. Thus 2000 = β' or $,\beta$. A twenty-eighth symbol, M, was used to represent 10,000, and a numeral above the M indicated the number of ten thousands. Thus $\overset{\eta}{M} = 80{,}000$.

[4] The numerals for 10, 20, · · · , 90 in the Greek system are the letters ι, κ, λ, μ, ν, ξ, o, π, ϙ; the numerals for 100, 200, · · · , 900 are the letters ρ, σ, τ, υ, ϕ, χ, ψ, ω, ϡ.

the sum of ten and two. Twenty-three was represented by ∩∩|||, which is twenty plus three; twenty is formed by repetition of two tens and three is formed by repetition of three ones. Ten tens, the next higher unit, was represented by a scroll or coiled rope 𓍢.

The Greeks did not employ the principle of repetition to form their numerals. Their alphabet was the source of an easy numerical notation. Beginning with eleven, the principle of addition provided the basis for numerals between 10 and 20. Eleven was represented by $\iota\alpha$, that is, $\iota + \alpha$, or ten plus one, and sixteen was represented by ιF. Thus a base ten was clearly indicated in the Greek system.

The Greeks also made use of the *principle of multiplication.* As mentioned in the second footnote to Table 1, a superscript following a numeral or a subscript written before a numeral indicated multiplication by one thousand. For example, ϵ' or $,\epsilon$ meant 1000×5, or 5000. Likewise, multiplication was expressed by the numeral $\overset{\gamma}{\text{M}}$, which meant $3 \times 10{,}000$, or 30,000. The Romans also placed a bar above a number to indicate multiplication by 1000. For example, $\overline{\text{XXXI}}$ DCC LIX meant $31 \times 1000 + 500 + 200 + 50 + 9$, or 31,759.

EXERCISE 3

1. Write 17 in each of the Mayan, Egyptian, Greek, and Roman systems of notation for numbers.

2. Write 10, 20, 30, 40, 50, and 60 in each of the Mayan, Egyptian, Greek, and Roman systems of notation for numbers.

3. Write 531 in each of the Egyptian, Greek, and Roman systems of notation for numbers.

4. Write the numbers 300, 400, 500, and 600 in each of the Mayan, Egyptian, and Roman systems of notation for numbers.

5. Write 2787 in each of the Egyptian, Greek, and Roman systems of notation for numbers.

6. Write 67,896 in each of the Greek and Roman systems of notation for numbers.

7. Translate the following numbers to our present-day system of notation:

(a) LXXIX *(b)* MDCCCL *(c)* $\overset{\bullet\bullet\bullet}{\equiv}$ *(d)* $\bullet\bullet\bullet \quad \equiv$

8. Translate the following numbers to our present-day system of notation:

(a) $\overline{\text{XIV}}$CCCC *(b)* MDCCLXXV *(c)* 𓍢𓍢∩∩∩∩∩||| *(d)* 𓆼𓆼𓆼𓍢∩∩|||||

9. Translate the following numbers to our present-day system of notation:

(a) $\sigma\kappa\beta$ *(b)* $\epsilon'\phi\kappa\theta$ *(c)* $\overset{\delta}{\text{M}}\gamma'$ ϡϙη *(d)* $\overline{\text{MDCLI}}$DCCLXI

10. Translate the following numbers to our present-day system of notation:

(*a*) ୨୨୨∩∩∩||| ୨୨୨∩∩∩||| (*b*) • ═ ⊗ (*c*) •••• $\overset{\cdots}{\equiv}$ ⊗ (*d*) $\overset{\epsilon}{\mathrm{M}}\rho\nu\zeta$

11. Find from your library how the early Babylonians represented numbers.

12. What symbols other than those shown in Table 1 were used by the early Egyptians to represent numbers?

13. Explain how the modern terms "score," "dozen," "gross," "great gross," "fortnight," "pair," and "quartet" are related to number bases different from ten.

2.4 PLACE-VALUE SYSTEMS OF NOTATION

Many historians believe that as early as 500 B.C. the Asiatic Indians had begun to develop a system of notation for numbers which was remarkably different from other systems in that only ten different symbols were needed to represent any number, no matter how large. These symbols or digits were the forerunners of our modern digits. They are known as Arabic numerals, since it is believed that they reached Europe by way of Arabia.

The Indians employed what is called the *place-value principle* in writing numerals. The digit to the extreme right represents the number of ones in the number, the next digit to its left, the number of tens, and so on. In this representation each of the digits has two meanings. Consider the numeral 235, for example. The digit 3 tells the reader that it is three of something. This may be called the *absolute value* or the *form value* of 3. The position of the 3 also tells the reader that it represents not 3 ones but 3 tens, or 30, since it occupies the second place from the right. This is called the *place value* of the 3. Likewise, each of the other two digits has these two meanings.

Consider next the numeral 203. The 3 indicates 3 ones and the 2 indicates 2 hundreds. The 0 in the second place indicates no tens. This new digit, called zero, is not a natural number, but it is very necessary to any place-value system of notation. Although it is used to express "no units" in certain places in a numeral, zero should *not* be thought of as "nothing." It will be seen later that it has properties that set it apart from the natural numbers.

It should be noted that the Egyptian, Greek, and Roman systems of notation, as described in Table 1, had no symbols for zero. A little contemplation on the part of the reader will convince him that no zero is needed in the Roman numeral CCIII, in the Egyptian ୨୨||| and in the Greek $\sigma\gamma$ because of the additive method of forming the numerals in these systems. Two hundred three, the number indicated in each of the above, cannot be written without a zero in either the Asiatic-Indian or the Mayan system of notation. If it is so written, the number becomes 23 in the first system and .. ... in the other, both of which are incorrect.* Very little is known about the evolution of the zero symbol in India, since the materials employed by the Indians to make their records were not very substantial. Some historians state that the first actual record of a zero appeared many centuries after the birth of Christ. However, the records of the Mayas show that their symbol for zero was in use around the time of the birth of Christ. The Mayas' zero had no influence on our present number system because of the lack of cultural contact between the civilizations of America and India.

The Asiatic Indians were not the sole inventors of a place-value system of notation. Historical evidence shows that the ancient Sumerians did rely on such a system to a limited extent, using a base of sixty, even though they had special numerals for ten and one hundred in their earlier system of numeration. We owe the division of an hour and that of a degree of an arc of a circle into sixty minutes, or 3600 seconds, to the Sumerians. The Mayas' place-value system of notation was certainly developed independently of the Asiatic system and, as far as is known, at about the same time. The Mayas, as mentioned earlier, had a base of twenty. It is believed by some that they combined ones, twenties, four hundreds, eight thousands, and so on, in writing their numbers. They therefore used the powers of twenty. However, in astronomical calculations they had a rather curious variance, in that ones and twenties occupied the first two places but that three hundred sixty was the first three-place number, followed by seven thousand two hundred as the first four-place number, and so on. One explanation offered for the use of three hundred sixty in this manner is that it may have corresponded to the number of days in the Mayan year.

EXERCISE 4

1. In addition to the principle of place value, what other principle is used in a place-value system of notation?

2. Let a, b, c represent the digits one, two, three, respectively, in the Sumerian place-value system of notation. Express the value of the number abc in base ten.

3. Express the value of the Mayan numeral, ..., in base ten
(*a*) if the left-hand place value is 400,
(*b*) if the left-hand place value is 360.

4. Explain the differences among the numbers in base ten:

4050 4005 405.

* Instead of two hundred three, we are using the analogous numeral .. ⊗ ... in Mayan notation, which represents eight hundred three. The Mayan numeral .. ... , without the zero, represents forty-three.

5. Write each of the numbers of problem 4 in the Roman number system for purposes of comparison.

2.5 EXPONENTS

Let n be any natural number and b any real number*; then the expression b^n is defined as follows:

$$b^n = b \cdot b \cdot b \cdots b \qquad (n \text{ factors}).$$

Thus

$$b^2 = b \cdot b, \qquad b^3 = b \cdot b \cdot b, \qquad 2^4 = 2 \cdot 2 \cdot 2 \cdot 2.$$

In the equation $b^n = z$, b is called the *base*, n is the *exponent*, and z is the *power*. There are several ways in which this statement can be read: (1) "b, exponent n, is z," (2) "b raised to the nth power is z," and (3) "z is the nth power of b." If n is 2, it is proper to say "b squared is z," and if n is 3 the equation may be read "b cubed is z." Mathematicians sometimes use abbreviated ways of reading $b^n = z$, which can be confusing to beginning students. Teachers should be very careful to use nonabbreviated statements in discussing this notation.

To the definition of b^n, add the following two definitions:

$$b^0 = 1 \quad \text{and} \quad b^{-n} = \frac{1}{b^n}, \quad \text{provided that } b \neq 0.$$

It can be shown that the following laws of exponents hold for all positive and negative integers and for 0. Assume that a and b are not zero.

1. $$b^m \cdot b^n = b^{m+n}.$$

2. $$\frac{b^m}{b^n} = b^{m-n}.$$

3. $$(b^m)^n = b^{nm}.$$

4. $$(ab)^n = a^n \cdot b^n.$$

5. $$\left(\frac{a}{b}\right)^n = \frac{a^n}{b^n}.$$

The definitions of b^0 and b^{-n} are consistent with the laws of exponents as follows:

$$b^0 = b^{m-m} = \frac{b^m}{b^m} = 1 \quad \text{for } b \neq 0 \text{ and } m \text{ any natural number.}$$

$$b^{-n} = b^{0-n} = \frac{b^0}{b^n} = \frac{1}{b^n}, \quad \text{for } b \neq 0 \text{ and a natural number } n.$$

* The reader who has no elementary knowledge of the positive and negative integers and the real number system should consult section 19.4 or a first-year algebra text before studying this section.

Example. Find the value of each of the following:

(*a*) $b^3 \cdot b^2 =$ (*b*) $\dfrac{b^6}{b^2} =$ (*c*) $\dfrac{b^2}{b^7} =$

(*d*) $b^7 \cdot b^{-2} =$ (*e*) $(2x)^3 =$ (*f*) $10^0 + 10^{-2} + 10^3 =$

(*g*) $\left(\dfrac{2}{3}\right)^3 =$ (*h*) $10^{-3} =$ (*i*) $10^8 \cdot 10^{-3} =$

(*j*) $10^0 =$ (*k*) $(b^{-2})^3 =$

Solution. (*a*) $b^3 \cdot b^2 = b^{3+2} = b^5$ (*b*) $\dfrac{b^6}{b^2} = b^{6-2} = b^4$

(*c*) $\dfrac{b^2}{b^7} = b^{2-7} = b^{-5} = \dfrac{1}{b^5}$ (*d*) $b^7 \cdot b^{-2} = b^{7-2} = b^5$

(*e*) $(2x)^3 = 2^3 \cdot x^3 = 8x^3$

(*f*) $10^0 + 10^{-2} + 10^3 = 1 + \dfrac{1}{100} + 1000 = 1001.01$

(*g*) $\left(\dfrac{2}{3}\right)^3 = \dfrac{2^3}{3^3} = \dfrac{8}{27}$ (*h*) $10^{-3} = \dfrac{1}{10^3} = \dfrac{1}{1000} = .001$

(*i*) $10^8 \cdot 10^{-3} = 10^5 = 100{,}000$ (*j*) $10^0 = 1$

(*k*) $(b^{-2})^3 = b^{-6} = \dfrac{1}{b^6}$

Problem. Find the value of each of the following:

(*a*) $2^3 \cdot 2^4 =$ (*b*) $\dfrac{3^6}{3^3} =$ (*c*) $(100)^0 =$

(*d*) $4 \cdot 10^0 =$ (*e*) $10^0 + 10^{-1} =$ (*f*) $10^{-4} =$

(*g*) $10^5 \cdot 10^3 =$ (*h*) $\left(\dfrac{2}{3}\right)^2 =$

(*i*) $2 \cdot 3^3 + 4 \cdot 3^2 + 2 \cdot 3 + 3^0 =$ (*j*) $\left(\dfrac{3}{4}\right)^3 =$

(*k*) $3^0 \cdot 3^{-1} =$

2.6 PLACE-VALUE SYSTEMS OF NOTATION USING OTHER BASES

It has been noted that bases other than ten have been used in place-value systems of notation. As stated earlier in section 2.3, the Sumerians worked with a principle of repetition to construct some of their numerals up to sixty, but they did employ sixty as a base. In order to avoid their clumsy notation for symbols required to represent the numbers zero to fifty-nine, let us use the following: the digits 0, 1, 2, 3, 4, 5, 6, 7, 8, 9, as usual, and

Table 2

(Base) Ten	Two	Seven	Eight	Twelve[1]	Sixteen[2]
0	0	0	0	0	0
1	1	1	1	1	1
2	10	2	2	2	2
3	11	3	3	3	3
4	100	4	4	4	4
5	101	5	5	5	5
6	110	6	6	6	6
7	111	10	7	7	7
8	1,000	11	10	8	8
9	1,001	12	11	9	9
10	1,010	13	12	*t*	*u*
11	1,011	14	13	*e*	*v*
12	1,100	15	14	10	*w*
13	1,101	16	15	11	*x*
14	1,110	20	16	12	*y*
15	1,111	21	17	13	*z*
16	10,000	22	20	14	10
17	10,001	23	21	15	11
18	10,010	24	22	16	12
19	10,011	25	23	17	13
20	10,100	26	24	18	14
21	10,101	30	25	19	15
22	10,110	31	26	1*t*	16
23	10,111	32	27	1*e*	17
24	11,000	33	30	20	18
25	11,001	34	31	21	19
26	11,010	35	32	22	1*u*
27	11,011	36	33	23	1*v*
28	11,100	40	34	24	1*w*
29	11,101	41	35	25	1*x*
30	11,110	42	36	26	1*y*
31	11,111	43	37	27	1*z*
32	100,000	44	40	28	20

[1] Let t = ten, e = eleven.

[2] Let u, v, w, x, y, z represent the digits ten, eleven, twelve, thirteen, fourteen, and fifteen.

then the alphabet $a, b, c, \cdots, z$ to represent the numbers from ten to thirty-five, followed by $a', b', c', \cdots, w', x'$ for the numbers thirty-six to fifty-nine. The orders in this system would be determined by the powers of sixty. Expressed in base ten they are $60^0 = 1$, $60^1 = 60$, $60^2 = 3600$, and so on. In the base-sixty system any number from zero to fifty-nine, inclusive, would be a one-place numeral, or a digit. Any number from sixty to 3599 would be a two-place numeral, and so on. The numeral $2cx'$, base sixty, represents the number $2(60^2) + c(60) + x'(1)$, or, expressed in base ten, $2(3600) + 12(60) + 59(1) = 7979$.

Present-day automatic digital computers perform their operations by using a base two. This gives rise to a simple arithmetic which is suitable for machine computation, inasmuch as electric pulses (corresponding to ones) and their absence (corresponding to zeros) can be used in the computers. Again we note that the orders are determined by the powers of the base, namely, $2^0, 2^1, 2^2, 2^3$, and so on. Thus the base-two numeral 11,011, when expressed in base ten, is $1(2^4) + 1(2^3) + 0(2^2) + 1(2) + 1(1)$, or $16 + 8 + 0 + 2 + 1 = 27$ base ten. Although arithmetic in base two is simple, two is not a practical base, since it would take too much space to write even comparatively small numbers. In fact, most digital computers are set up to change from base two to a larger base so that answers may be reported in less space. A larger base could be base twenty, used by the Mayas. However, it has been found more convenient to use base sixteen in some digital computers.

An examination of Table 2 will give the reader a better understanding of the effect of the base on the writing of a number in other bases as compared to base ten.

In Table 2 it is seen that the number twelve is represented by the numerals 12, base ten, 1100, base two, 15, base seven, 14, base eight, 10, base twelve, and w, base sixteen. The base must be noted for each numeral. Verification of each of these numerals can be obtained by changing to base ten. Consider 1100, base two. This means $1(2^3) + 1(2^2) + 0(2) + 0(1) = 8 + 4 + 0 + 0 = 12$, base ten. Likewise 15, base seven is $1(7) + 5(1) = 12$, base ten. Thus it is seen that *in changing a numeral expressed in a given base to the equivalent numeral expressed in base ten it is necessary only to write out the meaning of the numeral in terms of the powers of its base expressed in base ten.* A series of multiplications followed by a series of additions gives the numeral expressed in base ten.

The inverse problem is that of changing a given numeral, base ten, to the equivalent numeral, expressed in a new base. Since the inverse of addition is subtraction and the inverse of multiplication is division, it would be expected that the operation could be done by a series of divisions and subtractions. The following example shows how a simple algorithm can be developed to make the required change from base ten to another base.

Example 1. Express 29, base ten, in base eight.

Solution. The powers of eight are 1, 8, 64, $\cdots$. Since 29 is less than 64, it is necessary only to determine how many eights there are in 29. This requires division. Thus

```
8 | 29 | 3
    24
     5
```

Since the remainder is 5, the next question is, "How many ones are there in 5?" Again the answer is found by division. By rewriting the foregoing expression, we arrive at the complete solution:

```
8 | 29 | 3
    24
1 |  5 | 5
     5
     0
```

Hence 29, base ten, is equivalent to $3(8) + 5(1)$, or 35, base eight. This may be checked in the table or by changing back to base ten.

Let it be agreed that hereafter in this book, *when numbers are written to different bases, the base will appear as a subscript which is always in base ten.* Thus 16_{12} means 16, base twelve, 332_{16} means 332, base sixteen, and 456_{10} means 456, base ten.

Example 2. Change 1957_{10} to base twelve.

Solution. The powers of twelve are 1, 12, 12^2, 12^3, $\cdots$, or 1, 12, 144, 1728, $\cdots$. Hence

```
1728 | 1957 | 1
       1728
 144 |  229 | 1
        144
  12 |   85 | 7
         84
   1 |    1 | 1
          1
          0
```

Thus $1957_{10} = 1(12^3) + 1(12^2) + 7(12) + 1(1) = 1171_{12}$. Note that if this algorithm is used the required number can be read directly as the set of quotients resulting from the successive divisions, the highest order occurring at the top.

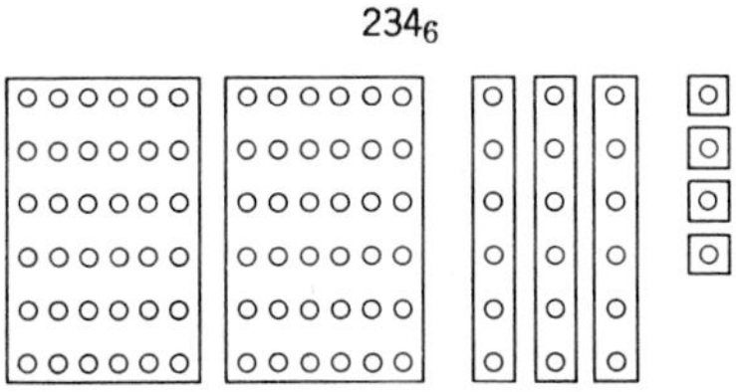

234_6

Diagram 1(*a*)

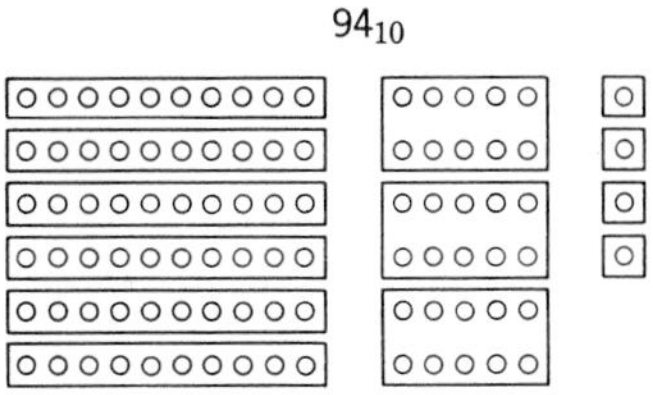

94_{10}

Diagram 1(*b*)

Example 3. Change 4907_{10} to base twelve.

Solution. Let t represent "ten" and e represent "eleven." It follows that

$$\begin{array}{r|r|l} 1728 & 4907 & 2 \\ & 3456 & \\ 144 & 1451 & t \\ & 1440 & \\ 12 & 11 & 0 \\ & 0 & \\ 1 & 11 & e \\ & 11 & \\ & 0 & \end{array}$$

Hence $4907_{10} = 2t0e_{12}$.

A little reflection will indicate that two processes, one of synthesis, or putting together, and the other of analysis, or taking apart, are used in changing numerals expressed in one base to numerals expressed in another base. Both processes involve a regrouping of units, as described in the following illustrations.

Consider the numeral 234_6. This numeral represents the collection of objects shown above in diagram 1(*a*).

In diagram 1(*b*) the objects of diagram 1(*a*) have been regrouped into familiar collections of tens and ones, showing 9 tens and 4 ones. The count of 9 tens and 4 ones can be obtained by putting together $2(36) + 3(6) + 4(1)$, which is the same as $72 + 18 + 4$, or 94.

The opposite process is illustrated in diagrams 2(*a*) and 2(*b*), in which 68_{10} is regrouped as 152_6.

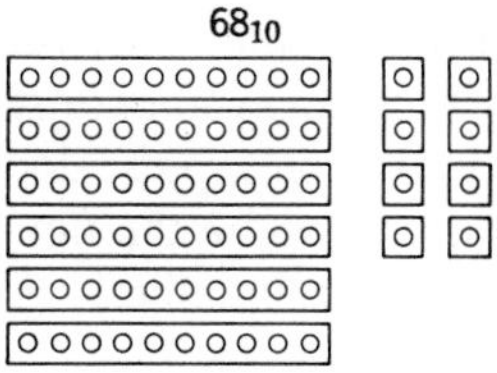

68_{10}

Diagram 2(*a*)

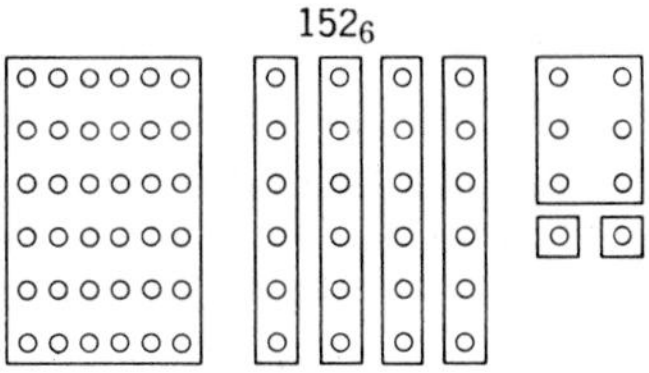

152_6

Diagram 2(*b*)

In diagram 2(*b*) the objects of diagram 2(*a*) have been separated into sets of 6×6, 6, and 1, to obtain one set of 6^2, five sets of 6, and two sets of 1. These sets are represented in 152_6. Regroupings for other bases could be treated in a similar manner.

EXERCISE 5

1. Write the following numbers as powers of ten:
(*a*) 3762_{10}, (*b*) 5060_{10}, (*c*) 2345_{10}.

2. Write the following numbers as powers of their bases:
(*a*) 231_4, (*b*) 76_{16}, (*c*) $37{,}156_8$, (*d*) $27te_{12}$ (t = ten, e = eleven), (*e*) $10{,}111_2$.

3. Change each of the numbers in problem 2 to base ten.

4. Change the following numbers to base ten:
(*a*) 234_5, (*b*) 234_{12}, (*c*) $6te_{12}$, (*d*) 503_7, (*e*) 555_{16}.

5. Change each of the following numbers to base seven:
$7_{10} = 10_7$, $10_{10} = 13_7$, $28_{10} =$ ——, $72_{10} =$ ——, $49_{10} =$ ——, $85_{10} =$ ——, $99_{10} =$ ——, $123_{10} =$ ——, $343_{10} =$ ——, $1000_{10} =$ ——.

6. Assume that each number is given in base ten and change it to base six:
6 18 35 78 218

7. Assume that each number is in base ten and change it to base twelve:
12 30 69 143 432 1000

8. Assume that each number is in base ten and change it to base two:
7 12 32 44 127 300

9. Change the number 1776_{10} to the following bases:
(*a*) base twelve, (*b*) base eight, (*c*) base five, (*d*) base two.

10. Change the number 4096_{10} to the following bases:
(*a*) base two, (*b*) base eight, (*c*) base twelve, (*d*) base twenty.

11. Solve each equation for the value of the unknown base:
$23_{10} = 25_b$ $67_{10} = 61_b$ $60_{10} = 50_b$ $38_{10} = 123_b$.

12. A number expressed in base ten is 324. Using a base b, the number is expressed as 642.
(*a*) Write the equation in b from which the value of b can be determined.
(*b*) Find the value or values of b which can be used as the base of 642.

2.7 NUMERATION

The art of expressing numbers in terms of words is called *numeration.* In an earlier section a numeral was defined as the abstract symbol or set of symbols representing a number. Numbers may also be represented by number names. Thus in English the first-order numbers are the familiar zero, one, two, three, and so on. The first second-order number, ten, is, of course, the base. The next two, 11 and 12, are eleven and twelve, believed to have been derived from the old Teutonic names meaning ten and one left over and ten and two left over. The remaining second-order numbers up to and including 19 are the familiar "teens," thirteen, fourteen, fifteen, sixteen, seventeen, eighteen, and nineteen.

These numbers are said to be in the first and second *decades*. Thus the first-order numbers 0, 1, · · · , 9 are sometimes called the ones decade, the numbers from 10 up to and including 19 are the second-decade numbers, sometimes called the "teens" decade.

Names of the remaining second-order numbers are formed as hyphenated words, consisting of the number of tens and the number of units. Thus 21 is written twenty-one, 57 is written fifty-seven, 93 is written ninety-three. Likewise, the decades are the twenties decade, the thirties decade, and so on.

Third-order numbers are the hundreds. The best way of reading such numbers is shown by the illustrations in Table 3.

Table 3

Numeral	Number Name
327	Three hundred twenty-seven
509	Five hundred nine
700	Seven hundred

Of course, there are other ways of reading these numbers. For example, 700 may be read seventy tens, but this is seldom done. A method of reading 327 by inserting an "and" between the three hundred and the twenty-seven is sometimes used, but it should be discouraged, since it may cause ambiguity when reading mixed decimal fractions, as is shown in a later chapter.

The units, tens, and hundreds orders are grouped in what is called the first *period* of a numeral. Similarly, the next three higher orders form the second period, and so on. Table 4 illustrates the relations between orders and periods and also shows the proper number names for the various orders.

Using the table, one would read the numeral 342,981,735,273,462 as three hundred forty-two trillion, nine hundred eighty-one billion, seven hundred thirty-five million, two hundred seventy-three thousand, four hundred sixty-two.

The following facts should be noted in Table 4 and the illustrative numerals. The periods are set off by commas, both in the numerals and the number names. They are given the name of the first order in each, with the exception of the first period, in which ones are understood.

Table 4

Order	Period	Power of Ten	Number Names
1		$10^0 = 1$	Units (or ones)
2	1	$10^1 = 10$	Tens
3		$10^2 = 100$	Hundreds
4		$10^3 = 1{,}000$	Thousands
5	2	$10^4 = 10{,}000$	Ten thousands
6		$10^5 = 100{,}000$	Hundred thousands
7		$10^6 = 1{,}000{,}000$	Millions
8	3	$10^7 = 10{,}000{,}000$	Ten millions
9		$10^8 = 100{,}000{,}000$	Hundred millions
10		$10^9 = 1{,}000{,}000{,}000$	Billions
11	4	$10^{10} = 10{,}000{,}000{,}000$	Ten billions
12		$10^{11} = 100{,}000{,}000{,}000$	Hundred billions
13		$10^{12} = 1{,}000{,}000{,}000{,}000$	Trillions
14	5	$10^{13} = 10{,}000{,}000{,}000{,}000$	Ten trillions
15		$10^{14} = 100{,}000{,}000{,}000{,}000$	Hundred trillions

As mentioned before, alternate methods could be used, even though they are not so desirable for reading numbers. Thus in reading the numeral for a date, 1959, for example, the best way is one thousand, nine hundred

Table 5

First Number in Period	English-German Name	Equivalent French-American Names
$10^0 = 1$	Units	Units
$10^6 = (1000000)^1$	Millions	Millions
$10^{12} = (1000000)^2$	Billions	Trillions
$10^{18} = (1000000)^3$	Trillions	Quintillions
$10^{24} = (1000000)^4$	Quadrillions	Septillions

fifty-nine. However, the common method is nineteen hundred fifty-nine. It should be noted that this method avoids the fourth order and expresses the number in third-, second-, and first-order number names only.*

* It is becoming common practice, in referring to large quantities, to speak of a million million items or a million billion items, and so on.

Unfortunately, the number names for numbers beyond the hundred millions are not the same in all countries. England and Germany, for example, divide their numbers into periods of six orders each and name these periods as millions, billions, trillions, and so on. Historically, these were the original names, but when the French changed their periods to three orders each in the 1600's the same names were used to represent the new three-order periods. The United States as well as many other countries followed the lead of the French. Table 5 illustrates the English-German system of numeration.

EXERCISE 6

1. Define the following concepts:
(*a*) order, (*b*) period (French-American usage), (*c*) period (English-German usage).

2. Write the following number words as numerals:
(*a*) seven thousand, three hundred seventy-five,
(*b*) six million, two hundred thirty-five thousand, one hundred four,
(*c*) one trillion, one million, one thousand, one,
(*d*) four million, forty-five thousand, three hundred two,
(*e*) twenty-three million, twenty-three thousand, twenty-three.

3. Write the following number words as numerals:
(*a*) eight hundred three thousand, twenty-four,
(*b*) six million, two hundred eighty thousand, fifty-six,
(*c*) two hundred eighty-three thousand, three hundred eighteen,
(*d*) four trillion, sixty-eight billion, five thousand,
(*e*) seventy billion, eight million, four hundred three,
(*f*) one million million,
(*g*) one million billion.

4. Write the number names of each of the following numerals:
(*a*) 2,372, (*b*) 73,501, (*c*) 62,045, (*d*) 3,617,235, (*e*) 43,078,650, (*f*) 4,851,732,334, (*g*) 76,058,490,209.

5. Write the number names of each of the following numerals:
(*a*) 28,603, (*b*) 16,075, (*c*) 186,300,
(*d*) 92,900,000, (*e*) 821,639,748, (*f*) 11,011,060,053,
(*g*) 7,846,783,056,012.

6. What is the largest number that could be read the same in both the English-German and the French-American systems of numeration?

7. Discuss the concept of a place-value number system, including the notions of absolute value, place value, and base and power of a base. Give examples of these concepts.

8. Explain why zero is important in a place-value number system.

9. Make a diagram similar to diagram 1(*a*)–1(*b*) to show the equivalence of 354_7 and 186_{10}.

10. Make a diagram similar to diagram 1(*a*)–1(*b*) to show the equivalence of 316_8 and 248_9.

11. Change the numerals 2364_7 and $3t1e_{12}$ to base ten.

12. Change the numerals 654_{10} and 1865_{10} to base twelve.

13. If the British pound is worth $2.80, is a bequest of a billion pounds in England worth as much as a bequest of two and a half trillion dollars in the United States of America?

14. Construct a number system base five and use the names of some of our collections of money to describe its place-value orders (e.g., 1, 5, 25, 125 cents have what common names?). Is the number represented by 1234_5 as large as the number 234_{10}?

EXERCISE 7

(*a*) *Brief review of numbers and numerals*

Write the following numbers in Arabic numerals:

1. Thirty-five

3. Five hundred four

5. Six thousand five

7. Forty thousand eight hundred three

9. Fifteen billion ten million eight thousand seven

Write the following numbers in words:

2. 43

4. 609

6. 10,027

8. 503,001

10. 37,000,000,600,040

Write Roman numerals to represent the following numbers:

11. The numbers 1 through 25

13. 84

15. 347

17. 1842

19. 1964

Write the following numbers in Arabic numerals:

12. XIV

14. XCIV

16. MDCLXVI

18. $\overline{\text{CXLVII}}$

20. MDCCIX

(*b*) *Preliminary practice in adding and subtracting whole numbers*

Add or subtract as indicated.

21.	**22.**	**23.**	**24.**
24	35	68	346
7	56	53	805
5	21	74	667
+8	+99	+28	+259

25.	**26.**	**27.**	**28.**
798	812	58113	30925
990	938	60094	7168
756	779	33345	59000
+623	+842	+98984	+8668

29. 334 -98 **30.** 6053 -965 **31.** 83455 -66997 **32.** 60004 -34567

33. 600 -283 **34.** 555 -495 **35.** 782034 -686868

36. Add each column of numbers, first downward, then upward for a check.

3456	5567	3092	8834	6993	9988	7703	8000
2105	6008	8192	6053	1111	2365	8993	6502
7862	2244	5678	8003	6565	4288	7990	6888
1123	9984	9746	6000	8333	3346	8907	9983
3354	2121	6663	7002	3597	6800	2115	1234
8255	6843	2386	7793	5964	3359	7198	8235

37. Subtract in each example and check by adding the subtrahend to the difference.

66666	81234	71000	68032	89896	73402	60000	78123
−12345	−55555	−38245	−31794	−56789	−64572	−35812	−66995

REFERENCES

Apostle, H. G., *A Survey of Basic Mathematics*, pp. 29–46.
Banks, J. H., *Learning and Teaching Arithmetic*, pp. 20–72.
Bell, E. T., *The Magic of Numbers*, pp. 148–157.
Dantzig, Tobias, *Number, the Language of Science*, pp. 20–77.
Dubisch, Roy, *The Nature of Number*.
Eulenberg, M. D., and T. S. Sunko, *Introductory Algebra, A College Approach*, pp. 7–35.
Kasner, E., and J. Newman, *Mathematics and the Imagination*, pp. 3–64.
Marks, J. L., C. R. Purdy, L. B. Kinney, *Teaching Arithmetic for Understanding*, pp. 61–78.
Mueller, Francis J., *Arithmetic, Its Structure and Concepts*, pp. 13–47.
Smith, D. E., and J. Ginsburg, *Number and Numerals*.
Swain, R. L., *Understanding Arithmetic*, pp. 1–35.

3

Addition

3.1 DEFINING ADDITION

The way to designate a place in a series was described in Chapter 2 by an ordinal number and the way to designate the number of objects in a collection was described by a cardinal number. When a study is made of a group of objects, it might be found that certain properties are common to every member of that group. If a group of three chairs is combined with another group of two chairs, this new group has a number property that is the result of addition. This leads us to the following definition:

Addition of natural numbers is the process of determining the cardinal number of a single set of objects when that set is made up of two or more nonoverlapping sets whose cardinal numbers are known.

The number zero 0 is included with the natural numbers in the set for which addition is initially defined.* At the close of this chapter a more general definition of addition is discussed.

The procedures used in carrying out the process of addition will depend considerably on the number system selected. First steps in addition will rest on counting, thereafter various rules for performing the operation can be developed. In all number systems certain reductions will have to be made. Some of these reductions can be observed in the following examples:

Illustration. Add the numbers in each system.

XXVIII	∩∩ |||| ||||	28 → 20 + 1 + 7
+XXXIX	+ ∩∩∩ |||| |||||	+39 → 30 + 9
XXXXX X V	∩∩ ||||| |||	50 + 10 + 7
III − I	∩∩∩ ||||| ||||	
L X V II	∩∩∩ |||	67 ← 60 + 7
	∩∩∩ ||||	

* The numbers in this set are sometimes called the *whole numbers*.

Discussion. In the Roman number system on the left the tens (X) are grouped and five (V) is added. The one (I) in nine (IX) is subtracted from three ones (III). In the Egyptian system, center, ten ones are regrouped to form ten, ∩ .

The result in addition is known as the *sum.* The sign for addition is the plus sign (+). The numbers added to make the sum are called *addends.* In the example $2 + 3 = 5$, two and three are the addends and five is the sum.

3.2 LAWS FOR THE OPERATION OF ADDITION

The addition of 3 and 5 could be written horizontally as $3 + 5 = 5 + 3$ or vertically as $\begin{array}{r} 3 \\ +5 \\ \hline \end{array}$ or $\begin{array}{r} 5 \\ +3. \\ \hline \end{array}$ The sum of 3 and 5 is the same as the sum of 5 and 3. This principle is stated as the *commutative law of addition.* In algebraic symbols it is written

$$a + b = b + a.$$

The sum of an addition is not affected by the order or sequence of its addends.

The sum of $(2 + 3) + 5$ is the same as that of $2 + (3 + 5)$ since $5 + 5$ gives the same result in addition as $2 + 8$. This principle is stated as the *associative law of addition.* In algebraic symbols it reads

$$(a + b) + c = a + (b + c).$$

The sum of an addition is not affected by the combinations or groupings of the addends. The two laws of addition are applied by a pupil when adding $7 + 8 + 3$ if he regroups and combines the 7 and 3 first and to the sum of 10 adds 8 for a total of 18.

In Chapter 2 number names were given for numerals; 327 is read three hundred twenty-seven. This means that the numeral is composed of three hundreds, two tens, and seven ones. If 327 and 251 are to be added the procedure could be performed by considering 327 and 251 as follows:

$$\begin{array}{l} 327 = 300 + 20 + 7 = 3 \text{ hundreds} + 2 \text{ tens} + 7 \text{ ones} \\ 251 = 200 + 50 + 1 = \underline{2 \text{ hundreds} + 5 \text{ tens} + 1 \text{ one}} \\ \qquad\qquad\qquad\qquad\quad\; 5 \text{ hundreds} + 7 \text{ tens} + 8 \text{ ones or } 578. \end{array}$$

3.3 THE COUNTING FRAME

A counting frame is a device consisting of beads or balls strung on wires, for example, ten on each wire, either vertically or horizontally. Primitive and modern abaci are counting frames with nine or fewer beads on each wire.

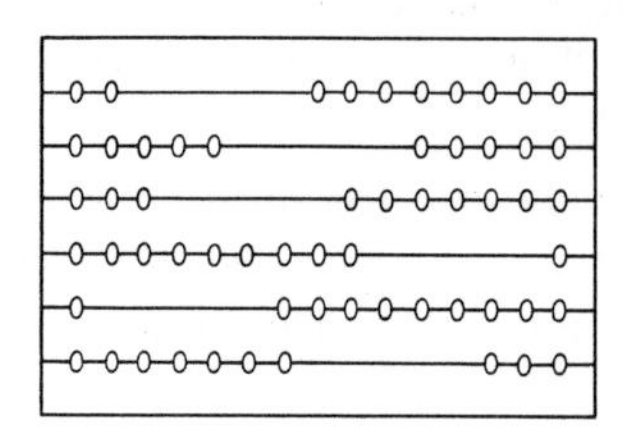

Fig. 1. Counting frame or abacus.

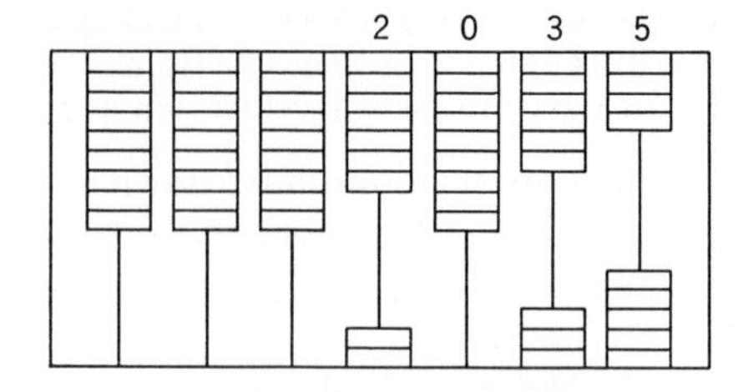

Fig. 2. Russian abacus.

The Russian abacus has vertical strings, each of which represents a group: ones, tens, hundreds, thousands, and so on. The number 2035 is shown on the Russian abacus.

The Chinese abacus has five beads on each wire below the dividing bar and two beads above the bar. The number 72,406 is shown on the Chinese abacus. Many small shops and department stores in the Orient today still use the abacus. In Yokohama, during one of the annual festivals, a contest is held in which sets of problems are worked, one group with abaci and another with adding machines and modern calculators. It is always a close contest. For the last three years of the 1950's the champion was a Japanese who did his calculations on the abacus.

Another type of abacus is used by the Japanese. This one has only one bead above the dividing bar and four beads below it. This abacus requires mental calculation not needed in other types. Although it calls for more concentration on the part of the user, there is more rapid calculation. On the 5-2 and 4-1 types of abaci the beads above the bar are worth five times as much as those below the bar.

Setting up the addition problem of 327 and 251 on a vertically strung, ten-bead counting frame is done as follows. The strings represent ones, tens, and hundreds from right to left. The number 327 is shown by pushing up seven beads in the ones column, two beads on the tens column, and

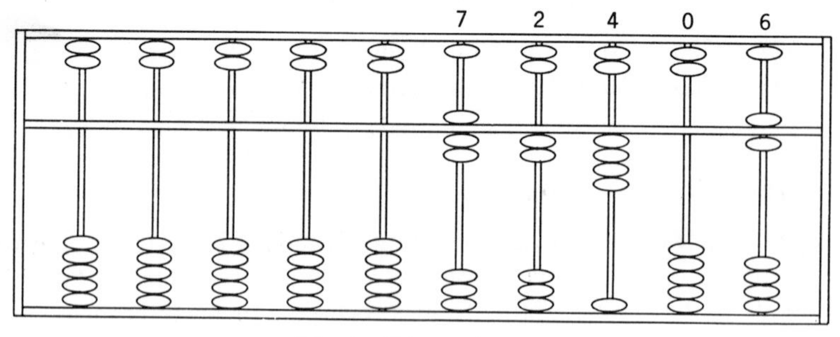

Fig. 3. Chinese abacus.

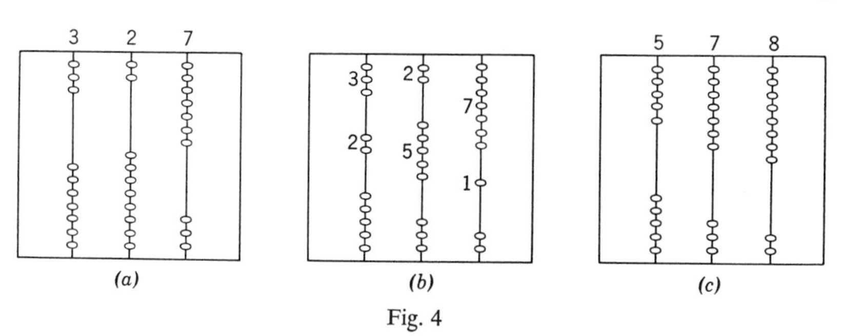

(a) (b) (c)

Fig. 4

three on the hundreds column. Diagram (*a*) in Fig. 4 reads 327. Diagram (*b*) illustrates 251, which is to be added. Diagram (*c*) shows the combination, giving the sum of 578. This problem is considered simple addition, since no carrying is involved.

3.4 METHODS OF ADDITION

The problem 68 + 47 is worked by four different methods.

(*a*) *Method of the counting frame.* 68 + 47. Diagram (*a*) in Fig. 5 reads 68. To add 7 of the 47, seven beads must be pushed up in the ones column, but there are only two beads left. Pushing up these two uses all ten beads in the ones column. One bead is pushed up in the tens column and all ten beads in the ones column are returned to the original starting position. Then the remaining five beads required for the 7 are pushed up. Diagram (*b*) shows the result of adding 7 to 68, which is 75. Next, to add the 4 tens of the 47, four beads in the tens column are needed to be pushed up. However, there are only three beads remaining. These three are pushed up, making all ten of the tens beads pushed up, which puts one bead up in the hundreds column, and the ten beads in the tens column are returned to their starting position on the wire. Now one more ten bead (remaining from the four to be added) is pushed up. The sum of 115 is indicated in diagram (*c*).

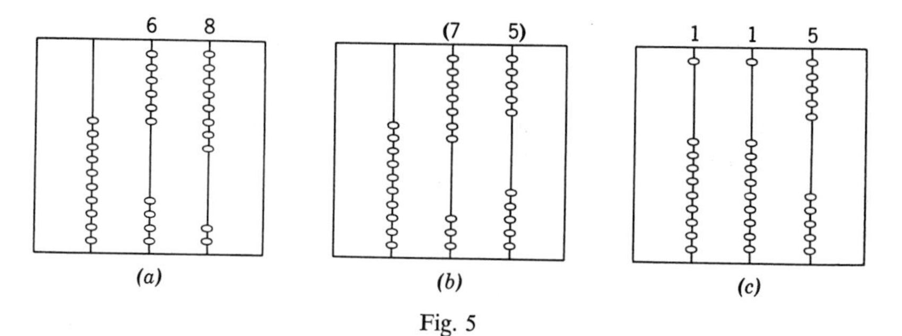

(a) (b) (c)

Fig. 5

(*b*) *Method of analysis.*

68 means 60 + 8 or 6 tens + 8 ones
47 means 40 + 7 or 4 tens + 7 ones

The sum is 10 tens + 15 ones, but 15 ones form 1 ten + 5 ones which gives 11 tens and 5 ones, but 10 tens make one hundred; hence we have 1 hundred + 1 ten + 5 ones. The sum is 115.

(*c*) *Civil service method.*

```
  68    Add 8 and 7, writing down 15.
  47
  --
  15    Add 6 and 4, writing 10, one column to the left,
 10     since 6 and 4 are tens.
 ---
 115
```

The sum is 115.

Another example of the civil service method is shown.

```
 347
 289
 345
 821
 ---
  22
 18
16
----
1802
```

The sum of the units column is 22.
The sum of the tens column is 18.
The sum of the hundreds column is 16.
The final sum is 1802.

A supposed advantage of this method is that if a clerk were interrupted it would be easy for him to find the place where he had been working. He would not have to remember what he had to carry in this method.

(*d*) *European scratch method.*

```
                  15     15
          10     10     10̸
  68      6̸8     6̸8̸     6̸8̸
  47      4̸7     4̸7̸     4̸7̸
  --      --     --     ---
                        115
 (a)     (b)    (c)    (d)
```

Beginning at the left, add 6 and 4, (*a*); scratch them out and write 10 above, (*b*). Add 8 and 7, scratch them out and put 15 above, (*c*). Since 1 and 0 equal 1, the 0 can be scratched, and the final sum is written underneath (*d*).

Another example by the scratch method is shown below. This time the steps are all in the addition problem as they would be when worked. Can you follow each step?

Example. Add 743 and 982 by the scratch method.

$$\begin{array}{r} 5 \\ 7 \\ 12 \\ 16 \\ 743 \\ \underline{982} \\ 1725 \end{array}$$

EXERCISE 1

1. What is the definition of addition according to the dictionary? Write a definition of addition in your own words.

2. Illustrate the addition of 427 and 356 by four methods.

3. Give in your own words, and illustrate, the commutative law and the associative law of addition.

4. Which pairs involve like terms and can be added?

(*a*) 2 desks, 3 chairs
(*b*) 3 cars, 4 cars
(*c*) 5 eggs, 2 eggs
(*d*) 3 dogs, 3 cats
(*e*) 4 kittens, 5 kittens
(*f*) 4 scissors, 5 knives
(*g*) 3 pencils, 2 pens
(*h*) 6 cups, 3 cups
(*i*) 7 tops, 3 spools
(*j*) 6, 3
(*k*) $\frac{1}{3}, \frac{1}{2}$
(*l*) $\frac{5}{6}, \frac{3}{6}$

Consider the "unlike" pairs in this problem. Is it possible to find some common characteristics by which the pairs might be grouped and then combined? If so, name them.

5. (*a*) Tell how many hundreds, how many tens, how many ones are in each number:

374 564 402 20 17

(*b*) The number 358 has how many hundreds? How many ones? How many tens?
(*c*) What digit has a place value of thousands in 8617?
(*d*) Express the numerals 782 and 1354 in terms of ones, tens, and so on.
(*e*) Why is a zero needed to form the numeral 10?

6. Consider the illustration of frying an egg in a pan: does it matter which comes first, the shortening or the egg? Why? Give one practical illustration of the commutative law of addition in which the law is valid and one in which it does not hold. Do the same for the associative law of addition.

7. Copy this problem in the form for column addition and add by the civil service method: 429 + 587 + 342 + 896 + 521. Has this method any advantages? Any disadvantages?

8. Give the advantages of having a counting frame with ten beads on the wire in contrast to the Chinese abacus with the dividing bar and five beads below it. Which would you prefer and why?

9. Sketch an abacus to show the numeral and then sketch the positions of the beads to show 437 added to 386.

10. (*a*) Add 7654 and 2189 by the method of analysis and then by the method of ordinary addition.

(*b*) Consider the addition problem:

$$\begin{array}{r} 7654 \\ 2189 \\ \hline 9843 \end{array}$$

(i) Adding 9 and 4, 3 is written down and 1 is "carried."

(ii) 5 and 8 and 1 are added, 4 is written down, and 1 "carried." Is the 1 in part (i) the same as the 1 in part (ii)? Why or why not?

3.5 ADDITION FACTS

At first children are fascinated by the attention they receive when counting. Oftentimes their counting is rote, and it may be 1, 2, 3, 4, 7, 10, 8, 12, · · · , according to words they recall. Later on the child learns to count rationally and enjoys counting his pennies, his fingers, his toes, and other groups of objects. When the child realizes that two apples combined with three apples make a sum of five apples, he is applying the process of addition. The first work in addition is very simple and is illustrated with concrete objects. The teacher has two pencils on the desk and one more pencil is added. How many pencils are now on the desk? A similar procedure can be used to act out all of the addition facts. After understanding has been gained by the use of concrete objects, the combinations can be illustrated with pictures of objects. Following the use of these semiconcrete materials, the abstract forms of writing the combinations can be developed.

The *basic addition facts* are derived from the number combinations in which the ten one-digit numbers are added two at a time in all possible ways. These one hundred addition combinations are shown in Table 6.

The commutative law reduces the number of distinct addition combinations to 55. When the pupil fully understands this principle, that $5 + 3 = 3 + 5$, for example, he can easily learn the facts below the double line in the table as the reverse facts of those above the double line. The zero facts need special attention and are usually postponed until some of the others without zeros have been mastered. Once the principle that zero added to any number gives the same number is understood, there should be little difficulty with the top row in the table. The twenty-five most important facts, which must be learned early, are those with sums of ten or less; these are shown in the shaded area of the table. The facts below the single line and to the right of the double line can be delayed for a time. The twenty-five facts with sums of ten or less are developed ordinarily as part of the work in grades 1 and 2; the zero facts are brought in during or before grade 3.

Table 6

Basic Addition Combinations

0 0	1 0	2 0	3 0	4 0	5 0	6 0	7 0	8 0	9 0
0 1	1 1	2 1	3 1	4 1	5 1	6 1	7 1	8 1	9 1
0 2	1 2	2 2	3 2	4 2	5 2	6 2	7 2	8 2	9 2
0 3	1 3	2 3	3 3	4 3	5 3	6 3	7 3	8 3	9 3
0 4	1 4	2 4	3 4	4 4	5 4	6 4	7 4	8 4	9 4
0 5	1 5	2 5	3 5	4 5	5 5	6 5	7 5	8 5	9 5
0 6	1 6	2 6	3 6	4 6	5 6	6 6	7 6	8 6	9 6
0 7	1 7	2 7	3 7	4 7	5 7	6 7	7 7	8 7	9 7
0 8	1 8	2 8	3 8	4 8	5 8	6 8	7 8	8 8	9 8
0 9	1 9	2 9	3 9	4 9	5 9	6 9	7 9	8 9	9 9

Many teachers develop the addition facts in number families. The "5" family is made up of 5 + 0, 0 + 5, 4 + 1, 1 + 4, 2 + 3, 3 + 2. After subtraction has been studied, 5 − 0, 5 − 5, 5 − 1, 5 − 4, 5 − 2, 5 − 3 can be combined with the "5" family. Little stories can be made up to go along with the study of these number families.

Consider the number facts whose sums are greater than ten. These can be treated in terms of facts whose sums are ten, 9 + 1, 8 + 2, 7 + 3,

$6 + 4$, $5 + 5$, $4 + 6$, $3 + 7$, $2 + 8$, $1 + 9$, on which much emphasis should be placed. When the child knows that $6 + 4 = 10$ and he is confronted with the problem $6 + 5 = ?$, his thinking can be directed to the realization that 5 is one more than 4. Since $6 + 4$ equal 10, then $6 + 5$ equal 11; that is, $6 + 5$ is the same as $6 + 4 + 1$, or 11. If the problem is $8 + 4$, the child realizes that $6 + 4$ equal 10, and 8 is 2 more than 6, so $8 + 4$ equal 12; or again, 8 and 2 are 10, and 4 is 2 more than 2, so 8 and 4 are 12. In symbols, $8 + 4$ is considered as $2 + (6 + 4)$ or as $(8 + 2) + 2$. The child must be made to feel that the addition facts have meaning because he has manipulated objects to find the sums and has also worked them out on a counting frame.

3.6 HIGHER DECADE ADDITION

The addition facts may be divided into two groups: those whose sums are less than ten and those whose sums are ten or more than ten. If the student knows that $5 + 2 = 7$, then his knowledge can be expanded by showing that $15 + 2 = 17$, $25 + 2 = 27$, $35 + 2 = 37$, $55 + 2 = 57$, or that $5 + 12 = 17$, $5 + 22 = 27$, $5 + 32 = 37$, and so on, all sums being in the same decade as that of the larger addend. If the student knows that $9 + 4 = 13$ and that this sum is more than ten, then he knows that the sum of $19 + 4$ or that of $9 + 14$ is in the decade next higher than that of the larger addend. Thus $29 + 4 = 33$, $49 + 4 = 53$, $9 + 14 = 23$, or $9 + 34 = 43$. In each case the sum is one decade higher than that of the larger addend. *Higher decade addition* (or adding by endings) is the name given to the process of *adding a single-digit number to a two-digit number, provided the sum is less than one hundred.*

EXERCISE 2

1. Give the sums:

23	47	56	25	45	50	43	36	79	84
9	7	6	2	8	5	4	8	8	7
53	12	25	46	43	52	16	64	92	65
8	9	7	5	9	9	8	4	6	9

2. To 7, 27, 57, 37, 47, 97, 67, 87, 17, 77, add 2, giving sums as 9, 29, 59, and so on. To the same numbers add 4; add 7; add 9.

3. To 12, 35, 68, 74, 46, 59, 25, 81, 43, 87, add 3; add 6; add 8.

4. Explain in your own words what is meant by "adding by endings." How does the pupil know whether to give the sum in the same decade or the next higher decade of the addends?

3.7 COLUMN ADDITION

In adding single columns of three, four, or more digits, higher decade addition applies. For example, 11 + 6, 17 + 8, 25 + 5 are higher decade combinations that appear in adding downward in the column at the right. Adding upward, 13 + 6, 19 + 7, 26 + 4 are also higher decade additions. Some teachers recommend using the associative law and picking out sums of ten or two tens, such as 4 + 6 and 7 + 8 + 5. Checking can be done by adding in the opposite direction. It is generally recommended that pupils learn to add consistently in one direction and to check by adding in the opposite direction.

```
 4
 7
 6
 8
 5
--
30
```

3.8 ADDITION OF NUMBERS REPRESENTED BY TWO-AND THREE-DIGIT NUMERALS

Problems involving the sums of two- and three-digit numbers* are usually divided into two groups: those with sums obtained without carrying and those with sums obtained with carrying. Consider the following problems.

1. Finding the sum of 23 and 34 is a problem without carrying.

23	is	20 + 3	or	2 tens + 3 ones
34	is	30 + 4	or	3 tens + 4 ones
The sum is				5 tens + 7 ones or 57.

The pupil must realize that 23 is 20 + 3 and that 34 is 30 + 4, hence the sum is 50 + 7. Too often the problem 23/34 is considered as 2/+3 3/+4, two separate addition problems.

2. Finding the sum of 35 and 78 is a problem with carrying.

35	is	30 + 5	or	3 tens + 5 ones
78	is	70 + 8	or	7 tens + 8 ones
The sum is				10 tens + 13 ones (13 ones become 1 ten and 3 ones)
which is the same as				10 tens 1 ten + 3 ones
The sum now becomes				11 tens + 3 ones (11 tens become 1 hundred and 1 ten)
This is		1 hundred +		1 ten + 3 ones or 113.

* It is common practice to refer to numbers represented by numerals made up of one or more digits simply as numbers having one or more digits. In general, this practice is followed in this book.

The solution of this problem is usually abridged as follows:

35	35	5 + 8 = 13, put down 3 and carry 1 (ten)
78	78	3 + 7 + 1 = 11 (tens), write down 11,
	113	making 1 hundred and 1 ten.

The sum is 113.

EXERCISE 3

Find the following sums:

1.

9	8	6	5	8	6	2	7	6	7
2	2	4	6	9	7	6	7	4	5
9	9	7	3	5	9	3	3	3	2
7	8	3	6	8	3	8	9	9	6
					4	5	4	8	5

2.

612	245	385	450	45	43	732
234	324	14	430	22	26	146

3.

37	58	63	67	54	37	58	25	43	79
46	49	58	57	76	69	89	57	38	52

4.

28	62	19	60	187	776	882	903
76	53	82	55	603	198	712	714
43	44	73	76	982	633	403	246
99	87	48	34	435	495	200	777

5.

586	939	240	830	2074	5903	274	8803
717	658	406	131	59	465	3987	2965
427	497	154	92	909	37	54	4476
			687	1294	634	123	3098

3.9 SUMMARY OF ADDITION

The following outline shows a number of different types of addition problems which the reader should study carefully.

1. Basic addition facts
   (*a*) Those with sum less than ten such as $5 + 2$
   (*b*) Those with sum ten or more such as $7 + 4$
2. Single column addition
   (*a*) Using only the basic addition facts

   3
   2
   4

3. Addition by endings (higher decade addition without bridging)
   (*a*) Sums in same decade

   15
   4

4. Addition of two-digit numbers without carrying

37
21

5. Single column additions
   (*a*) Sums less than twenty

9
4
6

6. Addition by endings (higher decade addition with bridging)
   (*a*) Sums in the next higher decade

28
3

7. Addition of two-digit numbers with carrying
   from the units column

38
24

8. Single column addition
   (*a*) Sums greater than or equal to twenty

4
9
8
7

9. Addition of two-or-more digit numbers with
   multiple carrying

63
84
45
57

3.10 CHECKS FOR ADDITION—THE CHECK BY CASTING OUT NINES

Pupils should develop the habit of checking their work. A general method involving whole numbers is discussed below. This is the check called "casting out nines." It is also applied to checking addition. However, two other methods of checking addition are given.

The *check by nines* is based on properties of a place-value number system with base ten. It is a check that can be used to trace any one of the four fundamental operations with whole numbers and it is rather easy to apply.

Consider the remainder obtained by dividing any power of ten by 9: for example, 1,000,000, or 1000, or 100. Since $1{,}000{,}000 = 999{,}999 + 1$, 9 divides this number with a remainder of 1. Similarly, $1000 = 999 + 1$, and 9 divides this number with a remainder of 1. Quite generally any power of ten is just one more than a multiple of 9; hence the remainder on division by 9 will be 1. Now, 2000 would have a remainder of 2; 5,000,000 would have a remainder of 5, and so on.

Any number in base ten can be separated in a manner similar to that shown in the following example:

$$2345 = 2000 + 300 + 40 + 5.$$

By removing all 9's from each of the parts of this number, we obtain remainders 2, 3, 4, and 5. When these remainders are combined, an additional 9 can be removed to obtain a final remainder of 5. In this manner a remainder 0 to 8 can be obtained as a representative for any whole number. Thus any whole number can be shown to belong to one and only one remainder class, among nine classes, according as its remainder is 0, 1, $\cdots$, or 8 when divided by 9.

The check by casting out nines consists in finding a representative or remainder for each entry in a problem and then performing the same operation on the representatives as was done on the original entries. Because the work with remainder classes preserves the results of operations on the numbers, the answer to a problem must occur in the number class determined by the representatives. The procedure is illustrated by the following example:

Example 1. Add and check by casting out nines.

$$\begin{array}{rlr}
234 \to & 2+3+4 \to 9 & \to 0 \\
605 \to & 6+5 \to 11 & \to 2 \\
138 \to & 1+8+3 \to 9+3 & \to 3 \\
493 \to & 4+3+9 \to 4+3 & \to 7 \downarrow \\
\hline
1470 \to & 12 \to \quad ③ \quad \leftarrow & \overline{12}
\end{array}$$

The work of finding remainders or representatives can be shortened materially in two ways when it is remembered that 9's are being subtracted and that powers of ten contribute separate remainders. These shortcuts are (1) dispense with any 9 or sum of 9 during the procedure: $138 \to \not{1}3\not{8} \to 3$, and (2) add remainders wherever feasible: $11 \to 1 + 1 \to 2$.

The check by nines applies to subtraction as well as multiplication and division. It is not an absolute check, however, since digit inversion errors are not detected. Thus $3187 \to 1$ and $3817 \to 1$.

Example 2. Subtract and check by casting out nines.

$$\begin{array}{rlr}
3686 \to & 9+14 \to 5 & 5 \downarrow \\
-2478 \to & 9+12 \to 3 & -3 \\
\hline
1208 \to & 9+\ \ 2 \to & ②
\end{array}$$

Example 3. Multiply and check by casting out nines.

$$\begin{array}{rlr}
348 \to & 15 \to & 6 \\
\times 23 \to & & \times 5 \\
\hline
1044 & & 30 \\
696 & & \downarrow \\
\hline
8004 \to & 12 \to & ③
\end{array}$$

Two other checks for addition are the following:

(*a*) *Add again.* After performing the addition, repeat the work. The resulting sum should be the same.

(*b*) *Add the columns in a different direction.* If the pupil usually adds from top to bottom, he should add the column again in the opposite direction, from bottom to top.

EXERCISE 4

1. Add each of the following downward and then check by reversing the direction adding upward:

23	68	11	48	83	62
46	74	64	80	57	48
85	22	93	75	94	59
94	53	44	63	23	88
12	89	72	29	16	71

2. Add each of the following and check by casting out nines:

3847	1158	4831	6203	9902
6531	9076	2764	4974	3944
2095	2594	9095	3842	4199
7734	3008	8837	3456	6604

3. What would be the remainder of each number when divided by 9?
(*a*) 38,645,207,611 (*b*) 73,483,906,255

4. Why is 345162 − 261543 exactly divisible by 9?

5. What number should be cast out in checking work with numbers in base twelve? What number should be used in checking in base eight?

6. Add the following items and check by casting out nines:

$384.62	$483.25	$1023.50
28.93	650.75	475.95
752.48	300.80	2264.73
602.54	566.40	3154.66

3.11 THE AVERAGE AND THE MEDIAN FOR A SET OF DATA

The *average* or *arithmetic mean* of a set of entries (scores or other numbers) is, by definition, the sum of the entries divided by the number of entries. To find the average for a set of entries, find their sum and divide this sum by the number of entries.

Example 1. Find the average of the following five scores made on a test: 16, 18, 24, 14, 10.

The scores are added and then divided by five, since there are five scores. The average is

$$\frac{16 + 18 + 24 + 14 + 10}{5} \quad \text{or} \quad \frac{82}{5} \quad \text{or} \quad 16\tfrac{2}{5}.$$

The *median* of a set of entries (scores or numbers) is the middle entry in the set of entries when they are arranged in ascending or descending order. To find the median, arrange the entries in ascending or descending order and count to the middle term. If the number of entries is even, then there is no median; however, the number half way between the two middle entries is often taken as the median in this case.

Example 2. Find the median in the foregoing example.
Solution. The scores are first arranged in descending order: 24, 18, 16, 14, 10. The third number, 16, is the median.

EXERCISE 5

1. Arrange these addition problems in order of increasing difficulty and tell how each problem differs from the preceding one:

37	27	7	3	15	9	28	9	5
12	15	6	2	2	4	19	8	2
		5	4				7	

2. (*a*) Find the average length of sticks in a bundle containing five sticks of lengths 32, 28, 17, 20, 26 inches.
(*b*) What is the median length?
(*c*) Which is greater, the median or the average? Is this always true? Why or why not?

3. Comparing the nine steps of addition procedure with techniques of increasing difficulty, which step do you consider offers the most difficulty? How would you overcome this difficulty in your teaching?

4. Which visual aid suggestion for addition in Appendix A do you consider the most effective for class work? Tell how you would use it and why you selected it.

5. Library research. What are magic squares? Where did they originate? How could they be used in a class?

3.12 ADDITION USING BASES OTHER THAN TEN

Below are some examples of addition in other number bases. Work with the fundamental operations in bases other than ten can give the student a better understanding of place value and a better grasp of the principles of carrying and regrouping.

Example 1. Add 231 and 22 when both numbers are given in base four.

231_4	$2 + 1 = 3,$	which is written down, since it is less than the base, 4.
22_4	$3 + 2$	gives 1 more than the base, which makes 1 for the column, and 1 carried to the next.
313_4	$2 + 1$	gives 3. The final answer is 313_4.

Check by changing to base ten:

$$\begin{array}{rl} 231_4 &= 2(4)^2 + 3(4) + 1 = 2(16) + 12 + 1 = 32 + 12 + 1 = 45_{10} \\ \underline{22_4} &= \qquad\quad 2(4) + 2 = \qquad\quad 8 + 2 = \qquad\qquad\quad \underline{10_{10}} \\ 313_4 &= 3(4)^2 + 1(4) + 3 = 3(16) + 4 + 3 = 48 + 4 + 3 = 55_{10} \end{array}$$

Example 2. Add 314 and 266, both numbers being given in base eight.

314_8	$4 + 6 =$	2 more than the base, 8. The 2 is written and eight 1's are carried as 1 of next order.
266_8	$6 + 1 + 1 =$	base eight. The 0 is written, and eight 8's are carried as 1 in the next column.
602_8	$3 + 2 + 1 =$	6. The answer is 602_8.

Check by changing to base ten:

$$\begin{array}{rl} 314_8 &= 3(8)^2 + 1(8) + 4 = 3(64) + 8 + 4 = 204_{10} \\ \underline{266_8} &= 2(8)^2 + 6(8) + 6 = 2(64) + 48 + 6 = \underline{182_{10}} \\ 602_8 &= 6(8)^2 + 0(8) + 2 = 6(64) + 2 \qquad = 386_{10} \end{array}$$

Thus 602 base eight = 386 base ten.

Problems in other bases can also be checked by casting out the number that is one less than the base. For example, to check in base eight, cast out sevens.

$$\begin{array}{l} 314_8 \rightarrow 1 + 7 \rightarrow 1 \\ \underline{266_8} \rightarrow 1 + 6 \rightarrow \underline{7} \\ 602_8 \rightarrow 10_8 \rightarrow \quad \textcircled{1} \end{array}$$

EXERCISE 6

1. Add the following quantities:

3 gross 4 dozen 7 ones	3 gallons 2 quarts 1 pint
5 gross 7 dozen 8 ones	5 gallons 3 quarts 1 pint

2. Make a list of basic addition facts for numbers up to 8 in base eight. Notice that 8 will appear as 10_8 in base eight.

3. (*a*) The expression "4 score and 7 years ago" implies what number as a base?

(*b*) Add and check by changing to base ten.

3 score and 10
4 score and 7
6 score and 4

(*c*) Rewrite the problem in part (*b*), using tens instead of scores, and add and check.

4. Find the sums of the numbers in each given base:

321_4	236_7	543_8	324_5	319_{12}
123_4	414_7	426_8	123_5	207_{12}

5. Check the answers in problem 4 by changing the numbers to base ten and adding.

6. Check the answers in problem 4 by casting out the number that is one less than the base in each case.

7. Find the average and the median score for the following set of test grades: 83, 75, 91, 68, 87, 72, 78.

8. Find the average value of the amount of money spent during a six-month period for food: \$128.50, \$110.75, \$122.60, \$98.80, \$120.25, \$115.10.

3.13 MORE ABOUT ADDITION (Optional topic)

Addition was defined for natural numbers at the beginning of this chapter. For the natural numbers and zero, addition is an operation in which a cardinal number is assigned to a set composed of two or more nonoverlapping sets whose cardinal numbers are known. In this section we shall consider addition as an operation that applies to a larger set of numbers than the natural numbers in which the natural numbers are a subset.

Addition as an abstract operation on numbers can be defined as outlined below. It is an operation on numbers that will satisfy certain properties. To be specific, we shall think of the operation as applying to the real numbers, which include the positive and negative integers, zero, fractions (or rational numbers), and irrational numbers (see section 10.1), such as $\sqrt{3}$, $\sqrt[3]{7}$, and π. Addition is an operation that assigns to any pair of real numbers a unique real number called their sum. This operation has the following properties:

Let $R = \{a, b, c, \cdots\}$ be the set of real numbers, for example, and let $+$ indicate the operation of addition.

1. $a + b = r$, where r is in the set R; that is, the *sum* of two numbers in a set is a *number of the set*. This property is called the *closure* property of addition.

2. $a + b = b + a$ for all choices of a and b in R. This property is called the *commutative* property of addition.

3. $a + (b + c) = (a + b) + c$ for all a, b, c in R. This property is called the *associative* property of addition.

4. There is in R a unique element, 0, such that $a + 0 = 0 + a = a$ for every a in R. This property asserts the existence of *zero*, which is also called the identity element for addition. Zero is the element which when added to any element of R will yield the original element; for example, $0 + 5 = 5$.

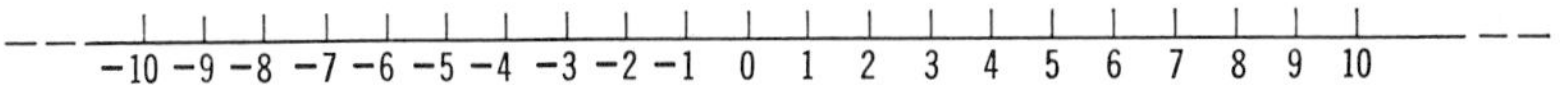

−10 −9 −8 −7 −6 −5 −4 −3 −2 −1 0 1 2 3 4 5 6 7 8 9 10

Fig. 6

5. Given any element a in R, there exists a unique element, $-a$ in R, called the negative of a, such that

$$a + (-a) = 0.$$

The element $-a$ is also called the *additive inverse* of a.

The set of natural numbers can be extended to form the set of *positive and negative integers* by taking the natural numbers and their additive inverses and zero.

All five of the properties listed for addition can be checked on the *real number line* (Fig. 6) on which the zero point and a unit distance are chosen. Positive numbers extend to the right of zero and negative numbers extend to the left. A fundamental postulate of the real number line is that there is a one-to-one correspondence between the real numbers and the points of a line on which a unit, a zero point, and a positive direction have been chosen. This permits the addition of segments on the line in order to add real numbers.

In adding, positive numbers are taken as segments measured to the right and negative numbers are taken as segments measured to the left. The student should verify that

$$3 + 4 = 7 = 4 + 3,$$

$$(-2) + (-3) = -5 = (-3) + (-2),$$

$$(-3) + 4 = 1 = 4 + (-3),$$

$$(-5) + 2 = -3 = 2 + (-5),$$

$$[2 + (-3)] + 5 = (-1) + 5 = 4,$$

$$2 + [(-3) + 5] = 2 + 2 = 4.$$

Some sets of numbers satisfying the properties of addition are (1) the set of positive and negative integers and zero, (2) the set of positive and negative fractions (including the integers), (3) the set of all possible decimal fractions and mixed decimals, finite or infinite, that represents the real numbers. Finally, the complex numbers, which we meet in intermediate algebra, also admits the operation of addition. Each of these systems is contained as a subsystem in the ones that follow it.

As an illustration of a finite set of elements that admits the operation of addition, we can take the set of remainders obtained on division by nine, namely 0, 1, 2, 3, 4, 5, 6,7, 8. A check of the following table will show that all of the properties of addition are satisfied:

Addition of Remainders for Divisor 9.

+	0	1	2	3	4	5	6	7	8
0	0	1	2	3	4	5	6	7	8
1	1	2	3	4	5	6	7	8	0
2	2	3	4	5	6	7	8	0	1
3	3	4	5	6	7	8	0	1	2
4	4	5	6	7	8	0	1	2	3
5	5	6	7	8	0	1	2	3	4
6	6	7	8	0	1	2	3	4	5
7	7	8	0	1	2	3	4	5	6
8	8	0	1	2	3	4	5	6	7

1. *Closure.* The sum of any two remainders is a unique remainder in the table.

2. *Commutative law.* Symmetry around the diagonal line from upper left to lower right shows the commutative property.

3. *Associative law.* The associative property can be verified for special cases. For example,

$$(2 + 3) + 4 = (5) + 4 = 0 \quad \text{and} \quad 2 + (3 + 4) = 2 + (7) = 0.$$

4. *Identity.* The zero, 0, is the identity for the table, as shown in the first row and the first column inside the table.

5. *Inverses.* The existence of an additive inverse for every element is shown by the fact that 0 occurs once and only once in every row and column of the table. To find the inverse of any element, such as 3, read along the row to find zero; above zero read the inverse. In this case the inverse of 3 is 6.

Problem. Construct a table for addition of remainder classes that would be obtained for the divisor 7. Every number would be in one of the classes 0, 1, 2, 3, 4, 5, 6. After making the table, verify the five addition properties from the table and give examples for each property.

EXERCISE 7

Preliminary practice in multiplication and division

1. Find the cost of (*a*) ten pens costing 35 cents each, (*b*) twenty packages of paper costing 28 cents each, (*c*) three books costing $1.50 each.

2. Work out each product.

20	29	40	62	23	64	38	95	73	97
× 3	× 6	× 5	× 7	×10	×20	×44	× 5	× 8	×61

3. Find each product.

23	75	234	703	86	93	615	774	508	672
×10	× 4	× 6	× 9	×20	×25	× 73	× 35	×123	×305

4. How far does a jet plane fly in twelve hours, if its average speed is
(*a*) 370 mph (*b*) 450 mph (*c*) 605 mph (*d*) 579 mph?

5. How far will a passenger train travel in fifteen hours, if its average speed is
(*a*) 30 mph (*b*) 48 mph (*c*) 56 mph (*d*) 63 mph?

6. Work out each product.

420	603	665	589	6154	8803
×305	× 18	×294	×490	× 306	× 557

7. Work out each product.

345	763	856	907	688	8813
×208	×442	×456	×309	×531	× 277

8. Find the total cost of: three shirts at $2.95, four ties at $1.75, and five pair of hose at 85 cents.

Find the quotient in each example:

9. $7\overline{)735}$

10. $6\overline{)6036}$

11. $5\overline{)2515}$

12. $13\overline{)2613}$

13. $23\overline{)23046}$

14. $8\overline{)1680}$

15. $17\overline{)3400}$

16. $15\overline{)21555}$

17. $28\overline{)14056}$

18. $6\overline{)2406}$

19. What is the cost of each small pie if eight of them are sold for $1.20?

20. What is the cost of one pencil if a gross of pencils (144) costs $4.32?

21. What is the equal share of each of five persons sharing an estate of $23,450?

22. What is the cost per gallon of gasoline if twelve gallons cost $4.68?

REFERENCES

Banks, J. H., *Learning and Teaching Arithmetic*, pp. 50–92 and 113–139.

Brueckner, L. J., and F. E. Grossnickle, *How to Make Arithmetic Meaningful*, pp. 170–242.

Larsen, H. D., *Arithmetic for Colleges*, pp. 31–62.
Layton, W. I., *College Arithmetic*, pp. 5–26.
Marks, J. L., C. R. Purdy, and L. B. Kinney, *Teaching Arithmetic for Understanding*, pp. 110–149.
Morton, R. L., *Teaching Arithmetic in the Elementary School*, Vol. 2, pp. 42–73.
Mueller, F. J., *Arithmetic, Its Structure and Concepts*, pp. 48–69.
Swain, R. L., *Understanding Arithmetic*, pp. 27–53.

4

Multiplication

4.1 INTRODUCTION AND DEFINITIONS

Among the basic addition facts, there are the following that contain equal addends: $1 + 1 = 2$, $2 + 2 = 4$, $3 + 3 = 6$, $4 + 4 = 8, \cdots,$ $9 + 9 = 18$. Another way of stating these facts is to say that two 1's are 2, two 2's are 4, two 3's are 6, and so on. In these cases two equal addends are combined to form the sum. *Multiplication* is the name given to this process of combining a collection of equal addends. The result is called the *product*. Multiplication can thus be thought of as a special case of addition: $20 + 20 + 20$ would be three 20's, or 60. Since 20 has been taken three times, one could say that 3 times 20 are 60. Horizontal and vertical forms of this statement are

$$3 \times 20 = 60 \quad \text{and} \quad \begin{array}{r} 20 \\ \times\ 3 \\ \hline 60 \end{array}$$

In a multiplication problem the first number (lower number) is called the *multiplier* and the second number (upper number) is the *multiplicand.* Thus in the example displayed above 3 is called the multiplier, 20 is the multiplicand, and 60 is the product. The numbers multiplied to form the product are called *factors* of the product. In the example of $3 \times 20 = 60$, 3 and 20 are two factors of 60. Other factors of 60 are 5 and 12; 2, 2, and 15; 3, 4, and 5. Any one of the factors of a product taken by itself is called a *divisor* of the product. Thus 2 or 5 or 12 or 30 $\cdots$ is a divisor of 60.

A commonly used symbol for multiplication is two small crossed lines similar to an "x", usually called "times." In algebra and in some other forms of calculation a small raised dot (·) sometimes indicates multiplication. Also in algebra letters written next to each other are used to indicate a product; for example, $abc = a \times b \times c$. In our notation (United

States) $2 \cdot 3$ means 2×3 and should not be confused with 2.3, which means two and three tenths. In Great Britain, however, a raised dot is a decimal point and a dot on the line is used for multiplication.

4.2 LAWS FOR MULTIPLICATION

In multiplying $3 \times 4 \times 5$, the factors could be grouped in the form $(3 \times 4) \times 5$ or $3 \times (4 \times 5)$ to obtain $12 \times 5 = 60$ or $3 \times 20 = 60$. This principle is the *associative law of multiplication* and it is stated as follows: *the product of a multiplication is not affected by the way in which the factors are grouped.* In algebraic symbols the associative law reads

$$(ab)c = a(bc) = abc, \quad \text{where } abc \text{ means } a \times b \times c.$$

When multiplying 3×4, it does not matter whether the factors are multiplied in the order given or in the reverse order, 4×3. This principle is the *commutative law of multiplication*, which is stated as follows: *the product of a multiplication is unaffected by the order in which the factors are multiplied.* In algebraic symbols the commutative law reads

$$a \times b = b \times a \quad \text{or} \quad ab = ba.$$

When multiplying $3 \times (4 + 6 + 10)$, it does not matter whether the sum of 4, 6, and 10 is multiplied by three to obtain 3×20 for the product of 60, or whether 4, 6, and 10 are individually multiplied by three to obtain 12, 18, and 30, which are then added to make 60. This principle is the *distributive law of multiplication with respect to addition.* Multiplication is said to be distributive with respect to addition. This law is stated as follows: *to obtain the product of a given number and the sum of several numbers, either add the several numbers and multiply their sum by the given number or multiply each of the several numbers by the given number and add the products.* In algebraic symbols the distributive law reads

$$a(b + c) = ab + ac.$$

Discussion.

1. What are the three laws governing multiplication? Give examples of each. What laws that govern addition were given?
2. Distinguish between the associative and commutative laws of multiplication.
3. Using the algebraic symbolism, $a(b + c + d) = ab + ac + ad$ is an application of what law?
4. What laws are applied if a student finds the product of $4 \times 2 \times 3 \times 5$ by taking 12×10 or 120?
5. To say that 5×4 is the same as 4×5 is an application of what law?

It is often stated that the multiplier is always an abstract number. This statement can lead to unnecessary confusion and misunderstanding, since all numbers should be abstracted for computational purposes. If

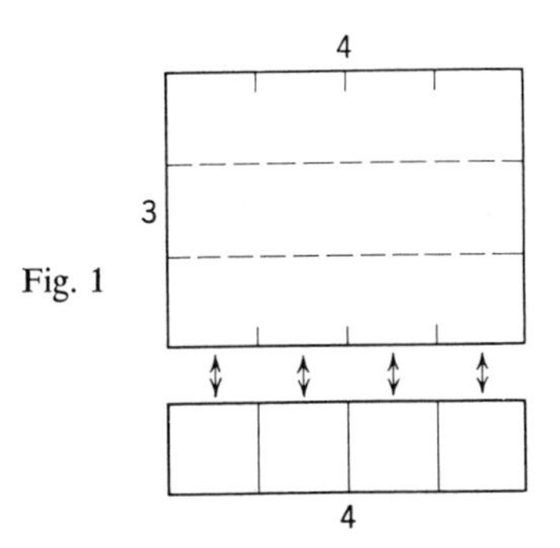

Fig. 1

there are three cartons each containing twelve eggs, then there are 3×12, or 36, eggs altogether in three cartons.

If the multiplier is always considered an abstract number and the product takes the name of the multiplicand, how would you explain that a garden plot 12 by 10 feet contains 120 square feet? One method of handling this situation is the following: set up a one-to-one correspondence between the *linear* units in one dimension of the rectangle whose area is to be found and the *square* units in a strip of squares one unit wide and exactly as long as the rectangle. Use the second dimension as a counter to count the number of strips of squares that would be needed to cover the rectangle. Such a product is dimensionally correct. See Fig. 1.

(number of strips) × (number of squares in each strip)
= (number of square units of area).

(3) × (4 square inches) = (12 square inches).

4.3 SUGGESTIONS FOR THE DEVELOPMENT OF THE MULTIPLICATION FACTS

(*a*) *Experience.* The multiplication facts should first be developed within the experiences of the children. These experiences should be well planned, but practice with the basic facts should involve their random arrangement. Special emphasis should be placed on the addition facts with equal addends when these are being developed; for example, adding 1 ball + 1 ball = 2 balls, 2 boats + 2 boats = 4 boats, 3 balloons + 3 balloons = 6 balloons, in which equal groups of like things are combined. The usual question is "how many?", and the formalized writing comes at a later time. If one ride at the school circus costs 3 cents, then how much would two rides cost?; three rides?; and so on.

(*b*) *Use of a counting frame.* The multiplication facts can be developed easily by using a counting frame in front of the class. The frame should have at least five strings or rows of beads with ten beads to each string or

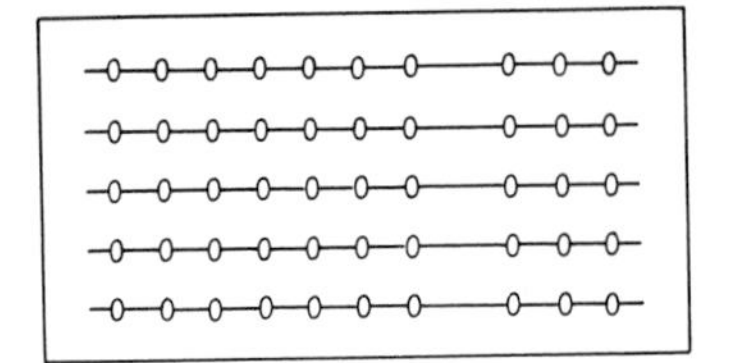

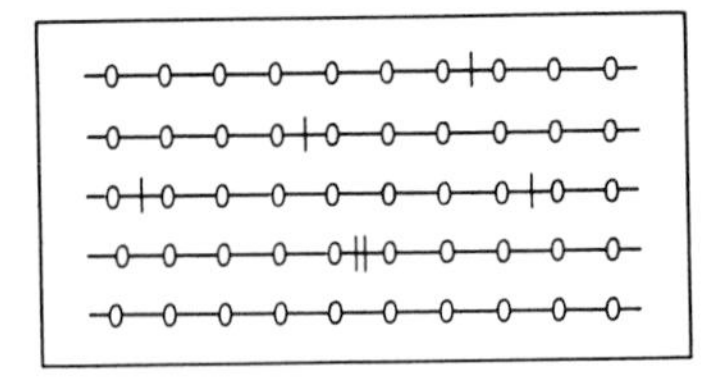

Fig. 2. Diagram *A*: five 7's are 35. Diagram *B*: five 7's are 35.

row. Some of the counting frames have ten rows and ten beads to the row, which is very acceptable. As an example, five 7's could be set up, as in diagram *A* Fig. 2, with five rows of seven beads to each row, or, as in diagram *B* Fig. 2, 7 could be counted off, followed by a space, and 7 counted off again, followed by a space, · · · , until 7 had been counted off five times. Has diagram *B* any advantage over diagram *A* in determining the product?

(*c*) *Recognition of groups.* In developing the group concept, small groups are used in the beginning.

$x\ x\ x$ $x\ x$	$x\ x\ x$ $x\ x$	$x\ x\ x$ $x\ x$	How many groups of x's? How many in each group? How many x's in all three groups together?

0 0 0 0	0 0 0 0	0 0 0 0	0 0 0 0	How many groups of 0's? How many in each group? How many in all four groups together?

(*d*) *Study of commutative products.* Equal products that arise in the application of the commutative law can be illustrated with objects and diagrams. To illustrate that four 3's give a product equal to three 4's, use the following diagrams:

Diagram of four 3's (4 rows with 3 in each row)		Diagram of three 4's (3 rows with 4 in each row)	
• • • • • • • • • • • •	Total 12	• • • • • • • • • • • •	Total 12

(*e*) *By developing and using the distributive law of multiplication.* For example:

$$4 \times 9 \text{ becomes } 4(3 + 6) \text{ or } 12 + 24 = 36$$

or

$$4 \times 9 \text{ becomes } 4(2 + 2 + 5) \text{ or } 8 + 8 + 20 = 36.$$

(*f*) *Counting and preparation of tables.* Children often count by 5's or 10's: 5, 10, 15 · · · . It should be pointed out to them that they are obtaining results for one 5, two 5's, three 5's, and so on.

A table or chart can be constructed to show counting by 2's and can be expanded to show counting by 4's and 8's.

Table 7

Counting by 2's, 4's, 8's

1	**2**	3	┘ **4**	5	**6**	7	┘ **8** ○	9	**10**
11	┘ **12**	13	**14**	15	┘ **16** ○	17	**18**	19	┘ **20**
21	**22**	23	┘ **24** ○	25	**26**	27	┘ **28**	29	**30**
31	┘ **32** ○	33	**34**	35	┘ **36**	37	**38**	39	┘ **40** ○
41	**42**	43	┘ **44**	45	**46**	47	┘ **48** ○	49	**50**
51	┘ **52**	53	**54**	55	┘ **56** ○	57	**58**	59	┘ **60**
61	**62**	63	┘ **64** ○	65	**66**	67	┘ **68**	69	**70**
71	┘ **72** ○	73	**74**	75	┘ **76**	77	**78**	79	┘ **80** ○
81	**82**	83	┘ **84**	85	**86**	87	┘ **88** ○	89	**90**
91	┘ **92**	93	**94**	95	┘ **96** ○	97	**98**	99	┘ **100**

The boldface numbers indicate counting by 2's; those with ┘ in the upper left corner of the square show counting by 4's and those with ○ in the upper right corner show counting by 8's.

Problem. Prepare a similar table for counting by 3's and include the 6's and 9's. List three uses of the table.

(*g*) *Multiplication tables.* You are probably familiar with tables showing multiplication facts up to twelve times twelve. Check the back cover of a household notebook in a ten cent store for these tables.

As teachers, you should know the multiplication facts up to 12 × 12, or twelve 12's. In some European countries the children are taught tables up to 15 × 15, and in India tables are learned up to 16 × 16. Most of the tables in the school books of today go only to 9 in Form A or Form B.

Table 8

Multiplication Table, Form A

	1	2	3	4	5	6	7	8	9
1	1	2	3	4	5	6	7	8	9
2	2	4	6	8	10	12	14	16	18
3	3	6	9	12	15	18	21	24	27
4	4	8	12	16	20	24	28	32	36
5	5	10	15	20	25	30	35	40	45
6	6	12	18	24	30	36	42	48	54
7	7	14	21	28	35	42	49	56	63
8	8	16	24	32	40	48	56	64	72
9	9	18	27	36	45	54	63	72	81

Multiplication Table, Form B

	0	1	2	3	4	5	6	7	8	9
0	0	0	0	0	0	0	0	0	0	0
1	0	1	2	3	4	5	6	7	8	9
2	0	2	4	6	8	10	12	14	16	18
3	0	3	6	9	12	15	18	21	24	27
4	0	4	8	12	16	20	24	28	32	36
5	0	5	10	15	20	25	30	35	40	45
6	0	6	12	18	24	30	36	42	48	54
7	0	7	14	21	28	35	42	49	56	63
8	0	8	16	24	32	40	48	56	64	72
9	0	9	18	27	36	45	54	63	72	81

(*h*) *Zero facts in multiplication.* The zero facts in multiplication should cause no difficulty if they are related to the child's experience when they are introduced. A boy might try twice to drop a bean into a jar and miss both times. How many beans did he drop into the bottle? How many times did he try? He received a score of 0 for two tries. $2 \times 0 = 0$. If a boy is shooting baskets and makes no baskets in three throws, the result can be expressed as $3 \times 0 = 0$. Too often zero is described as a place holder. In the numeral 320, which is 3 hundreds, 2 tens, 0 ones, could not 2 be considered a place holder since it indicates 2 tens? Likewise, the 3 holds the place to indicate 3 hundreds. Zero on a thermometer is used to indicate the point from which the scale of measurement starts. In algebra the origin, with coordinates (0, 0), separates positive x's from negative x's and positive y's from negative y's. In multiplication zero times any number, including zero, is zero. Hence

$$a \cdot 0 = 0 \cdot a = 0.$$

EXERCISE 1

1. Which multiplication table, Form A or Form B, do you prefer and why?

2. For what age group is the table Form A more desirable? Form B?

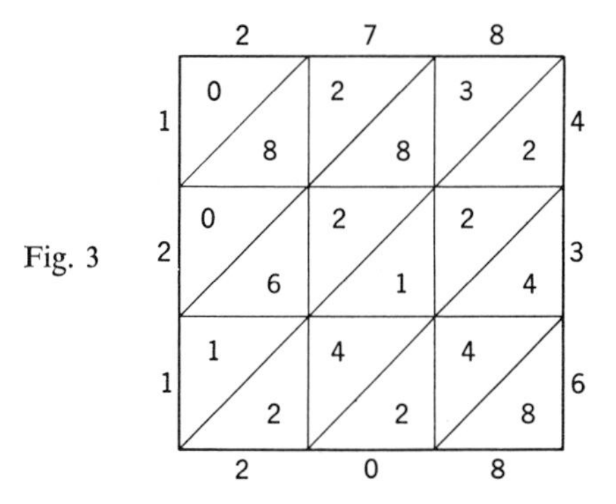

Fig. 3

3. Construct a multiplication table with entries up to 12 × 12.

4. Did you have any special difficulty with the zero facts when you first studied them? If so, how did you overcome the difficulty?

5. What generalization can you develop about the zero facts in multiplication?

4.4 THE LATTICE METHOD OF MULTIPLICATION

Multiplication with longer multipliers and multiplicands will require regrouping and work with partial products. Before turning to this work, it might be interesting to consider a method that uses only the multiplication facts and simple addition. The method referred to is the *lattice method*, which was introduced in Italy about five centuries ago. It is illustrated (Fig. 3) for the product of 278 × 436. The numerals 2, 7, and 8 are written across the top of a rectangle; the numerals 4, 3, and 6 are written along the right side, from the top down. A lattice of squares is drawn in the rectangle, and diagonals are drawn in each of the squares. Products of pairs of digits taken from the top and side of the rectangle are now entered in the squares, the ones' digit being written below the diagonal, the tens' digit above it. Diagonal sets of digits are added, with carrying used as needed, beginning at the lower right corner. The answer is read down the left side and across the bottom which is 121,208.

Problem. Multiply 368 × 723 and also 465 × 5819 by the lattice method.

4.5 MAKING SURE OF THE MULTIPLICATION FACTS

Practice is necessary to establish the multiplication facts after they have been developed within the experience of the student. Most of the tables of multiplication facts are set up with multiplicands as consecutive numbers. Some teachers feel that it is desirable to use a random order in achieving mastery. Teachers generally should provide this sort of random practice for their pupils.

4.6 PROGRESS IN MULTIPLICATION

Much has been written in arithmetic books, magazines, and periodicals about the analysis of skills involved in various types of multiplication problems. If the pupil has true insight into the meaning of multiplication, these problems will not be thought of as distinct types but as parts of a procedure in developing a desired generalization. Let us consider five stages in this development.

1. The multiplication facts. Examples: 8×7 and 6×9.
2. Multiplicands of two or three digits with one-digit multipliers.
   (*a*) Products involving no regrouping. Examples: $\begin{array}{r} 13 \\ \times 3 \\ \hline \end{array}$ $\begin{array}{r} 212 \\ \times 4 \\ \hline \end{array}$
   (*b*) Products involving regrouping. Examples: $\begin{array}{r} 15 \\ \times 3 \\ \hline \end{array}$ $\begin{array}{r} 316 \\ \times 4 \\ \hline \end{array}$
3. Multiplicands of two or more digits with multipliers of two or more digits. Examples: $\begin{array}{r} 36 \\ \times 32 \\ \hline \end{array}$ $\begin{array}{r} 378 \\ \times 24 \\ \hline \end{array}$
4. Multiplications involving zero in the multiplicand and in the multiplier.
5. Multiplications involving the multipliers 10, 100, and 1000.

4.6.1. Single digit multipliers. The multiplication facts have been discussed quite fully in the earlier part of this chapter. Let us consider now two- and three-digit numbers with a single-digit multiplier.

Example 1. $\begin{array}{r} 23 \\ \times 3 \\ \hline \end{array}$

From the multiplication facts we have $3 \times 3 = 9$. Before taking 3×20 the children would have to know the meaning of 20 which was developed in the meaning of number. The numeral 20 represents two groups of 10. In addition to manipulating bundles of tied sticks, two groups of 10, taken three times could be visualized diagrammatically (Fig. 4). All together there are six groups of 10 sticks, or 60 sticks. In the original problem the 20 could be considered as two groups of 10 ones, and three times this would give six groups of 10 ones, or 60. The problem 3×23 is the same as $3 \times (20 + 3)$ or $60 + 9$, which is 69.

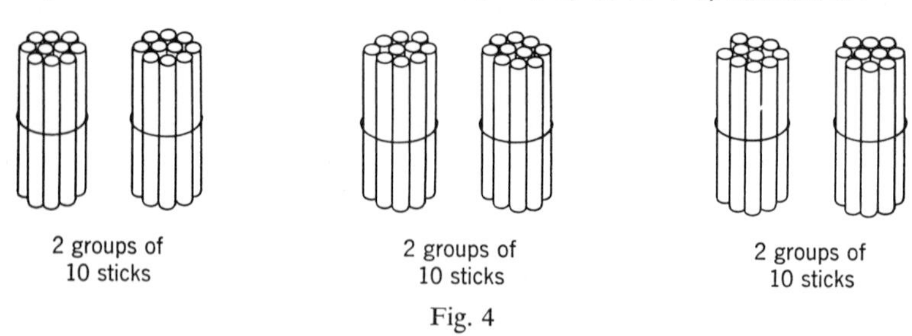

Fig. 4

Problem rationalization. $\begin{array}{r} 23 \\ \times 3 \\ \hline \end{array}$

by addition	by analysis		by partial products
$\begin{array}{r} 23 \\ 23 \\ 23 \\ \hline 69 \end{array}$	$\begin{array}{r} 23 \\ \times 3 \\ \hline \end{array} = \begin{array}{r} (20 + 3) \\ \times 3 \\ \hline 60 + 9 \\ \text{or } 69 \end{array}$	or $\begin{array}{r} 2 \text{ tens} + 3 \text{ ones} \\ \times 3 \quad\quad\quad\quad \\ \hline 6 \text{ tens} + 9 \text{ ones} \\ \text{or } 69 \end{array}$	$\begin{array}{r} 23 \\ \times 3 \\ \hline 60 \\ 9 \\ \hline 69 \end{array}$

Example 2. $\begin{array}{r} 234 \\ \times 2 \\ \hline \end{array}$

Solution.

by addition	by analysis	by partial products
$\begin{array}{r} 234 \\ 234 \\ \hline 468 \end{array}$	$\begin{array}{r} 234 \\ \times 2 \\ \hline \end{array} = \begin{array}{r} 2 \text{ hundreds} + 3 \text{ tens} + 4 \text{ ones} \\ \times 2 \quad\quad\quad\quad\quad\quad\quad\quad \\ \hline 4 \text{ hundreds} + 6 \text{ tens} + 8 \text{ ones} \\ \text{or } 468 \end{array}$	$\begin{array}{r} 234 \\ \times 2 \\ \hline 400 \\ 60 \\ 8 \\ \hline 468 \end{array}$

Example 3. $\begin{array}{r} 347 \\ \times 4 \\ \hline \end{array}$

Solution.

by addition	by analysis	by partial products
$\begin{array}{r} 347 \\ 347 \\ 347 \\ 347 \\ \hline 1388 \end{array}$	$\begin{array}{rrrr} 347 = & 3 \text{ hundreds} + & 4 \text{ tens} + & 7 \text{ ones} \\ & \times 4 & & \\ \hline & 12 \text{ hundreds} + & 16 \text{ tens} + & 28 \text{ ones} \\ \text{but 28 ones are} & & 2 \text{ tens} + & 8 \text{ ones} \\ \text{but 18 tens are} & 1 \text{ hundred} + & 8 \text{ tens} & \\ \text{but 13 hundreds:} & 1 \text{ thousand} + 3 \text{ hundred} & & \\ \hline & 1 \text{ thousand} + 3 \text{ hundred} + & 8 \text{ tens} + & 8 \text{ ones} \end{array}$ or 1388, the product.	$\begin{array}{r} 347 \\ \times 4 \\ \hline 1200 \\ 160 \\ 28 \\ \hline 1388 \end{array}$

The regrouping of ones to tens, tens to hundreds, and so on, is sometimes called "carrying" and sometimes "reduction." "Carrying" is quite prevalent today. For example, $\begin{array}{r} 347 \\ \times 4 \\ \hline \end{array}$ has previously been taught something like this:

$\begin{array}{r} 347 \\ \times 4 \\ \hline 1388 \end{array}$

four 7's are 28, write down 8 and carry 2,
four 4's are 16 and the 2 to carry makes 18,
write down 8 and carry 1,
four 3's are 12 and 1 to carry makes 13.
The product is 1388.

This is called "reduction" because 4 × 7 ones are 28 ones, and 28 ones are reduced to 2 tens and 8 ones. The 18 tens are reduced to 1 hundred and 8 tens, the 13 hundreds are reduced to 1 thousand and 3 hundreds. Is it incorrect to use the words "carry" and "reduce"? There is a tendency on the part of some students to substitute rules for understanding. We may say he is carrying 1, but it may be 1 ten or 1 hundred. To many students the word reduce means to make smaller. When 28 tens are "reduced" to 2 tens and 8 ones, some students may have the impression that the terms are not equivalent. To eliminate possible confusion, the terminology "regrouping" or "change of order" is desirable. Some students like the phrase "change of units" and others the word "simplify." These are not so meaningful as regrouping.

Problem. Find the products of

(*a*)	(*b*)	(*c*)	(*d*)	(*e*)	(*f*)	(*g*)	(*h*)	(*i*)	(*j*)
34	28	37	22	89	323	426	123	531	687
×2	×3	×5	×4	×6	×3	×4	×2	×5	×7

4.6.2. Methods of multiplication with multipliers of two or more digits

Example. Find the product of 36 × 32.

(*a*) *Method of factors or partial products.*

$$36 \times 32 = 6 \times 6 \times 32 = 6 \times 192 = 1152 \quad \text{or} \quad = 36 \times 4 \times 8 = 144 \times 8 = 1152$$

(*b*) *Method of decomposition* (applying the distributive law).

$$36 \times 32 = 36 \times (30 + 2) = 36 \times 30 + 36 \times 2 = 1080 + 72 = 1152$$
or
$$= (30 + 6) \times 32 = 30 \times 32 + 6 \times 32 = 960 + 192 = 1152$$

Another form is

$$\begin{array}{r}36\\ \times 32\\ \hline\end{array} \text{ equals } \begin{array}{r}36\\ \times 2\\ \hline\end{array} \text{ plus } \begin{array}{r}36\\ \times 30\\ \hline\end{array} \text{ or } 72 + 1080 \text{ or } 1152.$$

(*c*) *Other methods.*

(1)

$$\begin{array}{rl}36 & \\ \times 32 & \\ \hline 72 & (2 \times 36)\\ 1080 & (30 \times 36)\\ \hline 1152 & (32 \times 36)\end{array}$$

(2)

$$\begin{array}{r}36\\ \times 32\\ \hline 72\\ 108\\ \hline 1152\end{array}$$

The student is told to "indent" when multiplying by the tens digit in the multiplier.

(3)

$$\begin{array}{r}36\\ \times 32\\ \hline 12\\ 6\\ 18\\ 9\\ \hline 1152\end{array}$$

Form (1) is considered more meaningful, since 36 is being multiplied by 30. At a later time the pupil may invent his own technique for indenting, as illustrated in form (2), and that technique will be meaningful to him. Method (3) is just another version of the partial-products method.

EXERCISE 2

1. Give the advantages and disadvantages of methods (*a*) and (*b*) and the forms of writing the work.

2. Compare form (1) with form (2) in method (*c*). Which do you prefer and why?

3. Compare method (*c*) (2) and (*c*) (3). Why should a student prefer (*c*) (3) to (*c*) (1)? Which method has the greater possibility of error?

4. What benefit is it to a student to be able to write a product in terms of changing factors such as

$$160 = 2 \times 80 = 4 \times 40 = 8 \times 20 = 16 \times 10 = 32 \times 5 = 64 \times 2\tfrac{1}{2}?$$

5. Would you expect a student to find the product of 18×112 mentally? Suppose the problem were treated as $9 \times 2 \times 112$ or 9×224, would that change your reply?

6. Complete the problem: suppose a student has not had multiplication with 9 as a multiplier and was asked to find this product:
$9 \times 170 = 3 \times 3 \times 170 = 3 \times$ —— = ——.

7. Note that $65 = 9 \times 7 + 2$, since $65 = 63 + 2$.

Complete:
$38 = \ ? \times 9 + 2$
$57 = \ ? \times 6 + 3$
$39 = \ ? \times \ ? + 4$
$26 = \ ? \times 3 + \ ?$

4.6.3. Miscellaneous methods for products. Examine these different methods of finding the product of 378 and 24.

Example. 378
×24

Method a. $378 \times 24 = 378 \times 6 \times 4$ or $= 378 \times 8 \times 3$
$= 2268 \times 4$ $= 3024 \times 3$
$= 9072$ $= 9072$

Method b.

378		378		378		
×24	equals	×20	plus	×4		
	or	7560	+	1512	or	9072

Method c.

378 =	3 hundreds +	7 tens +	8 ones	or	7200
×24	×24				1680
					192
	72 hundreds +	168 tens +	192 ones		9072

Method d.

```
  378
 ×24
 1512 (4 × 378)
 7560 (20 × 378)
 9072
```

Method e.

```
  378
 ×24
   32
   28
 12
   16
 14
 6
 9072
```

Discussion

1. What was the principle used in multiplying 378 × 24 in method (*a*)?
2. Give the advantage and disadvantage of method (*c*) method (*d*) and method (*e*).
3. Make up an original problem involving a multiplicand of four digits and a multiplier of three digits and work this problem by two different methods.

4.6.4. Multiplication involving zero. These examples include zero in the multiplier, zero in the multiplicand, and then zero in both the multiplicand and the multiplier.

Example 1. 25 × 30 = 25 × 3 × 10
= 75 × 10
= 750

```
  25
 ×30
   0 (0 × 25)
 750 (3 tens × 25)
 750
```

Example 2.

```
 205
 ×7
```

205 is 2 hundreds 0 tens 5 ones
×7
14 hundreds 0 tens 35 ones
or 1 thousand 4 hundreds 3 tens 5 ones
or 1435 is the product.

```
 205        205
 ×7         ×7
 1400       1435
   35
 1435
```

Example 3.

```
 205
 ×70
```

205 × 70 = 205 × 7 × 10
= 1435 × 10
= 14,350

```
    205
    ×70
      0 (0 × 205)
 14,350 (7 tens × 205)
 14,350
```

4.6.5. Multiplying by 10's.

Discussion. What is 1 × 8? 1 × 4? 1 × 7? 1 × 5?

Generalize. Any number multiplied by 1 is ———. A number multiplied by 10 would be ten times greater. Ten 2's are 20, two 10's are 20, ten 3's are 30, ten 4's are 40, and so on. Can you generalize and make a statement regarding a short way of multiplying by 10? Can your statement be modified to include multiplication by 100 and by 1000?

EXERCISE 3

1. Complete the table.

×	10	100	1000	10,000
7	70			
13				130,000
203			203,000	
680		68,000		

2. Work out each part using two different methods.

(*a*) $\begin{array}{r} 450 \\ \times 63 \\ \hline \end{array}$ (*b*) $\begin{array}{r} 350 \\ \times 90 \\ \hline \end{array}$ (*c*) $\begin{array}{r} 509 \\ \times 68 \\ \hline \end{array}$ (*d*) $\begin{array}{r} 67 \\ \times 52 \\ \hline \end{array}$ (*e*) $\begin{array}{r} 408 \\ \times 98 \\ \hline \end{array}$ (*f*) $\begin{array}{r} 380 \\ \times 30 \\ \hline \end{array}$ (*g*) $\begin{array}{r} 937 \\ \times 6 \\ \hline \end{array}$ (*h*) $\begin{array}{r} 65 \\ \times 82 \\ \hline \end{array}$ (*i*) $\begin{array}{r} 541 \\ \times 70 \\ \hline \end{array}$ (*j*) $\begin{array}{r} 856 \\ \times 4 \\ \hline \end{array}$

(*k*) $\begin{array}{r} 638 \\ \times 29 \\ \hline \end{array}$ (*l*) $\begin{array}{r} 428 \\ \times 10 \\ \hline \end{array}$ (*m*) $\begin{array}{r} 312 \\ \times 100 \\ \hline \end{array}$ (*n*) 605×100, (*o*) 7329×100, (*p*) 895×10.

4.7 CHECKS IN MULTIPLICATION

The most common method of checking multiplication is by exchanging the multiplicand and the multiplier. Another method is to divide the product by the multiplier to obtain the same multiplicand.

Example 1. $\begin{array}{r} 72 \\ \times 34 \\ \hline 288 \\ 216 \\ \hline 2448 \end{array}$ *Check A.* $\begin{array}{r} 34 \\ \times 72 \\ \hline 68 \\ 238 \\ \hline 2448 \end{array}$ *Check B.* $\begin{array}{r} 72 \\ 34\overline{)2448} \\ 238 \\ \hline 68 \\ 68 \\ \hline \end{array}$

Check C. Another method of checking is to work the problem in another way.

$$\begin{aligned} 72 \times 34 &= 6 \times 12 \times 34 \\ &= 6 \times 408 \\ &= 2448. \end{aligned}$$

Check D. Estimation is considered one kind of check in multiplication.

Example 2. $3 \times 72 = 216$.

The student would reason something like this: 3×72 would be more than 3×70; but 3×70 is 210. My answer of 216 is more than 210, so it is a reasonable answer. (More precisely, think: my answer is *about* 210.)

Example 3. 32×40.

A boy wrote the answer as 128 and proceeded to check by estimation. $30 \times 40 = 1200$; the answer should be more than 1200. The boy then realized he had neglected to multiply by 10. The product should be 1280.

Problem. Estimate these products:

(*a*)	(*b*)	(*c*)	(*d*)	(*e*)
52×11	69×22	73×38	295×92	8924×307

Check E. Casting out nines is another check for multiplication. The nines are cast out as they are in addition, but the remainders of the multiplicand and of the multiplier are then multiplied and nines are again cast out. This remainder should be the same as the remainder for the product.

Example 4. Check by casting out nines:

$$\begin{array}{rlr} 543 & \rightarrow 5 + 4 + 3 \rightarrow & 3 \\ \times 85 & \rightarrow 8 + 5 \rightarrow & \times 4 \\ \hline 2715 & & \text{(multiply)} \\ 43440 & & 12 \downarrow \\ \hline 46{,}155 & \rightarrow 4 + 6 + 1 + 5 + 5 \rightarrow & \textcircled{3} \end{array}$$

Since the excess of nines in the multiplier and multiplicand when multiplied (3) equals the excess of nines in the product (3), the product is considered correct. This check can fail if compensating errors are made. For example, a product 45,255 would be incorrect in Example 4, even though it has a remainder 3 after casting out nines. Compensating errors of this kind appear only on rare occasions, but they can happen.

EXERCISE 4

1. (*a*) Check the following products by casting out nines:

(1)	(2)	(3)	(4)
654	582	2763	4921
×43	×376	×208	×37
28,122	218,832	77,364	172,077

(*b*) If any product did not check, find the correct product by multiplication.

(*c*) Find the product in (3) by actual multiplication. Why is this check of casting out nines not always satisfactory?

2. Describe another check for multiplication and tell of its advantages and disadvantages.

3. Check, by casting out nines, five of the products you obtained in the preceding set (*a*–*k*) at the end of section 4.6.5.

4. Check five more of the products (*a*–*k*) by interchanging multiplier and multiplicand.

5. What method do you ordinarily use to check multiplication? Is it satisfactory to you?

6. Work out each product and check by casting out nines:

386	2345	688	1728	8863
×27	×73	×462	×32	×456

7. It has been observed that the check by nines is not an absolute check. What statement can you make about this check that will always be valid?

4.8 ERRORS IN MULTIPLICATION

Many kinds of errors are made by pupils in performing the multiplication process, but most of them fall into one of these three groups:

1. Errors are made because the multiplication facts have not been mastered. Lack of mastery often leads to faltering, which is a cause of incorrect response. For example, if the pupil responds to 7×8 and hesitates, there is a tendency toward inaccuracy, particularly if the pupil has to resort to partial products or counting.

2. Errors are made in regrouping or in change of order.

(*a*) *Neglecting to regroup.* The pupil may have the problem 72×6 and he may write 4212 as the product, since $6 \times 2 = 12$ and $6 \times 7 = 42$. This is incorrect, for,

72 is 7 tens and 2 ones
×6
42 tens and 12 ones
or 43 tens and 2 ones, the product being 432.

(*b*) *Regrouping incorrectly.*

72 ×6 — A child reasons $6 \times 2 = 12$ ones or 1 ten and 2 ones.
7 tens and 1 ten = 8 tens.
$6 \times 8 = 48$.
The product is 482. (correct answer 432).

(*c*) *Making errors in regrouping, such as calling* 12 *ones* 1 *ten and* 3 *ones.*

3. Errors are made involving zero.

Example 1. 203 ×6 — A pupil may omit the 0 and write a product of 138 instead of 1218. Pupils sometimes think of 6×0 as 1 and give the incorrect product of 1278.

Example 2. 725 ×208 — A frequent source of error involving zero is one in which zero is in the tens place and the product using the hundreds digit ends in zero. The product should be formed with the partial products

5800
145000
150,800

EXERCISE 5

1. (*a*) Illustrate, by a diagram of groups, four 6's and six 4's.
(*b*) By what law or principle does $4 \times 8 = 8 \times 4$?
(*c*) Which is more meaningful to a student, four 6's are 24 or $4 \times 6 = 24$? Give reasons for your answer.

2. Describe how a child could work out 6×5, 6×6, and 6×7 if he knew 6×1, 6×2, 6×3, and 6×4.

3. What aids have been suggested for developing and mastering the multiplication facts?

4. What can be done to overcome the errors caused by zeros in the multiplicand and in the multiplier?

5. Give an advantage and a disadvantage of using the words "carrying," "reduction," "indentation," and "add two zeros to any number to multiply it by 100" to describe processes and techniques in multiplication.

6. Some teachers in preparing their pupils for multiplication with partial products greater than 9 write the kind of problem involving multiplication and addition given in this example, 47×3: 3×7 ones gives 21 ones or 2 tens and 1 one; 3×4 tens gives 12 tens and then 2 more tens make 14 tens. There is in this example the problem $3 \times 4 + 2$; note that $3 \times 4 + 3$ would not occur.

(*a*) Which of these would not occur in problems involving multiplication with a one-digit multiplier? What is the largest number of tens carried for each multiplier?

$4 \times 7 + 2$	$6 \times 6 + 2$	$8 \times 5 + 4$
$2 \times 8 + 3$	$5 \times 4 + 3$	$6 \times 8 + 9$
$6 \times 3 + 1$	$5 \times 6 + 7$	$8 \times 9 + 9$

(*b*) Make up ten additional product and addition combinations that might occur.

(*c*) What partial products and additions are used in finding the product of 8×7524?

7. Take the example

$$\begin{array}{r} 54 \\ \times 6 \\ \hline 324 \end{array}.$$

(*a*) Identify the multiplier, the product, the multiplicand.

(*b*) What are two factors of 324?

(*c*) Name some other factors.

8. Arrange a sequence of problems in order for developing the multiplication of 312 by each of these multipliers: 40, 10, 4, 45.

9. Arrange in order for teaching and tell how each differs from the preceding one:

$$\begin{array}{r} 62 \\ \times 3 \\ \hline \end{array} \quad \begin{array}{r} 402 \\ \times 5 \\ \hline \end{array} \quad \begin{array}{r} 32 \\ \times 3 \\ \hline \end{array} \quad \begin{array}{r} 437 \\ \times 2 \\ \hline \end{array} \quad \begin{array}{r} 301 \\ \times 2 \\ \hline \end{array} \quad \begin{array}{r} 68 \\ \times 4 \\ \hline \end{array} \quad \begin{array}{r} 8 \\ \times 9 \\ \hline \end{array} \quad \begin{array}{r} 203 \\ \times 3 \\ \hline \end{array} \quad \begin{array}{r} 46 \\ \times 2 \\ \hline \end{array} \quad \begin{array}{r} 4 \\ \times 3 \\ \hline \end{array}$$

10. Find the total cost of these decorations for a party:

24 badges at 7 cents per badge
15 hats at 10 cents per hat
8 spools at 19 cents per spool
3 sheets at 16 cents per sheet
102 yards of braid at 3 cents a yard

11. Completion.

(*a*) The result in multiplication is known as ———.

(*b*) Zero is used to form the number 20 because ———.

(*c*) In working the problem 49, a child wrote

$$\begin{array}{r} 49 \\ \times 32 \\ \hline \end{array} \qquad \begin{array}{r} 49 \\ \times 32 \\ \hline 98 \\ 147 \\ \hline \end{array}$$

Why was the 7 placed under the 9?

(*d*) In estimating products, a multiplicand of 4107 would be considered as ———, whereas 98, the multiplier, would be considered as ———.

(*e*) Five eights means ———.

12. Original projects.

(*a*) Make a list of errors in multiplication actually made by pupils in a classroom.

(*b*) Is it possible to classify these errors into groups? If so, what groups?

(*c*) How would you attempt to help the pupil to overcome these errors?

(*d*) Library research. Find other methods of multiplication. What are the distinguishing features of the Russian method? The finger method? Work a product problem using these methods.

4.9 MULTIPLICATION IN OTHER BASES

In the preceding discussion the student has become familiar with problems involving the addition of numbers in other number bases. In these problems multiples and powers of a new number base are combined or regrouped. These ideas can be carried over into work with multiplication, as illustrated in the following examples.

Example 1. Multiply 235 by 43, both numbers being given in base eight.

Solution.

$$\begin{array}{r} 235_8 \\ \times 43_8 \\ \hline 727 \\ 1164 \\ \hline 12567_8 \end{array}$$

Three 5's are 17 (base eight); write 7 and carry 1 eight. Three 3's are 11 (eights), plus 1 (eight) make 12; write 2 and carry 1 (eight eights). Three 2's are 6 (of eight eights), plus 1 make 7. Four 5's are 24 (eights); write 4 and carry 2 (of eight eights). Four 3's are 14 (of eight eights), plus 2 make 16; write 6 and carry 1. Four 2's are 10, plus 1 make 11; write 1 and carry 1.

In adding the partial products, observe that 7 and 6 are 15_8; write 5 and carry 1.

To check this problem, cast out sevens.

$$\begin{array}{rl} 235_8 \rightarrow 3 + 7 \rightarrow & 3 \\ \times 43_8 \rightarrow 7 \rightarrow 0 \rightarrow & \times 0 \downarrow \\ \hline 12567_8 \rightarrow 2 + 5 + 1 + 6 + 7 \rightarrow & \textcircled{0} \end{array}$$

Another check is obtained by changing to base ten.

$$\begin{array}{rl} 235_8 \rightarrow 2(64) + 3(8) + 5 \rightarrow 128 + 24 + 5 & = 157_{10} \\ \times 43_8 \rightarrow \qquad 4(8) + 3 \rightarrow \qquad 32 + 3 & = \times 35_{10} \\ \hline 12567_8 \rightarrow 1(4096) + 2(512) + 5(64) + 6(8) + 7 & = 5495_{10} \end{array}$$

Since 35 × 157 = 5495 (base ten), the solution checks.

Example 2. Multiply $2te$ by 23 in base twelve and check by casting out elevens.

Solution.

$$\begin{array}{lll} 2te_{12} & \to 2 + t + e \to & 1 \\ \times 23_{12} & \to 2 + 3 \quad\;\; \to & \times 5 \\ \hline 889 & & \\ 59t & & \downarrow \\ \hline 6669_{12} & \to 23_{12} \to 5 \;\; \to & \textcircled{5} \end{array}$$

To do problems of this kind efficiently in a different base, we would have to learn the addition and multiplication facts for the new base. For example, to work rapidly in base six, we would have to know the following tables.

Addition, base six

+	0	1	2	3	4	5
0	0	1	2	3	4	5
1	1	2	3	4	5	10
2	2	3	4	5	10	11
3	3	4	5	10	11	12
4	4	5	10	11	12	13
5	5	10	11	12	13	14

Multiplication, base six

×	0	1	2	3	4	5
0	0	0	0	0	0	0
1	0	1	2	3	4	5
2	0	2	4	10	12	14
3	0	3	10	13	20	23
4	0	4	12	20	24	32
5	0	5	14	23	32	41

EXERCISE 6

1. Multiply in each case, doing all of the work in the given base.

$$\begin{array}{r} 236_8 \\ \times 17_8 \\ \hline \end{array} \qquad \begin{array}{r} 467_8 \\ \times 53_8 \\ \hline \end{array} \qquad \begin{array}{r} 6t4_{12} \\ \times e5_{12} \\ \hline \end{array} \qquad \begin{array}{r} 812_{12} \\ \times 35_{12} \\ \hline \end{array}$$

2. Check each example in problem 1 by casting out the number that is one less than the base.

3. Check each example in problem 1 by changing the numbers and their product to base ten.

4. Multiply in the given base and check by casting out the number that is one less than the base.

$$\begin{array}{r} 345_6 \\ \times 52_6 \\ \hline \end{array} \qquad \begin{array}{r} 501_6 \\ \times 243_6 \\ \hline \end{array} \qquad \begin{array}{r} 378_9 \\ \times 46_9 \\ \hline \end{array} \qquad \begin{array}{r} 607_9 \\ \times 453_9 \\ \hline \end{array}$$

5. Use the tables given for base six to obtain values for the following where all numerals are expressed in base six:

$(2 + 3) + 4$, $2 + (3 + 4)$, $(2 \times 3) \times 4$, $2 \times (3 \times 4)$,
$3 + 4 + 5$, $3 \times 4 \times 5$, $2 \times (3 + 4)$, $(2 \times 3) + (2 \times 4)$.

6. Make a table of addition facts and a table of multiplication facts for numerals in base eight.

7. Use these tables in problem 6 to find the following in which all numerals are written in base eight.

$$2 + 4 + 3 = \qquad 5 + 7 = \qquad 2 \times 3 \times 4 = \qquad 5 \times 7 =$$

8. Work the first two examples in problem 1 by using the tables in problem 6.

REFERENCES

Apostle, H. G., *A Survey of Basic Mathematics*, pp. 76–82.
Banks, J. H., *Learning and Teaching Arithmetic*, pp. 139–157.
Brueckner, L., and F. Grossnickle, *How to Make Arithmetic Meaningful*, pp. 266–277.
Drewes, Mermer, and von Boenigk, *Practical Plans for Teaching Arithmetic*, pp. 14–33.
Larsen, H. D., *Arithmetic for Colleges*, pp. 76–97.
Lay, L. C., *Arithmetic, An Introduction to Mathematics*, pp. 17–25.
Marks, J. L., C. R. Purdy, and L. B. Kinney, *Teaching Arithmetic for Understanding*, pp. 150–189.
McSwain and Cooke, *Understanding and Teaching Arithmetic in the Elementary School*, pp. 74–94.
Wheat, H. G., *How to Teach Arithmetic*, pp. 125–192.

5

Subtraction

5.1 INVERSE OPERATIONS

An operation is said to be the inverse of a first operation if it undoes what the first operation has done. Thus untying a knot is the inverse of the operation of tying a knot. Likewise, the first operation may be considered as the inverse of the second. Thus tying a knot is the inverse of untying a knot. In Chapter 3 addition was considered. The purpose of this chapter is to consider the inverse of addition.

EXERCISE 1

1. What is the inverse of driving from home to school?
2. What is the inverse of putting on one's shoes?
3. Not all operations have inverses. Name at least three such operations.

5.2 INTRODUCTION TO SUBTRACTION

Addition has already been defined as the process of finding the number property of a group obtained by the combination of two or more groups. In particular, consider two groups having the number properties a and b. Let the number property of the combined group be s. This combined group may be represented by $a + b = s$; a and b are called addends and s is called the sum.

Suppose one of the addends b and the sum s are known. The process of finding the other addend is called *subtraction*. The unknown addend a may be indicated as follows: $s - b = a$. When a, b, and s are numbers involved in a subtraction problem, s is called the *minuend*, b is the *subtrahend*, and a is the *difference* or *remainder*. Consider the examples

$$5 + 2 = 7$$

$$7 - 2 = 5.$$

The first may be read 5 and 2 are 7; the second, from 7 subtract 2 to give 5. The important thing to note is that 2 is added to 5 to give 7, and from 7 the number 2 is subtracted to restore the original 5. Hence the second operation is the inverse of the first, and conversely. A similar examination of the two statements

$$a + b = s$$
$$s - b = a$$

shows that subtraction is the inverse of addition and likewise addition is the inverse of subtraction.

It should be noted that subtraction of natural numbers is not always possible. For example, the answer to $2 - 7$ is not a natural number. It is a negative number, -5, the inverse of 5 with respect to addition; that is $-5 + 5 = 0$. See section 3.13 or 19.4.

Obviously, the introduction of subtraction as the inverse of addition to an elementary pupil is not likely to result in clear understanding at all. Hence it is necessary to consider other concepts of subtraction. These concepts are illustrated below by situations familiar to the child.

1. John has six apples. He gives four apples to his friends. How many apples has he left? John will take four apples from his group of apples and then count the number he has left. The count, which is two, is the answer to the problem. This concept is called the *take-away*, or *subtractive concept*.

2. Richard has five cents. He wants a piece of candy that costs eight cents. How much more money does Richard need to buy the candy? Richard may think "5 and *what* are 8," and if he remembers that $5 + 3 = 8$, then his response will be 3. However, he could obtain his answer by counting 6, 7, 8. Thus he needs three cents more. This concept is generally called the *additive concept* of subtraction.

3. George has seven marbles and Jim has four marbles. How many more marbles has George than Jim? This problem illustrates a third concept of subtraction, which is called *comparison*. The boys in this problem may compare their marbles by pairing them one-to-one until Jim runs out of marbles. The number of marbles remaining, which is three, is then the answer, or George has three marbles more than Jim. Actually the answer to this problem may be obtained by either the additive or the take-away concept of subtraction.

EXERCISE 2

In each of the first five problems indicate the concept of subtraction best suited for the problem.

1. James has \$12. A friend borrows \$7 from James. How much money is left?

2. Esther has \$12. She wants to buy a jacket costing \$18. How much more money will she need to buy the jacket?

3. A baseball team of nine players has only six suits. How many more suits are needed?

4. Robert has six pieces of candy. He eats five pieces. How many pieces of candy has he left?

5. A teacher has twenty-four pencils. She gives twenty to her students. How many has she left?

6. Explain how the take-away concept of subtraction may be illustrated with concrete objects for the example $7-3$.

7. Explain how the additive concept of subtraction may be used to perform the subtraction $7 - 3$. How would you use concrete objects in this example?

8. Write two problems in which subtraction is used for comparison. Indicate the concept of subtraction you would prefer to use in working each problem.

5.3 THE BASIC SUBTRACTION FACTS

It will be recalled that in the chapter on addition the basic addition facts were defined as sums obtained by adding pairs of one-digit numbers in all possible ways. This led to one hundred basic addition facts of which only a little over one fourth had to be memorized if certain general facts and methods were used. The following table gives the one hundred addition facts in a different form from that used in Chapter 3.

Table 9

	0	1	2	3	4	5	6	7	8	9
0	0	1	2	3	4	5	6	7	8	9
1	1	2	3	4	5	6	7	8	9	10
2	2	3	4	5	6	7	8	9	10	11
3	3	4	5	6	7	8	9	10	11	12
4	4	5	6	7	8	9	10	11	12	13
5	5	6	7	8	9	10	11	12	13	14
6	6	7	8	9	10	11	12	13	14	15
7	7	8	9	10	11	12	13	14	15	16
8	8	9	10	11	12	13	14	15	16	17
9	9	10	11	12	13	14	15	16	17	18

The numbers in the column to the left of the vertical line and those in the row above the horizontal line are the addends. Thus the sum of 4 and 7 may be found in the row in which 4 occurs and the column in which 7 occurs.

This table may also be used as a subtraction table. The numbers lying to the right of the vertical line and below the horizontal line may be used as minuends and those in the column to the left of the vertical line may be used as subtrahends. As an example, the problem $15 - 8 =$ is solved by finding 8 in the subtrahend column, following it across the row until 15 is reached, and then reading the number 7 at the top of this column. Thus $15 - 8 = 7$.

Many teachers prefer that pupils learn subtraction facts in terms of common differences. The set of problems

$$\begin{array}{rrrrrrrrrr} 9 & 10 & 11 & 12 & 13 & 14 & 15 & 16 & 17 & 18 \\ -0 & -1 & -2 & -3 & -4 & -5 & -6 & -7 & -8 & -9 \\ \hline 9 & 9 & 9 & 9 & 9 & 9 & 9 & 9 & 9 & 9 \end{array}$$

is called the nine family, and the six family is the set

$$\begin{array}{rrrrrrrrrr} 6 & 7 & 8 & 9 & 10 & 11 & 12 & 13 & 14 & 15 \\ -0 & -1 & -2 & -3 & -4 & -5 & -6 & -7 & -8 & -9. \\ \hline 6 & 6 & 6 & 6 & 6 & 6 & 6 & 6 & 6 & 6 \end{array}$$

These families may be read very easily in Table 9. The minuends for the nine family all lie below the 9 in the last column. The subtrahends lie in the first column on the left. The family method of learning the basic subtraction facts leads to one hundred facts that should be memorized. The total number may be shortened by noting in the zero family

$$\begin{array}{rrrrrrrrr} 1 & 2 & 3 & 4 & 5 & 6 & 7 & 8 & 9 \\ -1 & -2 & -3 & -4 & -5 & -6 & -7 & -8 & -9 \\ \hline 0 & 0 & 0 & 0 & 0 & 0 & 0 & 0 & 0 \end{array}$$

that zero is always the difference when a number is subtracted from itself. Likewise, subtracting zero from a number does not change the number.

$$\begin{array}{rrrrrrrrrr} 0 & 1 & 2 & 3 & 4 & 5 & 6 & 7 & 8 & 9 \\ -0 & -0 & -0 & -0 & -0 & -0 & -0 & -0 & -0 & -0 \\ \hline 0 & 1 & 2 & 3 & 4 & 5 & 6 & 7 & 8 & 9 \end{array}$$

Another method of cutting down the number of basic subtraction facts to be memorized is to learn only those in which the minuends are ten or less. Facts for which the minuends are ten or greater would then be carried out as follows:

For example, take

$$\begin{array}{r} 13 \\ -8 \\ \hline \end{array}$$

which may be rewritten

$$\begin{array}{r} 10 + 3 \\ -8. \\ \hline \end{array}$$

Subtract 8 from 10 and add the remainder to 3, obtaining 5. Thus $13 - 8 = 5$. It should be noted that only the subtraction fact $10 - 8$ is needed. This, with the addition fact $2 + 3 = 5$, gives the required remainder.

This procedure makes use of the place-value system of our notation and is the basis of a method of subtraction called the complementary method, which is explained more fully in a later section. However, it may be pointed out now that the complement of a number is the difference between the base used and the number. Thus in the foregoing example the complement of 8 is 2, which is added to 3. In subtracting 8 from 13, the complement of 8 is added to 3 to give 5. Consider another example, $15 - 6 = \ $. The complement of 6 is 4; therefore the answer is $4 + 5 = 9$.

EXERCISE 3

1. Write the "five" family of basic subtraction facts.

2. Write the "seven" family of basic subtraction facts.

3. Write all of the basic subtraction facts for which the minuends are ten or less. How many are there? If zero facts are excluded, how many facts are there?

4. Show that $15 - 7 = 8$ by use of the complementary method.

5. Show that $12 - 8 = 4$ by use of the complementary method.

6. It was stated that subtraction is the inverse of addition. From the addition fact, $8 + 4 = 12$, one such inverse is $12 - 4 = 8$. Write another inverse. Is it always possible to get two inverses from each addition fact? Why?

5.4 HIGHER DECADE SUBTRACTION

Higher decade addition has been defined as an addition in which a one-place number is added to a two-place number and for which the sum is a two-place number. Furthermore, this addition is to be done by endings and not by carrying. Since subtraction is the inverse of addition, it is reasonable to define higher decade subtraction as the inverse of higher decade addition.

Consider the following higher decade additions:

$$(a)\ \begin{array}{r} 14 \\ 3 \\ \hline 17 \end{array} \qquad (b)\ \begin{array}{r} 28 \\ 4 \\ \hline 32 \end{array} \qquad (c)\ \begin{array}{r} 33 \\ 9 \\ \hline 42 \end{array}.$$

From (*a*) two inverses are obtained:

$$\begin{array}{r} 17 \\ -3 \\ \hline 14 \end{array} \qquad \begin{array}{r} 17 \\ -14 \\ \hline 3 \end{array}.$$

From (*b*),

$$\begin{array}{r} 32 \\ -4 \\ \hline 28 \end{array} \qquad \begin{array}{r} 32 \\ -28 \\ \hline 4 \end{array},$$

and, from (*c*),

$$\begin{array}{r} 42 \\ -9 \\ \hline 33 \end{array} \qquad \begin{array}{r} 42 \\ -33. \\ \hline 9 \end{array}$$

These are examples of higher decade subtractions, if the remainders are obtained by the method of endings and not by a borrowing or carrying process.

Higher decade subtraction may be defined as subtraction performed by the method of endings, involving an inverse of a higher decade addition. There are two cases of higher decade subtraction:

1. A subtraction of a one-digit number from a two-digit number, resulting in a two-digit remainder, which is performed by the method of endings.
2. A subtraction of a two-digit number from a two-digit number, resulting in a one-digit remainder, by the method of endings.

In each case, to be considered as higher decade subtraction, the operation must be done by the method of endings and not by borrowing or carrying. The two cases of higher decade subtraction are illustrated:

$$16 - 3 = 13, \qquad 19 - 9 = 10, \qquad 23 - 22 = 1,$$
$$37 - 29 = 8, \qquad 57 - 9 = 48, \qquad 20 - 15 = 5.$$

The following are not higher decade subtractions. Why?

$$17 - 9 = 8, \qquad 22 - 10 = 12, \qquad 101 - 99 = 2,$$
$$10 - 7 = 3, \qquad 37 - 19 = 18, \qquad 5 - 2 = 3.$$

Higher decade addition was found to be useful in column addition—in fact, it is necessary if column addition is to be done with reasonable speed. An analogous operation does not exist in subtraction, but the following illustrations will give applications of higher decade subtraction.

If a method of division by repeated subtraction is used, the quotient may be determined as the number of times the divisor can be subtracted from the dividend (see Chapter 6, section 6.3). Thus, to divide 36 by 9,

$$\begin{array}{r} 36 \\ -9 \\ \hline 27 \end{array} \qquad \begin{array}{r} 27 \\ -9 \\ \hline 18 \end{array} \qquad \begin{array}{r} 18 \\ -9 \\ \hline 9 \end{array} \qquad \begin{array}{r} 9 \\ -9. \\ \hline 0 \end{array}$$

The quotient is 4, the number of subtractions needed. It should be noted that the first two are higher decade subtractions of the type identified by (1) in the second definition.

Again, higher decade subtraction is necessary for short division (see section 6.9). Consider the example $3897 \div 9$ in which the answer is to be found by the short division process. Writing the example and solution in the usual form, we obtain this result:

$$9\overline{)\,3897}^{\;433}.$$

The steps in turn are as follows: $38 \div 9 = 4$, $4 \times 9 = 36$, $38 - 36 = 2$, $29 \div 9 = 3$, $3 \times 9 = 27$, $29 - 27 = 2$, $27 \div 9 = 3$, $3 \times 9 = 27$, $27 - 27 = 0$. It should be noted that each of the subtractions used in this division is a higher decade subtraction of the type identified by (2) in the second definition of higher decade subtraction.

EXERCISE 4

1. Which of the following subtractions may be carried out as higher decade subtractions? Which are basic subtraction facts, and which are neither?

(*a*) $16 - 3 = 13$. (*b*) $16 - 11 = 5$.
(*c*) $47 - 19 = 28$. (*d*) $17 - 8 = 9$.
(*e*) $13 - 13 = 0$. (*f*) $107 - 9 = 98$.
(*g*) $18 - 9 = 9$. (*h*) $10 - 2 = 8$.
(*i*) $28 - 19 = 9$. (*j*) $20 - 10 = 10$.

2. Using the method of subtraction, find the quotient when 56 is divided by 8. What higher decade subtractions are used?

3. Divide 31920 by 5, using short division. What higher decade subtractions are used?

4. The type of higher decade subtraction identified by (2) in the definition is used in short division. Is it possible to have the type identified by (1) in short division?

5.5 SUBTRACTION METHODS

Subtraction examples beyond the primary and higher decade subtraction facts may be classed in two groups. The first group includes those for which each digit in the subtrahend is less than or equal to the corresponding digit in the minuend. The second group contains those for which at least one of the digits in the subtrahend is greater than the corresponding digit in the minuend.

Examples in the first group offer little difficulty, particularly if the pupil has mastered the place-value meaning of numbers. Thus in the example

$$\begin{array}{r} 875 \\ -234, \\ \hline \end{array}$$

if the pupil rewrites the numbers using hundreds (h), tens (t), and units (u), and subtracts, he has

$$\begin{array}{r} 8h + 7t + 5u \\ -(2h + 3t + 4u) \\ \hline 6h + 4t + 1u, \end{array} \qquad \text{or} \qquad 641.$$

Many teachers use cents, dimes, and dollars and other devices to give meaning to this type of subtraction in preparation for the examples in the second group which are more difficult.

In considering subtractions of the second group, the example

$$\begin{array}{r} 924 \\ -279 \\ \hline \end{array}$$

will serve as an illustration. The situation here is quite different from examples in the first group. Thus 9 units cannot be subtracted from 4 units, nor can 7 tens be subtracted from 2 tens. Four different methods of subtraction result from the use of the additive or subtractive methods combined with borrowing or carrying.

5.5.1. Take-away-borrow method. This method is explained by the example given above. Since this is a subtractive method, the first step is to try to take 9 from 4, which cannot be done. From the 2 tens, 1 ten is borrowed and added to 4. Now 14, take away 9, is 5. Since 1 ten was borrowed from the 2 tens in the minuend, the next step is 1 ten, take away 7 tens—not possible. Hence borrow 1 hundred from the 9 hundreds, leaving 8 hundreds. The 1 hundred borrowed is 10 tens, and these added to the 1 ten make 11 tens. Now 11 tens, take away 7 tens, leaves 4 tens. Finally, 8 hundreds, take away 2 hundreds, is 6 hundreds. The answer may be written 645.

$$\begin{array}{rrrr} & 8 & 11 & 1 \\ & \not{9} & \not{2} & 4 \\ - & 2 & 7 & 9 \\ \hline & 6 & 4 & 5 \end{array}$$

This is sometimes called the *decomposition method.* It has been employed extensively during the present century in this country.

5.5.2. Take-away-carry method. This method is still a subtractive method, but, instead of borrowing, the process of carrying is used. Thus in the subtraction fact $6 - 4 = 2$ the same remainder is obtained if 10 (or any other number) is added to both the minuend and the subtrahend, since $16 - 14 = 2$. Because of these equal additions to both minuend and subtrahend, the take-away-carry method is sometimes called the *equal additions method.*

Briefly, the steps used, employing the preceding example as an illustration, are as follows: 4, take away 9—not possible. Add 10 to 4 to give 14. Add 10 (in the form of 1 ten) to the 7 tens in the subtrahend to give 8 tens; 14, take away 9, is 5; 2, take away 8—not possible. Add 1 hundred, or 10 tens, to the 2 tens in the minuend. To compensate, 1 hundred is added to the subtrahend, which changes the 2 in the hundreds place to 3. Now, 12 tens, take away 8 tens, is 4 tens, and 9 hundreds, take away 3 hundreds, is 6 hundreds. The answer may be written 645.

$$\begin{array}{rrrr} & & 1 & \\ & 9 & 2 & 4 \\ & 3 & 8 & \\ - & \not{2} & \not{7} & 9 \\ \hline & 6 & 4 & 5 \end{array}$$

The take-away-carry method was popular throughout the nineteenth century and is still in use.

5.5.3. Addition-borrow method. This method combines the additive idea of subtraction with a borrowing process. These are the steps, using the same example. What must be added to 9 to give 4? Not possible. Hence borrow 1 ten from the 2 tens in the minuend, leaving 1 ten in the tens place and giving 10 and 4, or 14 units; 9 and 5 are 14. What must be added to 7 to give 1? Not possible. Borrow 1 hundred (or 10 tens) from the 9 hundreds, leaving 8 hundreds, thus making 10 tens and 1 ten, or 11 tens; 7 and 4 are 11; 2 and 6 are 8. Hence the answer is 645.

```
8 11 1
 9 2 4
 2 7 9
------
 6 4 5
```

This method has never been widely adopted. However, it is still possible, on occasion, to find a person who uses it.

5.5.4. Addition-carry method. In this method the additive principle of subtraction is combined with a carrying process. The steps, following the same illustrative example, are these:

What must be added to 9 to give 4? Not possible. Hence add 10 to 4 to make 14. To compensate, add 10 to the subtrahend but, instead of adding it to the 9, add it to the 7 tens, thus making 8 tens. Now it is seen that 5 is the number that must be added to 9 to give 14. Moving to the tens column, what must we add to 8 to give 2? Not possible. Therefore, we add 1 hundred (10 tens) to the 2 tens in the minuend to make 12 tens. To compensate, we add 1 hundred to the 2 hundreds in the subtrahend, to make 3 hundreds. Now 8 tens and 4 tens are 12 tens; 3 hundreds and 6 hundreds are 9 hundreds. Hence the answer is 645.

```
   1 1
  9 2 4
  3 8
- 2 7 9
-------
  6 4 5
```

This method has been used extensively, principally in the 1920's. It is sometimes called the Austrian method, since it was believed to have reached the United States from Austria.

The foregoing completes the description of the four methods of subtraction obtained by various combinations of subtractive, additive, borrowing, and carrying ideas. However, during Colonial times and perhaps as late as 1800 another method (or possibly a series of methods) was in use. This method is now known as the complementary method and may be carried out with a take-away or an additive process, with either the carrying or the borrowing idea.

5.5.5. Complementary method. It will be recalled that the complement of a one-digit number was defined as the difference between the base and the number. Thus the complement of 8 is $10 - 8 = 2$, base ten. If the base is twelve, the complement of 7 is 5. These are simple primary number facts that are easily learned. As shown before (see section 5.3), to subtract 7 from 15, think of $10 + 5 - 7$ or $10 - 7 + 5$. Now $10 - 7 = 3$ is the complement of 7. This is added to 5 to give 8, the answer. With this review, the complementary method of subtraction may be developed.

As mentioned before, this method may be combined with a subtractive or an additive process of subtraction and either borrowing or carrying. It is illustrated by the same example employed in the four preceding methods. A subtractive method is used with carrying. Since 9 in the

$$\begin{array}{r} 9\ 2\ 4 \\ 3\ 8\ \ \\ -\ \not{2}\ \not{7}\ 9 \\ \hline 6\ 4\ 5 \end{array}$$

subtrahend is larger than 4 in the minuend, the complement of 9, which is 1, is added to 4 to give 5, and since taking the complement of 9 is equivalent to adding 10 to the minuend 1 ten is added to the 7 tens in the subtrahend to give 8 tens. In a similar manner, the complement of 8 is 2; $2 + 2 = 4$, and, to compensate, the 2 in the subtrahend is changed to 3. Now take 3 from 9. The answer is 645. To fix this method in mind, con-

$$\begin{array}{r} 8\ 4\ 5 \\ 6\ 7\ \ \\ -\ \not{5}\ \not{6}\ 8 \\ \hline 2\ 7\ 7 \end{array}$$

sider another example. Since 8 is larger than 5, the complement of 8, which is 2, is added to 5 to give 7. Carrying changes the 6 in the subtrahend to 7. Since 7 is larger than 4, the complement of 7, which is 3, is added to 4 to give 7. Carrying changes the 5 to 6; 8, take away 6, is 2. Hence the answer is 277.

This completes the various methods of subtraction. The question, which is best, naturally arises. As a rule, a person prefers to use the method he was taught when he was a child. Tests have been made on the relative values of some of the methods, but the results have not been universally accepted. From these results it appears that the take-away-borrow method is the one most easily understood by children. However, other tests show that the take-away-carry method gives faster and more accurate results.

To convince the reader of the relative ease with which the complementary method may be adapted to subtraction, this method and one of the other conventional subtraction methods should be used to solve a problem with an unfamiliar number base. In the subtraction problem

$$\begin{array}{r} z\ 9\ 5 \\ 3\ v\ \ \\ -\ \not{2}\ \not{u}\ x \\ \hline w\ y\ 8 \end{array}$$

given here the number base is sixteen. Let $u =$ ten, $v =$ eleven, $w =$ twelve, $x =$ thirteen, $y =$ fourteen, and $z =$ fifteen. The reader should carry out the subtraction by the method he was taught in elementary school. Then he should examine the subtraction outlined here, in which the complementary method is used. The solution follows:

The complement of x is 3; $3 + 5 = 8$; u is changed to v, since the base is carried. The complement of v is 5; $5 + 9 = y$. By the carrying process, 2 becomes 3; z, take away 3, is w.

EXERCISE 5

1. Carry out the steps in the following subtraction example with each of the five methods given in the text:

$$\begin{array}{r} 4621 \\ -1746 \\ \hline \end{array}$$

2. Subtract 2999 from 7543, using the take-away-borrow method first. Then work the same problem with the take-away-carry method. Which method seems to be best adapted for this particular example?

3. Work the example in (2), using the complementary method with carrying. How does this compare with the take-away-carry method for this particular example?

4. Use the complementary method and one other method for the following subtraction problems. *Note.* The base is indicated as a subscript written in base ten; u = ten, v = eleven.

(*a*) $\begin{array}{r} 723_{10} \\ -457_{10} \\ \hline \end{array}$ (*b*) $\begin{array}{r} 7342_{8} \\ -2564_{8} \\ \hline \end{array}$ (*c*) $\begin{array}{r} 8794_{12} \\ -2uv9_{12} \\ \hline \end{array}$

(*d*) $\begin{array}{r} 1101_{2} \\ -111_{2} \\ \hline \end{array}$ (*e*) $\begin{array}{r} 845_{11} \\ -3uu_{11} \\ \hline \end{array}$

5.6 METHODS OF CHECKING SUBTRACTION

Since addition is the inverse of subtraction, one of the best ways of checking subtraction is by adding the subtrahend to the difference. If the sum is the minuend, a check has been made. Another simple way of checking is to subtract by one of the other methods.

A check by casting out nines similar to that used in addition may be applied in subtraction. Using the given example, $924 - 278 = 646$, rewrite as shown at the left and cast out nines from each number; 8 cannot be subtracted from 6, but if 9 is added to 6 to make 15 then $15 - 8 = 7$, which is the required check. It should be noted that this is only a partial check. It simply states that if the casting out process is correctly done and if the difference is not equal to the number resulting from casting out nines from the answer to the original subtraction problem then the subtraction is incorrect.

$$\begin{array}{rcr} 924 & \rightarrow & 6 \\ -\,278 & \rightarrow & -8\downarrow \\ \hline 646 & \rightarrow & \textcircled{7} \end{array}$$

This method may be extended to other bases, provided the base is not two (see problem 4 in Exercise 6). For such bases a number one less than the base is always cast out. As an illustration, the following example will be checked where the numbers are written in base twelve. *Note.* u = ten, v = eleven.

Casting out elevens, as a check in base twelve,

$$\begin{array}{rll} 9\,4\,6 \rightarrow & 8 & \text{(nineteen minus eleven is eight)} \\ -\ 7\,u\,9 \rightarrow & -4\downarrow & \text{(twenty-six minus two elevens is four)} \\ \hline 1\,5\,9 \rightarrow & \textcircled{4} & \text{(fifteen minus eleven is four)} \end{array}$$

EXERCISE 6

1. Check each of the following subtraction problems by casting out nines:

(*a*) $\begin{array}{r} 732 \\ -275 \\ \hline 457 \end{array}$ (*b*) $\begin{array}{r} 4831 \\ -2477 \\ \hline 2345 \end{array}$ (*c*) $\begin{array}{r} 914 \\ -289 \\ \hline 625 \end{array}$

2. Check each of the examples in problem 1 by adding the subtrahends to the differences and comparing with the minuends. Explain why a mistake was discovered by this method that was not discovered by the method of casting out nines.

3. Determine which of the answers in the following subtraction problems are incorrect by casting out a number one less than the base. *Note.* u = ten, v = eleven.

(*a*) $\begin{array}{r} 432_8 \\ -157_8 \\ \hline 253_8 \end{array}$ (*b*) $\begin{array}{r} 453_9 \\ -268_9 \\ \hline 164_9 \end{array}$ (*c*) $\begin{array}{r} 956_{12} \\ -5uv_{12} \\ \hline 367_{12} \end{array}$

(*d*) $\begin{array}{r} 982_{11} \\ -3u3_{11} \\ \hline 58u_{11} \end{array}$ (*e*) $\begin{array}{r} 743_{10} \\ -279_{10} \\ \hline 564_{10} \end{array}$ (*f*) $\begin{array}{r} 421_5 \\ -234_5 \\ \hline 122_5 \end{array}$

4. Is the method of casting out ones, of any value when the base is two? Illustrate by attempting to determine which of the following subtractions is incorrect:

(*a*) $11110_2 - 1011_2 = 10011_2$
(*b*) $11110_2 - 1011_2 = 11011_2$

Is it possible to determine the incorrect answer by adding the subtrahend to the difference? Which answer is wrong?

5. Subtract in each example and check by adding the subtrahend to the difference.

$\begin{array}{r} 2836 \\ -1198 \\ \hline \end{array}$ $\begin{array}{r} 70035 \\ -43888 \\ \hline \end{array}$ $\begin{array}{r} 6273 \\ -2929 \\ \hline \end{array}$ $\begin{array}{r} 128{,}604 \\ -55{,}822 \\ \hline \end{array}$ $\begin{array}{r} 8811 \\ -4937 \\ \hline \end{array}$

6. Subtract in each example and check by casting out nines.

$\begin{array}{r} 2536 \\ -1722 \\ \hline \end{array}$ $\begin{array}{r} 8033 \\ -6155 \\ \hline \end{array}$ $\begin{array}{r} 6457 \\ -2388 \\ \hline \end{array}$ $\begin{array}{r} 666{,}123 \\ -437{,}298 \\ \hline \end{array}$ $\begin{array}{r} 7722 \\ -2277 \\ \hline \end{array}$

7. Subtract in base twelve and check by casting out elevens.

$\begin{array}{r} 9u33 \\ -34v5 \\ \hline \end{array}$ $\begin{array}{r} 50v8 \\ -1v2v \\ \hline \end{array}$ $\begin{array}{r} 7uvv \\ -6888 \\ \hline \end{array}$ $\begin{array}{r} 50{,}366 \\ -2u{,}v39 \\ \hline \end{array}$ $\begin{array}{r} uv88 \\ -88uv \\ \hline \end{array}$

8. Subtract, assuming all numbers are in base eight, and check by casting out sevens.

5467	3445	6033	23,456	6644
−2374	−1077	−3066	−17,264	−4466

9. Subtract and check by adding the subtrahend to the difference, base nine.

$12{,}350_9$	$68{,}475_9$	$300{,}825_9$	$7{,}300{,}000_9$
-8675_9	$-48{,}350_9$	$-218{,}585_9$	$-5{,}454{,}545_9$

10. Subtract in each case and check by casting out nines.

58,000	20,300	806,400	102,000
−23,456	−10,649	−72,450	−93,648

REFERENCES

Banks, J. H., *Learning and Teaching Arithmetic*, pp. 190–232.

Brueckner, L., and F. Grossnickle, *How to Make Arithmetic Meaningful*, pp. 250–265, 299–302.

Drewes, Mermer, and von Boenigk, *Practical Plans for Teaching Arithmetic*, pp. 10–13.

Larsen, H. D., *Arithmetic for Colleges*, pp. 63–75.

Lay, L. C., *Arithmetic, An Introduction to Mathematics*, pp. 1–16.

Marks, J. L., C. R. Purdy, and L. B. Kinney, *Teaching Arithmetic for Understanding*, pp. 110–112, 135–145.

McSwain and Cooke, *Understanding and Teaching Arithmetic in the Elementary School*, pp. 55–73.

Morton, R. L., *Teaching Arithmetic in the Elementary School*, Vol. I, pp. 76–206.

Spitzer, H. F., *The Teaching of Arithmetic*, pp. 110–115, 132–148, 159–163.

6

Division

6.1 DEFINITIONS

Division is properly defined as the inverse of multiplication. Thus, if the operation of division is indicated by the sign $\div$, then $a \div b = x$, where x is such that $x \cdot b = a$. In order to identify the various parts of a division example, the number a is the *dividend*, the number b is the *divisor*, and x is the *quotient*. Other methods of indicating division in common use are $a{:}b$, a/b, $\frac{a}{b}$, and $b\overline{)a}$. Each of these should be read *a divided by b*. In each of the ways of indicating division, with the exception of the last, the dividend a appears first, or at the top, making the phrase "a divided by b" seem natural. In the last case the divisor appears first; this has resulted in the unfortunate and meaningless "b into a" expression, which should be discouraged. Perhaps the older way of writing an indicated division, $\overline{a}\lfloor b$, should still be used.

An interesting observation in division is that 0 cannot be a divisor. Suppose that we assume that 0 can be used as a divisor; then $a \div 0 = x$, where x is such that $x \cdot 0 = a$. Clearly, this equation cannot be satisfied by any x if a is not zero; that is, $x \cdot 0 = 0$ for all x, and 0 is not equal to a. If, on the other hand, a is zero, then any number x will satisfy the statement that $0/0 = x$. The quotient $0/0$ is then said to be indeterminate. In either case, zero as a divisor does not give a meaningful quotient. Hence division by zero is not permissible.

A second observation about division is that if the dividend and the divisor are natural numbers it is not always possible to find a quotient that is a natural number. This leads to the notion of the remainder and ultimately to the extension of the number system.

6.2 MORE ABOUT DIVISION

The multiplication table, Form B, in Chapter 4 is reproduced here for reference. Since division is the inverse of multiplication, this table may be used as a division table. The division facts obtained from this table may very well be called the *basic division facts.*

Table 8B

	0	1	2	3	4	5	6	7	8	9
0	0	0	0	0	0	0	0	0	0	0
1	0	1	2	3	4	5	6	7	8	9
2	0	2	4	6	8	10	12	14	16	18
3	0	3	6	9	12	15	18	21	24	27
4	0	4	8	12	16	20	24	28	32	36
5	0	5	10	15	20	25	30	35	40	45
6	0	6	12	18	24	30	36	42	48	54
7	0	7	14	21	28	35	42	49	56	63
8	0	8	16	24	32	40	48	56	64	72
9	0	9	18	27	36	45	54	63	72	81

In the use of this table, note that any number to the right of the vertical line and below the horizontal line may be used as a dividend. Any number, except zero, to the left of the vertical line may be used as a divisor. In this case the quotient would then be found as one of the numbers above the horizontal line. However, these numbers may be used as divisors, in which case the quotients would be numbers to the left of the vertical line. Thus, to divide 24 by 4, follow the "4" row until you find 24. At the top of this column, which contains 24 read 6, the quotient. This quotient could be determined in another way by finding 24 in the "4" column.

Since zero cannot be used as a divisor, it is easy to see that there are 9×10, or ninety basic division facts. Nine of these facts have quotients equal to zero, namely, $0 \div 1$, $0 \div 2$, $0 \div 3$, $0 \div 4$, $0 \div 5$, $0 \div 6$, $0 \div 7$, $0 \div 8$, $0 \div 9$, which may then be summarized into the one fact that a zero dividend always gives a zero quotient. Once this fact is mastered, there are only eighty-one other basic facts to learn. Note particularly that *zero divided by any nonzero number gives zero as the quotient.*

Many teachers recommend that the basic division facts be learned with the corresponding multiplication facts. Therefore, since $7 \times 8 = 56$, $56 \div 7 = 8$ and $56 \div 8 = 7$. Although this procedure is not universally used, it is worth considering, especially in remedial work.

EXERCISE 1

1. Read each of the following division examples and give the names of the parts.

(*a*) $6 \div 2 = 3$. (*b*) $8:4 = 2$.

(*c*) $18/3 = 6$. (*d*) $\frac{36}{4} = 9$.

(*e*) $5\overline{)25}$ with quotient 5. (*f*) $\overline{72}\underline{|9}$ with quotient 8.

(*g*) $a \div 2 = 7$. (*h*) $48/b = 6$.

2. Use the table to find the quotient in each of these division problems:

(*a*) $56/7$ (*b*) $54/6$

(*c*) $72/8$ (*d*) $32/8$

(*e*) $27 \div 3$ (*f*) $49 \div 7$

(*g*) $40 \div 5$ (*h*) $35 \div 7$

3. What division facts are associated with the following multiplication facts?

(*a*) $4 \times 9 = 36$. (*b*) $3 \times 15 = 45$.

(*c*) $8 \times 8 = 64$. (*d*) $7 \times 7 = 49$.

(*e*) $6 \times 7 = 42$. (*f*) $4 \times 7 = 28$.

6.3 ELEMENTARY ASPECTS OF DIVISION

In the first section of this chapter division was defined as the inverse of multiplication. It is doubtful that this definition will have much meaning in the lower grades. Hence we approach division in a different manner.

One such approach has been called *division by partition*. An example illustrates the method. A mother wishes to give each of her three children an equal share of twelve pieces of candy. She starts with one child by giving him the first piece. The second piece is given to the second child and the third piece to the third child. She repeats this process, starting again with the first child, and continues until no candy remains. If the last piece goes to the third child, the candy has been distributed equally. Furthermore, the number of pieces of candy given to any one child is the quotient of 12 divided by 3.

Another approach to division has been called *division by measurement* or *division by subtraction*. In dividing 12 by 3, the question is, "How many 3's are there in 12?" This can be answered by measuring 12 in terms of a unit three times as large as the 1 unit. Thus 12 may be a length in feet with the foot as the unit of measure. Using the yard (three feet) as a measure, the answer is 4. In general, it is easier to get the answer by repeated subtraction of 3 from 12. Thus $12 - 3 = 9, 9 - 3 = 6, 6 - 3 = 3, 3 - 3 = 0$. Since 3 has been subtracted four times, 4 is the answer.

This method of division is used whenever division is carried out with a desk calculator; the machine performs division by doing repeated subtraction.

The notions of sharing and measuring are readily grasped by children and can be introduced in the primary grades. Simple examples should be used in introducing the ideas.

Example 1. Five boys are going to share twenty cents. How much is each boy's share?

Solution. Each boy receives one fifth of twenty cents, or one of five equal parts.
Separate twenty cents into five equal shares.

$$20 \text{ cents} = 4 + 4 + 4 + 4 + 4 \text{ cents}.$$

Each share is four cents. Here one fifth of 20 is 4, which is the same as the result in the division, $20 \div 5 = 4$. The notion used is that of partition.

Example 2. How many five-cent articles can a child buy for twenty cents?

Solution. The child can take four nickels out of twenty cents, or a nickel can be measured out four times. This is the notion of measurement, with five cents as the unit of measure. It is found that 5 is contained in 20 four times.

Example 3. How many quarts are contained in one gallon?

Solution. By filling a quart jar four times when pouring from a gallon jar, we can show that there are four quarts in one gallon. One fourth of a gallon is contained four times in one gallon. This is again the notion of measurement.

EXERCISE 2

1. Show how each of the following division examples may be carried out by the method of partition and also by the method of measurement:

(*a*) $8 \div 2$ (*b*) $33 \div 11$ (*c*) $14 \div 2$

2. (*a*) A boy has fifteen books he wishes to distribute equally among three friends. How many does he give to each friend?
(*b*) Which method of division is better for this problem? Why?

3. (*a*) A girl buys ten feet of ribbon which she will cut into two-foot lengths for bows. How many bows can she make?
(*b*) Which method of division is better for this problem? Why?

4. Illustrate, by means of diagrams, each of the methods of division. Use the example $15 \div 3 = 5$.

5. A sum of thirty-five cents is divided by seven. Write one problem in which the notion of partition would be used to solve it. Write another problem in which measurement could be used.

6. Show by repeated subtraction that $42 \div 6$ is 7. Which notion of division is employed in this process?

7. A team of five players shares a prize of \$200. What is each player's share?

8. How many quarter dollars are there in \$3.50? How many $\frac{1}{4}$'s are there in $3\frac{1}{2}$? Which idea of division is used in this problem?

9. How many half hours are there in two and one half hours? What is the quotient of $2\frac{1}{2}$ divided by $\frac{1}{2}$?

10. How many $\frac{1}{4}$-inch pieces of wire can be cut from a four-inch piece of wire? What is the quotient of $4 \div \frac{1}{4}$?

6.4 DIVISION WITH REMAINDERS

An interesting property sometimes associated with a set of numbers and an operation is called the closure property. A set of numbers is said to have this property of closure with respect to a certain operation, provided that the result of the operation is in the same set. Thus, using the natural numbers and zero as the set under consideration, consider the sum of 3 and 6. The answer is 9, a number in the same set. Likewise, every two numbers in this set when added will give a number of the same set. Hence the closure property holds for these sets of numbers under the operation of addition. The closure property also holds for the operation of multiplication.

Consider now the operation of subtraction. Is it closed for the set of natural numbers and zero? $6 - 6 = 0, 7 - 3 = 4, 8 - 2 = 6, 2 - 0 = 2$ are a few examples in which the operation of subtraction with natural numbers and zero give numbers in the same set. However, $2 - 4 = ?$, $0 - 5 = ?$ are examples in which the answers, if indicated, would be in numbers that are not in the set of natural numbers and zero. Hence the closure property does not hold for the operation of subtraction on the set of natural numbers and zero.

Likewise, the closure property does not hold for the operation of division for the set of natural numbers and zero. Even with zero excluded as a divisor, it is easy to find examples in which division does not yield a number in the set under consideration. Such an example is $13 \div 4 = ?$. To represent such a quotient, a new type of number, the fraction, must be defined. This is done in a later chapter. A second method of handling this kind of division example is to subtract the divisor 4 three times from the dividend 13. The final subtraction remainder for this example in division is 1. This number is called the remainder.

Suppose a plumber needs a number of four-foot lengths of pipe. He has a thirteen-foot length on hand. How many four foot lengths can he make? Using the measurement method, he can subtract 4 from 13 three times, thus using 12 feet of pipe. Only one foot remains, which is not enough for another piece of the required length. This remainder, a one-foot length of pipe, may be used for some other job, but not for the immediate job. Hence, as far as the plumber is concerned, $13 \div 4 = 3$.

The correct answer to the question asked above is simply 3. If one asks a second question, "How much pipe is left?", then the remainder 1, is the answer.

Definition. The *remainder in a division that is not exact* is the number obtained by subtracting the divisor successively from the dividend until the remainder in subtraction is less than the divisor. If the division is exact, the remainder is zero. In either case the remainder is always one of the numbers 0, 1, 2, $\cdots$, up to the number that is one less than the divisor.

Since partition and measurement, as methods of division, are too slow, they should be used only to fix understanding of the division process. The inverse of multiplication can be used to advantage even when remainders exist. Note the following table.

$$
\begin{array}{ll}
8 = 1 \times 7 + 1 & 43 = 6 \times 7 + 1 \\
15 = 2 \times 7 + 1 & 50 = 7 \times 7 + 1 \\
22 = 3 \times 7 + 1 & 57 = 8 \times 7 + 1 \\
29 = 4 \times 7 + 1 & 64 = 9 \times 7 + 1 \\
36 = 5 \times 7 + 1 &
\end{array}
$$

This table gives a clue to division by 7 when the remainder is 1. Thus, $29 \div 7$ is 4 because $4 \times 7 = 28$, and the remainder is 1, since $29 - 28 = 1$. Tables with other remainders with the same divisor may be easily constructed. Thus, with 6 as the remainder, the table is as follows:

$$
\begin{array}{lll}
13 = 1 \times 7 + 6 & 34 = 4 \times 7 + 6 & 55 = 7 \times 7 + 6 \\
20 = 2 \times 7 + 6 & 41 = 5 \times 7 + 6 & 62 = 8 \times 7 + 6 \\
27 = 3 \times 7 + 6 & 48 = 6 \times 7 + 6 & 69 = 9 \times 7 + 6
\end{array}
$$

For example, $62 \div 7$ gives a quotient 8, and, since $8 \times 7 = 56$, the remainder R is $62 - 56$, or 6. A pupil will become proficient in division if he will make a series of these tables with various divisors and all possible remainders.

The general form exhibited in each of the tables is often called the *division transformation form*. Thus $29 \div 3 = 9$, R 2, may be written in the division transformation form as $29 = 9 \times 3 + 2$. Generally,

$$\text{dividend} = \text{quotient} \times \text{divisor} + \text{remainder}.$$

EXERCISE 3

1. Does the property of closure hold for the natural numbers under the operation of squaring?

2. Does the property of closure hold for the natural numbers under the operation of taking square roots?

3. Find the quotient and remainder mentally for the following division examples:

(*a*) $3\overline{)17}$ (*b*) $9\overline{)73}$

(*c*) $7\overline{)41}$ (*d*) $5\overline{)37}$

(*e*) $8\overline{)47}$ (*f*) $9\overline{)80}$

(*g*) $8\overline{)57}$ (*h*) $7\overline{)29}$

(*i*) $6\overline{)35}$ (*j*) $4\overline{)39}$

4. Library research: examine elementary school textbooks and other books on arithmetic to find other methods of writing the remainder in division.

5. Write each of the following division examples in the division transformation form, that is, *dividend* = *quotient* × *divisor* + *remainder*:

(*a*) $85 \div 9 = 9, R4$ (*b*) $107 \div 12 = 8, R11$

(*c*) $59 \div 7 = 8, R3$ (*d*) $49 \div 7 = 7, R0$

(*e*) $31 \div 4 = 7, R3$

6. Can the remainder in a division example be equal to or greater than the divisor? Explain.

7. Write the division transformation for a quotient of 7 and show all possible remainders, using the numbers below as divisors.

(*a*) 4, (*b*) 9, (*c*) 5, (*d*) 6, (*e*) 3.

Solution for (*a*) $4 \cdot 7 + 0 = 28$, $4 \cdot 7 + 1 = 29$, $4 \cdot 7 + 2 = 30$, $4 \cdot 7 + 3 = 31$.

8. Consider random whole numbers, such as 23, 154, 205, $\cdots$, as dividends. On the average, how often will division by a single-digit divisor for such dividends come out with a remainder:

(*a*) if the divisor is 3? (*b*) if the divisor is 7?

(*c*) if the divisor is 5? (*d*) if the divisor is 9?

6.5 SINGLE-DIGIT DIVISORS

Problems involving single-digit divisors can be classified according to increasing difficulty as follows.

1. Exact division facts, the basic facts. Examples are

$$18 \div 6, \qquad 72 \div 8, \qquad 25 \div 5.$$

2. Remainder facts, in which the division is not exact. Examples are

$$23 \div 4, \qquad 69 \div 8, \qquad 85 \div 9.$$

3. Longer dividends, with exact division

(*a*) without carrying,

$$396 \div 3, \qquad 255 \div 5,$$

(*b*) with carrying,

$$204 \div 6, \qquad 175 \div 7.$$

4. Longer dividends, with remainders. Examples are

$$249 \div 6, \qquad 269 \div 7, \qquad 764 \div 9.$$

5. Dividends involving zeros. Examples are

$$240 \div 8, \qquad 204 \div 5, \qquad 2003 \div 4.$$

6. Quotients involving zeros. Examples are

$$162 \div 8, \qquad 2414 \div 6, \qquad 2403 \div 6.$$

The principle of place value is fundamental to the understanding and performance of division in all groups involving longer dividends. The process of long division, which is discussed in section 6.6, can be used in introducing many of these examples.

Examples. Work out the quotients for the division problems:

$$249 \div 6, \qquad 240 \div 8, \qquad 2414 \div 6, \qquad 2403 \div 6.$$

Solutions.

41 *R* 3* 6⌋249 240 9 6 3	24 tens divided by 6 is 4 tens; write 4. 6 × 40 equals 240. 9 ones divided by 6 is 1; write 1. 6 × 1 = 6. *R* = 3.	30 8⌋240 240 0	24 tens divided by 8 is 3 tens; write 3. 8 × 30 = 240. The division comes out exact.
402 *R* 2* 6⌋2414 2400 14 12 2	2400 divided by 6 is 400; write 4. One ten is not divisible by 6; write 0. 14 divided by 6 is 2, with *R* 2.	400 *R* 3* 6⌋2403 2400 03	2400 divided by 6 is 400; write 4. 0 tens divided by 6 is 0; write 0. 3 ones divided by 6 is 0; write 0. *R* = 3.

EXERCISE 4

1. Work out each of the following examples, using place value:

$$204 \div 6, \qquad 175 \div 7, \qquad 269 \div 7, \qquad 204 \div 5.$$

2. Work out each of the following examples, using place value:

$$2003 \div 4, \qquad 2403 \div 6, \qquad 162 \div 8, \qquad 1545 \div 5.$$

3. Work out each of the following examples, using place value:

$$2709 \div 3, \qquad 2709 \div 4, \qquad 2709 \div 5, \qquad 2709 \div 9.$$

4. Write two examples, each, as illustrations for groups 3, 4, 5, and 6 shown in the text, making one example of the exact type (no remainder) and one of the remainder type.

* For another form of writing the remainder, see Chapter 10 on operations with fractions.

6.6 THE LONG-DIVISION ALGORITHM

With two-digit divisors it becomes necessary to set up some sort of mechanical procedure whereby such a division can be accomplished. The common algorithm used in division is shown below in two forms, with a one-digit divisor for illustrative purposes.

```
     178            178
  3 |534         3 |534
     300            3
     ---            -
     234            23
     210            21
     ---            --
      24             24
      24             24
      --             --
       0              0
```

The form at the left is used by some teachers who feel that it has more meaning. Thus, if 534 is divided by 3, what is the partial quotient figure in the hundreds place? It is 1, and, to indicate that it represents hundreds, it is placed above the 5. The next step is a subtraction, $534 - 300$, as indicated in the example. The difference is divided by 3 to determine the partial quotient in the tens place, and so on. It should be pointed out that the measurement idea of division is used in this algorithm, since at each step a number of 3's is subtracted from the dividend. The total number of 3's subtracted is the quotient.

The second form of long division is the method used by a majority of teachers. The usual method of carrying out the division is as follows: $5 \div 3 = 1$, $3 \times 1 = 3$, $5 - 3 = 2$, bring down the 3; $23 \div 3 = 7$, $3 \times 7 = 21$, $23 - 21 = 2$, bring down the 4; $24 \div 3 = 8$, $3 \times 8 = 24$, $24 - 24 = 0$.

If the divisor is a two- or higher place number, it becomes more difficult to determine the partial quotients. The following example is given to illustrate the method that is sometimes used.

```
       134 R 41
  62 |8349
      62
      --
      214
      186
      ---
       289
       248
       ---
        41
```

The steps are as follows. Since 62 rounds off to 60, 83 divided by 60 is 1. (How many 60's are there in 83?) Now, $62 \times 1 = 62$ and $83 - 62 = 21$. Bringing down the 4, the next partial quotient is obtained by dividing 214 by 60, which gives 3. Then, $62 \times 3 = 186$ and $214 - 186 = 28$. After bringing down the 9, $289 \div 60$ gives the next partial quotient 4. $62 \times 4 = 248$ and $289 - 248 = 41$. Since 41 is less than 62, the remainder is 41 and the quotient is 134.

In the preceding example all partial quotients obtained by dividing by 60 were correct. If the divisor is changed to 65, the problem of finding the partial quotients may become more difficult. Consider the following example:

```
        8
      1 2 9̸ R 2 9
 6 5 ) 8 3 4 9
       6 5
       1 8 4
       1 3 0
         5 4 9
         5̶ 8̶ 5̶
         5 2 0
           2 9
```

If again the 65 is rounded to 60 and the partial quotients are obtained as before, the last partial quotient, 9, is found to be incorrect, for 65×9 gives 585, a number too large to be subtracted from the difference remaining in the preceding step. Instead of 9, the last partial quotient must be 8, as indicated in the example. In general, such trouble may be expected when the divisor ends in 5 or a number close to 5, such as 4 or 6. Also, if the first number in the divisor is small, the indicated partial quotients may not always be the correct ones.

6.7 TWO-DIGIT DIVISORS

As has been indicated in the section on long division, the estimating of partial quotients depends considerably on the nature of the divisor. The two-digit divisor examples can be classified according to increasing difficulty as follows.

(*a*) *Divisors ending in* 0, 1, 2, or 3. In this group we round the divisor down to the number of tens indicated by the tens' digit for a trial divisor. This method is sometimes called the *apparent method* for estimating the partial quotient.

Example 1. Find the quotient of 2265 ÷ 82.

Solution.

```
      27 R51
82 ) 2265
     164
      625
      574
       51
```

80 appears to divide 200 tens, 20 times; write 2 (tens). 80 appears to divide 600 ones, 7 times; write 7 (ones). The remainder is found to be 51.

The apparent method gives the correct estimate more frequently when the second digit (in the ones' place) is 0 or 1.

(*b*) *Divisors ending in* 7, 8, or 9. In this group we round the divisor upward to the number of tens one greater than the tens' digit for a trial divisor. This method is sometimes referred to as the *increase-by-one method.* (The quantity increased by one is the tens' digit.)

Example 2. Find the quotient of 18356 ÷ 68.

Solution.

```
       269 R64
68 ) 18356
     136
      475
      408
       676
       612
        64
```

70 appears to divide 180 hundreds, 200 times; write 2 in the hundreds place. 70 appears to divide 470 tens, 60 times; write 6 (tens). 70 appears to divide 670 ones, 9 times; write 9 (ones). The remainder is 64.

The increase-by-one method gives the correct estimate of the partial quotient more frequently when the second digit of the divisor is an 8 or a 9.

(*c*) *Divisors ending in* 4, 5, or 6. This group of divisors is the most troublesome. The only guide to estimating partial quotients is that the divisor is about half way between the number of tens obtained by rounding down to the tens' digit and the number of tens obtained by rounding upward one more than the tens' digit.

Example 3. Find the quotient of 25456 ÷ 64.

Solution.

```
       397 R48
64 ) 25456
     192
      625
      576
       496
       448
        48
```

60 would divide 250 hundreds, 400 times, but 70 would divide only 300 times; try 3 (hundreds). 70 would not divide 620 tens, 90 times, but a number somewhat smaller than 70 would divide 90 times; try 9. 60 would divide 490, 8 times, but 70 would divide only 7 times; try 7. $R = 48$.

6.8 THE GALLEY METHOD OF DIVISION

A scratch method of historical interest that serves for doing long division is called the *galley method of division*; it was in general use before the adoption of the present method, which the Italians began developing about A.D. 1300, and generally adopted about A.D. 1600. The galley method appears to have originated with the Hindus, some eight or nine centuries ago, and it was known among Europeans for several centuries before A.D. 1600. Division by this method is performed as follows.

Example 1. Find the quotient of $7862 \div 24$ by the galley method.

Solution. (The steps (*a*) to (*f*) illustrate details; see Example 2 below for a compact form of solution.)

```
      (a)                 (b)                 (c)

                                               2
1                   16                        16
7862    3           7862    3                 7862    32
24                  244                       244
                     2                         2
```

(*a*) Write divisor 24 beneath 78, which it will divide three times. Three 2's are 6, $7 - 6 = 1$; scratch 2 and 7; write 1 above 7.

(*b*) Three 4's are 12, $18 - 12 = 6$; scratch 4 and 8; write 6 above 8. Write divisor 24, one place to the right, beneath 66.

(*c*) Sixty-six divided by 24 is 2; write 2 in quotient. $2 \times 2 = 4$, $6 - 4 = 2$; scratch 2 of divisor, 6 of dividend; write 2 above 6.

```
      (d)                 (e)                 (f)
1                    1                        11
2                    24                       24
168                  168                      1684
7862    327          7862    327              7862    327.
2444                 2444                     2444
 22                   22                       22
```

(*d*) Two 4's are 8; $26 - 8 = 18$; scratch 4, 2, 6; write 1 and 8. Write divisor 24, one place to right; 24 divides 182 seven times.

(*e*) Seven 2's are 14; $18 - 14 = 4$; scratch 2, 1, 8; write 4 above 8.

(*f*) Seven 4's are 28; $42 - 28 = 14$. The remainder is 14. The quotient of $7862 \div 24$ is 327 *R* 14.

Example 2. Find the quotient of $48731 \div 63$ by the galley method.

Solution.

```
  23
 444
 6622
48731     773          The answer is 773 R 32.
 6333
  66
```

EXERCISE 5

1. Perform the following division examples by using the first form for the long division algorithm:

(*a*) 4176 ÷ 32, (*b*) 3892 ÷ 19.

2. Perform the following division examples by rounding off the divisor properly to obtain partial quotients:

(*a*) 2835 ÷ 82, (*b*) 98,342 ÷ 68,

(*c*) 478 ÷ 23, (*d*) 8972 ÷ 19,

(*e*) 19,342 ÷ 13, (*f*) 6835 ÷ 40,

(*g*) 23,765 ÷ 22, (*h*) 18,300 ÷ 37.

3. Why does the method fail so often when the divisor is a number in the low teens?

4. Perform each division by the galley method:

(*a*) 8381 ÷ 23, (*b*) 6432 ÷ 52.

5. Perform each division by the galley method:

(*a*) 18492 ÷ 29, (*b*) 33864 ÷ 48.

6. Perform the following divisions by the usual method:

(*a*) 72106 ÷ 54, (*b*) 6305 ÷ 21,

(*c*) 8375 ÷ 35, (*d*) 6374 ÷ 46.

7. Try to discover short cuts for carrying out the galley method of division in examples such as those in problems 4 and 5.

6.9 SHORT DIVISION

Short division is a method of doing a division problem mentally and recording only the quotient and remainder, if there is a remainder. Consider the problem $2\overline{)8356}$ with quotient 4178. The steps are carried out as follows. $8 \div 2 = 4$, $2 \times 4 = 8$, $8 - 8 = 0$. $3 \div 2 = 1$, $2 \times 1 = 2$, $3 - 2 = 1$. $15 \div 2 = 7$, $2 \times 7 = 14$, $15 - 14 = 1$. $16 \div 2 = 8$, $8 \times 2 = 16$, $16 - 16 = 0$. It should be noted that higher decade subtraction is needed for short division if the pupil is to become proficient with this method.

The question which should be taught first, long division or short division often arises. For years nearly every teacher gave short division first and followed it by long division. Since short division is a short cut, this order seems to be the wrong way of presenting division. As a result of much agitation against the older order, the teaching of long division first has now been accepted. Unfortunately, however, in many schools the use of long division is carried to the extreme in that no second method is given. Occasionally pupils are forbidden by their teachers to use the short form. Children should be encouraged to use short division as soon as they are ready for it and should eventually be expected to adopt it exclusively for one-digit divisors.

EXERCISE 6

1. Do the following division examples by short division, giving the quotient and remainder.

(*a*) $2846 \div 2$, (*b*) $567 \div 3$,
(*c*) $8937 \div 9$, (*d*) $2153 \div 5$,
(*e*) $67{,}812 \div 6$, (*f*) $735 \div 8$,
(*g*) $2473 \div 4$, (*h*) $8231 \div 7$,
(*i*) $9432 \div 8$, (*j*) $10{,}432 \div 3$.

2. Although short division is not generally used when the divisor is a number having more than one place, see if you can do the following by short division.

(*a*) $288 \div 12$, (*b*) $3978 \div 13$,
(*c*) $12{,}575 \div 25$, (*d*) $4515 \div 15$,
(*e*) $37{,}962 \div 18$, (*f*) $733 \div 12$,
(*g*) $3943 \div 13$, (*h*) $250{,}077 \div 25$,
(*i*) $2428 \div 22$, (*j*) $8734 \div 15$.

6.10 CHECKING DIVISION BY CASTING OUT NINES

The best check for division is by multiplication of the divisor by the quotient, followed by the addition of the remainder. Thus $8734 \div 15 = 582$ with a remainder of 4. To check, $582 \times 15 = 8730$, $8730 + 4 = 8734$.

If the division is written in the division transformation form, the example becomes

$$8734 = 582 \times 15 + 4.$$

This may be checked by casting out nines from each part and performing the indicated operations to give

$$4 = 6 \times 6 + 4,$$
$$4 = 36 + 4,$$
$$4 = 0 + 4, \quad \text{which checks.}$$

Again, as in other places in which casting out nines is used, it should be noted that this is not an absolute check.

EXERCISE 7

1. Determine which of the following divisions are correct by using the check, *quotient × divisor + remainder = dividend:*

(*a*) $824 \div 17 = 48\ R\,8$, (*b*) $9325 \div 47 = 222\ R\,3$,
(*c*) $182{,}754 \div 781 = 234\ R\,0$, (*d*) $102{,}556 \div 1423 = 72\ R\,100$,
(*e*) $1735 \div 23 = 75\ R\,5$.

2. Check each of the following division problems by the method of casting out nines:

(*a*) $3645 \div 135 = 27\ R\ 1$, (*b*) $3278 \div 54 = 60\ R\ 38$,
(*c*) $75{,}831 \div 74 = 1024\ R\ 54$, (*d*) $5438 \div 201 = 28\ R\ 11$,
(*e*) $7834 \div 28 = 297\ R\ 22$.

3. Are you certain that the check by casting out nines will pick out all errors in problem 2? Recheck by the method used in problem 1.

4. Check each of the division examples in problem 1 by the method of casting out nines.

5. Divide in each case and check by casting out nines.

(*a*) $23{,}761 \div 42$, (*b*) $68{,}745 \div 55$,
(*c*) $16{,}403 \div 13$, (*d*) $85{,}200 \div 39$.

6. Divide in each case, noting that rounding depends on the second digit of the divisor. Check by casting out nines.

(*a*) $\underline{218}\overline{)86125}$, (*b*) $\underline{683}\overline{)223456}$.

7. What are the second, or ones', digits in the two-digit divisors for which the *apparent method* is used? For what divisors is the *increase-by-one method* used?

8. A gallon contains 231 cubic inches and a cubic foot contains 1728 cubic inches. How many gallons are there in a cubic foot and what is the remainder? About what fraction of a gallon is there in this remainder?

9. A bushel contains 2150.42 cubic inches. How many cubic feet (1728 cubic inches per cubic foot) are there in 100 bushels and what is the remainder?

10. Explain by using place value why the quotient of $2856 \div 14$ must be 204.

11. Find the average amount of the cost for the following items:

3 items at 36 cents, 5 items at 42 cents, 7 items at 30 cents,
6 items at 45 cents.

Note that there are 21 items altogether.

12. One meter = 39.37 inches and one foot = 12 inches. How many feet are there in 100 meters and what is the remainder?

13. If seventeen persons share equally a prize of $35,020, what is the share of each person?

14. A mile is equal to 5280 feet. How many yards are there in one mile? How long is a quarter of a mile, in feet? How many feet are there in one sixteenth of a mile?

15. One cubic foot is equal to 1728 cubic inches and 231 cubic inches are equal to one gallon. How many cubic feet would a tank hold (to the nearest whole number) if it contained 1000 gallons?

EXERCISE 8. Cumulative Review

(*a*) *Completion test.* Write the word or group of words that should be used to complete the following statements:

1. The four fundamental operations with numbers are ———.

2. Although the Egyptian system for representing numbers did not use place value, it did make use of the two principles of ———.

3. The inverse of the operation of addition is the operation of ———.

4. The number four in base *ten* would be ——— in base *two*.

5. A division problem has three parts: the answer is called the ———, and the names of the other parts of the problem are ———.

6. The fact that the grouping of the various elements in addition or multiplication will not affect the result is known as the ——— principle.

7. The art of expressing numbers in terms of words is called ———.

8. The commutative principle applies to the operations of ———.

9. The special class of fractions in which the denominators are ten or some higher power of ten is known as the ——— fractions.

10. The difference between the base and the number of a one-digit number is called the ——— of the number.

(*b*) *True-false statements*. Copy the numbers of these statements on your paper. Then, if a statement is always true, write *T* after its number. If a statement is not always true, write *F* after its number.

1. Drill in the form of well-planned games and activities is a valid part of the arithmetic learning program.

2. The elements of algebra are points, lines, and planes.

3. Operations with fractions are parallel to those with whole numbers.

4. The principle that repeated practice with basic facts of arithmetic is sufficient for mastery is known as the drill theory.

5. The cardinal meaning of a number is sometimes called the series meaning of the number.

6. Multiplication is the inverse of addition because $2 + 2 + 2$ is the equivalent of three 2's.

7. The incidental-learning theory has the advantage of ease of administration.

8. If the additive principle of subtraction is used with a carrying process, it is known as the addition-carry method of subtraction.

9. In the multiplication and division of fractions the notion of a common denominator is important.

10. Fourteen divided by three yields a remainder of two thirds.

11. A micrometer measurement of .0015 inch has two significant digits.

12. The number six in base ten is represented by 110 in the base two.

13. In writing 333 in the Hindu-Arabic system, the principle of repetition is used, not the principle of place value.

14. In the partition view of division the divisor is a quantity that is measured from the dividend.

15. The digits in a numeral have a place value that varies with the position of the digit.

(*c*) *Numerical examples and problems*

1. Translate the following to our present system of notation.

$$\text{XLII}, \quad \overset{\bullet\bullet\bullet}{\equiv}, \quad 99\cap|, \quad \lambda\delta$$

2. Use the method of analysis to add 347 and 282.

3. Change $346_{\text{base }8}$ to base ten.

4. Write 14 in each of the Egyptian, Greek, Roman, and Mayan systems of numerals.

5. Add 432 and 44 when both numbers are given in base five.

6. Write the number names of each of the following numerals

27,864   91,009,000

7. Write $4208_{\text{base }10}$ as a power of ten (scientific notation).

8. Add and check by casting out nines.

$$\begin{array}{r} 4263 \\ 7819 \\ 5432 \\ 1769 \\ \underline{8251}. \end{array}$$

9. Change $343_{\text{base }10}$ to base seven.

10. Find the product of 437 and 84 by three different methods.

11. Subtract and check by adding the subtrahend to the difference.

$$\begin{array}{r} 673_{\text{base }9} \\ \underline{485_{\text{base }9}}. \end{array}$$

12. Divide and check by using (quotient × divisor) + remainder = dividend

$$328\overline{)726{,}549}.$$

13. A survey by Lewers and Cooke, Ltd., revealed that the following employees had been with the company more than 30 years:

G. Kililikani	47 years	F. Chang	34 years	N. Miguel	34 years
J. C. Quon	45 years	S. Okai	36 years	A. Gomez	33 years
K. H. Young	42 years	A. Burgo	35 years	H. Iwamoto	33 years
H. Wong	39 years	W. Nobriga	35 years	I. Martin	32 years
I. Hayashi	38 years	O. K. Auerbach	34 years	A. Miranda	31 years
J. Iwamoto	37 years	H. Ahio	34 years		

How many years of service is represented by these men? What is the average number of years of service for the group?

14. Hawaii has a six-year road program which calls for funds to be distributed to the islands as follows: Oahu, $113,012,382.00; Hawaii, $23,789,360.00; Maui, $13,371,950.00; Kauai, $8,618,600.00. What is the total amount for the road program? Under the Federal-aid system, $87,745,405.00 is subject to reimbursement. What is the amount not subject to reimbursement?

15. Mr. Kane drove from San Francisco to Los Angeles in nine hours. His speedometer registered the distance as 424 miles and his car used twenty-four gallons of gasoline. What was his average speed per hour? What was his gasoline bill if the price was 31 cents per gallon? How many miles per gallon did he average?

(*d*) *Preliminary practice problems in the work with fractions*

1. Give an example each of a proper fraction, an improper fraction, a mixed number.

2. What is the principle used to write the equivalent fractions

(*a*) $\frac{4}{5} = \frac{16}{20}$ (*b*) $\frac{25}{40} = \frac{5}{8}$ (*c*) $\frac{34}{51} = \frac{2}{3}$ (*d*) $\frac{3}{4} = \frac{15}{20}$?

3. Change to equivalent fractions as shown.

(*a*) $\frac{7}{18} = \frac{\ }{54}$ (*b*) $\frac{3}{4} = \frac{\ }{56}$ (*c*) $\frac{48}{144} = \frac{\ }{3}$ (*d*) $\frac{5}{12} = \frac{\ }{96}$.

4. Write in lowest terms. (*a*) $\frac{25}{55} =$ (*b*) $\frac{14}{36} =$ (*c*) $\frac{24}{72} =$ (*d*) $\frac{75}{125} =$.

5. Write in the form of improper fractions.

(*a*) $2\frac{5}{8}$ (*b*) $1\frac{3}{4}$ (*c*) $8\frac{5}{12}$ (*d*) $37\frac{1}{2}$.

6. Find (*a*) $\frac{2}{5}$ of 250 (*b*) $\frac{1}{2}$ of $12\frac{2}{3}$ (*c*) $\frac{2}{3}$ of $21\frac{3}{5}$.

7. (*a*) $2\frac{1}{2}$ is what fractional part of 4? (*b*) 18 is what fractional part of 9?

8. Reduce to lowest terms.

(*a*) $\frac{25 \times 54 \times 63}{35 \times 75 \times 36} =$ (*b*) $\frac{32 \times 72 \times 81}{27 \times 48 \times 108} =$.

9. Reduce to lowest terms.

(*a*) $\frac{45 \times 48 \times 38}{64 \times 57 \times 80} =$ (*b*) $\frac{28 \times 96 \times 51}{49 \times 85 \times 64} =$.

10. Change to fractions with a lowest common denominator.

(*a*) $\frac{7}{2}$ and $\frac{5}{3}$; (*b*) $\frac{5}{8}$ and $\frac{7}{18}$; (*c*) $\frac{3}{4}$ and $\frac{5}{8}$; (*d*) $\frac{7}{16}$ and $\frac{5}{12}$.

11. Add (*a*) $2\frac{1}{3} + 5\frac{1}{8} + 3\frac{5}{12}$ (*b*) $3\frac{1}{4} + 8\frac{3}{5} + 6\frac{7}{10}$ (*c*) $11\frac{1}{2} + 7\frac{2}{3} + 9\frac{8}{9}$.

12. Add (*a*) $3\frac{2}{3} + 7\frac{7}{12} + 4\frac{3}{8}$ (*b*) $5\frac{1}{2} + 1\frac{2}{3} + 9\frac{5}{6}$ (*c*) $15\frac{3}{5} + 2\frac{5}{6} + 23\frac{4}{15}$.

13. Subtract (*a*) $\begin{array}{r} 7\frac{2}{3} \\ \underline{4\frac{1}{3}} \end{array}$ (*b*) $\begin{array}{r} 14\frac{5}{8} \\ \underline{9\frac{3}{4}} \end{array}$ (*c*) $\begin{array}{r} 8 \\ \underline{2\frac{3}{5}} \end{array}$ (*d*) $\begin{array}{r} 42\frac{1}{2} \\ \underline{34\frac{9}{10}} \end{array}$

14. Subtract (*a*) $\begin{array}{r} 9\frac{1}{2} \\ \underline{3\frac{1}{4}} \end{array}$ (*b*) $\begin{array}{r} 16\frac{7}{8} \\ \underline{13\frac{11}{12}} \end{array}$ (*c*) $\begin{array}{r} 7 \\ \underline{2\frac{5}{8}} \end{array}$ (*d*) $\begin{array}{r} 38\frac{2}{3} \\ \underline{21\frac{3}{4}} \end{array}$

REFERENCES

Banks, J. H., *Learning and Teaching Arithmetic*, pp. 158–189.

Brueckner, L., F. Grossnickle, *How to Make Arithmetic Meaningful*, pp. 277–298, 303–325.

Drewes, Mermer, von Boenigk, *Practical Plans for Teaching Arithmetic*, pp. 34–54.

Larsen, H. D., *Arithmetic for Colleges*, pp. 98–109.
Lay, L. C., *Arithmetic, An Introduction to Mathematics*, pp. 26–38.
Marks, J. L., C. R. Purdy, and L. B. Kinney, *Teaching Arithmetic for Understanding*, pp. 150–170, 177–183.
McSwain and Cooke, *Understanding and Teaching Arithmetic in the Elementary School*, pp. 95–135.
Morton, R. L., *Teaching Arithmetic in the Elementary School*, Vol. II, pp. 127–170.
Spitzer, H. F., *The Teaching of Arithmetic*, pp. 170–208.
Wheat, H. G., *How to Teach Arithmetic*, pp. 122, 152, 174, 185–191, 198–208.

7

More about Numbers

7.1 PRIME NUMBERS

By examining the first twenty natural numbers the student will discover that some of them are even or divisible by 2; some of them are divisible by 3 or 5 and so on. Chart A shows the first twenty natural numbers, with the even numbers (except 2) and the multiples of 3 (except 3) crossed out.

Chart A

①	2	3	~~4~~	5	~~6~~	7	~~8~~	~~9~~	~~10~~	/ divisible by 2
11	~~12~~	13	~~14~~	~~15~~	~~16~~	17	~~18~~	19	~~20~~	\ divisible by 3

This small sample of the natural numbers is sufficient to show that they can be separated into three classes: (1) the natural numbers that have no divisors except themselves and 1, (2) the natural numbers that have divisors other than themselves and 1, and (3) the natural number 1. This leads us to the following definitions:

PRIME NUMBER

Any natural number greater than or equal to 2 that has no divisor other than itself and 1 is a *prime number.*

COMPOSITE NUMBER

Any natural number that has divisors other than itself and 1 is a *composite number.*

The number "1" is neither prime nor composite. It is generally considered in a class of its own and is called a *unit.*

Example 1. List the numbers in Chart A that are prime numbers.

Solution. 2 (this is the only even prime), 3, 5, 7, 11, 13, 17, 19.

Example 2. List the numbers in Chart A that are composite numbers.
Solution. 4, 6, 8, 9, 10, 12, 14, 15, 16, 18, 20.

A *divisor* of a given natural number is another natural number that divides the given one exactly, that is, without remainder. For example, 2 is a divisor of 6. Every number has itself and 1 as divisors; these are sometimes called trivial or *improper divisors.* Divisors other than the number itself and the number 1 are called *proper divisors.* A prime number has no proper divisors, but a composite number has.

A *multiple* of a natural number is any number that contains the given natural number as a divisor. Thus 6 is a multiple of 3, and 12 is a multiple of 2, 3, 4 and 6, and also of 12 and 1.

Euclid (about 300 B.C.) proved that there are infinitely many prime numbers. This proof is discussed in a later section of this chapter. Eratosthenes (276–195 B.C.) showed how to obtain a sequence of primes by taking all of the natural numbers, beginning with 1, 2, 3, · · · , in a given list, and deleting the composite numbers.

7.2 THE SIEVE OF ERATOSTHENES

The sieve method for determining prime numbers is illustrated in Table 10.

Table 10

Prime Numbers. The Sieve of Eratosthenes

①	2	3	4	5	6	7	8	9	10
11	12	13	14	15	16	17	18	19	20
21	22	23	24	25	26	27	28	29	30
31	32	33	34	35	36	37	38	39	40
41	42	43	44	45	46	47	48	49	50
51	52	53	54	55	56	57	58	59	60
61	62	63	64	65	66	67	68	69	70
71	72	73	74	75	76	77	78	79	80
81	82	83	84	85	86	87	88	89	90
91	92	93	94	95	96	97	98	99	100

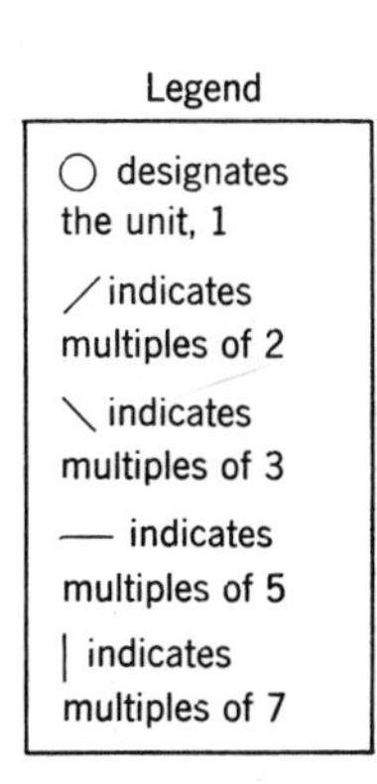

In the sieve method a large list of numbers, for example, the first 1000 natural numbers, is made on a page of material (originally a parchment scroll). The first even number, 2, is noted and left unmarked; then all of the even numbers following 2 are crossed out, or punched out, of the page. Thus 4, 6, 8, · · · , 98, 100 are all crossed out to the end of the given list of natural numbers. Next, 3 is noted and left unmarked, but all other multiples of 3 are crossed out. Thus 6, 9, 12, · · · , 99 are crossed out. Following this, 5 is noted and all other multiples of 5 are crossed out. The next unmarked number, 7, is prime; its multiples are crossed out. Following it, 11 is the next prime; its multiples are crossed out and so on. This method is analyzed further in section 7.3.

In the original use of the sieve method, credited to the Greek mathematician, Eratosthenes, the composite numbers were punched out or cut out of a parchment scroll. After the multiples of the prime numbers were punched out, the scroll contained a list of the prime numbers. Because it was filled with holes, the punched-out scroll had the appearance of a sieve and in effect it operated as such by permitting the composite numbers to pass through but retaining the prime numbers. Tables of prime and composite numbers with their factors have been published for the first ten million natural numbers, and others have been worked out as far as one-hundred million. The principle underlying the sieve method is still used in some investigations of prime numbers, particularly those being conducted on electronic digital computers.

7.3 A CLOSER LOOK AT THE FIRST TWENTY-FIVE PRIMES

The prime numbers among the first one hundred natural numbers will be investigated a little further. It has already been stated that all even numbers are divisible by 2. It is evident that, except for 2, none of the even numbers can be prime. If we count by 5's, the numbers always end in 5 or 0. Any number ending in 5 or 0 is divisible by 5. Except for 5, all such numbers are composite. Consider other numbers than the multiples of 2 and of 5, up to 100; they are given in Chart B.

Chart B

3	7	9	11	13	17	19	21	23	27	29	31
33	37	39	41	43	47	49	51	53	57	59	61
63	67	69	71	73	77	79	81	83	87	89	91
93	97	99									

Suppose we count by 3's: 3, 6, 9, 12, 15, · · · , and so on. Every other number is an even number (6, 12, 18, · · ·), which means it is divisible by 2, but all of the numbers are also divisible by 3.

Problem. Copy the numbers of Chart B and draw a line through each number other than 3 which is divisible by 3.

Discussion. How many numbers did you cross out? You should have thirteen: 9, 21, 27, 33, 39, 51, 57, 63, 69, 81, 87, 93, 99. The numbers that remain are 3, 7, 11, 13, 17, 19, 23, 29, 31, 37, 41, 43, 47, 49, 53, 59, 61, 67, 71, 73, 77, 79, 83, 89, 91, 97.

Problem. Examine the remaining numbers carefully. Are there any numbers in this group besides 7 that are divisible by 7? Yes, 49, 77, 91. These are not prime numbers. Draw a line through them.

Discussion. Are there any numbers in the list, other than 11, divisible by 11? No. Are there any numbers, other than 13, divisible by 13? No. Are there any other than 17, divisible by 17? No. We conclude that the numbers remaining in the list are prime. The prime numbers less than 100 are given in Chart C.

Chart C

Prime Numbers Less Than 100

2	3	5	7	11	13	17	19	23	29	31	37	
41	43	47	53	59	61	67	71	73	79	83	89	97

It is good practice to write the prime numbers between 1 and 100 several times and to check them against Chart C. *Reminder*: omit all even numbers except 2, all those divisible by 3, except 3, any number divisible by 5, except 5, and those numbers other than 7 which are divisible by 7.

7.4 COMPOSITE NUMBERS

Consider some of the numbers less than 100 and not on the list of primes; for example, 12, 49, 72, 99. Recall that these are composite numbers. How quickly can you tell what "composes" them or what their factors are?

12 is 2×6, or 3×4, or 1×12, or $2 \times 2 \times 3$.

49 is 1×49, or 7×7.

72 is 2×36, or 3×24, or 4×18, or 6×12, or 8×9, or $2 \times 2 \times 2 \times 3 \times 3$.

99 is 9×11, or $3 \times 3 \times 11$.

As defined in section 4.1, the numbers multiplied to form a product (number) are called the factors of the product (number). Any one of the factors of a number, taken by itself, is called a divisor of the number. Thus 2 and 6 are factors of 12 and 3 and 4 are factors of 12.

If the factors of a number are prime numbers, they are called *prime factors* of the number. Thus 2, 2, and 3 are the prime factors of 12, since $2 \times 2 \times 3 = 12$. The prime factors of 72 are 2, 2, 2, 3, 3, since $2 \times 2 \times 2 \times 3 \times 3 = 72$.

Problem. In Chart D the prime numbers are shown in boldface type. Copy the chart and complete it by filling in the prime factors with their proper exponents for the composite numbers shown in lightface type.

Chart D

Prime and Composite Numbers Less Than or Equal to 100

①	**2**	**3**	4 2^2	**5**	6 2×3	**7**	8 2^3	9 3×3	10 2×5
11	12 $2^2 \times 3$	**13**	14	15	16	**17**	18	**19**	20
21	22	**23**	24	25	26	27	28	**29**	30
31	32	33	34	35	36	**37**	38	39	40
41	42	**43**	44	45	46	**47**	48	49	50
51	52	**53**	54	55	56	57	58	**59**	60
61	62	63	64	65	66	**67**	68	69	70
71	72	**73**	74	75	76	77	78	**79**	80
81	82	**83**	84	85	86	87	88	**89**	90
91	92	93	94	95	96	**97**	98	99	100

7.5 TESTS FOR DIVISIBILITY

To determine whether a given number is prime or composite and to factor numbers, a check should be made by using some simple rules for divisibility.

(*a*) *Divisibility by 2.* A number is divisible by 2 if it is even, in which case it ends in 0, 2, 4, 6, or 8. Thus the ones' digit must be divisible by 2.

The fact that the last digit of a number is a sufficient test for divisibility by 2 rests on the structure of the number system with base ten. Any number in base ten can be separated into two parts: (1) a multiple of ten and (2) the ones' digit. Since any multiple of ten is divisible by 2, if the ones' digit also is divisible by 2, the distributive law guarantees that the number is divisible by 2.

Example 1. 1234 is divisible by 2, since it ends in 4. The reason for this is that $1234 = 1230 + 4$. Since both numbers contain 2 as a divisor, the whole number contains 2 as a divisor.

(*b*) *Divisibility by 4.* A number is divisible by 4 if the number formed by its last two digits is divisible by 4.

This test follows from the fact that any number in base ten can be separated into two parts consisting of a number of hundreds and a remainder given by the last two digits. Every hundred is divisible by 4, and if the last two digits of the number is divisible by 4 the distributive law guarantees that 4 will be a divisor of the entire number.

Example 2. 31548 is divisible by 4 because it ends in 48, which is divisible by 4. $31548 = 31500 + 48 = 4 \times 25 \times 315 + 4 \times 12 = 4(25 \times 315 + 12) = 4(7887)$.

(*c*) *Divisibility by 8 and by 16.* If the number formed by the last three digits of a number is divisible by 8, the entire number is divisible by 8. Similarly, if the number formed by the last four digits is divisible by 16, the entire number is divisible by 16.

Example 3. 13128 is divisible by 8, since 128 is divisible by 8.

$$13128 = 13000 + 128 = 8 \times 125 \times 13 + 8 \times 16 = 8(1625 + 16) = 8(1641).$$

The reason that any number of 1000's must be divisible by 8 is that

$$1000 = 10^3 = (2 \times 5)^3 = 2^3 \times 5^3 \quad \text{and} \quad 2^3 = 8.$$

(*d*) *Divisibility by 3.* A number is divisible by 3 if the sum of its digits is divisible by 3.

Every ten or power of ten yields a remainder of 1 on division by 3; for example, $1000 = 3(333) + 1$. In any given number, then, the remainders for each place in the number are the digits in those places. Hence the number is divisible by 3, if the sum of its digits is divisible by 3.

Example 4. 21522 is divisible by 3 since the sum of its digits is 12, which is divisible by 3.

$$\begin{array}{rcl} 20{,}000 & \rightarrow & 2 \\ 1{,}000 & \rightarrow & 1 \\ 500 & \rightarrow & 5 \rightarrow 2 \\ 20 & \rightarrow & 2 \\ 2 & \rightarrow & 2 \\ \hline & & 12 \text{ or } 9 \rightarrow 0. \end{array}$$

Briefly: $2 + 1 + 5 + 2 + 2 = 12 \rightarrow 3 \rightarrow 0$, or, $12 = 4 \times 3$; hence the division by 3 will come out exact.

(*e*) *Divisibility by 5.* A number is divisible by 5 if it ends in 5 or 0.

This rule depends on the fact that any number can be separated into a collection of tens and a single digit remainder. The collection of tens will always contain 5 as a divisor; hence, if the ones' digit is divisible by 5, the distributive law guarantees that the entire number will have 5 as a divisor.

Example 5. 310875 is divisible by 5 since it ends in 5.

$$310875 = 310870 + 5 = 31087 \times 10 + 5 = 5(31087 \times 2 + 1) = 5(62175).$$

(*f*) *Divisibility by 9.* A number is divisible by 9 if the sum of its digits is divisible by 9.

The basis of this test is the same as that used in developing the check by casting out nines (see section 3.10).

Example 6. 31452786 is divisible by 9 since the sum of its digits is 4×9.

$$31452786 \rightarrow (3 + 6) + (1 + 8) + (4 + 5) + (2 + 7) \rightarrow 0.$$

(*g*) *Divisibility by 11.* A number is divisible by 11 if the sum of its digits in the odd places, counting from the right, minus the sum of its digits in the even places, is divisible by 11.

This rule follows from the fact that the powers of ten in the 1's, 100's, 10,000's, · · · places give a remainder of 1 on division by 11, hence digits in these positions contribute toward an excess in the division by 11. The powers of ten in the 10's, 1000's and 100,000's places give remainders of -1 on division by 11; hence the digits in these positions contribute toward a deficit in the division by 11. This method can be used to obtain remainders in division by 11, and a *check by elevens* can be used for the operations with whole numbers.

Example 7. 61534 is divisible by 11, since

$$6 + 5 + 4 = 15, 1 + 3 = 4; \qquad 15 - 4 = 11 \rightarrow 0.$$

Example 8. Work each example and check by casting out 11's.

$$\begin{array}{r} 2345 \\ +6842 \\ \hline \end{array} \qquad\qquad \begin{array}{r} 15821 \\ -6392 \\ \hline \end{array} \qquad\qquad \begin{array}{r} 6885 \\ \times 23 \\ \hline \end{array}$$

Solutions.

$$\begin{array}{rl} 2345 \rightarrow 8 - 6 \rightarrow & 2 \\ +6842 \rightarrow 10 - 10 \rightarrow & +0 \downarrow \\ \hline 9187 \rightarrow 8 - 17 \rightarrow 19 - 17 \rightarrow & 2 \end{array}$$

$$\begin{array}{rl} 15821 \rightarrow 10 - 7 \rightarrow & 3 \\ -6392 \rightarrow 5 - 15 \rightarrow 16 - 15 \rightarrow & 1 \\ \hline 9429 \rightarrow 13 - 11 \rightarrow & 2 \end{array}$$

$$\begin{array}{rlr} 6885 & \rightarrow 13 - 14 \rightarrow 24 - 14 \rightarrow & 10 \\ \times 23 & \rightarrow 3 - 2 \rightarrow & \times 1 \\ \hline 20655 & & 10 \\ 13770 & & \downarrow \\ \hline 158355 & \rightarrow 13 - 14 \rightarrow 24 - 14 \rightarrow & 10 \end{array}$$

Note that several times in the checks an eleven was added to the remainder so that a positive difference could be obtained. Adding or subtracting an eleven does not change the remainder class; it changes the representative of that class.

Checks for divisibility other than the ones enumerated here can be developed, but in general they are complicated, and it is easier to divide directly to test for divisibility. This is true, for example, of the divisor 7.

It should be noted, of course, that a number is not divisible by a composite number unless it is divisible by each prime factor of the composite number. Thus a number is not divisible by 6 unless it is divisible by both 2 and 3.

The tests for divisibility discussed above are necessary as well as sufficient, which means that a number is divisible by a given integer if and only if it satisfies the test for divisibility by that integer.

Example 9. Test the number 1078 for divisibility by 2, 3, 4, 5, 8, 9, 11.

Solution.

1078 is *divisible* by 2, since it ends in an even digit.

1078 is *not divisible* by 3, since the sum of its digits is 16, which is not a multiple of 3.

1078 is *not divisible* by 4, since it ends in 78, which is not divisible by 4.

1078 is *not divisible* by 5, since it does not end in 0 or 5.

1078 is *not divisible* by 8, since it ends in 078, not a multiple of 8.

1078 is *not divisible* by 9, since the sum of its digits is 16.

1078 is *divisible* by 11, since $0 + 8 = 1 + 7$, as required in the test.

7.6 DETERMINING WHETHER A NUMBER IS PRIME

To determine whether a given number is prime, test for divisibility by 2, 3, 5, 7, 11, 13, $\cdots$. The divisions for 7 and 13 and larger primes have to be carried out directly. However, only prime numbers need be tried, since a composite number will not divide a given number unless its prime factors divide the number.

In testing to see whether a number is prime, the question how far in the list of primes we should go must be considered. Only those divisors up to or equal to the square root of the number need to be tried. This follows from the fact that if a number is divided by its square root the quotient is equal to the square root. If the divisor is increased, the quotient must decrease; hence if a number has a prime factor larger than its square root, it must also have another factor smaller than its square root. If the smaller factor exists, it will be found, in testing prime numbers, smaller than or equal to the square root. (Either the smaller factor or one of its factors will be found in this way.)

Example. Is 97 prime?

97 is not divisible by 2, 3, 5, or 7, and since $\sqrt{97}$ is less than 10 it is not necessary to test for divisibility by 11 or 13 or 17 to conclude that 97 is prime.

EXERCISE 1

1. Make a table, with twelve columns and fifteen rows, containing the numbers 1, 2, 3, $\cdots$, 180. Use the sieve method to obtain the sequence of primes less than 180. How far in the list of primes (2, 3, 5, $\cdots$) is it necessary to go in crossing out multiples in order to be sure that the list in the table contains only primes?

2. Test the following numbers to see whether they are prime:
(*a*) 137, (*b*) 267, (*c*) 301, (*d*) 323, (*e*) 641.

3. Complete the following table:

Number	8338	54	1384	12345	13560	495
Divisible by 2	yes					
Divisible by 4		no				
Divisible by 3			no			
Divisible by 5				yes		
Divisible by 9					no	
Divisible by 11						yes

4. Which of the following numbers are divisible by 3?
(*a*) 123456, (*b*) 60733, (*c*) 238512, (*d*) 238442, (*e*) 111111.

5. Which numbers in problem 4 are divisible by 4?

6. Which of the numbers in problem 4 are divisible by 6?

7. Work the following examples and check by casting out elevens:

(*a*)	(*b*)	(*c*)	(*d*)	(*e*)
2384	6844	8275	7831	77777
+6591	+1939	−6944	−2599	−34567

8. Work the following examples and check by casting out elevéns:

(*a*)	(*b*)	(*c*)	(*d*)	(*e*)
6831	19643	8301	9934	70803
×28	×85	×66	×71	×69

9. Find the prime factors of each number:
(*a*) 285, (*b*) 289, (*c*) 360, (*d*) 128, (*e*) 1331.

10. Distinguish between the terms *factor*, *divisor* and *multiple* and give examples.

7.7 DETERMINING FACTORS OF A NUMBER

At times numbers can be used more effectively if their factors are known. Factors were developed for numbers in completing Chart D, for the first one hundred integers, but how should we proceed in general to obtain the prime factors of a number? Two methods are discussed.

Method 1. Divide by prime numbers, continuing the process as long as possible.

Example 1. What are the prime factors of 360?

Solution. The number is even, hence divisible by 2:
Divide by 2 again:
Divide by 2 again:
45 is not even but is divisible by 3; divide by 3:
Divide by 3 again:
The quotient, 5, is a prime number.

2	360
2	180
2	90
3	45
3	15
	5

The prime factors of 360 are 2, 2, 2, 3, 3, 5. Thus $360 = 2^3 \times 3^2 \times 5$.

Method 2. Take as factors any numbers that will make the product and simplify them into prime factors.

Example 2. What are the prime factors of 360?

Solution. $360 = 12 \times 30$,

but $12 = 4 \times 3$ and $30 = 3 \times 10$,

and again $4 = 2 \times 2$ and $10 = 2 \times 5$.

The prime factors of 360 are

(2, 2, 3) and (2, 5, 3), (factors of 12) and (factors of 30).

Method 2, by diagram:

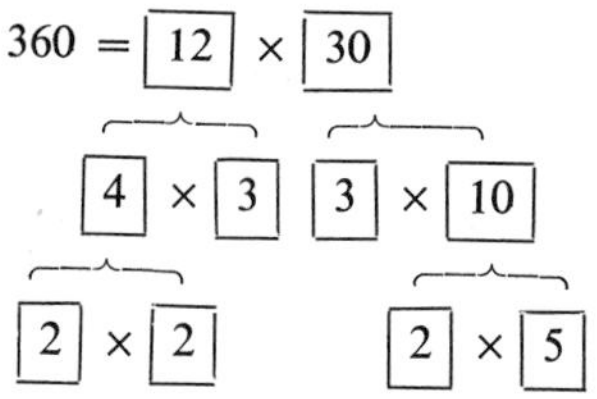

$$360 = \boxed{12} \times \boxed{30}$$

$$\boxed{4} \times \boxed{3} \quad \boxed{3} \times \boxed{10}$$

$$\boxed{2} \times \boxed{2} \qquad \boxed{2} \times \boxed{5}$$

Hence the prime factors of 360 are 2, 2, 2, 3, 3, 5.

In this method write any factors easily obtained and factor any that are not prime. Continue factoring until all of the factors are prime numbers. Rearrange the factors, with the smaller ones first and write the prime factors with their appropriate exponents.

Example 3. What are the prime factors of 48?

Solution.

Method 1.

```
2 | 48
2 | 24
2 | 12
2 |  6
     3
```

Prime factors of 48 are 2, 2, 2, 2, 3.

Method 2.

$48 = 4 \times 12$

$4 = 2 \times 2$ and $12 = 2 \times 6$

or $12 = 2 \times 3 \times 2$

$48 = 2 \times 2 \times 2 \times 3 \times 2$

Prime factors of 48 are 2, 2, 2, 2, 3.

7.8 GREATEST COMMON DIVISOR

In performing calculations with fractions, it is necessary to know when numbers have a common divisor and to find their greatest common divisor, which is often abbreviated as G.C.D.

Definition. *The greatest common divisor* of two or more natural numbers is the largest natural number that is a divisor of each of them.

The greatest common divisor of a set of natural numbers is also referred to as their *highest common factor* (H.C.F.). The reader should note that the H.C.F. of a set of natural numbers cannot be larger than any one of the numbers. This implies that the H.C.F. cannot be larger than, but can be equal to, the smallest number of the set. The set of numbers, 6, 24, and 36, is an example of a set whose H.C.F. is equal to the smallest number in this set.

Example 1. What is the greatest common divisor of 48 and 36?

Solution. 48 is equivalent to $2 \times 2 \times 2 \times 2 \times 3$.
36 is equivalent to $2 \times 2 \times 3 \times 3$.

Two is a factor of 48, and 2 is also a factor of 36; hence 2 is a *common factor* of 48 and 36. Three is also a common factor of 48 and 36. It is evident that 48 and 36 are divisible by 2, by 2×2, by 3, by 2×3, and by $2 \times 2 \times 3$. All of these are *common* divisors of 48 and 36. The *greatest* common divisor of 48 and 36 is $2 \times 2 \times 3$, or 12.

Check. $48 \div 12 = 4$, $36 \div 12 = 3$.

The 4 and the 3 have no common factor (other than 1). Two such numbers are said to be relatively prime.

Example 2. What is the greatest common divisor of 180 and 240?

Solution. Factors of 180 are 18, 10; factors of 240 are 24, 10. Evidently 10 is a common factor of 180 and 240.

Since $6 \times 3 = 18$ and $6 \times 4 = 24$, 6 is also a common factor of 180 and 240, supplementing the factor 10. Since 3 and 4 have no factor other than 1 in common, the highest common factor of 180 and 240 is 6×10, or 60. In this solution the meaning of the highest common factor is emphasized. It is not always necessary to analyze numbers completely into their prime factors in order to construct the highest common factor, although that method (prime factors) is quite general.

Check. $180 \div 60 = 3$, $240 \div 60 = 4$; 3 and 4 are relatively prime.

Example 3. What is the greatest common divisor of 90 and 70?

Solution. Factors of 90 are 2, 3, 3, 5.
Factors of 70 are 2, 5, 7.
The G.C.D. is 2×5, or 10.

Check. $90 \div 10 = 9$, $70 \div 10 = 7$; 9 and 7 are relatively prime.

Summary: To find the greatest common divisor of two or more natural numbers, express each number in terms of its prime factors. Write each prime factor that is a divisor of all of the given numbers and repeat it only as many times as it appears the least in any of the numbers.

Refer to Example 1:

$$48 = 2 \times 2 \times 2 \times 2 \times 3, \qquad 36 = 2 \times 2 \times 3 \times 3.$$

The common prime factors are 2 and 3.

The least number of times that 2 appears is twice.

The least number of times that 3 appears is once; hence the G.C.D. is $2 \times 2 \times 3$, or $2^2 \times 3$, which is equal to 12.

Refer to Example 2. To emphasize the general method of prime factors, we solve this problem as follows.

$$180 = 2 \times 2 \times 3 \times 3 \times 5, \qquad 240 = 2 \times 2 \times 2 \times 2 \times 3 \times 5.$$

The common factors are 2, 3 and 5.

The least number of times that 2 appears is twice; the least number of times that 3 and 5 appear is once. Hence, the G.C.D. is $2^2 \times 3 \times 5$, or 60.

7.9 EUCLID'S ALGORITHM

A procedure for determining the highest common factor for two natural numbers, known as *Euclid's algorithm*, was developed by Euclid in his work in geometry and arithmetic. It is analogous to a repeated division algorithm and is illustrated in the following examples:

Example 1. Find the highest common factor for 72 and 54.

Solution.

$$\begin{array}{r} 1 \\ 54\overline{)72} \\ 54 \\ \hline 18 \end{array} \qquad \begin{array}{r} 3 \\ 18\overline{)54} \\ 54 \\ \hline 0 \end{array} \qquad 18 = \text{H.C.F.} \quad \text{(or G.C.D.).}$$

Divide the smaller number into the larger, then divide the remainder into the preceding divisor. Repeat this process until the division is exact. The divisor that yields an exact division is the highest common factor.* (The highest common factor can be 1, in which case the numbers are relatively prime.)

Example 2. Find the highest common factor for 91 and 39.

Solution.

$$\begin{array}{r} 2 \\ 39\overline{)91} \\ 78 \\ \hline 13 \end{array} \qquad \begin{array}{r} 3 \\ 13\overline{)39} \\ 39 \\ \hline 0 \end{array} \qquad 13 = \text{H.C.F.}$$

Example 3. Find the highest common factor of 25 and 36.

Solution.

$$\begin{array}{r} 1 \\ 25\overline{)36} \\ 25 \\ \hline 11 \end{array} \qquad \begin{array}{r} 2 \\ 11\overline{)25} \\ 22 \\ \hline 3 \end{array} \qquad \begin{array}{r} 3 \\ 3\overline{)11} \\ 9 \\ \hline 2 \end{array} \qquad \begin{array}{r} 1 \\ 2\overline{)3} \\ 2 \\ \hline 1 \end{array} \qquad \begin{array}{r} 2 \\ 1\overline{)2} \\ 2 \\ \hline 0 \end{array}$$

1 is the highest common factor; hence the numbers are relatively prime.

EXERCISE 2

1. Find the prime factors of each number:

(*a*) 144, (*b*) 60, (*c*) 108, (*d*) 63, (*e*) 96.

2. What factor is common to all of the numbers in problem 1? What is the largest factor common to the first three numbers in problem 1?

3. Find the highest common factor of 60 and 108. Use the method of factoring each number into prime factors. Check by using Euclid's algorithm. Can you find the highest common factor by inspection?

* See the Appendix for a discussion of the proof of this algorithm.

4. Find the highest common factor of 63 and 144. Also find the highest common factor of 144 and 96.

5. Find the highest common factor of 28, 70, and 42. Also find the highest common factor of 18, 36, and 72.

6. Use Euclid's algorithm to find the highest common factor of 117 and 143; also of 35 and 77.

7. Use Euclid's algorithm to find the highest common factor of 247 and 323; also of 437 and 551.

8. Use Euclid's algorithm to find the highest common factor of the three numbers, 273, 429, and 221. First find the highest common factor of two of the numbers and then the highest common factor between that result and the third number. Check your work by starting with a different pair of original numbers.

7.10 LEAST COMMON MULTIPLE

Suppose we are counting by 2's. It is found that the even numbers obtained are divisible by 2; hence each of these numbers is a *multiple* of 2. Thus we find that

$$4 \text{ is } 2 \times 2 \qquad 6 \text{ is } 2 \times 3 \qquad 8 \text{ is } 2 \times 4 \qquad 10 \text{ is } 2 \times 5 \qquad 12 \text{ is } 2 \times 6.$$

Similarly, 6, 9, and 12 are all multiples of 3. Since 12 is a multiple of 2 and a multiple of 3, 12 is a common multiple of 2 and of 3. However, 6 is a multiple of 2 and also of 3. In this case, 6 is the *least common multiple* of 2 and 3. Other common multiples of 2 and 3 are 12, 24, 36, and 30, but none of these is the least common multiple.

Definition. *The least* (*or lowest*) *common multiple* of a set of numbers is the smallest number that contains each of the given numbers as a divisor. The abbreviation for this term is L.C.M.

Remember that a *multiple* of a number always contains that number as a divisor; hence the multiple is greater than or equal to the number. A *factor* or divisor of a number is always equal to or less than the number. Thus, for the numbers 12 and 24, 24 is the L.C.M., whereas 12 is the H.C.F.

Example 1. Find the least common multiple of 12 and 30.

Solution. Factors of 12 are 2, 2, 3.

Factors of 30 are 2, 3, 5.

The different factors are 2 and 3 and 5, but the 2 appears twice in one number. The L.C.M. is thus $2^2 \times 3 \times 5$, or 60.

Check.

$$12\overline{)60}^{\;5} \qquad 30\overline{)60}^{\;2} \qquad \text{5 and 2 are relatively prime.}$$

In this example 60 is the smallest number that contains both 12 and 30 as divisors. Both 12 and 30 would divide 120, 360, 720, and so on. To keep calculations to a minimum, it is desirable to work with the least common multiple rather than any other common multiple.

Example 2. Find the least common multiple of 72 and 90.

Solution. Factors of 72 are 2, 2, 2, 3, 3.
Factors of 90 are 2, 3, 3, 5.
The L.C.M. is $2^3 \times 3^2 \times 5$, or 360.

Check.

$$72\overline{)360}^{\,5} \qquad 90\overline{)360}^{\,4}$$

5 and 4 are relatively prime.

It might also be noted that $72 = 18 \times 4$ and $90 = 18 \times 5$; hence the L.C.M. is $18 \times 4 \times 5$, or 360.

Summary. To find the least common multiple of two or more numbers, express each number in terms of its prime factors. The L.C.M. is the product of the prime factors, each of which is given an exponent equal to the greatest number of times it appears in one or more of the numbers.

Refer to the two examples above for finding the L.C.M.

First example.

$12 = 2 \times 2 \times 3.$

$30 = 2 \times 3 \times 5.$

The different prime factors are 2 and 3 and 5.
The factor 2 appears twice as a factor of 12.
The other factors appear only once.
The L.C.M. is $2^2 \times 3 \times 5$, or 60.

Second example.

$72 = 2 \times 2 \times 2 \times 3 \times 3.$

$90 = 2 \times 3 \times 3 \times 5.$

The 2 appears at most three times as a factor.
The 3 appears at most twice as a factor.
The 5 appears as a factor just once.
Therefore, the L.C.M. $= 2^3 \times 3^2 \times 5$, or 360.

The L.C.M. can often be determined by inspection, but we must be certain that it is the *least* common multiple that has been selected.

Example 3. Find the least common multiple of 3, 8, and 12.

A student may state that 48 is a common multiple of 3, 8, and 12, which it is; but 24 is the L.C.M.

The method used in working the foregoing examples in finding the L.C.M. is called the *factor method.* Another method sometimes used in schools is the *common divisor method*, which is illustrated in the following examples.

Example 4. Find the least common multiple of 12 and 30.

Solution. Select 2, a common divisor that is prime, and divide by 2, then use 3 as a common divisor:

$$\begin{array}{r|l} 2 & 12 - 30 \\ \hline 3 & \;\;6 - 15 \\ \hline & \;\;2 - \;\;5. \end{array}$$

The L.C.M. is $2 \times 3 \times 2 \times 5$, or 60.

Review of steps. Divide 12 and 30 by 2, obtain 6 and 15; divide 6 and 15 by 3. The quotients 2 and 5 are prime, with no common factor; hence the L.C.M. is $2 \times 3 \times 2 \times 5$, or 60.

Example 5. Find the least common multiple of 3, 8, and 12.

Solution.

$$\begin{array}{r|l} 2 & 3 - 8 - 12 \\ \hline 2 & 3 - 4 - \ 6 \\ \hline 3 & 3 - 2 - \ 3 \\ \hline & 1 - 2 - \ 1 \end{array}$$

The L.C.M. is
$2 \times 2 \times 3 \times 2 = 24$.

Comment. The common divisor selected must divide at least two of the numbers to be useful. If a number is not divisible by the common divisor selected, the number is repeated in the next line, as in the case of 3 which is not divisible by 2 or 2 which is not divisible by 3.

Example 6. Find the least common multiple of 12, 30, and 70 by both methods.

Solution.

Common divisor method

$$\begin{array}{r|l} 2 & 12 - 30 - 70 \\ \hline 3 & \ 6 - 15 - 35 \\ \hline 5 & \ 2 - \ 5 - 35 \\ \hline & \ 2 - \ 1 - \ 7 \end{array}$$

L.C.M. is $2 \times 3 \times 5 \times 2 \times 7$, or 420.

Factor method

$12 = 2 \times 2 \times 3$

$30 = 2 \times 3 \times 5$

$70 = 2 \times 5 \times 7$

L.C.M. is $2^2 \times 3 \times 5 \times 7$, or 420.

Check.

$$12\overline{)420}^{\,35} \qquad 30\overline{)420}^{\,14} \qquad 70\overline{)420}^{\,6}$$

35, 14, and 6 have no common factor.

EXERCISE 3

1. State briefly the tests for divisibility by 2, 3, 5, and 9. Give examples of five-digit numbers that are divisible by the given divisor.

2. List the prime numbers between 1 and 150, not counting the number 1.

3. Show the composition of the following numbers which characterizes them as composite numbers: 12, 18, 25, 34, 42, 51, 56, 66, 72, 87, 91, 93.

4. Explain and illustrate: common factor, common divisor, common multiple

5. Which of the following are prime numbers?

17	35	51	63	67	73	91	97	103
117	134	179	229	341	391	589	625	641.

6. Find common divisors for each pair of numbers and name the G.C.D.

(8, 12), (12, 18), (30, 42), (36, 64), (22, 55),
(323, 437), (323, 391), (87, 203), (57, 95).

7. Write a condensed form of each number, using exponents:

(*a*) $2 \times 2 \times 2 \times 3 \times 3 \times 5$, (*b*) $2 \times 3 \times 3 \times 3 \times 5 \times 5$,
(*c*) $7 \times 7 \times 11 \times 13$, (*d*) $2 \times 2 \times 2 \times 5 \times 5 \times 7 \times 7$,
(*e*) $2 \times 3 \times 3 \times 3 \times 5 \times 7 \times 7$.

8. Expand and find the value of

(*a*) $2^2 \times 3 \times 5$, (*b*) $2 \times 3^2 \times 5^2$, (*c*) $2^4 \times 5$, (*d*) $3^3 \times 5^2$,
(*e*) $5^5 \times 7^2$, (*f*) $3^2 \times 5^2 \times 7^2$, (*g*) $3^4 \times 5^4$, (*h*) $2^5 \times 3^3$.

9. Find the L.C.M.'s of

(*a*) 12 and 32, (*b*) 16 and 20, (*c*) 10, 12, and 15,
(*d*) 6 and 14, (*e*) 12 and 27, (*f*) 14, 18, and 30,
(*g*) 8 and 12, (*h*) 10 and 25, (*i*) 8, 12, and 16.

10. Without actually dividing, but applying the tests for divisibility, show whether 9240 is divisible by 2; by 3; by 4; by 5; by 6; by 8; by 9; by 11; by 15; by 20.

Note on common factors. Numerical calculations can sometimes be simplified by dividing out common factors in both numerators and denominators in a continued series of operations.

Example. Simplify and evaluate: $\dfrac{6 \times 12 \times 30 \times 40.}{8 \times 3 \times 4 \times 5}$

$$\frac{6 \times \overset{3}{\cancel{12}} \times \overset{10}{\cancel{30}} \times \overset{\overset{1}{\cancel{5}}}{\cancel{40}}}{\underset{1}{\cancel{8}} \times \underset{1}{\cancel{3}} \times \underset{1}{\cancel{4}} \times \underset{1}{\cancel{5}}} = \frac{6 \times 3 \times 10 \times 1}{1 \times 1 \times 1 \times 1} = 180.$$

Divide by common factors of 8, 3, 4, and 5, as shown.

EXERCISE 4

Evaluate by dividing out common factors in numerators and denominators:

1. $\dfrac{16 \times 15 \times 27 \times 280}{72 \times 40 \times 70}$, **2.** $\dfrac{9 \times 4 \times 21 \times 10}{4 \times 3 \times 20 \times 4}$,

3. $\dfrac{3 \times 4 \times 95 \times 9 \times 17}{19 \times 51 \times 36 \times 5}$, **4.** $\dfrac{8 \times 18 \times 35 \times 22}{55 \times 36 \times 12 \times 7}$,

5. $\dfrac{34 \times 24 \times 14 \times 4}{16 \times 18 \times 17 \times 7}$, **6.** $\dfrac{65 \times 75 \times 85 \times 55}{39 \times 25 \times 51 \times 22}$.

Application to problems involving cost of paper for printing:

7. Find the cost of 5250 sheets of 40-pound weight bond paper at $42 per 100 pounds. (40-pound weight means 40 pounds per 1000 sheets of 17 × 11 inch stock, or 500 sheets of 17 × 22 inch stock.)

$$5250 \times \frac{40}{1000} \times \frac{42}{100} =$$

8. Find the cost of 125 sheets of 32-pound weight paper at $30 per 100 pounds.

$$125 \times \frac{32}{1000} \times \frac{30}{100} =$$

9. Find the cost 5500 sheets of 32-pound weight paper at $40 per 100 pounds.

$$5500 \times \frac{32}{1000} \times \frac{40}{100} =$$

10. Reduce each fraction to lowest terms. Use Euclid's algorithm if necessary.

(*a*) $\frac{38}{65} =$ (*b*) $\frac{108}{192} =$ (*c*) $\frac{69}{115} =$ (*d*) $\frac{221}{323} =$ (*e*) $\frac{324}{342} =$

7.11 THE NUMBER OF PRIMES IS INFINITE

We began this chapter by considering the first few prime numbers; we observed that there were twenty-five primes between 1 and 100. The question naturally arises whether there are always new primes as we go further out in the list of integers or whether the list of primes comes to a end at some finite point. Euclid answered this question with the following theorem.

Theorem. Given any list of prime numbers, it is always possible to construct a new prime number not in the list; hence the number of primes is infinite.

Proof. Suppose there is a list of primes, $p_1, p_2, p_3, \cdots, p_n$, which might even include all possible primes, beginning with 2, 3, 5, 7, 11, $\cdots$, out to some fixed prime number p_n.

Construct the following number

$$p_1 \times p_2 \times p_3 \times \cdots \times p_n + 1,$$

which is the product of all of the given primes, increased by 1. We shall call this number N; the closure laws for products and sums tell us that N is some natural number.

The natural number N is either prime or composite.

1. If N is composite, it has at least two prime divisors, but *neither is in the list*, $p_1, p_2, p_3, \cdots, p_n$; hence there is a new prime not in the original list. The reason that there must be a new prime if N is composite is that none of the given primes will divide N exactly; every one of the primes, $p_1, p_2, p_3, \cdots, p_n$ leaves a remainder 1 when divided into N.

2. If N is prime, it is a *new prime*, being one more than some multiple, for all of the given primes. Hence, in either case, we have found a prime which is not in the given list.

Proceeding step by step, we can incorporate new primes into the list as we construct them, which means that the number of primes is infinite.

Several properties of integers (or natural numbers) were assumed tacitly in the proof, the principal assumption being that the number N could be factored uniquely into prime factors if it was composite. This property is guaranteed by the *unique factorization theorem*, which says that any integer can be factored in only one way into prime factors if no attention is paid to the order of the factors. We have assumed the uniqueness of our factoring throughout the discussions in this chapter.

7.12 SOME PROPERTIES OF THE NATURAL NUMBERS

Many interesting properties of the natural numbers have been known for centuries. We shall discuss several of these properties in this and in

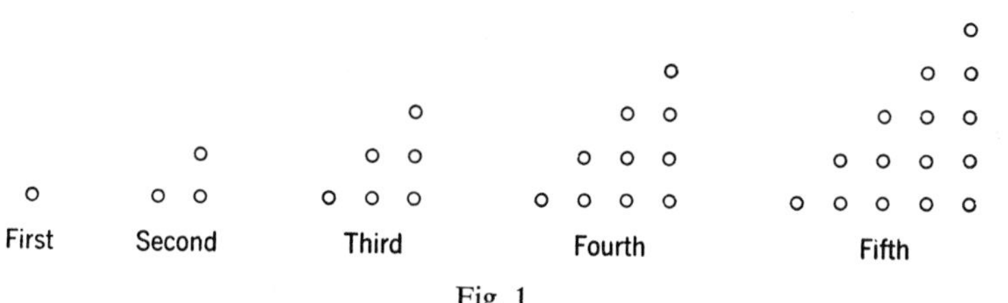

Fig. 1

succeeding sections of this chapter. The ancient Greeks, particularly the Pythagoreans, did a considerable amount of work in systematizing the early work in this field.

7.12.1. The triangular numbers. A glance at the diagram in Fig. 1 will reveal why a certain sequence of numbers is called "the triangular numbers."

The following are known as the *triangular numbers*:

$$1, 3, 6, 10, 15, 21, 28, 36, \cdots$$

These numbers, suggested in the diagram (Fig. 2), are the sums of the numbers 1; 1 and 2; 1, 2, and 3; 1, 2, 3, and 4, and so on. There are several ways of obtaining an expression or formula for these numbers.

In the diagrams at the left the triangular numbers are represented by squares instead of dots. The diagrams at the right show that the number of squares for each triangular number is one half the product of the ordinal number for the triangle times the next larger ordinal number. Thus the third triangular number is given by $(3 \times 4)/2$, or 6; the fourth triangular number is given by $(4 \times 5)/2$, or 10; and so on. Generally, the nth triangular number is given by

$$\frac{n(n + 1)}{2}$$

This result also gives the *sum of the first n natural numbers.*

It might be noted that a number of writers of textbooks for elementary schools recommend that in grouping for place value *ten* can be represented

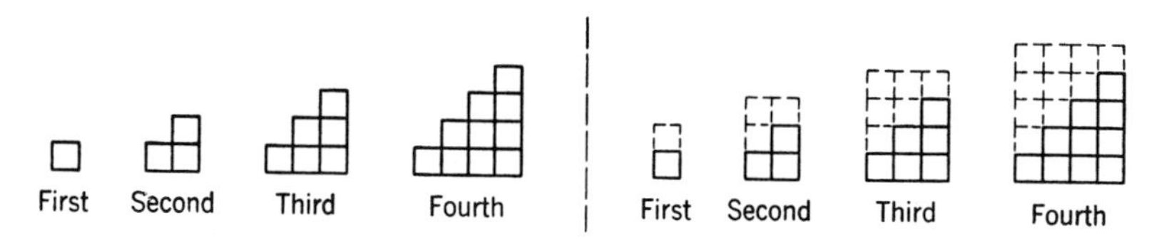

Fig. 2

as a cross section of a bundle of ten sticks. *Ten* is thus shown essentially as the fourth triangular number.

Ten is a group represented by Fig. 3.

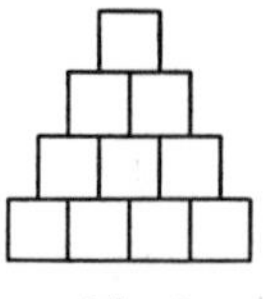

Fig. 3

7.12.2. The square numbers. A glance at the diagram in Fig. 4 will show why a certain sequence of numbers is called "the square numbers."

Fig. 4

The following are known as the *square numbers*:

$$1, \quad 4, \quad 9, \quad 16, \quad 25, \quad 36, \quad 49, \quad 64, \cdots$$

These numbers are very easy to represent by means of an expression:

The nth *square number* $= n^2$.

The reader should look closely at the diagrams in Fig. 5 for the square numbers and try to imagine them separated into two triangular numbers. Which triangular numbers make up the square numbers?

The second square number is made up from the first and ——— triangular numbers. The third square number is made up from the second and ——— triangular numbers. The fourth square number is made up from the ——— and ——— triangular numbers. Check these facts by using the two lists of numerals for the square and the triangular numbers.

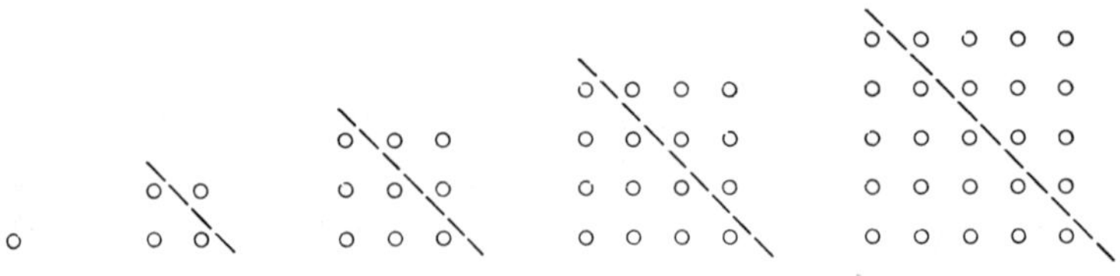

Fig. 5

EXERCISE 5

1. What are the successive differences among the triangular numbers? Use this fact to extend the list of triangular numbers to twenty terms.

2. Use the formula for the *n*th triangular number to find the twentieth triangular number and thus check the twentieth term in problem 1.

3. What are the successive differences among the square numbers? Use this fact to construct a list of the first twenty squares.

4. What should the twentieth square number be? What should the sum of the nineteenth triangular number and the twentieth triangular number be?

5. Use Euclid's construction to obtain at least one new prime number from 2, 3, and 5. Do the same, using 2, 3, 5, and 7.

6. Find the sum of the first twenty-nine numbers (twenty-ninth triangular number) and the sum of the first thirty numbers. What is the total of these two sums?

7. Find the seventy-ninth and eightieth triangular numbers, and the eightieth square number.

8. Use Euclid's method to construct a new prime by using 3, 5, and 7.

7.13 PERFECT NUMBERS

Among the numbers of interest to the Pythagoreans and other Greek mathematicians, as well as amateur and professional mathematicians of more recent times, were the *perfect numbers*. These were of the following sort: any composite number was considered by the Greeks to have divisors 1, and all other numbers which would give zero remainder, except the number itself. Thus 8 would have divisors 1, 2, and 4. A perfect number was then defined as follows:

Definition. A *perfect number* is one whose divisors have a sum equal to the number itself.

The first perfect number is easily seen to be the number 6, for its divisors are 1, 2, and 3, and

$$1 + 2 + 3 = 6.$$

The next perfect number is 28, since

$$1 + 2 + 4 + 7 + 14 = 28.$$

Euclid gave the rule that an even number would be perfect if it had the form

$$2^{p-1}(2^p - 1),$$

and if $2^p - 1$ is a prime.

A simple proof involving only intermediate algebra can be given to show that these numbers are perfect. (See Appendix B.)

The numbers $2^p - 1$ are known as *Mersenne's numbers*, since he conjectured (about A.D.1640) that eleven values of p, up to $p = 257$, would give prime values of $2^p - 1$. He was wrong in part. At present, the following values of p are among those which are known to give prime values of $2^p - 1$.

$$2, \quad 3, \quad 5, \quad 7, \quad 13, \quad 17, \quad 19, \quad 31, \quad 61, \quad 89, \quad 107, \quad \text{and} \quad 127.$$

EXERCISE 6

1. Construct the Euclidean-type perfect numbers for $p = 5$ and $p = 7$; that is, evaluate $2^4(2^5 - 1)$ and $2^6(2^7 - 1)$. Show that these numbers satisfy the definition of perfect numbers.

2. Look up the definition and give one or two examples of each of the following kinds of numbers:

(*a*) amicable numbers, (*b*) sociable numbers,
(*c*) abundant numbers, (*d*) defective numbers.

3. Construct a sequence of pentagonal numbers by placing dots in successive pentagonal (five-sided) patterns. The first pentagon is a single point. The second pentagon has two points on each side (the two adjacent vertices); the third pentagon has three points on each side (two vertices and a point between them), and so on. Each successive pentagon contains the preceding ones inside it. (See the diagram of the successive square numbers.) Write the value of each of the first four pentagonal numbers.

REFERENCES

Apostle, H. G., *A Survey of Basic Mathematics*, pp. 29–33.
Banks, J. H., *Learning and Teaching Arithmetic*, pp. 92–111.
Bell, E. T., *Men of Mathematics*, pp. 56–72, 218–269.
Dantzig, T., *Number, the Language of Science*, pp. 37–57.
Dubisch, R., *The Nature of Number.*
Larsen, H. D., *Arithmetic for Colleges*, pp. 109–119.
Lay, L. C., *Arithmetic, An Introduction to Mathematics*, pp. 47–62.
Swain, R. L., *Understanding Arithmetic*, pp. 113–134.
Taylor, E. H., C. N. Mills, *Arithmetic for Teacher-Training Classes*, fourth edition, pp. 115–127.
Titchmarsh, E. C., *Mathematics for the General Reader*, pp. 13–36.

8

Introduction to Measurement, Area, and Volume

8.1 INTRODUCTION

Measurement is everywhere about us. At the breakfast table the toast is made from the standard pound or pound-and-one-half loaf, the coffee is measured before being put into the coffee pot, which already contains a measured amount of water. The milk is poured from a quart or half-gallon carton. The packaged cereal has its weight printed on the carton. Likewise, measurements of time, distance, and temperature are familiar to all of us.

This chapter is concerned with linear and surface measure and discusses the perimeters of triangles, squares, rectangles, and circles as well as the area of the square and the rectangle. Other common figures are discussed in a later chapter, when areas and volumes are studied in detail.

8.2 LINEAR MEASURE

Measurement along a line is called linear measure. A child who wants to know how tall he is usually stands against a wall and someone marks his height. Measurement is then made along an imaginary line from that point to the floor. Common linear units are inches, feet, and yards. In the metric system linear units include millimeters, decimeters, centimeters, meters, kilometers, and so on. In a track meet yards are used for some events, such as the 220- 440- or 880-yard dash, whereas the high jump is most often measured in terms of feet and inches. Some events are taken in terms of meters (for example, Whitefield once set a 1 minute, 49.2 second mark as the record for 800 meters). Distance between towns and cities may be expressed in terms of miles, another linear unit.

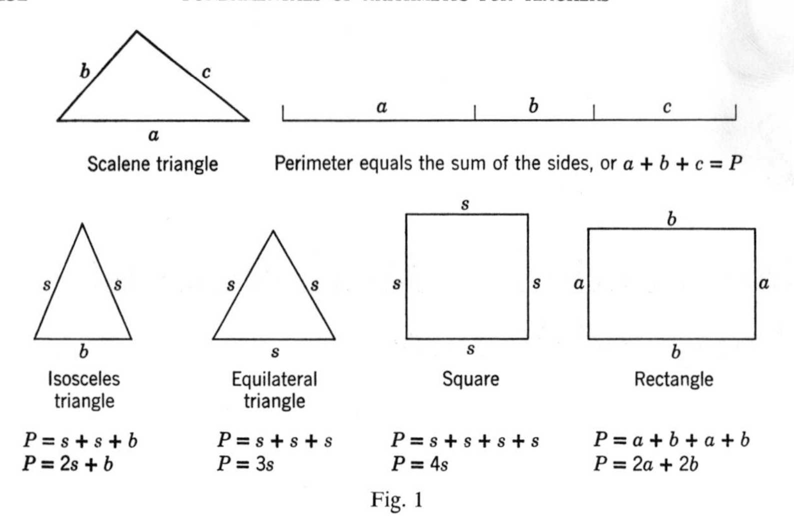

Fig. 1

8.3 PERIMETER

The distance around a room is called the perimeter, as is the distance around any plane figure, as a rule. We could be asked to find the perimeter of a playground. This measurement is expressed in linear units. Above are some common geometric figures and their formulas for perimeter (Fig. 1).

8.4 THE NATURE OF π

The Greek letter π is used to represent the ratio of the circumference of a circle to the diameter of the circle (Fig. 2). The value of π is about $\frac{22}{7}$ or, more precisely, $3.1416 \cdots$. However, the value of π is an irrational number, that is, a number which cannot be expressed exactly by the ratio of two natural numbers (see Chapter 10). As a mixed decimal number, π is a nonrepeating, nonterminating decimal expression. Archimedes (287–212 B.C.) and other Greek mathematicians showed how to approximate the value of π by comparing the perimeters of inscribed regular polygons in a circle with the diameter of the circle. As the number of sides of the inscribed polygon is increased, by doubling the number successively,

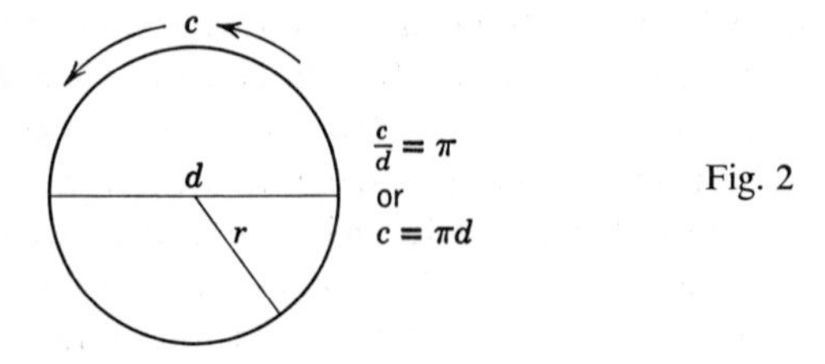

Fig. 2

for example, the perimeter of the polygon becomes as nearly equal to the perimeter of the circle as we could wish. By this method, Archimedes showed that the value of π was larger than $3\frac{10}{71}$ but smaller than $3\frac{1}{7}$. In recent decades the value of π has been computed to more than 2000 decimal places on electronic digital computers.

Project. Find an approximate value of π by measuring the length of a string stretched around a tomato can or other circular object and comparing it with the measured diameter of the object.

By using a value of π, we can find the circumference and the area of a circle. The formula $c = \pi d$ gives the circumference of the circle, and the formula $A = \pi r^2$ gives the number of square units of area of the circular disk.

Example. Find the area and the circumference of a circle whose diameter is 10 inches.

Solution.

$$d = 10, \qquad r = \tfrac{1}{2}d = 5.$$

$$c = \pi d = 3.1416 \times 10 = 31.416$$

The circumference of the circle is 31.416 inches. The circumference of the circle is its perimeter.

$$A = \pi r^2 = 3.1416 \times 5^2 = 3.1416 \times 25 = 78.540$$

The area of the circle is 78.540 square inches.

EXERCISE 1

1. Find the perimeter of a triangle with sides 3 inches, 4 inches, and 5 inches; with sides 2 feet 3 inches, 5 feet 4 inches, 3 feet 7 inches.

2. A square is 3 feet on a side. What is its perimeter?

3. A rectangle is twice as long as it is wide, and it is 8 inches wide. What is the perimeter of the rectangle?

4. One of the equal sides of an isosceles triangle is 11 inches and the base is 4 inches. What is the perimeter of this triangle?

5. If a square has a perimeter of 100 yards, what is the length of one side?

6. A rectangle has a perimeter of 280 feet. If its width is 45 feet, what is the length?

7. A playground surrounded by buildings is in the shape of an equilateral triangle and a path separates the buildings from the playground. If the length of the outer edge of the path on one side is 56 feet, what is the perimeter of the outer edge of the path?

8. Find the perimeter of a circle, called the circumference, if the circle has a radius of 7 inches; a radius of 11 inches; and one with a radius of 4 feet. Also find the areas of these circles.

9. Find the circumferences of the circles with diameters of (*a*) 14 feet; (*b*) 7 yards; (*c*) 2 feet. Find the areas of these circles.

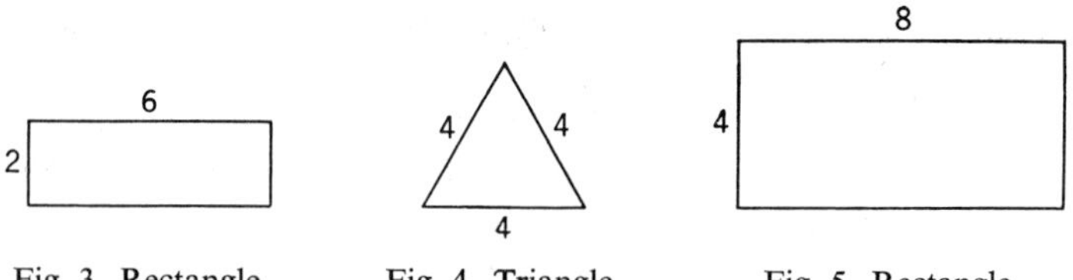

Fig. 3. Rectangle Fig. 4. Triangle Fig. 5. Rectangle

10. How many units difference in perimeter will there be between the rectangle shown in Fig. 5 and the rectangle shown in Fig. 3, assuming that the units are the same kind?

11. By how many units does the perimeter of the rectangle in Fig. 3 exceed that of the perimeter of the triangle in Fig. 4?

12. Subtract the perimeter of the rectangle in Fig. 5 from the sum of the perimeters of the diagrams in Fig. 3 and Fig. 4.

8.5 AREA

The surface enclosed by any of the foregoing figures is expressed in square units of measure, not linear measure, (Fig. 6). Here is a linear measure of one inch, ______1 inch______. Fig. 6 is a square inch.

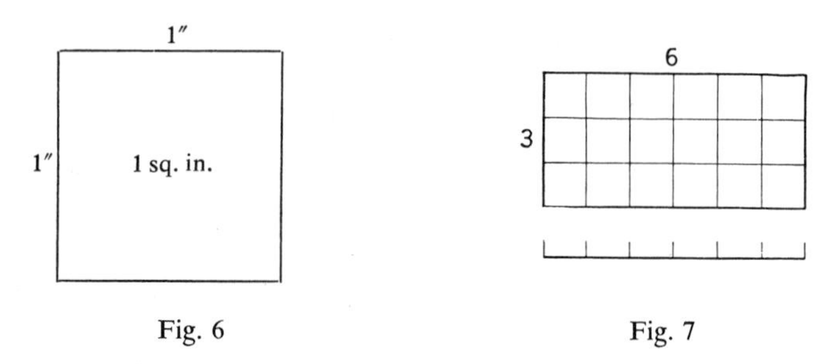

Fig. 6 Fig. 7

Square measure is always used in measuring surface areas (Fig. 7). The units may be square inches, square feet, square yards, square meters, and so on. If a rectangle is 6 units long and 3 units wide, its surface or area is 18 square units. There are three rows each of 6 square units.

If the 6 and the 3 were measured in inches the area would be 18 *square* inches. If the 6 and the 3 had been measured in feet, the area would be 18 *square* feet. *Note.* Some teachers prefer to speak of the area *enclosed* by a rectangle rather than the area of the rectangle.

EXERCISE 2

1. In the above cross section paper (Fig. 8), consider the lines to be drawn one inch apart. Find the area of each of the outlined figures by counting the number of squares.

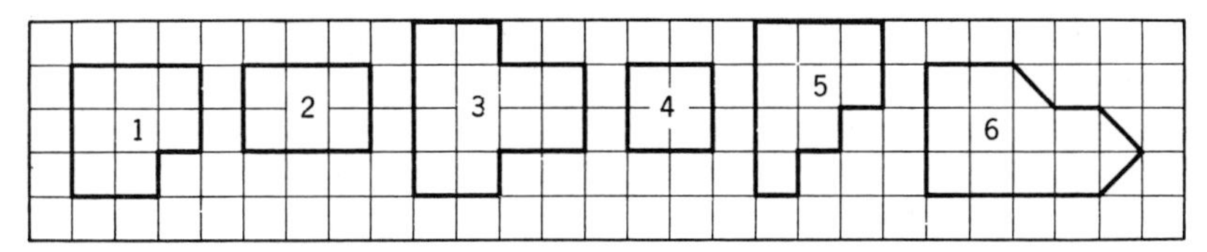

Fig. 8

2. In Fig. 8 by how much does the sum of the areas indicated by 1 and 2 exceed the area indicated by 3?

3. In Fig. 8 which has the greater area, areas of 2 and 6 combined or areas 4 and 5 combined?

4. In Fig. 8 what is the total of the areas 1, 2, 3, 4, and 5?

5. Is there any difference between an inch square and a square inch? Illustrate. Is there any difference between 2 square feet and a 2 foot square? Illustrate.

8.6 FORMULAS FOR AREAS OF CERTAIN FIGURES

Rectangle. The area of a rectangle is the product of the number of units in its base and the number of units in its altitude (Fig. 9).

$$A = ba$$

(Sometimes this is referred to as the product of the length and width, the width being the altitude, and the length, the base. Thus $A = lw$.)

Example 1. Find the area of a rectangle with base 6 inches and altitude 4 inches.

Solution. $A = ba$, $A = 6 \times 4$

$A = 24$ square inches.*

Square. The area of a square is the number of linear units of the side, multiplied by itself.

$$A = s \times s \quad \text{or} \quad A = s^2$$

Example 2. Find the area of a square of side 6 inches (Fig. 10).

Solution. $A = s^2$, $s = 6$,

$A = 6^2$,

$A = 6 \times 6$,

$A = 36$ square inches.*

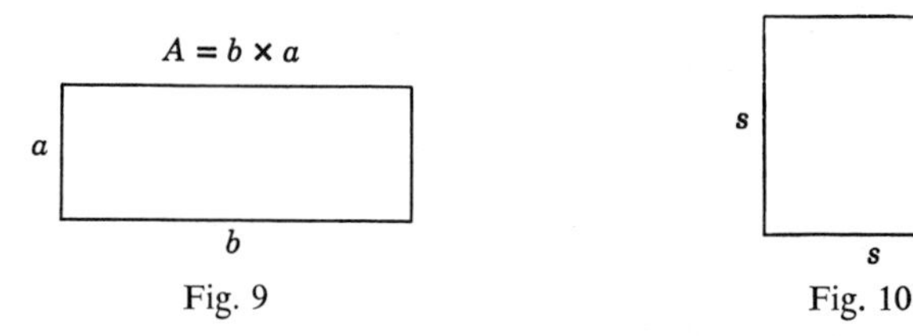

Fig. 9

Fig. 10

* For convenience in writing solutions, the units are omitted in all except the last step of the work.

Example 3. A rectangle with 45 square feet of area has an altitude of 5 feet. What is its base?

Solution. Formula for area: $A = ba$.

Then, $45 = 5b$ or $b = 9$, (Dividing both numbers by 5.)

The base is 9 feet long.

Example 4. A square has an area of 225 square inches. What is the length of one side?

Solution. Formula for area: $A = s^2$.

Then, $225 = s^2$ or $s^2 = 225$; $s = \sqrt{225} = 15$ inches.

EXERCISE 3

1. How many square inches are there in one square foot? How can a student not make the error of thinking 12 inches = 1 square foot?

2. How many square feet are there in one square yard? What are the advantages of having a square yard painted on the classroom floor and dividing it into square feet?

3. The floor of a bookkeeping class room is 40 feet long and 30 feet wide. What is its area?

4. If a room is 30 feet long, 20 feet wide, and 10 feet high, what is the area of the walls and ceiling, allowing 70 square feet for the doors and windows?

5. If a gymnasium floor is 100 feet long and 65 feet wide, how many square feet of surface does it contain?

6. Find the area of a rectangle 25 feet long and 12 feet wide.

7. A rectangle has an area of 220 square yards. If it is 20 yards long, how wide is it?

8. What is the side of a square that contains the same area as that of a rectangle that is 4 feet wide and is four times as long as it is wide?

9. How does the area of a rectangle change if its base is doubled when the height remains the same? When the height is doubled and the base remains the same? When both the base and height are doubled?

10. A lawn measures 28 by 18 feet. Over how many square feet of lawn can the child of the house play?

11. A square measures 10 feet on a side. What is its perimeter? What is its area? How are these changed if the side is doubled?

12. The dimensions of a rectangle are given in inches but the answer is requested in square feet. Which is better and why: to change the inches to feet and obtain the answer in square feet or to find the area in square inches and then change them to square feet?

13. A rectangular lawn has an area of 1545 square feet. If the lawn is 15 feet wide, how long is it?

14. How many gallons of paint are required for painting the outer sides of a barn if its walls are 10 feet high and the dimensions of the floor are 25 feet and 40 feet? Assume that one gallon of paint will cover a surface of 250 square feet.

15. Find the area of a football field 100 yards long and 50 yards wide.

8.7 CORRESPONDENCE OF LINEAR AND SURFACE MEASURE

In discussing surface area, it has been pointed out that the result is a number of square units, although the dimensions of the figure are given in linear units. To arrive at a correct relation between the dimensional units involved, the problem can be treated in the following way (Fig. 11):

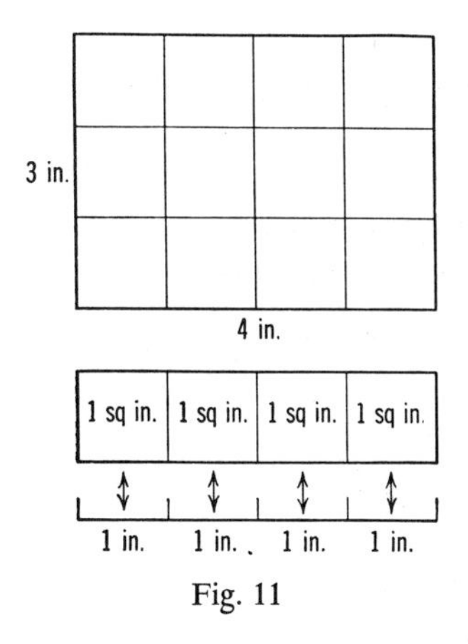

Fig. 11

A one-to-one correspondence should be set up between the linear units in one dimension of the rectangular region and an equivalent number of unit squares. This corresponds to constructing a strip of unit squares of length equal to one side of the rectangle and of width one unit. Strips of this kind can be placed side by side on the rectangle. The number of strips required is given by the number of linear units in the other dimension of the rectangle. Thus, if one side of a rectangle is 4 inches long and an end of the rectangle is 3 inches long, strips of four 1-inch squares can be placed side by side three times to cover the rectangle. The area of the rectangle is then

$$3 \times \text{(4 square inches)} = 12 \text{ square inches.}$$

EXERCISE 4

1. Make a sketch and set up a correspondence, in two distinct ways, between the length of one side and an equivalent number of unit squares, to measure the area of a rectangle with dimensions 3 and 5 inches.

2. Proceed as in problem 1, with a rectangle which is $5\frac{1}{2}$ by 4 inches. How many square inches are in a strip as long as the rectangle if the strip is 1 inch wide and as long as the rectangle? How many strips of length 4 inches and width 1 inch are needed to cover the area? Make sketches for the discussions.

3. Show that there are 9 square feet in 1 square yard by making a diagram and using strips 3 feet long by 1 foot wide to cover the square yard.

4. Give a discussion and a sketch to show why there are 144 square inches in one square foot.

8.8 CORRESPONDENCE OF SURFACE MEASURE AND VOLUME MEASURE

To find the volume of a rectangular box, or other container, a correspondence can be set up between the number of square units of area in one surface of the box and an equal number of unit cubes that can be placed one-to-one on the square units of surface. The container can then be thought of as filled with these layers of cubes. The *number of layers* of cubes is given by the number of units in the third dimension of the box.

Example 1. If a box measures 3 by 2 by 2 (Fig. 12), then one surface of the box

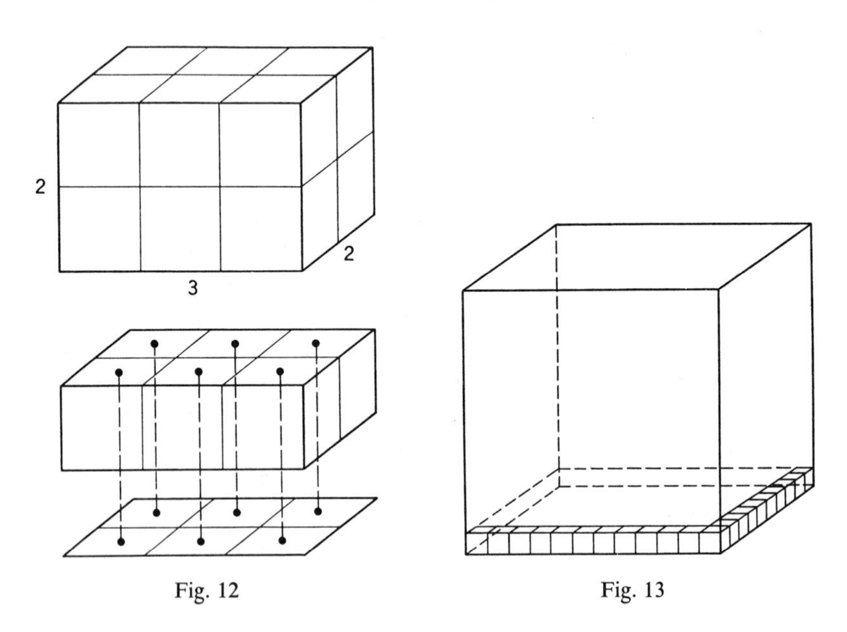

Fig. 12 Fig. 13

will have an area of 3×2, or 6 square units. A layer of 6 unit cubes can be placed on this surface. Two layers of cubes will fill the box. The volume will be $2 \times (6 \text{ cubic units}) = 12$ cubic units.

Example 2. A cubic foot container, 12 by 12 by 12 inches, can be filled with 12 layers of 144 cubic inches, each layer fitting exactly over a 12 by 12 square-inch surface (Fig. 13). There will be a volume of 12 × (144 cubic inches), or 1728 cubic inches in the container.

EXERCISE 5

1. Make a sketch showing that there are three layers of 6 cubic units in a box with dimensions of 3 by 2 by 3; hence there are 3 × (6 cubic units), or 18 cubic units content in the box.

2. Make a sketch showing that there are three layers of 9 cubic feet (9 one-foot cubes) in one cubic yard; show that there are 27 cubic feet in one cubic yard.

3. Find the volume of a box that is 4 by 5 by 3 feet. Make a sketch.

4. If the base of a rectangular bin is 3 by 6 feet, how deep must the bin be if it is to hold 54 cubic feet?

5. A gallon is equal to 231 cubic inches. About how deep should a carton be if its base is 5 by 5 inches and it holds one gallon?

6. How many gallons (231 cubic inches) will a carton hold if its dimensions are 6 by 7 by 11 inches?

Project. Obtain some one-inch blocks with which to fill a chalk box or similar container to demonstrate the use of layers of cubes to fill the box. This device is useful in discussing the notion of volume.

EXERCISE 6

Preliminary practice problems in the work with fractions.

1. Add (*a*) $\begin{array}{r} 3\frac{1}{4} \\ 4\frac{5}{8} \\ \hline \end{array}$ (*b*) $\begin{array}{r} 5\frac{2}{3} \\ 2\frac{5}{12} \\ \hline \end{array}$ (*c*) $\begin{array}{r} 8\frac{3}{8} \\ 5\frac{2}{5} \\ \hline \end{array}$ (*d*) $\begin{array}{r} 3\frac{3}{8} \\ 14\frac{7}{10} \\ \hline \end{array}$.

2. Subtract (*a*) $\begin{array}{r} \frac{3}{4} \\ \frac{1}{8} \\ \hline \end{array}$ (*b*) $\begin{array}{r} \frac{2}{3} \\ \frac{3}{7} \\ \hline \end{array}$ (*c*) $\begin{array}{r} 7\frac{3}{5} \\ 6\frac{2}{3} \\ \hline \end{array}$ (*d*) $\begin{array}{r} 5\frac{7}{8} \\ 4\frac{2}{3} \\ \hline \end{array}$.

3. Perform the indicated operations.

(*a*) $\frac{2}{5} \times 4\frac{1}{2}$ (*b*) $3\frac{3}{4} \times 5\frac{1}{3}$

(*c*) $2\frac{3}{5} \times 4$ (*d*) $5\frac{1}{2} \times 6\frac{3}{8}$

(*e*) $\frac{3}{4} \div \frac{3}{8}$ (*f*) $\frac{2}{3} \div 5$

(*g*) $3 \div \frac{4}{7}$ (*h*) $8\frac{1}{2} \div 5\frac{2}{3}$.

4. How much will $\frac{7}{8}$ pound of food cost if the price is 40 cents per pound?

5. What is the cost per yard if $3\frac{1}{2}$ yards of goods cost $2.80?

6. A paper $11\frac{2}{3}$ inches long will make how many pieces each $2\frac{1}{3}$ inches long?

7. If candy costs 60 cents per pound, how much can be purchased for 40 cents?

8. A jar holds $\frac{2}{5}$ quart liquid. How many such jars are needed to hold 10 quarts?

9. If $2\frac{3}{4}$ pounds lard cost 66 cents, how many pounds can be purchased for $2.00?

REFERENCES

Apostle, H. G., *A Survey of Basic Mathematics*, pp. 221–227.
DeMay, Amy, *Guiding Beginners in Arithmetic*, pp. 155–163.
Drewes, Mermer, von Boenigk, *Practical Plans for Teaching Arithmetic*, pp. 93–98.
Larsen, H. D., *Arithmetic for Colleges*, pp. 185–198.
Lieber, Lillian, *The Education of T. C. Mits*, pp. 22–78.
Marks, J. L., C. R. Purdy, and L. B. Kinney, *Teaching Arithmetic for Understanding*, pp. 273–298.
McSwain and Cooke, *Understanding and Teaching Arithmetic in the Elementary School*, pp. 244–256.
Wheat, H. G., *How to Teach Arithmetic*, pp. 236–239, 280–289, 297–308.

9

Introduction to Fractions

9.1 INTRODUCTION TO FRACTIONS

Children in elementary school soon become acquainted with fractions. They eat half an apple, drink half a glass of water, or share a candy bar. If a candy bar is divided into two equal parts, then halves of the candy bar are obtained. The fact that halves must be equal parts can be emphasized by having a child share his candy with a friend. If the child is told that he will have to take the remaining part of the bar after his friend has first choice, he will make the pieces as nearly equal as he can, and the pieces will be almost true halves. It should be noted that the word "half" is used loosely in ordinary language and does not always refer to one of two equal parts of a whole. Emphasis on equality of parts for thirds and fourths can be made in a similar manner. There must be three equal parts of the whole for thirds, four equal parts of the whole for fourths, and so on.

Whole quantities, such as candy bars, apples, oranges, and glasses of water, can be discussed with children early in the grades. Similarly, the teacher can talk about half a candy bar, half an apple, half an orange, half a glass of water, and so on. In speaking of a whole, a whole unit is meant, whether the unit is one apple, one pie, one square, or one circle. To describe a part of a whole, a fraction is used, the simplest examples being one half ($\frac{1}{2}$) and one fourth ($\frac{1}{4}$). Consider what is meant by one half dollar or one quarter hour. Each is a part of a whole quantity of its given kind. Relations of the cubes of a pound of butter to the whole pound and similar situations can also be discussed by the teacher in the primary grades.

For more advanced groups, the teacher may ask each child to fold a sheet of paper so that it is divided into two equal parts. The pupil is then asked to tell what part of the whole sheet is in each part. On each part can be written $\frac{1}{2}$. The child folds another sheet into four equal parts and again is asked to tell what part of the entire sheet is in each part. He then writes $\frac{1}{4}$ on each of the four parts. This procedure can be used to show that two halves equal one whole, that four quarters equal one whole, and that two quarters equal one half.

9.2 DEFINITION

A fraction is an indicated quotient of two natural numbers. A fraction is also a quantity or number showing *how many of the equal parts* of a whole unit are being considered *in all of the equal parts* into which the unit has been divided. The numbers $\frac{1}{2}$, $\frac{3}{4}$, $\frac{2}{3}$ are examples; these are examples of *common fractions*. The 1, 3, or 2 above the bar is the numerator of each fraction. The 2, 4 or 3 below the bar is the denominator of each fraction. The *numerator* gives the number of parts that are being considered and the *denominator* states the total number of parts into which the whole has been divided. The fraction $\frac{3}{4}$ indicates that the whole has been divided into four equal parts and that three of them are taken. In the fraction $\frac{a}{b}$, a is the numerator and b is the denominator. The whole has been divided into b equal parts, and a of them are being considered. The numerator can be referred to as the *dividend*, and the denominator, as the *divisor*. The numerator and denominator are often referred to as the *terms* of a fraction.

9.3 READING FRACTIONS

The numerator of a fraction is read as a natural number, but the denominator usually has a "ths" suffix added to the number. If the denominator is two, it is read as halves; if it is three, it is read as thirds.

Examples. $\frac{3}{4}$ is read three fourths, $\frac{2}{3}$ is read two thirds, and $\frac{7}{8}$ is read seven eighths.

When a fraction appears combined with a natural number, such as $3\frac{2}{5}$, it is read as three and two fifths and means $3 + \frac{2}{5}$. Such an expression is called a *mixed number*. In discussing fractions orally, great care must be exercised to distinguish between three fours (4, 4, 4) and the fraction $\frac{3}{4}$, which is three fourths.

Discussion Problem. What is the difference between three eights and three eighths? Three eights means 8, 8 and 8, or 24. The difference would be $24 - \frac{3}{8}$, or $23\frac{5}{8}$.

9.4 REPRESENTING FRACTIONS

There are different ways of representing the same fraction. The fraction with numerator 5 and denominator 6 may be written (1) in words, five

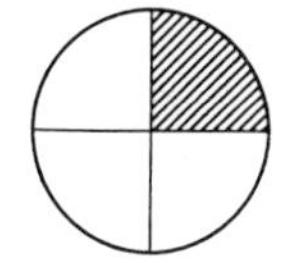 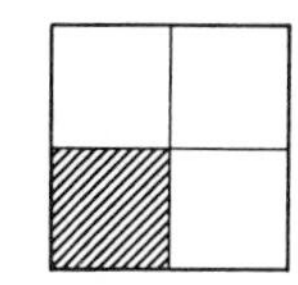 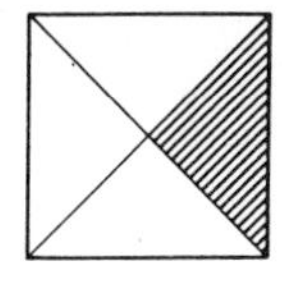 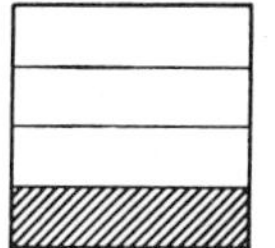

Fig. 1

sixths; (2) in symbol and word, 5 sixths; (3) in symbols as $\frac{5}{6}$ with horizontal bar, as 5/6 with diagonal bar, as 5 : 6 in which two dots replace the bar, or as 5 to 6, using the word "to" in place of the bar; and (4) as a division problem, $5 \div 6$ or $\overline{5}|\underline{6}$. The diagonal bar is very confusing to primary children and should not be used in grades 1, 2, and 3. Its principal advantage is the ease with which it is written on a typewriter.

9.5 USES OF FRACTIONS

Four important uses of a fraction are discussed.

1. To represent part of a whole.
2. To represent part of a group.
3. To compare two or more things or to express a ratio.
4. To express certain measurements.

9.5.1. Fractions to represent part of a whole. A fraction may be used to represent a segment of a whole; that is, the segment is one or more of the equal parts of the whole unit. In the diagrams in Fig. 1 the whole has been divided into four equal parts and one of them (one quarter or one fourth) is shaded.

In each of the plane figures in the diagram in Fig. 2 the whole has been divided into three equal parts; two of them are shaded, or $\frac{2}{3}$ of the figure is shaded.

EXERCISE 1

1. Consider the fraction $\frac{2}{5}$. (*a*) What is the numerator? (*b*) What is the denominator? (*c*) How many parts are taken? (*d*) What is the name of these parts? (*e*) Into how many parts was the whole divided? (*f*) What name other than the numerator could describe the 2? (*g*) Which is the divisor, 5 or 2?

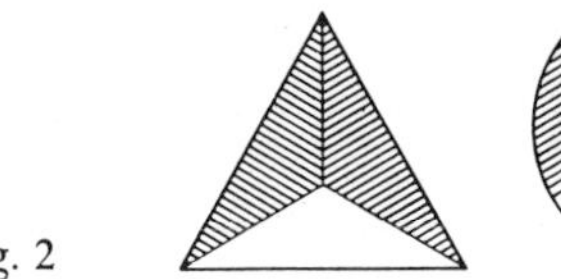 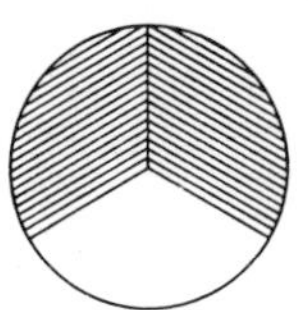 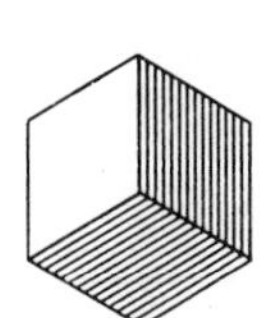

Fig. 2

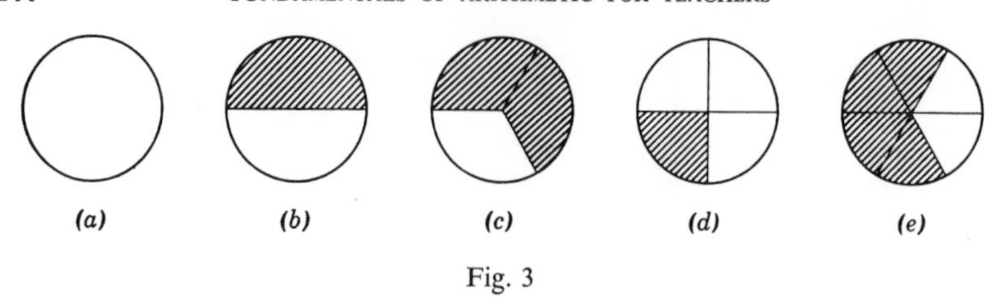

Fig. 3

2. Tell how the whole was divided in each of the circles in the diagram in Fig. 3. What is the name of each part? How many parts are shaded? What fraction tells the part that is shaded or not shaded? As the number of parts into which the whole is divided is increased, 2, 3, 4, 6, etc., what change takes place in the size of each part?

3. Let the line AB in the diagram represent one unit. What fractional part of AB is represented by these parts: AQ, AS, AP, AV, AR, QU, RV, VB? Fig. 4.

4. Draw a sketch to illustrate

$$1 = \frac{2}{2} = \frac{3}{3} = \frac{4}{4} = \frac{6}{6} = \frac{8}{8}.$$

5. What is the dictionary meaning of "fraction"? Give an illustration of how the word "fraction" is used in a nonmathematical situation and tell how this meaning is related to the mathematical meaning.

6. *Reference Problem.* Obtain a copy of the *Ahmes Papyrus* from your library and study the Egyptian method for representing fractions, or refer to other sources for this information.

9.5.2. Fractions to represent a part of a group. In addition to its function as a part of a whole unit, a fraction may be used to indicate a part of a group. Suppose there are six pencils on the desk and Mary is told to take one half of them. The six pencils would be considered as a group, and Mary would take three pencils, or one half of the group of six pencils. To take one half of any number is the same as dividing that number by two. This is the partition notion of division. The partition concept implies that a fraction such as $\frac{3}{4}$ may mean not only "three of four equal parts of one unit" but also "one of four equal parts of three units."

9.5.3. Fractions to compare two or more things. One table is half as long as another table. Jane is one third taller than Mary. Paul saved one fourth as much money as John. Comparisons can be made only of like things. In the preceding illustrations we compared the length of one table

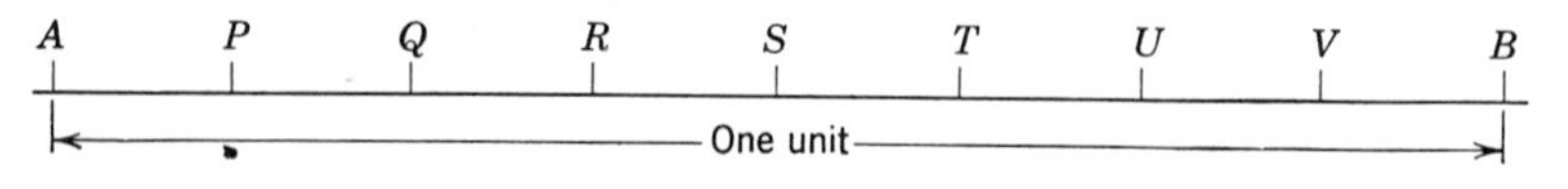

Fig. 4

with the length of another. We cannot compare the length of a table with money saved. The notion of comparison is similar to the notion of a ratio.

Sometimes fractions are used to express a ratio. The ratio of the width of a table which is 3 feet wide to the length of the table, which is 6 feet, could be expressed as the ratio 3 to 6, or in fractional form $\frac{3}{6}$. Ratios are usually expressed in the simplest form. The ratio 3 to 6 becomes 1 to 2, 1 : 2, or $\frac{1}{2}$. John is 5 feet tall and Henry is 6 feet tall. The ratio of their heights would be 5 to 6, 5 : 6, or $\frac{5}{6}$, that is, the ratio in the order named. In order to compare two quantities by means of a ratio, these quantities must be expressed in the same units. All ratios are then expressed in the simplest terms.

Example 1. Find the ratio of 6 inches to $1\frac{1}{2}$ feet.

Solution. Changing to the same units, $1\frac{1}{2}$ feet becomes 18 inches; the ratio then is $\frac{6}{18} = \frac{1}{3}$, or 1 to 3. The problem could be worked out this way also: 6 inches is $\frac{1}{2}$ foot. The ratio of 6 inches to $1\frac{1}{2}$ feet becomes $\frac{1}{2}/1\frac{1}{2}$ which is not in its simplest form. Multiplying both the numerator and the denominator by 2 does not change the value of the fraction; it gives $\frac{1}{2} \times 2/(1\frac{1}{2} \times 2)$ or $\frac{1}{3}$, which is a ratio in its simplest form.

If two ratios are known to be equal, they can be set up to form a proportion, such as $\frac{2}{3} = \frac{4}{6}$, which is read 2 is to 3 as 4 is to 6. There are four terms in a proportion: 2 is the first term, 3, the second term, 4, the third term, and 6, the fourth term. In any proportion such as $a/b = c/d$, a is the first term, b is the second term, c is the third term, and d is the fourth term. The *first* and *fourth terms* in any proportion are called the *extremes*. The *second* and *third terms* are called the *means*. In algebra the principle is stated as follows: "In any proportion the product of the means equals the product of the extremes." In other words, if two fractions are equal, the product of the numerator of the first and the denominator of the second is equal to the product of the denominator of the first fraction and the numerator of the second; that is, if $\frac{2}{3} = \frac{4}{6}$, then $2 \times 6 = 3 \times 4$, or if the two fractions are $a/b = c/d$, then $a \times d = b \times c$. Knowing this principle, we can easily solve for a missing term if three terms of the proportion are given. It can be seen that interchanging the means in a proportion preserves the equality; thus $a/c = b/d$. Likewise, the extremes can be interchanged.

Example 2. If 3 pounds of apples cost 50 cents, what will 5 pounds cost at the same rate?

Solution. The problem can be solved by setting up a ratio of pounds to pounds equals cost to cost: $\frac{3}{5} = \frac{50}{x}$. In this case the product of the middle terms equals the product of the end terms: $3x = 250$. Divide by 3 to solve for the unknown x: $x = (5 \times 50)/3$ or $\frac{250}{3}$ or $83\frac{1}{3}$. The answer is $83\frac{1}{3}$ cents. It would also be possible to compare ratios of pounds to cost and pounds to cost by exchanging the means in the proportion. Again, the problem could be solved by finding the cost of one pound of apples and multiplying that cost by 5 to obtain the cost of 5 pounds of apples. Proportions are special cases of equations; both equations and proportions are discussed in the chapter on algebra (Chapter 19).

EXERCISE 2

Write in simplest terms the fractional form of the following ratios:

1. 3 months to 1 year.
2. 200 cents to 4 dollars.
3. 12 ounces to 3 pounds.
4. 3 yards to 16 feet.
5. 2 yards to 40 inches.
6. 1 mile to 880 yards.
7. 36 hours to 30 days.
8. 5 days to 1 month.
9. 1 month to 1 year.
10. 2 quarts to 2 pints.

Write the fraction or ratio or missing number that is required in the following:

11. There were twenty-four chairs in the room. Eight of them were removed. What fraction represents the part of the group removed?

12. In a class of thirty pupils eighteen are boys and twelve are girls. What fraction represents the part of the class that is boys? Girls? What is the ratio of the number of boys to the number of girls? What is the ratio of the number of girls to the number of boys?

13. John is 5 feet tall; the ratio of James's height to John's is 5 to 4. How tall is James?

14. In a certain recipe for jam the ratio of the number of cups of berries to the number of cups of sugar is 4 to 3. How much sugar is needed for 10 cups of berries? How many cups of berries are needed for 8 cups of sugar?

15. If 5 yards of cloth cost \$1.80, what will 12 yards cost at the same rate?

16. A man drove 400 miles in 8 hours. At the same rate how far would he drive in $5\frac{1}{2}$ hours?

17. A tree casts a shadow 30 feet long at the same time a 3-foot stick casts a 5-foot shadow. How high is the tree?

18. Simplify these ratios:

$$\frac{2\frac{1}{2}}{5}, \frac{\frac{3}{4}}{6}, \frac{5}{7\frac{1}{2}}, \frac{\frac{2}{3}}{\frac{1}{2}}.$$

19. If $7x = 5y$, what is the ratio of x to y? Check your ratio by the principle of the "product of the means equals the product of the extremes."

20. Solve for x in these proportions:

$$\frac{x}{2} = \frac{3}{8}; \quad \frac{4}{8} = \frac{5}{x}; \quad 8 = \frac{2}{x}; \quad \frac{3}{x} = 6; \quad 4 = \frac{x}{3}; \quad \frac{2}{3} = \frac{x}{1.5}.$$

9.5.4. Fractions to express certain measurements. The use of fractions to express measurements is somewhat different from their use in comparing objects.

Examples. Certain fractional measures become independent quantities by common usage: A half dollar is a whole object, but it is of less value than the whole dollar. Similarly, a pint carton is a whole container, but it contains less than the quart carton. These fractional parts of a whole quantity are complete items in their own right.

EXERCISE 3

1. Give the following values in terms of a smaller unit: what is one quarter of (*a*) a dollar, (*b*) an hour, (*c*) a quart, (*d*) a yard, (*e*) a pound? What is one fifth of (*a*) a dollar, (*b*) an hour, (*c*) a ton, (*d*) a year? (*e*) What is one eighth of a day?

2. Express the following in form of a ratio:
(a) One day in every five during the winter is rainy.
(b) A girl obtains six out of ten marks.
(c) Seven men in every ten own motor cars.
(d) Two pupils in every 100 are absent from school.

3. What are the four uses of fractions described in this chapter? Give an example of each use.

4. Find and copy articles in newspapers, magazines, or advertising that illustrate the four uses of fractions.

9.6 KINDS OF FRACTIONS

Fractions are classified in several ways. With regard to form, a fraction may be *simple*, *complex*, or *compound*. With regard to the kinds of denominators, fractions may be *similar* or *dissimilar* fractions. A simple fraction is one for which both the numerator and denominator are natural numbers. Thus

$$\frac{1}{2}, \quad \frac{3}{4}, \quad \frac{7}{10}, \quad \frac{a}{b}$$

are simple fractions (where a and b are natural numbers). Such simple fractions are generally known as common fractions.* A complex fraction is one in which the numerator or the denominator or both are simple fractions. Thus

$$\frac{\frac{2}{3}}{4}, \quad \frac{6}{\frac{3}{4}}, \quad \frac{\frac{2}{3}}{\frac{3}{4}}$$

are complex fractions. A fraction whose numerator or denominator or both contain indicated operations on fractions or natural numbers is called a compound fraction. Examples of compound fractions are

$$\frac{2+3}{5 \times 2}, \quad \frac{6-1}{4}, \quad \frac{\frac{1}{2}+5}{\frac{2}{3}}.$$

* See G. James and R. C. James, *Mathematics Dictionary*, second edition.

The combination of an integer and a fraction, such as $5\frac{3}{4}$, is called a mixed number.

With regard to denominators, there are the following types of fractions: *Similar fractions* are those with the same denominator. Thus

$$\frac{2}{4}, \quad \frac{7}{4}, \quad \frac{27}{4}$$

are similar fractions, since they have the same denominator, 4. *Dissimilar fractions* have different denominators. $\frac{2}{3}$ and $\frac{5}{7}$ are dissimilar fractions.

With regard to value, a fraction may be classified as *proper* or *improper*. When the numerator of a fraction is less than the denominator, the fraction is called a proper fraction; $\frac{1}{2}$, $\frac{3}{4}$ and $\frac{1}{10}$ are proper fractions. When the numerator of a fraction is equal to or greater than the denominator, the fraction is called an improper fraction; $\frac{10}{7}$, $\frac{5}{3}$, $\frac{4}{4}$ and $\frac{12}{4}$ are improper fractions.

To change the form of a mixed number to that of an improper fraction, the whole number must be expressed as a fraction with the same denominator as the fraction of the mixed number. The fractions are then combined.

Example 1. To change $3\frac{3}{4}$ to an improper fraction, proceed as follows:

$$3 = \frac{12}{4}, \quad \frac{12}{4} + \frac{3}{4} = \frac{15}{4}.$$

$$3\tfrac{3}{4} = \frac{15}{4}.$$

To change $6\frac{2}{3}$ to an improper fraction, proceed with

$$6 = \frac{18}{3}, \quad \frac{18}{3} + \frac{2}{3} = \frac{20}{3}.$$

$$6\tfrac{2}{3} = \frac{20}{3}.$$

To change the form of an improper fraction to a mixed number, the denominator is divided into the numerator and the remainder is written as a fractional part of the denominator or divisor.

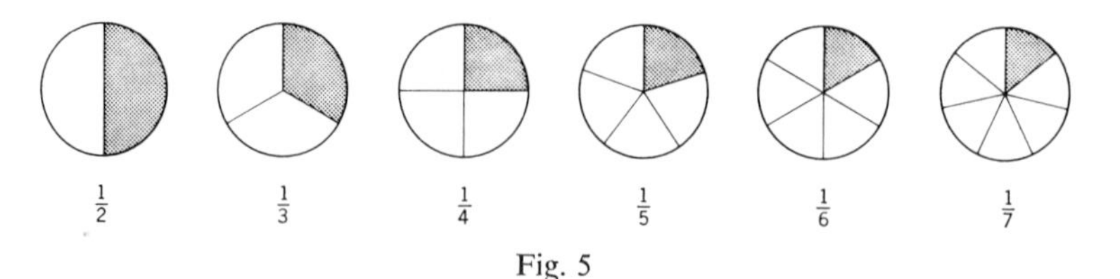

Fig. 5

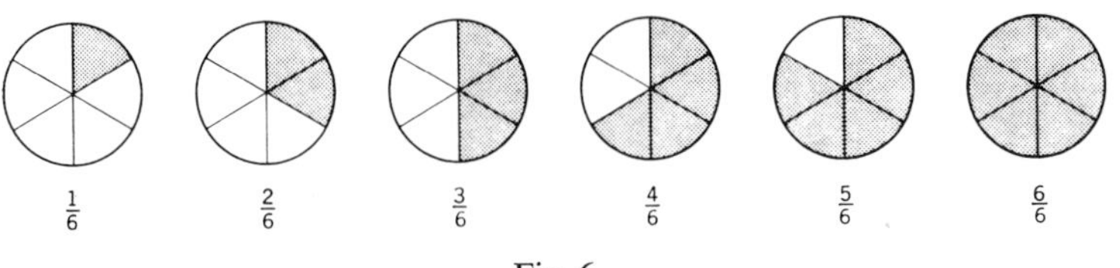

Fig. 6

Example 2. To change $\frac{13}{4}$ to a mixed number, proceed as follows:

$$13 \div 4 = 3 \text{ with remainder 1, which yields } \frac{1}{4}.$$

$$\frac{13}{4} = 3\tfrac{1}{4}.$$

Similarly, $$\frac{17}{5} = 3 \text{ and 2 remainder;} \qquad \frac{17}{5} = 3\tfrac{2}{5}.$$

Fractions with one or unity as the numerator are called *unit fractions*. In ancient Egypt all fractions except two thirds were unit fractions, a fact which is evident in the Ahmes Papyrus.

Unit fractions serve well to show that the larger the denominator of a fraction, with a fixed numerator, the smaller the value of the fraction (Fig. 5).

On the other hand, for fractions with fixed denominator, the larger the numerator, the larger the value of the fraction (Fig. 6).

Fractions with the same value are called *equivalent fractions*.

$$\frac{1}{3} = \frac{2}{6}, \qquad \frac{1}{2} = \frac{2}{4}, \qquad \frac{3}{4} = \frac{6}{8}$$

are pairs of equivalent fractions. Pairs of equivalent fractions can be illustrated with circle and rectangle diagrams (Fig. 7).

Equivalent fractions are used to change the form but not the value of the fraction. Equivalent fractions can be obtained by the application of one or both of these principles.

Principle 1. Multiplying both the numerator and the denominator by the same number, not zero, does not change the value of the fraction. Thus $\frac{1}{2} = \frac{4}{8} = \frac{9}{18}$, and so on.

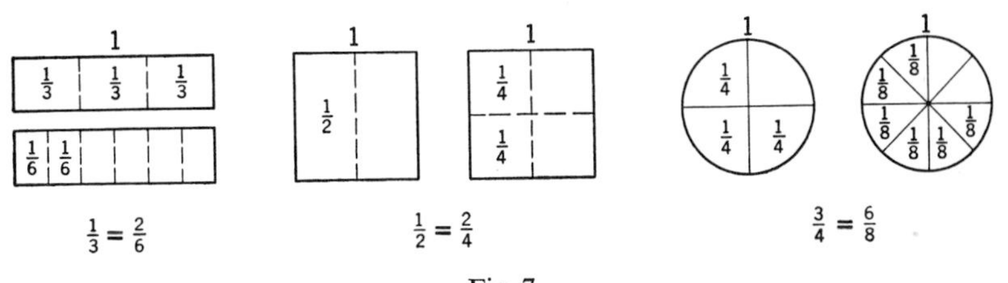

Fig. 7

Principle 2. Dividing both the numerator and the denominator by the same number, not zero, does not change the value of the original fraction.

Examples: $\frac{12}{18} = \frac{12 \div 6}{18 \div 6} = \frac{2}{3}$. $\frac{3}{4} = \frac{3 \times 5}{4 \times 5} = \frac{15}{20}$.

Although the fraction consists of different natural numbers, $\frac{2}{3}$ has the same value as $\frac{12}{18}$. Likewise, $\frac{15}{20}$ has the same value as $\frac{3}{4}$. The terms of the fraction have been changed, but the value has not. A test to determine whether two fractions are equivalent is the following: does the product of the first numerator and the second denominator equal the product of the first denominator and second numerator? Are the fractions $\frac{6}{8}$ and $\frac{15}{20}$ equivalent? They are if 6×20 equals 8×15. This is an application of the principle that in any proportion the product of the means equals the product of the extremes.

Discussion Problems.

1. Discuss the change in value of a given fraction if only the numerator is
   (*a*) multiplied by a natural number greater than 1;
   (*b*) divided by a natural number greater than 1.
2. Discuss the change in value of a given fraction if only the denominator is
   (*a*) multiplied by a natural number greater than 1;
   (*b*) divided by a natural number greater than 1.

EXERCISE 4

1. Which of the fractions in this group are proper fractions? Which are improper fractions?

$$\frac{7}{4}, \frac{3}{8}, \frac{7}{23}, \frac{6}{2}, \frac{5}{3}, \frac{21}{4}, \frac{3}{2}, \frac{7}{8}, \frac{1}{3}, \frac{7}{2}.$$

2. Classify each of these fractions as simple, complex, or compound:

$$\frac{2}{3}, \frac{\frac{1}{2}}{3}, \frac{6}{4}, \frac{7}{8}, \frac{2}{3\frac{1}{2}}, \frac{7}{\frac{1}{2}}, \frac{2}{23}, \frac{7\frac{1}{2}}{3}, \frac{1}{\frac{2}{3}}, \frac{7}{16}.$$

3. Which of these fractions are equivalent to $\frac{2}{3}$ or to $\frac{3}{4}$?

$$\frac{6}{9}, \frac{\frac{2}{3}}{1}, \frac{15}{20}, \frac{10}{15}, \frac{1}{\frac{4}{3}}, \frac{27}{36}, \frac{16}{24}, \frac{\frac{3}{2}}{2}, \frac{1}{1\frac{1}{2}}, \frac{36}{48}.$$

4. From the group, select (*a*) the unit fractions, (*b*) the mixed numbers, (*c*) the improper fractions.

$$\frac{3}{3}, \frac{1}{3}, 2\tfrac{3}{4}, \frac{7}{4}, 3\tfrac{1}{2}, \frac{1}{8}, \frac{3}{10}, \frac{6}{8}, \frac{1}{32}, \frac{1}{10}.$$

5. Select pairs or triples of (*a*) similar fractions, (*b*) equivalent fractions.

$$\frac{2}{3},\ \frac{1}{2},\ \frac{7}{8},\ \frac{5}{10},\ \frac{4}{8},\ \frac{4}{6},\ \frac{21}{24},\ \frac{7}{3},\ \frac{7}{2},\ \frac{3}{8}.$$

6. Express $\frac{1}{3}$ as ninths, twelfths, sixtieths.
Express $\frac{3}{5}$ as tenths, fifteenths, hundredths.
Express $\frac{1}{2}$ as quarters, tenths, sixteenths.

7. Supply the missing numerator or denominator as indicated by the "?."

(*a*) $\frac{1}{2} = \frac{24}{?}$ (*b*) $\frac{2}{3} = \frac{?}{24}$ (*c*) $\frac{5}{6} = \frac{?}{24}$

(*d*) $2\frac{3}{4} = 1\frac{?}{4}$ (*e*) $\frac{7}{8} = \frac{?}{72}$ (*f*) $\frac{48}{96} = \frac{?}{2}$

(*g*) $7\frac{1}{6} = 6\frac{?}{6}$ (*h*) $\frac{144}{288} = \frac{?}{4}$ (*i*) $\frac{7}{3\frac{1}{2}} = \frac{3\frac{1}{2}}{?}$

(*j*) $5\frac{2}{3} = 4\frac{5}{?}$.

8. Change the mixed numbers to improper fractions and the improper fractions to mixed numbers:

$$2\tfrac{5}{6},\ \frac{18}{3},\ 7\tfrac{1}{2},\ \frac{27}{7},\ 4\tfrac{2}{3},\ \frac{19}{3},\ 25\tfrac{1}{2},\ \frac{123}{123},\ 12\tfrac{3}{4},\ \frac{23}{7}.$$

9. Arrange according to size from the smallest to the largest:

$$\frac{4}{5},\ \frac{1}{2},\ \frac{2}{3},\ \frac{1}{4},\ \frac{5}{6},\ \frac{1}{6},\ \frac{3}{4},\ \frac{3}{8},\ \frac{2}{5},\ \frac{5}{8}.$$

Check your order by drawing ten circles and shading in the part represented by the fraction. Does the amount shaded become increasingly greater?

10. State the principle or method by which the second form is obtained from the first:

(*a*) $\frac{7}{8} = \frac{70}{80}$ (*b*) $8\frac{5}{6} = \frac{53}{6}$ (*c*) $\frac{36}{108} = \frac{1}{3}$

(*d*) $\frac{2\frac{1}{2}}{5} = \frac{20}{40}$ (*e*) $\frac{7}{10} = \frac{3\frac{1}{2}}{5}$ (*f*) $\frac{72}{5} = 14\frac{2}{5}$

(*g*) $\frac{91}{28} = \frac{13}{4}$ (*h*) $\frac{5}{12} = \frac{2\frac{1}{2}}{6}$ (*i*) $8\frac{2}{3} = 7\frac{5}{3}$

(*j*) $\frac{24}{60} = \frac{2}{5}$.

11. Sketch diagrams to show the difference between $\frac{1}{4}$ of 3 and $\frac{1}{4}$ taken three times.

12. Devise a method to compare two fractions, that is, to determine which fraction is the larger: (*a*) when the numerators are the same, (*b*) when the denominators are the same, (*c*) when both numerators and denominators are different.

13. Develop a fractional equivalent chart, using circles instead of rectangular bars, for $\frac{1}{2} = \frac{2}{4} = \frac{4}{8} = \frac{8}{16}$. Do the same for $\frac{2}{3} = \frac{4}{6} = \frac{8}{12}$.

EXERCISE 5

Review of terminology and structure of fractions. Are the following statements true or false?

1. Improper fractions can always be changed to mixed numbers. Give illustrations to defend your answer.

2. In the fraction $\frac{2}{3}$, 2 can be considered a dividend.

3. The part of a fraction below the line is called the numerator.

4. A proper fraction is equal to one or more than one.

5. Examples of improper fractions are $\frac{5}{5}$, $\frac{7}{3}$.

6. The numerator of a fraction gives the name to the kind of parts into which the whole unit has been divided.

7. The denominator of a fraction can be smaller than the numerator.

8. Examples of mixed numbers are 14, 25, $\frac{30}{7}$.

9. The value of a proper fraction is always less than one.

10. A mixed number can always be changed to a proper fraction.

11. In $\frac{5}{6}$, 6 is called the denominator.

12. The numerator of a fraction can be larger than the denominator.

13. A number composed of a whole number and a common fraction is called an improper fraction.

14. Equivalent fractions are fractions with the same number above the line.

15. Equivalent fractions must have the same denominator.

16. A unit fraction always equals one.

17. Similar fractions have the same denominator.

18. Equivalent fractions have the same value, although the terms differ.

19. A ratio is an indicated division.

20. The value of a fraction is unchanged if the same number is subtracted from both the numerator and the denominator.

21. A unit fraction has one as the numerator.

22. Examples of unit fractions are $\frac{1}{4}$, $\frac{1}{8}$, $\frac{1}{2}$.

REFERENCES

Banks, J. H., *Learning and Teaching Arithmetic*, pp. 233–264.
Brueckner, L. J., and F. E. Grossnickle, *Making Arithmetic Meaningful*, pp. 326–349.
DeMay, Amy, *Guiding Beginners in Arithmetic*, pp. 142–154.
Hooper, A., *An Arithmetic Refresher*, pp. 48–64.
Larsen, H. D., *Arithmetic for Colleges*, pp. 121–130.
Marks, J. L., C. R. Purdy, and L. B. Kinney, *Teaching Arithmetic for Understanding*, pp. 192–226.
McSwain and Cooke, *Understanding and Teaching Arithmetic in the Elementary School*, pp. 136–147.
Taylor, E. H., and C. N. Mills, *Arithmetic for Teacher-Training Classes*, fourth edition, pp. 128–143.
Wheat, H. G., *How to Teach Arithmetic*, pp. 206–219.

10

Operations with Fractions

10.1 INTRODUCTION

As stated in Chapter 9, it is known that a fraction has two terms, the numerator, which gives the number of parts, and the denominator, which gives the kind of part or how the whole was divided. Thus it is seen that the fraction is a new kind of number quite different from the natural number (or whole number) first studied. In mathematics fractions belong to the set of numbers called the *rational numbers*, which are defined as numbers of the form p/q, where p and q are natural numbers or zero, with the restriction that q cannot be zero. It does not seem unreasonable, therefore, to expect the fundamental operations of addition, subtraction, multiplication, and division to be somewhat different from the corresponding operations with the natural numbers and zero.

It should be noted that there are real numbers, called irrational numbers, which cannot be represented by the ratio of two natural numbers. Thus a number whose square equals the natural number 2 is irrational. The positive square root of 2 is represented by the symbol $\sqrt{2}$. Proof is given in Appendix B to show that no rational number can serve as the square root of 2. There are numerous other irrational numbers such as $\sqrt[3]{7}$ (the cube root of 7), $\sqrt[5]{3}$, arising as solutions of algebraic equations, the number π, the values of trigonometric ratios for various angles, and so on.

Mathematically, we would define the addition of two rational numbers, or fractions, in the following manner:

$$\frac{a}{b} + \frac{c}{d} = \frac{ad + cb}{bd}.$$

However, this abstract definition of addition of fractions is not suitable for students in elementary school. Hence the following principles are offered as a more suitable method of introducing the addition of fractions. It will be recalled that similar fractions, such as $\frac{3}{5}$ and $\frac{4}{5}$, have the same denominators.

10.2 ADDITION OF FRACTIONS

Three important principles give aid in adding fractions.

Principle 1. Similar fractions can be combined by addition without changing the forms of the fractions. Thus $\frac{3}{4}$ and $\frac{6}{4}$ can be added, whereas $\frac{1}{4}$ and $\frac{2}{3}$, in their present form, cannot.

Principle 2. In adding similar fractions, add only the numerators and keep the same denominator. For example,

$$\frac{3}{4}+\frac{6}{4}=\frac{9}{4}, \qquad \frac{2}{x}+\frac{5}{x}=\frac{7}{x}, \qquad \frac{a}{3}+\frac{b}{3}=\frac{a+b}{3}.$$

Principle 3. Fractions that are not similar can be made into similar fractions by the process of constructing their equivalents with a common denominator (see Chapter 9). For example, to add $\frac{1}{4}$ and $\frac{2}{3}$, the fractions are changed as follows:

$$\frac{1}{4}=\frac{3}{12}, \quad \text{and} \quad \frac{2}{3}=\frac{8}{12}$$

Therefore, $\frac{1}{4}+\frac{2}{3}$ becomes $\frac{3}{12}+\frac{8}{12}$, which is $\frac{11}{12}$.

10.3 GROUPS OF EXAMPLES IN ADDITION OF FRACTIONS

In the addition of fractions various difficulties can be dealt with separately by treating successive types of examples. These groups of examples will be studied for some time in the intermediate grades. Each should be mastered before going to the next.

(*a*) *Similar fractions with like denominators.* In this group Principles 1 and 2 mentioned above are applied.

Example 1. Add $2\frac{1}{3}$
$+3\frac{1}{3}$

Solution. In this first example $\frac{1}{3}$ and $\frac{1}{3}$ are added; they make two thirds. Next 2 and 3 are added; the answer is $5\frac{2}{3}$. This example could be introduced by means of the problem: if a mother buys $3\frac{1}{3}$ yards of cloth for a dress for herself and $2\frac{1}{3}$ yards of cloth for a dress for her daughter, how much cloth does she buy all together? Note that the fraction $\frac{2}{3}$, in the answer, is a proper fraction which is not reducible.

Example 2. Add $\frac{3}{4}+\frac{1}{4}$.

Solution. In this example $\frac{3}{4}+\frac{1}{4}=\frac{4}{4}=1$. The example can be illustrated by a diagram (Fig. 1).

Note that the answer is an improper fraction which reduces to a natural number.

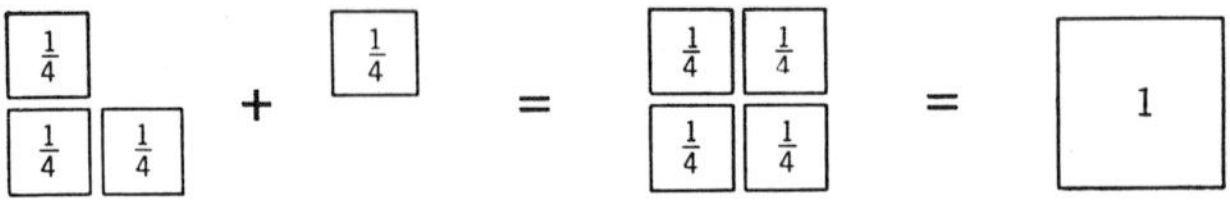

$$\frac{1}{4}\ \frac{1}{4}\ \frac{1}{4} + \frac{1}{4} = \frac{1}{4}\ \frac{1}{4}\ \frac{1}{4}\ \frac{1}{4} = 1$$

Fig. 1

Example 3. (*a*) Add $\frac{2}{3} + \frac{2}{3}$, (*b*) add $\frac{3}{8} + \frac{1}{8}$, (*c*) add $\frac{5}{8} + \frac{5}{8}$.

Solution. By adding two thirds and two thirds we get a total of four thirds; thus

$$(a)\ \frac{2}{3} + \frac{2}{3} = \frac{2+2}{3} = \frac{4}{3} = 1\tfrac{1}{3}.$$

The answer is an improper fraction which reduces to a mixed number. The example can be illustrated by a diagram (Fig. 2).

$$(b)\ \frac{3}{8} + \frac{1}{8} = \frac{4}{8} = \frac{1}{2} \qquad \text{(the answer is reducible).}$$

$$(c)\ \frac{5}{8} + \frac{5}{8} = \frac{10}{8} = \frac{5}{4} = 1\tfrac{1}{4}.$$

Example 4. Add $\frac{8}{24} + \frac{6}{24} + \frac{3}{24}$.

Solution. In this case we have

$$\frac{8}{24} + \frac{6}{24} + \frac{3}{24} = \frac{8+6+3}{24} = \frac{17}{24}.$$

Note that these fractions would appear in the example: $\frac{1}{3} + \frac{1}{4} + \frac{1}{8}$.

The examples given above indicate that there are as many as five different kinds of answers in the addition of fractions. These are (1) proper fractions not reducible to lower terms, (2) proper fractions that are reducible, (3) improper fractions reducible to natural numbers, (4) improper fractions reducible to lower terms, which can be changed to mixed numbers, and (5) improper fractions, not reducible, which can be changed to mixed numbers.

(*b*) *Dissimilar fractions with unlike denominators.* In this group of examples all three principles apply. There are three subgroups of examples:

1. Fractions with common denominator included among the given denominators.

Example 5. Add $\frac{3}{4} + \frac{5}{8} + \frac{1}{2}$.

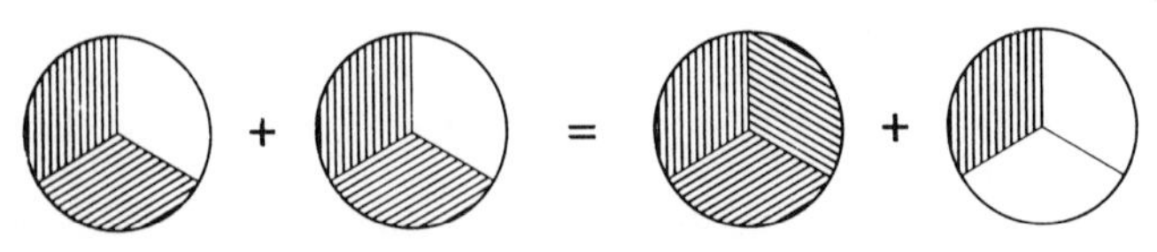

Fig. 2

Solution. In this example the denominator 8 contains the others as divisors hence 8 is the lowest common denominator. The solution is worked out as follows:

$$\frac{3}{4} + \frac{5}{8} + \frac{1}{2} = \frac{6}{8} + \frac{5}{8} + \frac{4}{8} = \frac{15}{8} = 1\tfrac{7}{8}.$$

The main problem here is to find the equivalent of $\frac{3}{4}$ and $\frac{1}{2}$ in terms of eighths. Once these fractions have been written in terms of eighths, the example will fall in group (*a*), previously discussed.

Example 6. Add $\begin{array}{r} 3\frac{5}{12} \\ +4\frac{1}{4} \\ \hline \end{array}$

Solution. The denominator 12 is required in the solution.

$$\begin{array}{rcr} 3\frac{5}{12} & \rightarrow & 3\frac{5}{12} \\ +4\frac{1}{4} & \rightarrow & +4\frac{3}{12} \\ \hline 7\frac{2}{3} & \leftarrow & 7\frac{8}{12} \end{array}$$

Note that the fraction in the answer is reducible.

2. Fractions in which the common denominator is the product of the given denominators.

Example 7. Add $\frac{1}{2} + \frac{1}{3}$.
Solution. The common denominator is 6, the product of 2 and 3.

$$\frac{1}{2} + \frac{1}{3} = \frac{3}{6} + \frac{2}{6} = \frac{5}{6}.$$

Example 8. Add $\frac{1}{2} + \frac{2}{3} + \frac{3}{5}$.
Solution. The common denominator is $2 \times 3 \times 5 = 30$.

$$\frac{1}{2} + \frac{2}{3} + \frac{3}{5} = \frac{15}{30} + \frac{20}{30} + \frac{18}{30} = \frac{53}{30} = 1\tfrac{23}{30}.$$

3. Common denominator by inspection or by special methods.

Example 9. Add $\frac{1}{3} + \frac{1}{4} + \frac{1}{6}$.
Solution. The common denominator must contain 3, 4, and 6 as divisors. Since 6 is contained in 3×4, 12 is the common denominator.

$$\frac{1}{3} + \frac{1}{4} + \frac{1}{6} = \frac{4}{12} + \frac{3}{12} + \frac{2}{12} = \frac{9}{12} = \frac{3}{4}.$$

This example can be illustrated on the one-foot ruler, the ruler 12 inches long being taken as the unit (Fig. 3).
The total is $\frac{4}{12} + \frac{3}{12} + \frac{2}{12}$, which is $\frac{9}{12}$ or $\frac{3}{4}$.

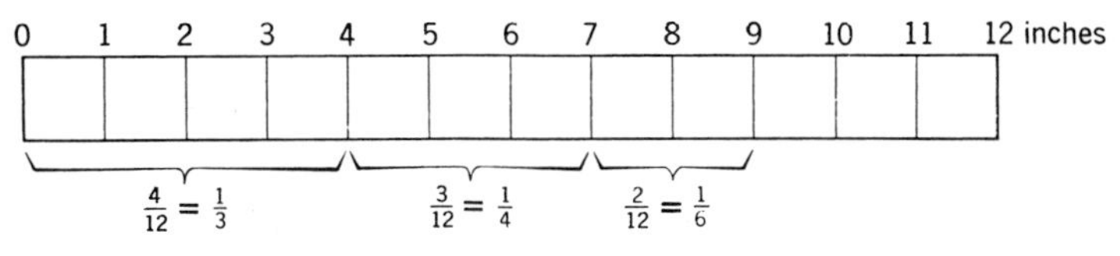

Fig. 3

Example 10. Add $\frac{7}{30} + \frac{5}{28} + \frac{8}{21}$.

Solution. The least common multiple of 30, 28, and 21 is obtained as follows:

$$30 = 2 \times 3 \times 5,$$
$$28 = 2 \times 2 \times 7,$$
$$21 = 3 \times 7.$$

The L.C.M. is $2^2 \times 3 \times 5 \times 7$, or 420. Thus we have

$$\frac{7}{30} + \frac{5}{28} + \frac{8}{21} = \frac{98}{420} + \frac{75}{420} + \frac{160}{420} = \frac{98 + 75 + 160}{420} = \frac{333}{420} = \frac{111}{140}.$$

This example illustrates the general method of finding the lowest common denominator, which can be used when necessary. However, the common denominator can often be found by inspecting the given denominators.

EXERCISE 1

Add

1. $\frac{2}{7} + \frac{3}{7}$,
2. $\frac{1}{4} + \frac{3}{4}$,
3. $\frac{5}{3} + \frac{2}{3}$,
4. $\frac{4}{6} + \frac{3}{6}$,
5. $\frac{4}{8} + \frac{5}{16}$,
6. $\frac{7}{4} + \frac{1}{2} + \frac{5}{8}$,
7. $\frac{3}{6} + \frac{5}{12} + \frac{2}{3}$,
8. $\frac{2}{3} + \frac{1}{2}$,
9. $\frac{1}{4} + \frac{1}{5}$,
10. $\frac{3}{5} + \frac{2}{3}$,
11. $\frac{7}{8} + \frac{3}{5}$,
12. $\frac{1}{2} + \frac{1}{3} + \frac{1}{4}$,
13. $\frac{3}{6} + \frac{2}{6} + \frac{5}{6}$,
14. $\frac{2}{3} + \frac{5}{6}$,
15. $\frac{3}{4} + \frac{2}{3} + \frac{5}{6}$,
16. $\frac{7}{8} + \frac{5}{16}$,
17. $\frac{7}{8} + \frac{1}{6} + \frac{1}{3}$,
18. $\frac{a}{5} + \frac{b}{5}$,
19. $\frac{4}{x} + \frac{3}{x}$,
20. $\frac{a}{b} + \frac{c}{d}$,
21. $\frac{7}{8} + \frac{2}{3} + \frac{1}{4}$,
22. $\frac{3}{16} + \frac{5}{8} + \frac{1}{2}$,
23. $\frac{4}{15} + \frac{7}{20} + \frac{8}{45}$,
24. $\frac{3}{16} + \frac{7}{24} + \frac{5}{18}$.

10.4 SUBTRACTION OF FRACTIONS

Three principles similar to those for adding fractions give aid in subtraction.

Principle 1. Similar fractions can be combined by subtraction without change in the forms of the fractions. Examples of this type are $\frac{3}{5} - \frac{1}{5}$ and $\frac{7}{8} - \frac{3}{8}$.

Principle 2. In subtracting fractions, the operation of subtraction applies only to the numerators. The denominators remain the same. The examples above have these solutions:

$$\frac{3}{5} - \frac{1}{5} = \frac{3-1}{5} = \frac{2}{5} \text{ and } \frac{7}{8} - \frac{3}{8} = \frac{7-3}{8} = \frac{4}{8}, \text{ or } \frac{1}{2}.$$

Principle 3. Fractions that are not similar can be made into similar fractions by the process of changing to equivalent fractions with the lowest common denominator. Thus

$$\frac{7}{8} - \frac{2}{3} = \frac{21}{24} - \frac{16}{24} = \frac{21-16}{24} = \frac{5}{24}.$$

The groups of examples for subtraction are the same as those given for addition:

1. Subtraction of similar fractions, like denominators.
2. Subtraction of dissimilar fractions, unlike denominators.
   (*a*) Common denominator is included among the given denominators.
   (*b*) Common denominator is the product of the given denominators.
   (*c*) Common denominator is found by inspection or by special methods.

Work with subtraction of fractions can follow closely after that with addition of fractions. Groups of examples in subtraction are generally similar to those in addition.

Example 1. Subtract $\frac{5}{12} - \frac{3}{12}$.

Solution. $\frac{5}{12} - \frac{3}{12} = \frac{5-3}{12} = \frac{2}{12} = \frac{1}{6}.$

Example 2. Subtract $\frac{3}{4} - \frac{2}{5}$.

Solution. $\frac{3}{4} - \frac{2}{5} = \frac{15}{20} - \frac{8}{20} = \frac{15-8}{20} = \frac{7}{20}.$

Example 3. Combine $\frac{3}{4} + \frac{2}{3} - \frac{5}{6}$.

Solution. Vertical form: $\frac{3}{4} = \frac{18}{24}$

Add $\frac{2}{3} = \frac{16}{24}$

$\frac{34}{24}$

Subtract $\frac{5}{6} = \frac{20}{24}$

$\frac{7}{12} = \frac{14}{24}$

Example 3. Combine $\frac{3}{4} + \frac{2}{3} - \frac{5}{6}$.

Solution. Horizontal form:

$$\frac{3}{4} + \frac{2}{3} - \frac{5}{6} = \frac{18}{24} + \frac{16}{24} - \frac{20}{24} = \frac{18 + 16 - 20}{24} = \frac{14}{24} = \frac{7}{12}.$$

EXERCISE 2

Subtraction, with some addition:

1. $\frac{5}{7} - \frac{2}{7}$
2. $\frac{3}{4} - \frac{1}{4}$
3. $\frac{5}{6} - \frac{1}{3}$
4. $\frac{2}{3} - \frac{1}{2}$
5. $\frac{3}{5} - \frac{1}{5}$
6. $\frac{2}{3} - \frac{3}{5}$
7. $\frac{7}{8} - \frac{3}{4}$
8. $\frac{3}{4} - \frac{7}{12}$
9. $\frac{2}{3} + \frac{3}{4} - \frac{5}{6}$
10. $\frac{7}{8} + \frac{3}{4} - \frac{2}{3}$
11. $\frac{7}{12} - \frac{5}{12}$
12. $\frac{3}{4} + \frac{7}{8} - \frac{11}{12}$
13. $\frac{4}{x} - \frac{1}{x}$
14. $\frac{x}{5} - \frac{y}{5}$
15. $\frac{a}{b} - \frac{x}{y}$
16. $\frac{7}{8} - \frac{2}{5} - \frac{3}{10}$
17. $\frac{7}{15} + \frac{5}{16} - \frac{9}{20}$
18. $\frac{5}{32} + \frac{11}{12} - \frac{7}{18}$

10.5 ADDITION AND SUBTRACTION OF MIXED NUMBERS

In dealing with the addition and subtraction of mixed numbers, the natural numbers and the fractions are considered separately and then combined, as in section 10.3, or the mixed numbers may be changed to improper fractions, as shown in some of the following examples.

Example 1. Add $5\frac{3}{8} + 2\frac{3}{8}$.

Solution. Horizontal form:

$$5 + 2 = 7 \quad \text{and} \quad \frac{3}{8} + \frac{3}{8} = \frac{6}{8}$$

the sum is $7\frac{6}{8}$ or $7\frac{3}{4}$.

Solution. Vertical form.

$$\begin{array}{r} 5\frac{3}{8} \\ +2\frac{3}{8} \\ \hline 7\frac{6}{8} \end{array} \quad \text{or} \quad 7\frac{3}{4}.$$

Example 2. Add $2\frac{3}{4} + 3\frac{2}{3}$.

Solution.

Method 1. $2\frac{3}{4} + 3\frac{2}{3} = 2\frac{9}{12} + 3\frac{8}{12} = 5\frac{17}{12} = 6\frac{5}{12}$.

Method 2. $2\frac{3}{4} + 3\frac{2}{3} = \frac{11}{4} + \frac{11}{3} = \frac{33}{12} + \frac{44}{12} = \frac{77}{12} = 6\frac{5}{12}$.

Example 3. Subtract $6\frac{7}{8} - 2\frac{3}{8}$.

Solution.

Method 1. $6\frac{7}{8} - 2\frac{3}{8} = 4\frac{4}{8} = 4\frac{1}{2}$.

Method 2. $6\frac{7}{8} - 2\frac{3}{8} = \dfrac{55}{8} - \dfrac{19}{8} = \dfrac{36}{8} = 4\frac{4}{8} = 4\frac{1}{2}$.

Example 4. Subtract $5\frac{1}{3} - 2\frac{3}{4}$.

Solution.

Method 1.

$$\begin{array}{rl} 5\frac{1}{3} = 5\frac{4}{12} = & 4\frac{16}{12} \\ -2\frac{3}{4} = 2\frac{9}{12} = & 2\frac{9}{12} \\ \hline & 2\frac{7}{12}. \end{array}$$

Check.

$$\begin{array}{r} 2\frac{7}{12} \\ +2\frac{9}{12} \\ \hline 4\frac{16}{12} = 5\frac{4}{12} = 5\frac{1}{3}. \end{array}$$

Method 2. $5\frac{1}{3} - 2\frac{3}{4} = \dfrac{16}{3} - \dfrac{11}{4} = \dfrac{64}{12} - \dfrac{33}{12} = \dfrac{31}{12} = 2\frac{7}{12}$.

EXERCISE 3

1. $2\frac{3}{4} + 1\frac{1}{3}$

2. $4\frac{2}{3} - 1\frac{2}{3}$

3. $6\frac{3}{4} + 2\frac{1}{3} + 3\frac{5}{6}$

4. $9\frac{11}{12} - 2\frac{5}{12} + 3\frac{7}{12}$

5. Add

$$\begin{array}{r} 12\frac{1}{3} \\ 60\frac{5}{12} \\ 5\frac{3}{4} \\ \hline \end{array}$$

6. Add

$$\begin{array}{r} 35\frac{5}{7} \\ 22\frac{7}{12} \\ 13\frac{1}{3} \\ \hline \end{array}$$

7. $6\frac{1}{2} - 2\frac{3}{4} + 1\frac{2}{3}$

8. $25 - 6\frac{2}{3}$

9. $16\frac{2}{3} - 5\frac{1}{3}$

10. $43\frac{13}{21} - 31\frac{2}{7}$

11. $3\frac{1}{4} - 2\frac{3}{4}$

12. $13\frac{5}{8} - 1\frac{7}{8}$

13. $7\frac{1}{3} - 2\frac{3}{4}$

14. $6 - 2\frac{3}{8}$.

10.6 OVERCOMING DIFFICULTIES

Many difficulties are experienced by students in performing operations involving the addition and subtraction of fractions and mixed numbers. The greatest difficulty lies in a lack of understanding of the meaning of a fraction. This is particularly true when a student writes $\frac{2}{3} + \frac{5}{3}$ and arrives at $\frac{7}{6}$, or $\frac{2}{3} + \frac{3}{4}$ and arrives at $\frac{5}{7}$, *both of which are incorrect.*

Some understanding should be gained by making diagrams to illustrate the examples (see Fig. 4).

Another difficulty is in finding the lowest common denominator (L.C.D.) in dealing with fractions having unlike denominators. In adding $\frac{2}{3}$ and $\frac{3}{4}$ the L.C.D. is 12, which is the product of the denominators, 3×4, but, in adding $\frac{2}{3}$, $\frac{3}{4}$, and $\frac{5}{8}$, the L.C.D. is not $3 \times 4 \times 8$, but only 3×8, or 24, since 4 is a factor of 8.

Students often encounter trouble when the solution involves an improper fraction. In finding the sum of $3\frac{1}{2}$ and $2\frac{5}{6}$, some students think

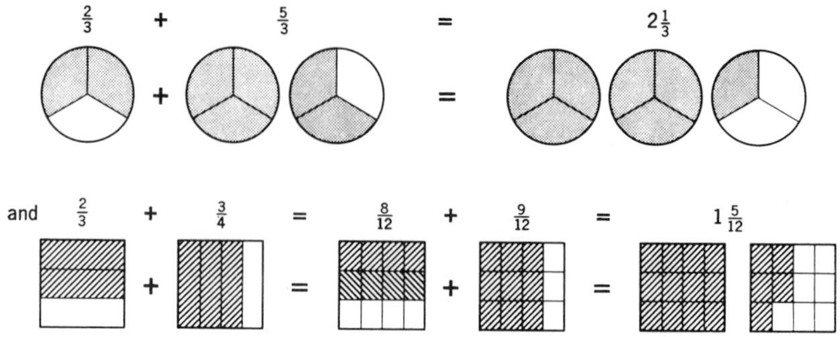

$\frac{2}{3} + \frac{5}{3} = 2\frac{1}{3}$

and $\frac{2}{3} + \frac{3}{4} = \frac{8}{12} + \frac{9}{12} = 1\frac{5}{12}$

Fig. 4

the answer $5\frac{8}{6}$ is incorrect, when it is just not finished and should be simplified to $6\frac{2}{6}$ or $6\frac{1}{3}$. All of these problems give rise to possible sources of error.

Probably more errors are made when the solution depends upon finding equivalent fractions or when regrouping is necessary than in any other phases of the work. Study the explanation of the following example.

Example. Subtract $5\frac{1}{4} - 3\frac{2}{3}$.

Solution. $5\frac{1}{4}$ becomes $5\frac{3}{12}$ and $3\frac{2}{3}$ becomes $3\frac{8}{12}$, but $\frac{8}{12}$ cannot be taken from $\frac{3}{12}$; $5\frac{3}{12}$ becomes $4 + 1 + \frac{3}{12}$ or $4 + \frac{12}{12} + \frac{3}{12}$ or $4\frac{15}{12}$. Then $4\frac{15}{12} - 3\frac{8}{12} = 1\frac{7}{12}$.

Discussion. How should fractions be introduced and developed to eliminate these sources of error?

EXERCISE 4

1. Use a diagram of a one-foot ruler to illustrate that $\frac{1}{3} + \frac{1}{4} = \frac{7}{12}$.

2. Make a diagram showing fractions as parts of a disk to illustrate that $\frac{2}{3} + \frac{1}{2} = \frac{7}{6} = 1\frac{1}{6}$.

Perform the indicated operations:

3. $2\frac{3}{4} + 5\frac{7}{8}$

4. $3\frac{1}{2} + 4\frac{2}{3}$

5. $7\frac{1}{12} + 3\frac{1}{5}$

6. $\frac{5}{8} + \frac{3}{4} + \frac{7}{16}$

7. $11\frac{1}{3} + 5\frac{3}{8}$

8. $\frac{3}{24} + \frac{5}{8} + \frac{1}{3}$

9. $\frac{2}{3} + \frac{3}{4} + \frac{4}{5}$

10. $5\frac{1}{2} + 2\frac{1}{3} + 3\frac{1}{6}$

11. $\frac{2}{3} - \frac{2}{5}$

12. $\frac{3}{8} - \frac{1}{4}$

13. $5\frac{1}{8} - 2\frac{1}{4}$

14. $23\frac{1}{2} - 6\frac{7}{8}$

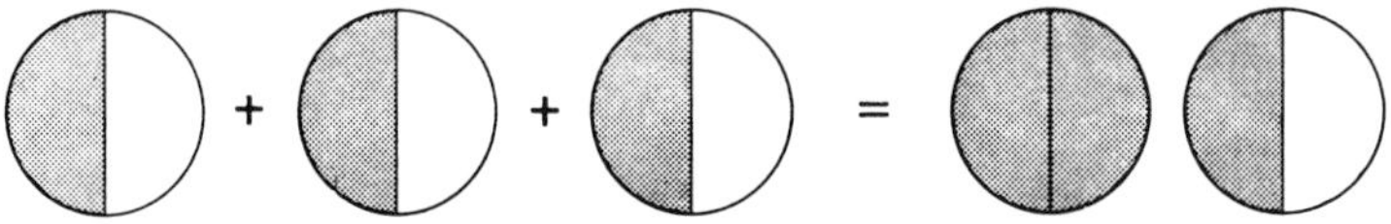

Fig. 5

15. $7\frac{3}{16} - 4\frac{5}{8}$ 16. $6\frac{3}{4} - 2\frac{5}{8}$

17. $27\frac{1}{3} - 18\frac{1}{2}$ 18. $8\frac{7}{24} - 3\frac{8}{15}$

10.7 MULTIPLICATION OF FRACTIONS

Problems in multiplication of fractions may be grouped as follows.

(*a*) *Multiplication of a fraction by a natural number.* In Chapter 4 multiplication was described as a shortened method of addition; three times $\frac{1}{2}$ could be $\frac{1}{2} + \frac{1}{2} + \frac{1}{2}$, that is, $\frac{1}{2}$ taken three times. In the diagram (Fig. 5) it is shown that three halves are equivalent to one whole and a half more, or

$$3 \times \frac{1}{2} = \frac{3}{2} = 1\frac{1}{2} \qquad \left(3 \times \frac{1}{2} = \frac{3 \times 1}{2} = \frac{3}{2}\right).$$

(*b*) *Multiplication of a natural number by a fraction.* The diagram illustrates three times one half. Applying the commutative law, $\frac{1}{2} \times 3 = 3 \times \frac{1}{2}$, but $\frac{1}{2} \times 3$ would also be equivalent to dividing 3 into two equal parts, which would give $1\frac{1}{2}$ in each part, as shown in the diagram (Fig. 6).

$$\frac{1}{2} \times 3 = \frac{1 \times 3}{2} = \frac{3}{2} = 1\frac{1}{2}.$$

Let us look more closely at the multiplication $\frac{1}{2} \times 3$ and the idea of multiplying any fraction times a natural number. We know that $3 \times \frac{1}{2}$, "three times one half," is $\frac{1}{2} + \frac{1}{2} + \frac{1}{2}$, or $1\frac{1}{2}$. By the commutative law of multiplication,

$$3 \times \frac{1}{2} = \frac{1}{2} \times 3,$$

hence "one half times three" is also $1\frac{1}{2}$. Since we know that one half *of* three is $1\frac{1}{2}$, we conclude that "one half *of* three" is equivalent to "one half

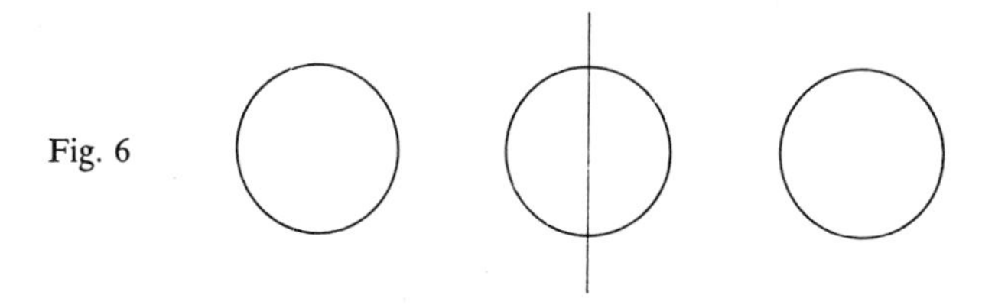

Fig. 6

times three." In general, *finding a fractional part of a quantity* is the same as *multiplying the fraction times the quantity*.

Example 1. Find $\frac{2}{3}$ of 5.

Solution. Finding $\frac{2}{3}$ of 5 is the same as multiplying 5 by $\frac{2}{3}$; thus

$$\frac{2}{3} \times 5 = \frac{2 \times 5}{3} = \frac{10}{3} = 3\tfrac{1}{3}.$$

Check.

$$\frac{2}{3} \times 5 = 5 \times \frac{2}{3} = \frac{2}{3} + \frac{2}{3} + \frac{2}{3} + \frac{2}{3} + \frac{2}{3} = \frac{10}{3}.$$

This example can also be solved by using the definition of a fraction and the notion of partition in division. By definition, $\frac{2}{3}$ of 5 means two of the three equal parts of 5. The partition notion of division tells us that one of the three equal parts of 5 is $5 \div 3$, or $\frac{5}{3}$. Thus two of the three equal parts of 5 will be $2 \times \frac{5}{3}$, or $\frac{10}{3}$.

Example 2. Find the cost of $3\frac{2}{3}$ yards of cloth at \$1.35 per yard.

Solution. The cost is $3\frac{2}{3} \times 135$, in cents. We have

$$3\tfrac{2}{3} \times 135 = \frac{11}{3} \times 135 = \frac{11 \times \overset{45}{\cancel{135}}}{\underset{1}{\cancel{3}}} = \frac{11 \times 45}{1} = 495.$$

The cloth costs 495 cents, or \$4.95.

(*c*) *Multiplication of a fraction by a fraction.* In section 8.6 we found that the area of a rectangle is given by the formula $A = b \times a$, where b and a are the base and altitude, respectively. This formula will help us to determine a proper definition of the product of two fractions.

Example 1. Find the product $\frac{1}{3} \times \frac{1}{2}$.

Solution. Draw a unit square (Fig. 7). Draw a horizontal line which cuts the square into halves. Next, by means of vertical lines, divide the unit square into thirds. These lines divide the unit square into six equal rectangles. The rectangle in the lower left-hand corner is shaded. This rectangle has a base $\frac{1}{3}$ and an altitude $\frac{1}{2}$. Hence the product $\frac{1}{3} \times \frac{1}{2}$ may be interpreted as the area of the shaded

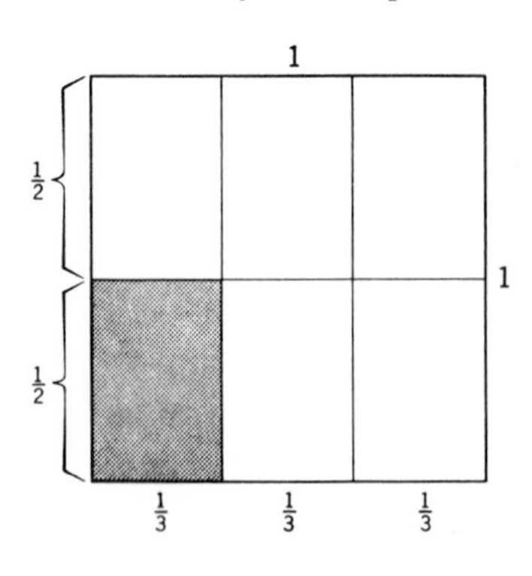

Fig. 7

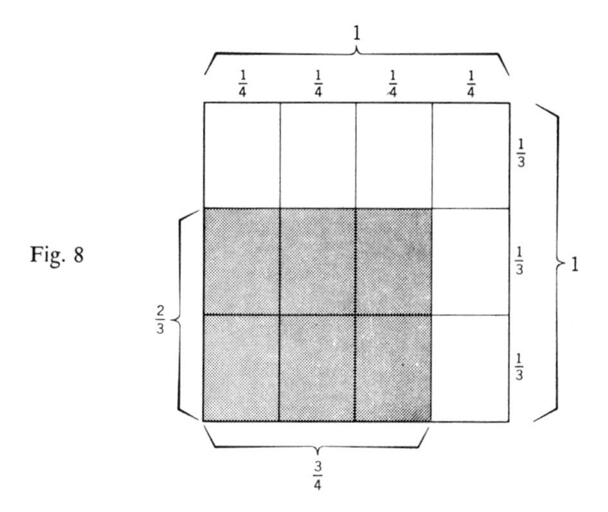

Fig. 8

portion of the unit square. Since this rectangle is one of the six equal parts of the whole, its area may be represented by $\frac{1}{6}$. Hence it is reasonable to say that $\frac{1}{3} \times \frac{1}{2} = \frac{1}{6}$.

Example 2. Find the product $\frac{3}{4} \times \frac{2}{3}$.

Solution. Draw three vertical lines in such a way that they divide a unit square into fourths (Fig. 8). Likewise, draw two horizontal lines that divide the same unit square into thirds. By observing Fig. 8, it is seen that the two sets of lines just drawn divide the unit square into twelve small equal rectangles. In the lower left-hand corner shade the rectangle whose base is $\frac{3}{4}$ and altitude is $\frac{2}{3}$. This rectangle covers six of the twelve small rectangles. Hence its area is $\frac{6}{12}$. This means that $\frac{3}{4} \times \frac{2}{3} = \frac{6}{12}$.

It should be observed in Examples 1 and 2 that the products may be obtained in each case by simply multiplying the numerators and the denominators of the fractions involved. This leads to the following definition or principle of multiplying one fraction by another.

Principle. To multiply one fraction by another multiply the numerator of the first times the numerator of the second and the denominator of the first times the denominator of the second, to obtain the new numerator and the new denominator of the product fraction. Using symbols, we have

$$\frac{a}{b} \times \frac{c}{d} = \frac{ac}{bd}.$$

Natural numbers may be considered as having a denominator of 1, and mixed numbers may be written as improper fractions. Factors common to a numerator and a denominator may be divided out, and the answers may then be left in simplified form. Dividing out factors that are common to a numerator and a denominator is sometimes referred to as cancellation. However, the use of the term "cancellation" is not recommended too early, for students sometimes make errors in trying to use it when it does not apply. They might make errors such as $\frac{12}{26} = \frac{1}{6}$, which although not *true* is obtained by improperly canceling the 2's.

Example 1. $\frac{2}{3} \times \frac{4}{7} = \frac{2 \times 4}{3 \times 7} = \frac{8}{21}.$

Example 2. $3 \times \frac{2}{5} = \frac{3}{1} \times \frac{2}{5} = \frac{3 \times 2}{1 \times 5} = \frac{6}{5} = 1\frac{1}{5}.$

Example 3. $\frac{2}{5} \times \frac{3}{7} \times \frac{4}{9} = ?$

Method 1. $\frac{2 \times 3 \times 4}{5 \times 7 \times 9} = \frac{24}{315} = \frac{8}{105}$ (reducing the fraction to lower terms).

Method 2. $\frac{2 \times \overset{1}{\cancel{3}} \times 4}{5 \times 7 \times \underset{3}{\cancel{9}}} = \frac{8}{105}$ (dividing out the common factor 3).

Example 4. $\frac{2}{3} \times \frac{3}{4} \times \frac{4}{5} \times \frac{5}{6} = \frac{\overset{1}{\cancel{2}} \times \overset{1}{\cancel{3}} \times \overset{1}{\cancel{4}} \times \overset{1}{\cancel{5}}}{\underset{1}{\cancel{3}} \times \underset{1}{\cancel{4}} \times \underset{1}{\cancel{5}} \times \underset{3}{\cancel{6}}} = \frac{1 \times 1 \times 1 \times 1}{1 \times 1 \times 1 \times 3} = \frac{1}{3}.$

3 was divided by 3 in both the numerator and the denominator.
4 was divided by 4 in both the numerator and the denominator.
5 was divided by 5 in both the numerator and the denominator.
2 was divided by 2 in the numerator and 6 was divided by 2 in the denominator.

Example 5. $3\frac{2}{3} \times 4\frac{1}{4} = \frac{11}{3} \times \frac{17}{4} = \frac{187}{12} = 15\frac{7}{12}.$

Note. When multiplying mixed numbers less than 100, it is usually quicker for most students to change them to improper fractions. However, for mixed numbers larger than 99, direct multiplication is recommended.

Example 6. $40\frac{2}{3} \times 3\frac{1}{4}$.

Method 1. $\frac{122}{3} \times \frac{13}{4} = \frac{\overset{61}{\cancel{122}} \times 13}{3 \times \underset{2}{\cancel{4}}} = \frac{61 \times 13}{3 \times 2} = \frac{793}{6} = 132\frac{1}{6}.$

Method 2.

$$
\begin{array}{ll}
 & 40\frac{2}{3} \\
 & \times 3\frac{1}{4} \\
\hline
 & 10 \left(\text{obtained by } \frac{1}{4} \times 40\right) \\
 & \frac{1}{6} \left(\text{obtained by } \frac{1}{4} \times \frac{2}{3}\right) \\
 & 2 \left(\text{obtained by } 3 \times \frac{2}{3}\right) \\
 & 120 \text{ (obtained by } 3 \times 40). \\
\hline
 & 132\frac{1}{6}
\end{array}
$$

Method 3. $\left(40 + \frac{2}{3}\right) \times \left(3 + \frac{1}{4}\right)$, which becomes

$$40 \times 3 + 40 \times \frac{1}{4} + \frac{2}{3} \times 3 + \frac{2}{3} \times \frac{1}{4}, \text{ or}$$

$$120 + 10 + 2 + \frac{1}{6}, \text{ which equals } 132\tfrac{1}{6}.$$

EXERCISE 5

(*a*) Can you give these answers without using a pencil?

1. $\frac{1}{2} \times 10$ **2.** $\frac{1}{2} \times 16$ **3.** $\frac{2}{3} \times 12$

4. $\frac{3}{4} \times 16$ **5.** $100 \times \frac{1}{4}$ **6.** $100 \times \frac{2}{5}$

7. $21 \times \frac{3}{7}$ **8.** $50 \times \frac{7}{10}$ **9.** $240 \times \frac{3}{4}$

10. $\frac{3}{10} \times 15$ **11.** $\frac{4}{5} \times 60$ **12.** $48 \times \frac{5}{8}$

13. $\frac{2}{5} \times 8$ **14.** $14 \times \frac{5}{7}$ **15.** $80 \times \frac{9}{10}$

(*b*) Can you complete these in two minutes?

1. $\frac{1}{2} \times \frac{1}{2}$ **2.** $\frac{1}{2} \times \frac{1}{3}$ **3.** $\frac{2}{7} \times \frac{3}{5}$

4. $\frac{2}{5} \times \frac{3}{4}$ **5.** $\frac{2}{3} \times \frac{5}{8}$ **6.** $\frac{1}{3} \times \frac{9}{10}$

7. $\frac{4}{5} \times \frac{7}{8}$ **8.** $\frac{5}{2} \times \frac{66}{35}$ **9.** $\frac{4}{7} \times \frac{2}{3}$

10. $\frac{5}{100} \times \frac{3}{10}$ **11.** $\frac{7}{12} \times \frac{24}{49}$ **12.** $\frac{2}{3} \times \frac{9}{16}$

13. $\frac{3}{4} \times \frac{2}{3} \times \frac{4}{5}$ **14.** $\frac{1}{2} \times \frac{5}{7} \times \frac{2}{5}$ **15.** $\frac{3}{4} \times \frac{8}{9} \times \frac{15}{6}$

(*c*) Can you complete these in less than five minutes?

1. $2\frac{1}{3} \times 21$ **2.** $6\frac{1}{4} \times 12$ **3.** $4\frac{1}{5} \times 15$

4. $24 \times 3\frac{1}{8}$ **5.** $60 \times 3\frac{1}{12}$ **6.** $49 \times 2\frac{1}{7}$

7. $100 \times 3\frac{1}{4}$ **8.** $1\frac{1}{2} \times 4\frac{2}{3}$ **9.** $2\frac{1}{3} \times 2\frac{1}{7}$

10. $4\frac{1}{4} \times 2\frac{1}{8}$ **11.** $3\frac{1}{4} \times 2\frac{2}{3}$ **12.** $4\frac{2}{5} \times 3\frac{3}{4}$

13. $3\frac{1}{7} \times 16\frac{1}{3}$ **14.** $20\frac{4}{5} \times 2\frac{1}{5}$ **15.** $18\frac{2}{3} \times 1\frac{3}{4}$

(*d*) Do these problems by the direct method, keeping the mixed numbers. Check by changing to improper fractions and multiplying.

1. $234\frac{3}{5}$ $\times 400$	**2.** $72\frac{3}{4}$ $\times 42\frac{2}{3}$	**3.** $2000\frac{1}{3}$ $\times 435\frac{3}{4}$	**4.** $56\frac{3}{4}$ $\times 12\frac{1}{5}$	**5.** $1256\frac{1}{2}$ $\times 327\frac{2}{3}$

10.8 DIVISION INVOLVING FRACTIONS

Let us review the measurement meaning of division. Twelve divided by 3 equals the number of measures of 3 contained in 12, as illustrated in Fig. 9. There are twelve circles.

If we take three circles as a measure (Fig. 9), we see the measure is contained four times, or $12 \div 3 = 4$.

If we take two circles as a measure (Fig. 10), we see the measure is contained six times, or $12 \div 2 = 6$.

If we take one circle as a measure, the measure is contained twelve times, or $12 \div 1 = 12$. (Fig. 11).

If we take one half circle as a measure (Fig. 12), the measure is contained twenty-four times, or $12 \div \frac{1}{2} = 24$. In like manner, if $\frac{1}{3}$ circle were taken as the measure, it would be contained thirty-six times, or

$$12 \div \frac{1}{3} = 36$$

and also

$$12 \div \frac{1}{4} = 48.$$

Fig. 9

Fig. 10

Fig. 11

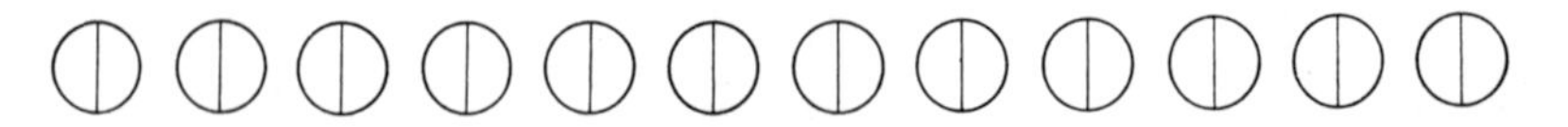

Fig. 12

These examples illustrate the divisor-dividend-quotient relation; that is, consider 12 as a fixed dividend, and, as the divisor decreases 3, 2, 1, $\frac{1}{2}$, $\frac{1}{3}$, $\frac{1}{4}$, the quotient increases 4, 6, 12, 24, 36, 48. Note particularly that *when the divisor is greater than one the quotient is less than the dividend,* but *when the divisor is less than one the quotient is greater than the dividend.*

Definition of Reciprocal. In the set of all fractions p/q, p and q natural numbers, there always exists a *reciprocal,* r such that $r \times p/q = 1$. The reciprocal takes the form q/p, or wq/wp, since

$$\frac{q}{p} \times \frac{p}{q} = \frac{qp}{pq} = 1,$$

or again

$$\frac{wq}{wp} \times \frac{p}{q} = \frac{wqp}{wpq} = 1, \qquad \text{where } w \neq 0.$$

Consider another application of the principle used in Chapter 9 to obtain equivalent fractions.

Principle. Multiplying or dividing both the numerator and the denominator of a fraction by the same number does not change the value of the fraction.

Example 1. Find the quotient of $10 \div \frac{2}{3}$.

Method 1. $10 \div \frac{2}{3}$ may be written $\dfrac{10}{\frac{2}{3}}$. If the denominator is multiplied by $\frac{3}{2}$, the denominator becomes unity. The numerator must also be multiplied by $\frac{3}{2}$ so as not to change the value of the fraction. The problem then becomes

$$\frac{10}{\frac{2}{3}} = \frac{\frac{3}{2} \times 10}{\frac{3}{2} \times \frac{2}{3}} = \frac{\dfrac{3 \times \overset{5}{\cancel{10}}}{\cancel{2}}}{\frac{1}{1}} = \frac{\frac{15}{1}}{1} = 15.$$

Note. $\frac{3}{2}$ was selected as the multiplier of both numerator and denominator, since it is the reciprocal of the divisor $\frac{2}{3}$, the reciprocal being such that its product with the given number equals the unit 1.

Method 2. Using the same principle, that is, $a/b = ka/kb$, we have

$$\frac{10}{\frac{2}{3}} = \frac{10 \times 3}{\frac{2}{3} \times 3} = \frac{30}{2} = 15.$$

Method 3. Some teachers prefer to make both the numerator and the denominator fractions with the same denominator and then divide only the numerators as shown below:

$$\frac{10}{\frac{2}{3}} = \frac{\frac{10}{1}}{\frac{2}{3}} = \frac{\frac{30}{3}}{\frac{2}{3}} = \frac{30}{2} = 15.$$

Method 4. Abridged form of Method 1.

$$10 \div \frac{2}{3} = \frac{10}{1} \times \frac{3}{2} = \frac{\overset{5}{\cancel{10}} \times 3}{1 \times \underset{1}{\cancel{2}}} = \frac{15}{1} = 15.$$

Example 2. Find the quotient of $\frac{11}{12} \div \frac{2}{3}$

Solution. Method 1.

$$\frac{\frac{11}{12}}{\frac{2}{3}} = \frac{\frac{3}{2} \times \frac{11}{12}}{\frac{3}{2} \times \frac{2}{3}} = \frac{\frac{\not{3}}{2} \times \frac{11}{\not{12}}}{\frac{1}{1}} = \frac{11}{8} = 1\tfrac{3}{8}.$$

Solution. Method 3.

$$\frac{\frac{11}{12}}{\frac{2}{3}} = \frac{\frac{11}{12}}{\frac{8}{12}} = \frac{11}{8} = 1\tfrac{3}{8}.$$

Problem. Work Example 2, using Methods 2 and 4, and give an advantage and disadvantage of each of the four methods.

To obtain a fraction with a denominator of one, the reciprocal of the denominator was used as a multiplier. This reciprocal of the divisor is the same as the divisor inverted; its use underlies the principle usually given regarding division involving fractions.

Principle. To divide a fraction by a fraction, multiply the dividend by the reciprocal of the divisor. In symbols,

$$\frac{a}{b} \div \frac{c}{d} = \frac{a}{b} \times \frac{d}{c} = \frac{ad}{bc}.$$

Example 1. $10 \div \frac{2}{3} = \frac{10}{1} \times \frac{3}{2} = \frac{30}{2}$

or

$$\overset{5}{\not{10}} \times \frac{3}{\underset{1}{\not{2}}} = \frac{15}{1} = 15.$$

Example 2. $\frac{11}{12} \div \frac{2}{3} = \frac{11}{12} \times \frac{3}{2} = \frac{11 \times \overset{1}{\not{3}}}{\underset{4}{\not{12}} \times 2} = \frac{11}{8} = 1\tfrac{3}{8}.$

10.9 DIVISION INVOLVING MIXED NUMBERS

Mixed numbers may be changed to the form of improper fractions before dividing. Then proceed according to the principles for dividing fractions. Study these examples.

Example 1. $5\tfrac{7}{8} \div \frac{8}{3} = \frac{47}{8} \times \frac{3}{8} = \frac{47 \times 3}{8 \times 8} = \frac{141}{64} = 2\tfrac{13}{64}.$

Example 2. $2\tfrac{1}{2} \div \frac{1}{2} = \frac{5}{\underset{1}{\not{2}}} \times \frac{\overset{1}{\not{2}}}{1} = \frac{5}{1} = 5.$

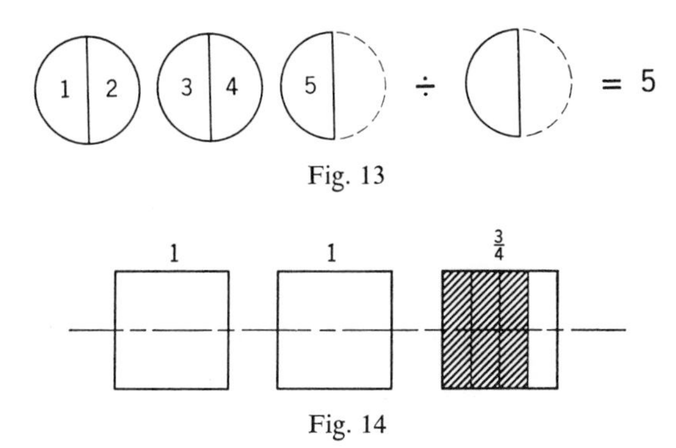

Fig. 13

Fig. 14

Example 3. $20\frac{3}{4} \div 2\frac{3}{40} = \dfrac{\overset{1}{\cancel{83}}}{\underset{1}{\cancel{4}}} \times \dfrac{\overset{10}{\cancel{40}}}{\underset{1}{\cancel{83}}} = \dfrac{10}{1} = 10.$

Example 4. $2\frac{1}{2} \div \dfrac{3}{4} = \dfrac{4 \times 2\frac{1}{2}}{4 \times \frac{3}{4}} = \dfrac{10}{3}.$

Example 5. $2\frac{3}{4} \div 2 = \dfrac{11}{4} \div \dfrac{2}{1} = \dfrac{11}{4} \times \dfrac{1}{2} = \dfrac{11}{8} = 1\frac{3}{8}.$

Example 6. $17 \div 2\frac{1}{3} = \dfrac{17}{1} \div \dfrac{7}{3} = \dfrac{17}{1} \times \dfrac{3}{7} = \dfrac{51}{7} = 7\frac{2}{7}.$

Comments. In the early work in division of fractions the ideas of measurement and partition, suitably diagrammed, should be used. In Example 2, for instance, how many $\frac{1}{2}$'s are contained in $2\frac{1}{2}$? (See Fig. 13.)

The diagram shows $\frac{1}{2}$ is contained in $2\frac{1}{2}$, five times. Measurement is the concept used in this case.

Again, in Example 5, dividing by 2 in $2\frac{3}{4} \div 2$ (Fig. 14) is the same as finding $\frac{1}{2}$ of $2\frac{3}{4}$. Thus we have $2\frac{3}{4} \div 2 = \frac{1}{2} \times 2\frac{3}{4}$.

$$\tfrac{1}{2} \times 2\tfrac{3}{4} = \tfrac{1}{2} + \tfrac{1}{2} + \tfrac{3}{8} = 1\tfrac{3}{8}$$

Partition is the concept used in this case.

EXERCISE 6

(*a*) Do as many of these problems as you can by partition and measurement. Use suitable methods for the others.

1. $16 \div \dfrac{1}{2}$ **2.** $12 \div \dfrac{2}{3}$ **3.** $16 \div \dfrac{3}{4}$

4. $100 \div \dfrac{1}{4}$ **5.** $100 \div \dfrac{2}{5}$ **6.** $21 \div \dfrac{3}{7}$

7. $50 \div \frac{7}{10}$
8. $240 \div \frac{3}{4}$
9. $\frac{3}{10} \div 15$
10. $\frac{2}{7} \div 14$
11. $48 \div 1\frac{3}{5}$
12. $\frac{2}{3} \div 8$
13. $14 \div \frac{5}{7}$
14. $35 \div \frac{7}{10}$
15. $\frac{4}{5} \div 60$

(*b*) Can you complete these in two minutes or less?

1. $\frac{1}{2} \div \frac{1}{2}$
2. $\frac{1}{2} \div \frac{1}{3}$
3. $\frac{2}{7} \div \frac{2}{5}$
4. $\frac{1}{2} \div \frac{3}{4}$
5. $\frac{1}{2} \div \frac{5}{8}$
6. $\frac{1}{9} \div \frac{9}{10}$
7. $\frac{4}{5} \div \frac{8}{9}$
8. $\frac{5}{3} \div \frac{6}{20}$
9. $\frac{4}{7} \div \frac{2}{3}$
10. $\frac{5}{100} \div \frac{3}{10}$
11. $\frac{2}{3} \div \frac{8}{9}$
12. $\frac{3}{4} \div \frac{4}{5}$
13. $\frac{5}{7} \div \frac{2}{5}$
14. $\frac{3}{4} \div \frac{8}{9}$
15. $\frac{7}{9} \div 4\frac{2}{3}$

(*c*) Time yourself on these problems. Between two and three minutes is excellent, between four and five minutes is satisfactory.

1. $12 \div 2\frac{1}{3}$
2. $20 \div 2\frac{1}{4}$
3. $4\frac{1}{3} \div 5$
4. $6\frac{1}{4} \div 2$
5. $24 \div 1\frac{1}{8}$
6. $60 \div 2\frac{1}{4}$
7. $49 \div 2\frac{1}{3}$
8. $100 \div 2\frac{2}{3}$
9. $4\frac{2}{3} \div 1\frac{1}{2}$
10. $2\frac{1}{3} \div 2\frac{1}{7}$
11. $4\frac{1}{4} \div 2\frac{1}{8}$
12. $3\frac{2}{3} \div 1\frac{5}{6}$
13. $66 \div 3\frac{1}{7}$
14. $50 \div 1\frac{2}{3}$
15. $3\frac{1}{2} \div \frac{7}{8}$

Applied problems.

EXERCISE 7

1. What is the cost of $\frac{3}{4}$ yard of cotton goods selling at $33\frac{1}{3}$ cents per yard?
2. How many strips $\frac{3}{16}$ inch wide can be cut from a strip $\frac{3}{4}$ inch wide?
3. What is the cost of $\frac{1}{2}$ gallon of kerosene retailing for $27\frac{1}{2}$ cents per gallon?
4. How much punch would be required to fill 36 special punch glasses if one quart will fill $6\frac{1}{2}$ glasses?
5. What is the cost of $2\frac{3}{4}$ pounds of meat listed at 79 cents a pound?
6. What is the cost of $12\frac{1}{2}$ tons of coal costing $45.00 per ton?
7. What is the cost of $\frac{3}{4}$ pound of tea at a special summer rate of $1.00 per pound?

8. If $\frac{2}{3}$ yard of goods cost 66 cents, what is the price per yard?

9. If 75 cents was paid for $\frac{3}{4}$ pound of candy, what is the price per pound?

10. If $3\frac{2}{3}$ gallons cost \$1.43, what is the cost of one gallon?

11. A recipe calls for $2\frac{1}{2}$ cups of flour, $1\frac{1}{3}$ cups of shortening, $\frac{3}{4}$ cup of sugar, $1\frac{1}{2}$ teaspoons of salt, $1\frac{1}{2}$ teaspoons of baking powder, and 1 cup of milk. How much of each ingredient should be used for three times the recipe?

12. How much of each ingredient should one use for one half the recipe in problem 11?

13. Explain carefully why one can always find half a given fraction by simply multiplying its denominator by 2. Give examples.

14. Find one half of each of the following quantities

$$(a)\,\frac{2}{3} \quad (b)\,\frac{3}{4} \quad (c)\,4\tfrac{1}{2} \quad (d)\,5\tfrac{1}{3} \quad (e)\,6\tfrac{4}{5}$$

15. A book $\frac{3}{4}$ inch thick contains 180 leaves. What is the thickness of one leaf in this book?

16. How many strips of lath $1\frac{1}{4}$ inch wide will it take to cover a space 60 inches wide if the laths are placed side by side? How many laths are needed if they are placed so that there is $\frac{1}{4}$ inch air space on the right side of each lath?

17. What is the perimeter (distance around) and what is the surface area of a rectangular floor that measures $12\frac{3}{4}$ feet by $16\frac{2}{3}$ feet?

18. How many square rods are there in a rectangular plot of ground $20\frac{3}{4}$ rods long by $15\frac{1}{2}$ rods wide?

19. What is the speed of a boat which travels $22\frac{1}{2}$ miles in $\frac{3}{4}$ of one hour?

20. Show by means of a diagram using circles divided into thirds, that $2 \div \frac{2}{3} = 3$.

10.10 FRACTIONAL PARTS OF 100

The diagram in Fig. 15 contains ten rows of ten columns, or one hundred squares. If it is cut into two equal parts, each part will contain one half of the one hundred squares, or fifty. If these parts are divided again each will contain one fourth of the original one hundred squares, or

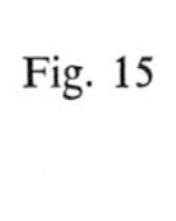
Fig. 15

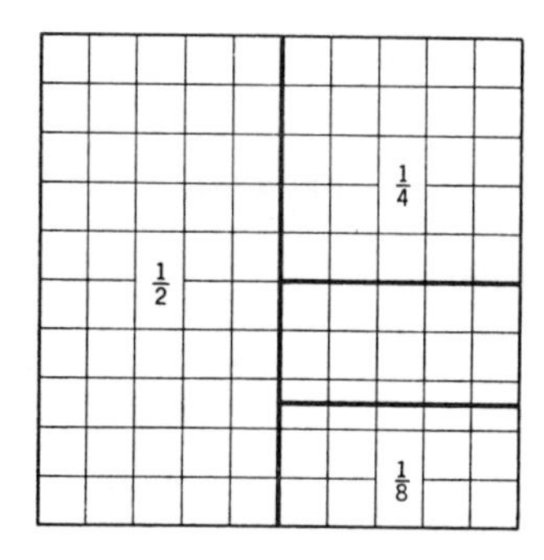

twenty-five. Cutting the quarter into two equal parts will leave $\frac{1}{8}$ in each part. One eighth of the original square is twelve and one half squares. The following fractional parts of 100 should be checked or verified by a method similar to the one just given, and the parts should be learned. The fractional parts of 100 are sometimes referred to as *aliquot parts.*

Fractional parts of 100.

$\frac{1}{2}$ of $100 = 50$,

$\frac{1}{3}$ of $100 = 33\frac{1}{3}$,

$\frac{2}{3}$ of $100 = 66\frac{2}{3}$,

$\frac{1}{4}$ of $100 = 25$,

$\frac{2}{4}$ or $\frac{1}{2}$ of $100 = 50$,

$\frac{3}{4}$ of $100 = 75$,

$\frac{1}{5}$ of $100 = 20$,

$\frac{2}{5}$ of $100 = 40$,

$\frac{3}{5}$ of $100 = 60$,

$\frac{4}{5}$ of $100 = 80$,

$\frac{1}{6}$ of $100 = 16\frac{2}{3}$,

$\frac{2}{6}$ or $\frac{1}{3}$ of $100 = 33\frac{1}{3}$,

$\frac{3}{6}$ or $\frac{1}{2}$ of $100 = 50$,

$\frac{4}{6}$ or $\frac{2}{3}$ of $100 = 66\frac{2}{3}$,

$\frac{5}{6}$ of $100 = 83\frac{1}{3}$,

$\frac{1}{8}$ of $100 = 12\frac{1}{2}$,

$\frac{2}{8}$ or $\frac{1}{4}$ of $100 = 25$,

$\frac{3}{8}$ of $100 = 37\frac{1}{2}$,

$\frac{4}{8}$ or $\frac{1}{2}$ of $100 = 50$,

$\frac{5}{8}$ of $100 = 62\frac{1}{2}$,

$\frac{6}{8}$ or $\frac{3}{4}$ of $100 = 75$,

$\frac{7}{8}$ of $100 = 87\frac{1}{2}$,

$\frac{1}{10}$ of $100 = 10$,

$\frac{2}{10}$ of $100 = 20$,

$\frac{3}{10}$ of $100 = 30$,

$\frac{4}{10}$ of $100 = 40$,

$\frac{5}{10}$ of $100 = 50$,

$\frac{6}{10}$ of $100 = 60$,

$\frac{7}{10}$ of $100 = 70$,

$\frac{8}{10}$ of $100 = 80$,

$\frac{9}{10}$ of $100 = 90$.

Other fractional parts of 100.

$\frac{1}{12}$ of $100 = 8\frac{1}{3}$,

$\frac{1}{20}$ of $100 = 5$,

$\frac{1}{25}$ of $100 = 4$,

$\frac{1}{50}$ of $100 = 2$.

Problem. Make a complete table for the fractional parts of 100
(*a*) on the basis of twelfths,
(*b*) on the basis of twentieths,
(*c*) on the basis of twentyfifths,
(*d*) on the basis of sixths.

Knowing these fractional parts of 100 permits the solution of problems with fewer calculations, as seen from these examples.

Short cuts.

1. To multiply by 25, multiply by 100 and divide by 4.

Example 1. $25 \times 12 = \dfrac{100 \times \overset{3}{\cancel{12}}}{\underset{1}{\cancel{4}}} = 300.$

Example 2. $25 \times 28 = \dfrac{100 \times 28}{4} = 700.$

2. To multiply by 125, multiply by 1000 and divide by 8.

Example 1. $125 \times 36 = \dfrac{\overset{500}{\cancel{1000}} \times \overset{9}{\cancel{36}}}{\underset{\underset{1}{\cancel{2}}}{\cancel{8}}} = 4500.$

Example 2. $125 \times 328 = \dfrac{1000 \times 328}{8} = 41{,}000.$

3. To multiply by $33\frac{1}{3}$, multiply by 100 and divide by 3.

Example 1. $33\frac{1}{3} \times 627 = \dfrac{100 \times 627}{3} = 20900.$

4. To multiply by $37\frac{1}{2}$, multiply by 300 and divide by 8, or divide by 8 and multiply by 300.

Example 1. $37\frac{1}{2} \times 408 = \dfrac{300 \times \overset{51}{\cancel{408}}}{\underset{1}{\cancel{8}}} = 15{,}300.$

5. To divide by 25, multiply by 4 and divide by 100.

Example 1. $\dfrac{650}{25} = \dfrac{650}{100} \times 4 = \dfrac{2600}{100} = 26.$

6. To divide by 50, multiply by 2 and divide by 100.

Example 1. $\dfrac{325}{50} = \dfrac{325}{100} \times 2 = \dfrac{650}{100} = \dfrac{65}{10} = \dfrac{13}{2}.$

EXERCISE 8

Develop the following rules.

1. Make a rule to use in multiplying by $16\frac{2}{3}$, using fractional parts of 100.

2. Make a rule to use in dividing by $16\frac{2}{3}$, using fractional parts of 100.

3. Make a rule to use in multiplying by $66\frac{2}{3}$, using fractional parts of 100.

4. Make a rule to use in dividing by $66\frac{2}{3}$, using fractional parts of 100.

5. Make a rule to use in multiplying by $87\frac{1}{2}$, using fractional parts of 100.

Use fractional parts of 100 when possible in these problems.

6. 25×72

7. $33\frac{1}{3} \times 48$

8. 50×128

9. $12\frac{1}{2} \times 688$

10. $16\frac{2}{3} \times 960$

11. $62\frac{1}{2} \times 408$

12. $83\frac{1}{3} \times 396$

13. $4350 \div 25$

14. $7859 \div 50$

15. $87\frac{1}{2} \times 728$

Solve each of the following groups of examples.

16. Find the required part(s) of each number.

(*a*) $\frac{1}{2}$ of 35 (*b*) $\frac{1}{3}$ of $7\frac{1}{2}$ (*c*) $\frac{3}{8}$ of 72

(*d*) $\frac{5}{6}$ of 84 (*e*) 7 of $3\frac{1}{2}$ (*f*) $\frac{5}{3}$ of $\frac{7}{10}$

(*g*) $1\frac{1}{4}$ of $2\frac{1}{2}$ (*h*) $3\frac{1}{4}$ of $\frac{2}{3}$ (*i*) $\frac{1}{8}$ of $\frac{3}{4}$

17. What part of the second number is the first?

(*a*) $\frac{1}{2}, \frac{3}{2}$ (*b*) $\frac{3}{4}, \frac{3}{2}$ (*c*) $\frac{2}{3}, \frac{1}{3}$

(*d*) $\frac{1}{2}, 2\frac{1}{2}$ (*e*) $3\frac{1}{3}, 1\frac{1}{2}$ (*f*) $\frac{5}{6}, \frac{5}{12}$

(*g*) $\frac{1}{8}, \frac{1}{2}$ (*h*) $2\frac{1}{2}$, 5 (*i*) $3\frac{1}{3}$, 10

18. Find the number such that

(*a*) $\frac{1}{3}$ of it is 2 (*b*) $\frac{3}{4}$ of it is 60 (*c*) $\frac{5}{4}$ of it is 20

(*d*) $3\frac{1}{2}$ of it is 70 (*e*) $\frac{1}{8}$ of it is 7 (*f*) $\frac{3}{8}$ of it is 12

(*g*) $\frac{4}{5}$ of it is 10 (*h*) $\frac{8}{5}$ of it is 24 (*i*) 5 of it is 35

Work out each of the following examples:

19. Add $8\frac{1}{3}$, $5\frac{3}{4}$, $2\frac{1}{2}$.

20. Subtract (*a*) $\begin{array}{r} 300\frac{1}{6} \\ 16\frac{2}{5} \\ \hline \end{array}$ (*b*) $\begin{array}{r} 290 \\ 195\frac{2}{3} \\ \hline \end{array}$ (*c*) $\begin{array}{r} 38\frac{1}{4} \\ 24\frac{5}{8} \\ \hline \end{array}$

21. Multiply (*a*) $\frac{3}{5} \times \frac{5}{9} \times \frac{4}{7} =$ (*b*) $15 \times 9\frac{3}{4} \times 12\frac{1}{3} =$

(*c*) $\begin{array}{r} 365\frac{3}{4} \\ 25 \\ \hline \end{array}$ (*d*) $\begin{array}{r} 258\frac{1}{2} \\ 34\frac{1}{3} \\ \hline \end{array}$

22. Divide (*a*) $4\frac{1}{4} \div 100$ (*b*) $12 \div 1\frac{2}{3}$ (*c*) $3\frac{2}{5} \div 2\frac{1}{2}$ (*d*) $27\frac{1}{2} \div \frac{1}{4}$.

23. Simplify (*a*) $\dfrac{\frac{3}{5}}{\frac{2}{3}}$ (*b*) $\dfrac{100}{62\frac{2}{3}}$ (*c*) $\dfrac{7 - 2\frac{1}{2}}{\frac{2}{3} + 6}$ (*d*) $\dfrac{5 \times 3\frac{1}{4}}{7\frac{1}{4} - 3\frac{3}{16}}$.

24. (*a*) Explain by means of a marked rectangle why $\frac{3}{4} \times \frac{3}{5} = \frac{9}{20}$.
(*b*) Explain by means of a diagram why $\frac{2}{3} \times 3 = 2$ and $3 \times \frac{2}{3} = 2$.
(*c*) Use circular discs divided in thirds to show why $2 \div \frac{2}{3} = 3$.

EXERCISE 9

Review of Fractions and Related Concepts

1. Prime numbers:

(*a*) What is a prime number? Give two examples.
(*b*) What is a prime factor? Give two examples.
(*c*) Find the prime factors of (*a′*) 304, (*b′*) 290.
(*d*) Write the prime numbers between 60 and 90.

2. List all of the common divisors of 16, 40, 328, 176. Which is the greatest common divisor?

3. (*a*) Find the lowest common multiple of 24, 30, 40, 48.
(*b*) State the rule and give an example for testing whether numbers are divisible by 3: also by 4.

4. (*a*) State three meanings of a fraction.
(*b*) Name the terms in the fraction.

5. Give an example of a proper fraction, an improper fraction, a mixed number, and a compound fraction.

6. State the principle used to write the equivalent fractions: (*a*) $\frac{3}{5} = \frac{12}{20}$, (*b*) $\frac{18}{30} = \frac{3}{5}$.

7. Write in lowest terms: $\frac{25}{45} =$, $\frac{14}{16} =$, $\frac{24}{42} =$, $\frac{16}{56} =$, $\frac{75}{100} =$, $\frac{39}{91} =$.

8. Write as improper fractions: $2\frac{3}{4}$, $1\frac{7}{8}$, $8\frac{5}{12}$, $66\frac{2}{3}$, $37\frac{1}{2}$.

9. Find (*a*) $\frac{2}{3}$ of 450, (*b*) $\frac{1}{2}$ of $16\frac{2}{3}$.

10. (*a*) $2\frac{1}{2}$ is what fractional part of 4? (*b*) 14 is what fractional part of 7?

11. Find the number of which (*a*) $7\frac{1}{2}$ is $\frac{3}{4}$ (*b*) 180 is $\frac{3}{5}$.

12. A clerk received a salary of $5500 last year. This year his salary was increased by $\frac{1}{10}$. What is his salary this year?

13. A clerk receives a salary of $5500 this year, which is $\frac{1}{10}$ more than he received last year. What was his salary last year?

14. If $\frac{2}{3}$ pound of candy costs 60 cents, what is the cost of one pound?

15. Find the cost of $2\frac{3}{4}$ pounds of cheese at 80 cents per pound.

16. 144 is $\frac{1}{8}$ more than a certain number. Find the number.

17. If a certain kind of candy bar weights $\frac{4}{5}$ of an ounce, how many of these bars would it take to make one pound of this candy? (16 ounces = one pound.)

18. At what rate in miles per hour does a boat travel if it goes 7 miles in 20 minutes?

REFERENCES

Banks, J. H., *Learning and Teaching Arithmetic*, pp. 265–279.

Brueckner, L. J., and F. E. Grossnickle, *How to Make Arithmetic Meaningful*, pp. 294–349.

Larsen, H. D., *Arithmetic for Colleges*, pp. 129–142.

McSwain and Cooke, *Understanding and Teaching Arithmetic in the Elementary School*, pp. 147–179.

Morton, R. L., *Teaching Arithmetic in the Elementary School*, Vol. 2., pp. 178–316.

Spencer, P., and M. Brydegaard, *Building Mathematical Concepts in the Elementary School*, Chapter 7.

Spitzer, H. F., *The Teaching of Arithmetic*, pp. 255–288.

Taylor, E. H., and C. N. Mills, *Arithmetic for Teacher-Training Classes*, fourth edition, pp. 144–183.

Wheat, H. G., *How to Teach Arithmetic*, pp. 219–226, 242–251.

11

Decimal Fractions

11.1 DEFINITIONS

In this book the term *fraction* is used to mean both the common fraction and the decimal fraction. It will be recalled that a common fraction (simple fraction) is one in which both the numerator and the denominator are natural numbers. Thus $\frac{3}{4}$, $\frac{17}{10}$, $\frac{5}{16}$ and $\frac{23}{100}$ are common fractions. A *decimal fraction* is defined as a fraction for which the *denominator is ten or a higher power of ten*. Examples of decimal fractions are $\frac{3}{10}$, $\frac{15}{100}$, $\frac{25}{1000}$. Decimal fractions are a subset of the set of all common fractions.

In Chapter 9 it was stated that an equivalent fraction is obtained if both the numerator and the denominator are multiplied by the same number $n \neq 0$. This fact is true not only when the multiplier is a natural number but also when it is a fraction. By allowing complex fractions in some cases, it is always possible to change a common fraction to a decimal fraction. Thus

$$\frac{1}{4} = \frac{25 \times 1}{25 \times 4} = \frac{25}{100},$$

a decimal fraction. Take as a second example, $\frac{1}{3}$, which is equivalent to

$$\frac{3\frac{1}{3} \times 1}{3\frac{1}{3} \times 3} = \frac{3\frac{1}{3}}{10}.$$

This is a *complex decimal fraction*, in contrast to a *simple decimal fraction*, for which the numerator is a natural number; in both cases the denominator is a power of ten.

In changing from common fractions to decimal fractions, an infinite number of representations is possible. For example, it was shown that $\frac{1}{4} = \frac{25}{100}$. This could likewise be represented by $\frac{250}{1000}$, $\frac{2500}{10,000}$ and so on.

The common fraction $\frac{1}{3}$ was changed to the decimal fraction $3\frac{1}{3}/10$. Other representations are $33\frac{1}{3}/100$, $333\frac{1}{3}/1000$, and so on.

In the chapter on fractions a proper fraction was defined as one for which the numerator is smaller than the denominator. The same definition applies to decimal fractions. However, a decimal fraction is more commonly called a *pure decimal fraction*. Examples are $\frac{3}{10}$, $\frac{42}{100}$, and so on.

An improper fraction was defined as one for which the numerator is equal to or greater than the denominator. If the numerator of an improper fraction is a multiple of the denominator, the value of the improper fraction may be expressed by a natural number. All other improper fractions may be expressed as mixed numbers. Improper decimal fractions must necessarily follow this pattern, and those which are not natural numbers may be called *mixed decimal fractions*. Examples are

$$\frac{312}{100} = 3\tfrac{12}{100}, \qquad \frac{182}{10} = 18\tfrac{2}{10}.$$

EXERCISE 1

1. Change the following decimal fractions to common fractions in lowest terms:

$(a)\ \frac{30}{100},\quad (b)\ \frac{26}{10},\quad (c)\ \frac{4}{100},\quad (d)\ \frac{230}{1000},\quad (e)\ \frac{4}{10{,}000}.$

2. Change the following common fractions to decimal fractions:

$(a)\ \frac{1}{2},\quad (b)\ \frac{1}{4},\quad (c)\ \frac{1}{8},\quad (d)\ \frac{2}{3},\quad (e)\ \frac{1}{7}.$

3. Change each of the following improper decimal fractions to either a natural number or a mixed decimal fraction:

$(a)\ \frac{10}{10},\quad (b)\ \frac{23}{10},\quad (c)\ \frac{5235}{1000},\quad (d)\ \frac{281}{10},\quad (e)\ \frac{1000}{10}.$

4. Which of the answers obtained in problem 1 still satisfy the definition of a decimal fraction?

11.2 THE DECIMAL POINT NOTATION

One of the most important inventions in arithmetical notation is the decimal mark, which in America is the period, in England, the raised period, and in certain other countries, the comma. The period, so used, is called the decimal point. With this notation, the decimal fractions $\frac{6}{10}$, $\frac{23}{100}$, and $\frac{54}{1000}$ may be represented, respectively, by .6, .23, and .054.* This short form of writing decimal fractions is called the *decimal point*

* In engineering such decimal point forms are usually written with a zero before the decimal point. Thus .36 is written 0.36, .0153 is written 0.0153, and so on.

form. It requires a decimal point followed by one digit when the denominator is 10, two digits when the denominator is 100, three digits when it is 1000 and so on. In the case of $\frac{54}{1000}$ a zero, placed between the decimal point and 54 is the necessary third digit. As many zeros as needed may be inserted in this manner. Thus $\frac{6}{10,000}$ would require a decimal point followed by four digits. The proper representation is .0006.

Changing the common fraction $\frac{1}{2}$ to a decimal fraction presents no difficulty, but changing $\frac{1}{3}$ to a decimal fraction leads to complex decimal fractions, such as $3\frac{1}{3}/10$, $33\frac{1}{3}/100$, $333\frac{1}{3}/1000$, and so on, which may be written in decimal point form as $.3\frac{1}{3}$, $.33\frac{1}{3}$, $.333\frac{1}{3}$, respectively. This sequence, customarily written in the form $.333\cdots$, may be continued indefinitely. The three dots at the end represent the continuation. In like manner $\frac{2}{3} = .666\cdots$ and $\frac{1}{6} = .1666\cdots$. Such decimal fractions are usually called *repeating or recurring decimal fractions.*

EXERCISE 2

1. Write the following decimal fractions in decimal point form:

(*a*) $\frac{3}{10}$ (*b*) $\frac{16}{100}$

(*c*) $\frac{6}{100}$ (*d*) $\frac{1471}{1000}$

(*e*) $\frac{4}{1000}$ (*f*) $\frac{42}{1000}$

(*g*) $\frac{370}{100}$ (*h*) $\frac{300}{1000}$

(*i*) $\frac{472}{10,000}$ (*j*) $\frac{6891}{10,000}$

2. Write the following decimal fractions in the form without the decimal point ($.8 = \frac{8}{10}$):

(*a*) .8 (*b*) .61
(*c*) .04 (*d*) .672
(*e*) .602 (*f*) .002
(*g*) .600 (*h*) .0023
(*i*) .0621 (*j*) .7345

3. Change each of the following decimal fractions to an equivalent common fraction ($.8 = \frac{8}{10} = \frac{4}{5}$.):

(*a*) .8 (*b*) $\frac{4}{100}$ (*c*) $\frac{21}{100}$ (*d*) .42 (*e*) .06

(*f*) $\frac{7}{100}$ (*g*) $\frac{232}{1000}$ (*h*) .045 (*i*) $\frac{111}{1000}$ (*j*) .137

4. Change the following common fractions to equivalent decimal fractions expressed in decimal point form:

(*a*) $\frac{2}{5}$ (*b*) $\frac{7}{8}$ (*c*) $\frac{3}{8}$ (*d*) $\frac{1}{12}$ (*e*) $\frac{1}{7}$

(*f*) $\frac{2}{7}$ (*g*) $\frac{1}{13}$ (*h*) $\frac{4}{5}$ (*i*) $\frac{3}{4}$ (*j*) $\frac{1}{9}$

5. Indicate which of the following decimal fractions are simple and which are complex:

$$.28\tfrac{2}{5},\quad 16.2,\quad 1.0,\quad .642,\quad .005,\quad \frac{7}{1000},\quad .25\tfrac{1}{4}.$$

6. Which of the decimal fractions in problem 5 are pure decimal fractions? Which are mixed decimal fractions?

11.3 READING DECIMAL FRACTIONS

Decimal fractions are read in the same way as other fractions. Just as $\frac{3}{4}$ is read three fourths, $\frac{3}{10}$ is read three tenths. If $\frac{3}{10}$ is written in the decimal point form, it is read in the same way. Similarly,

$\frac{7}{10}$ or .7 is read *seven tenths*;
$\frac{72}{100}$ or .72 is read *seventy-two hundredths*;
$\frac{725}{1000}$ or .725 is read *seven hundred twenty-five thousandths*;
$\frac{7253}{10,000}$ or .7253 is read *seven thousand two hundred fifty-three ten-thousandths*;
$\frac{72631}{100,000}$ or .72631 is read *seventy-two thousand six hundred thirty-one hundred-thousandths*.

Tenths, hundredths, thousandths, $\cdots$, are called the *orders* in a decimal fraction. They are known as the first, second, third, $\cdots$, order. Other successive orders are ten-thousandths, hundred-thousandths, millionths, and so on. Note the use of hyphens in the compound names of orders.

In reading a mixed decimal fraction, the decimal point is indicated by using the conjunction *and*. To illustrate, 23.83 is read *twenty-three and eighty-three hundredths*. The number 143.6 is read *one hundred forty-three and six tenths*, not one hundred and forty-three and six tenths. The only time a second *and* is used is in reading complex mixed decimal fractions. Thus $23.4\frac{1}{3}$ is read *twenty-three and four and one-third tenths.* This kind of mixed decimal fraction occurs in compound interest problems. For example, the accumulation factor in compound interest when the rate is 5 per cent compounded monthly is $1.00\frac{5}{12}$.

The improper use of *and* in reading a number may result in a number name that applies to an entirely different number. Thus, if .232 is incorrectly read as "two hundred and thirty-two thousandths," the number

200.032 is indicated. Hence in accordance with the rule, .232 must be read "two hundred thirty-two thousandths."

Because of these difficulties, many computers prefer to "dictate" numbers rather than read them. Thus 200.032 would become *two zero zero point zero three two.* The number .232 would be read *point two three two.* It is seen that no possible confusion can arise between these numbers when they are dictated as described.

Occasionally, certain forms of complex decimal fractions may be confusing. Thus $.015\frac{1}{3}$ is clearly fifteen and one third thousandths, but what would $.000\frac{1}{3}$ represent? This is *one third of a thousandth,* not one third of a ten-thousandth. The complex decimal fraction $.00\frac{1}{3}$ is one third of a hundredth, and $.0\frac{1}{3}$ is one third of a tenth. What then would $.\frac{1}{3}$ represent? Following the above system, it would be one third of one or simply $\frac{1}{3}$ For this reason the form $.\frac{1}{3}$ is *not used.*

11.4 EXPONENT FORM FOR DECIMAL FRACTIONS

Decimal fractions are not only fractions whose denominators are powers of ten, they are also *an extension of place value* in terms of negative powers of ten. It should be recalled from all of the work with place values and from the brief discussion of exponents in Chapter 2 that numbers can be written in terms of powers of ten. Thus

$$234 = 2(10^2) + 3(10^1) + 4(10^0)$$

and

$$6307 = 6(10^3) + 3(10^2) + 0(10^1) + 7(10^0).$$

It should also be recalled that

$$10^0 = 1, \quad 10^{-1} = \frac{1}{10}, \quad 10^{-2} = \frac{1}{10^2} = \frac{1}{100}, \quad 10^{-3} = \frac{1}{10^3} = \frac{1}{1000} \cdots.$$

In fact, it should be clear that

$$10^{-1} = \frac{1}{10} = .1, \qquad 10^{-2} = .01, \qquad 10^{-3} = .001, \qquad 10^{-4} = .0001.$$

Place value continues to the right of the decimal point. For example,

$$\begin{aligned} .234 &= 2(10^{-1}) + 3(10^{-2}) + 4(10^{-3}) \\ &= \frac{2}{10} + \frac{3}{100} + \frac{4}{1000}. \end{aligned}$$

Note that this expansion can be checked:

$$\frac{2}{10} + \frac{3}{100} + \frac{4}{1000} = \frac{200}{1000} + \frac{30}{1000} + \frac{4}{1000} = \frac{234}{1000}.$$

Example 1. Write the mixed decimal fraction 16.705 in exponential form.

Solution. 16.705 is equivalent to

$$1(10^1) + 6(10^0) + 7(10^{-1}) + 0(10^{-2}) + 5(10^{-3})$$

or

$$1(10) + 6(1) + \frac{7}{10^1} + \frac{0}{10^2} + \frac{5}{10^3}.$$

Example 2. Write the mixed decimal fraction 654.32 in exponential form.

Solution. 654.32 is equivalent to

$$6(10^2) + 5(10^1) + 4(10^0) + 3(10^{-1}) + 2(10^{-2})$$

or

$$6(100) + 5(10) + 4(1) + \frac{3}{10} + \frac{2}{100}.$$

11.5 FRACTIONS IN OTHER NUMBER BASES

Place value applies in work with fractions in other number bases. Naturally, denominators for these fractions will have to be powers of the given number base. Consider numbers in base twelve. Numbers in base twelve are often referred to as duodecimals and duodecimal fractions (duodecimal means "two and ten" or twelve). What would $\frac{1}{3}$ be in the duodecimal system?

$$\tfrac{1}{3} = \tfrac{4}{12} \quad \text{therefore} \quad \tfrac{1}{3} = .4_{12}$$

Example 1. Write the fractions $\frac{1}{2}, \frac{1}{6}, \frac{1}{5}, \frac{1}{24}$ as duodecimal fractions.

Solutions. $\frac{1}{2} = \frac{6}{12} = .6_{12}$, $\quad \frac{1}{6} = \frac{2}{12} = .2_{12}$,

$$\frac{1}{5} = \frac{1 \times 2\frac{2}{5}}{5 \times 2\frac{2}{5}} = \frac{2\frac{2}{5}}{12} = (.2\tfrac{2}{5})_{12}, \qquad \frac{1}{24} = \frac{6}{144} = .06_{12}$$

Example 2. Expand the following quantities and change them to common fractions.

$$.8_{12}, \quad .5_{12}, \quad .68_{12}, \quad .369_{12}:$$

Solutions. $.8_{12} = \frac{8}{12} = \frac{2}{3}$, $\quad .5_{12} = \frac{5}{12}$,

$$.68_{12} = \frac{6}{12} + \frac{8}{12^2} = \frac{1}{2} + \frac{8}{144} = \frac{1}{2} + \frac{1}{18} = \frac{10}{18} = \frac{5}{9},$$

$$.369_{12} = \frac{3}{12} + \frac{6}{12^2} + \frac{9}{12^3} = \frac{1}{4} + \frac{1}{24} + \frac{9}{1728}$$

$$= \frac{1}{4} + \frac{1}{24} + \frac{1}{192} = \frac{48 + 8 + 1}{192} = \frac{57}{192} = \frac{19}{64}.$$

Example 3. Expand the following quantities and reduce them to common fractions.

$$.6_8, \quad .34_8, \quad 32.16_8:$$

Solutions. $.6_8 = \frac{6}{8} = \frac{3}{4}, \qquad .34_8 = \frac{3}{8} + \frac{4}{64} = \frac{24 + 4}{64} = \frac{28}{64} = \frac{7}{16}.$

$$32.16_8 = 3(8) + 2(1) + 1(\tfrac{1}{8}) + 6(\tfrac{1}{64})$$
$$= 24 + 2 + \frac{1}{8} + \frac{3}{32} = 26\tfrac{7}{32}.$$

EXERCISE 3

1. Write the following decimal fractions in word form:
(*a*) .23, (*b*) .064, (*c*) 2.107, (*d*) .12345, (*e*) 23.0492.

2. Write the following decimal fractions in word form:
(*a*) .6, (*b*) .006, (*c*) 3.209, (*d*) .01503, (*e*) 16.0598.

3. Write the following numbers, using numerals in decimal point form:
(*a*) fifty-eight hundredths
(*b*) three hundred four thousandths
(*c*) three hundred and four thousandths
(*d*) four thousand three hundred twenty-one ten-thousandths.

4. Write the following decimal fractions in exponential form:
(*a*) .18, (*b*) .108, (*c*) .018, (*d*) 3.25, (*e*) 20.05.

5. Write the following as decimal fractions:
(*a*) $2(10^{-2}) + 3(10^{-3}) + 6(10^{-5})$, (*b*) $7(10^2) + 4(10^{-1}) + 5(10^{-3})$.

6. Write $6(10^2) + 4(10^0) + 7(10^{-2}) + 3(10^{-4})$ as a decimal fraction.

7. Write the following numbers, using numerals in decimal point form:
(*a*) Twenty-two thousandths
(*b*) Two hundred thirty-seven and five hundred eighty-seven ten-thousandths
(*c*) Five hundred and two thousandths
(*d*) Six thousand two hundred sixty-one and forty-nine and one third hundredths.

8. Show that $2(10^{-1}) + 5(10^{-2}) + 3(10^{-3})$ is equal to 253/1000.

9. Write the following decimal fractions in exponential form:
(*a*) 42.325, (*b*) 206.042, (*c*) 330.333.

10. Write the following decimal fractions in word form:
(*a*) 832.047, (*b*) 5.0006, (*c*) 8000.0039, (*d*) $7.0\frac{1}{3}$, (*e*) .63207.

11. The first decimal fraction order is called tenths. Name the next five in order.

12. The number 23.56_8 is written in base eight. Write this number in base ten.

13. The numbers $.38_{12}$ and 3.64_{12} are in base twelve. Express them in base ten.

14. Express the following common fractions as duodecimal fractions (base twelve):

(*a*) $\frac{5}{6}$, (*b*) $\frac{1}{24}$, (*c*) $\frac{13}{72}\left(\text{or } \frac{26}{144}\right)$, (*d*) $\frac{7}{8}$.

15. Express the following common fractions as fractions in base eight:

(*a*) $\frac{5}{8}$, (*b*) $\frac{1}{4}$, (*c*) $\frac{3}{32}$, (*d*) $\frac{7}{16}$, (*e*) $\frac{9}{256}$.

11.6 EQUIVALENT DECIMAL FRACTIONS—SIMILAR DECIMAL FRACTIONS

Two decimal fractions having the same value are said to be *equivalent*. Consider a decimal fraction of the form .24 or $\frac{24}{100}$. Since a fraction is unchanged if numerator and denominator are multiplied by the same number,

$$\frac{24}{100} = \frac{24 \times 10}{100 \times 10} = \frac{240}{1000} = .240.$$

Hence .24 is said to be equivalent to .240. Likewise, .24 = .2400 = .24000, and so on. This means that a decimal fraction in decimal point form is unchanged in value if zeros are annexed to the right end of the decimal fraction.

If two decimal fractions have the same order, they are said to be *similar*. (Their denominators are the same power of ten.) Thus .670, .023, and .004 are similar decimal fractions. If mixed decimal fractions are considered, the foregoing definition may be modified slightly to include such fractions. Thus, if the decimal fractional part of the mixed decimal fraction is of the same order as a pure decimal fraction or of the same order as the decimal fraction part of another mixed fraction, they are said to be similar decimal fractions. The following pairs are similar decimal fractions: .21 and 4.37; 28.305 and 899.001.

Two decimal fractions may be made similar by simply annexing a proper number of zeros to the decimal fraction of lower order. For example, .29 and .2 are not similar; hence write .2 as .20, an equivalent decimal fraction. Then .29 and .20 are similar decimal fractions.

EXERCISE 4

1. (*a*) Change the following decimal fractions to similar decimal fractions:

2.1, 73.82, 9.002.

(*b*) Is there more than one set of similar decimal fractions which can be written in 1(*a*)? Why?

2. Change each of the following decimal fractions to thousandths:

4.5, .06, $.85\frac{1}{2}$.

3. Compare the following decimal fractions, writing that of the largest value first, the next to largest, second, on down to the smallest:

.2, .37, .09, .195, .6, .078, .403, .75, .567.

4. Compare the following common fractions by changing them to similar decimal fractions of order three (thousandths). Arrange them in order of decreasing size.

$$\frac{1}{3},\quad \frac{3}{8},\quad \frac{5}{12},\quad \frac{7}{16},\quad \frac{13}{25},\quad \frac{27}{50},\quad \frac{61}{125}.$$

11.7 THE FUNDAMENTAL OPERATIONS AND DECIMAL FRACTIONS—DECIMAL POINT NOTATION

To illustrate addition, consider the example 2.38 + 15.6.

$$\begin{array}{r} 2.38 \\ +15.6 \\ \hline \end{array}$$

Rewrite this sum so that the mixed decimal fractions become similar decimal fractions, with the decimal point of one falling directly under the decimal point of the other. In this form it appears reasonable to add as integers are added. Thus we have

$$\begin{array}{r} 2.38 \\ +15.60 \\ \hline 17.98 \end{array}$$

That this is the proper procedure can be verified easily by changing each decimal fraction to common fraction form.

$$\begin{array}{rl} 2.38 \rightarrow & 2\tfrac{38}{100} \\ 15.60 \rightarrow & 15\tfrac{60}{100} \\ \hline 17.98 \quad & 17\tfrac{98}{100} \rightarrow 17.98. \end{array}$$

Another way of verifying the procedure is by writing each decimal fraction in the exponential forms. Thus

$$\begin{array}{rl} 2.38 = & \phantom{1(10^1) + {}} 2(1) + 3(10^{-1}) + 8(10^{-2}) \\ 15.6 \ = & 1(10^1) + 5(1) + 6(10^{-1}) \\ \hline \end{array}$$

Adding gives $1(10^1) + 7(1) + 9(10^{-1}) + 8(10^{-2})$, or 17.98.

This method again emphasizes the treatment of each of the orders of the numbers as integers. Thus, in

$$\begin{array}{r} 37.87 \\ +14.9 \\ \hline 52.77 \end{array}$$

it can be pointed out that the 7 hundredths is added to the zero (not indicated) hundredths in the second number, making 7 hundredths. Now 8 tenths and 9 tenths are 17 tenths, or 1 unit and 7 tenths. This 7 tenths is written and the 1 unit is carried to the units column, and so on.

It is obvious that the subtraction of decimal fractions may be carried out in the same way. Thus we have

$$\begin{array}{r} 43.760 \\ -8.394 \\ \hline 35.366 \end{array}$$

If the minuend had been 43.76 instead of 43.760, the zero could be annexed or it could be assumed to be there.

Consider now the problem of multiplication, using the example

$$2.37 \times 42.6.$$

Changing to improper common fraction form,

$$2.37 \times 42.6 = \frac{237}{100} \times \frac{426}{10} = \frac{237 \times 426}{1000}.$$

In other words, it again appears that the multiplication may be considered as the multiplication of natural numbers with the proper placing of the decimal point.

$$\begin{array}{r} 2.37 \\ \times\ 42.6 \\ \hline 1422 \\ 474 \\ 948 \\ \hline 100.962 \end{array}$$

The decimal point is placed to produce an answer in the thousandths, since the denominator is 1000 as indicated above.

It should be pointed out that the number of decimal places in the answer is the sum of those in the factors.

Example 1. Multiply $2 \times .03$.

Solution. $2 \times .03 = 2 \times \frac{3}{100} = \frac{2 \times 3}{100} = \frac{6}{100} = .06.$

$$\begin{array}{r} .03 \\ \times 2 \\ \hline .06 \end{array}$$

Two times three hundredths is six hundredths.

Example 2. Multiply $.05 \times 24$.

Solution. $.05 \times 24 = \frac{5}{100} \times 24 = \frac{120}{100} = \frac{12}{10} = 1.2.$

$$\begin{array}{r} 24 \\ \times .05 \\ \hline 1.20 \end{array} \quad \text{or} \quad 1.2$$

A zero at the right end of a decimal fraction may be dropped, changing it to a lower order.

Example 3. Multiply $.3 \times .02$.

Solution. $.3 \times .02 = \frac{3}{10} \times \frac{2}{100} = \frac{6}{1000} = .006.$

$$\begin{array}{r} .02 \\ \times .3 \\ \hline .006 \end{array}$$

Example 4. Multiply 2.63 × 1.07.

Solution. $2\frac{63}{100} \times 1\frac{7}{100} = \frac{263 \times 107}{10000}$,

$$\frac{263 \times 107}{10000} = \frac{28141}{10000} = 2.8141.$$

$$\begin{array}{r} 1.07 \\ \times\ 2.63 \\ \hline 321 \\ 642 \\ 214 \\ \hline 2.8141 \end{array}$$

The problem of changing a common fraction to decimal fraction form was discussed in section 11.1. To illustrate the method used, change $\frac{1}{2}$ to decimal fraction form. Multiply the numerator and denominator by 5 to obtain the equivalent forms

$$\frac{1}{2} = \frac{5}{10} = .5.$$

This problem may be considered as a division problem, written

$$\begin{array}{r} .5 \\ 2\overline{)1.0.} \end{array}$$

The steps used are as follows: 1 divided by 2 is not possible; change 1 to 10 tenths; 10 tenths divided by 2 gives .5. Thus $\frac{1}{2} \times \frac{10}{10} = \frac{5}{10}$.

The following are examples illustrating the division of decimal fractions. Different techniques are shown to emphasize the principles involved.

Example 1. Find the quotient of 24 ÷ .3.

Solution. $24 \div .3 = 24 \div \frac{3}{10} = 24 \times \frac{10}{3} = 80.$

Also

$$\frac{24}{\frac{3}{10}} = \frac{24 \times 10}{\frac{3}{10} \times 10} = \frac{240}{3} = 80.$$

Finally,

$$.3\overline{)24} = 3\overline{)240} = 80.$$

In the last form of the solution the divisor and the dividend have been multiplied by 10.

Example 2. Find the quotient of .60 ÷ 4.

Solution. $\frac{.60}{4} = \frac{1}{4} \times \frac{60}{100} = \frac{15}{100} = .15.$

Also

$$\begin{array}{r} .15 \\ 4\overline{).60} \end{array}$$ (.6 divided by 4 = .1, in the tenths place).

Example 3. Find the quotient of .08 ÷ .2.

Solution. $.08 \div .2 = \frac{\frac{8}{100}}{\frac{2}{10}} = \frac{8}{100} \times \frac{10}{2} = \frac{4}{10} = .4.$

Also

$$\frac{\frac{8}{100} \times 10}{\frac{2}{10} \times 10} = \frac{\frac{8}{10}}{2} = \frac{4}{10} = .4.$$

Finally,

$$.2\overline{)\,.08} = 2\overline{)\,.8} = .4.$$

In the last form the divisor and the dividend have been multiplied by 10. Consider now $20.664 \div 25.2$. Multiplying numerator and denominator by 10 gives $206.64 \div 252$, or $252\overline{)\,206.64}$; 206 is not divisible by 252, but 2066 tenths is. The computation is as follows; the first digit of the quotient is shown in the tenths place:

$$\begin{array}{r|l} & .8\,2 \\ \hline 252 & 206.64 \\ & 201\,6 \\ \hline & 5\,04 \\ & 5\,04 \\ \hline & 0 \end{array}$$

A little consideration on the part of the reader will convince him that if the divisor is changed to a natural number by multiplying by the proper power of ten (and, of course, multiplying the dividend by this same power of ten) then the decimal point in the answer will appear just above the position of the new decimal point in the dividend. Many teachers use what is popularly called the *caret method* of *indicating the multiplication of divisor and dividend by a power of ten.* Thus $25.2\overline{)\,20.664}$ becomes $25.2_{\wedge}\overline{)\,20.6_{\wedge}64}$. Now the decimal point in the answer appears over the caret in the dividend; thus $25.2_{\wedge}\overline{)\,20.6_{\wedge}64}$ with $.82$ written above.

EXERCISE 5

1. Perform the following operations:

(*a*) $23.1 + 6.64 =$ (*b*) $89.63 - 7.361 =$

(*c*) $821.5 \times 92.03 =$ (*d*) $30.34 \div 4.1 =$

(*e*) $.14091 \div 2.31 =$

2. In each of the following division examples state the proper power of ten required to make the divisor a natural number. Enter the carets in the proper place in each example.

(*a*) $2.1\overline{)\,4.32}$ (*b*) $2.34\overline{)\,2.478}$

(*c*) $.62\overline{)\,8.9832}$ (*d*) $.02\overline{)\,7456.1}$

(*e*) $.016\overline{)\,2.1}$

3. In the division example $.16 \div 4 =$, the quotient is .04.

(*a*) Explain in terms of place value why there are zero tenths in the answer.

(*b*) One fourth of sixteen hundredths is how much? What concept of division is used in this approach?

4. In the division problem, $15 \div .5$, what is the quotient? Is this example equivalent to $150 \div 5$? Why?

5. Again, in the problem $15 \div .5$ think of .5 as equivalent to $\frac{1}{2}$. $15 \div \frac{1}{2}$ asks the question, "how many halves are in fifteen units?" Answer this question. What concept of division is used in this case?

6. Work the following examples and justify your answer in at least two ways:

(*a*) $.035 \div 5$ (*b*) $28 \div .04$ (*c*) $.12 \div .04$ (*d*) $.032 \div .4$.

7. Use the concepts of partition or measurement in explaining the following examples:

(*a*) $.2\overline{)8}$ (*b*) $8\overline{).24}$ (*c*) $.03\overline{).24}$ (*d*) $15\overline{).60}$.

8. Work the examples in problem 7 by changing all numbers to decimal fractions with denominators that are tens or powers of ten. For example,

$$\frac{24}{100} \div \frac{3}{100} = ?$$

in part (*c*).

9. Add each group of decimal fractions.

(*a*) 1.23, .056, 5.3; (*b*) 28.07, 16.735, 18.2; (*c*) .803, .9, .008.

10. Perform the indicated operations.

$$\begin{array}{r} 13.75 \\ -6.92 \\ \hline \end{array} \qquad \begin{array}{r} 2.00 \\ -.83 \\ \hline \end{array} \qquad \begin{array}{r} 6.75 \\ -2.097 \\ \hline \end{array} \qquad \begin{array}{r} 11.22 \\ -5.3 \\ \hline \end{array}$$

11. Perform the indicated operations.

$$\begin{array}{r} .23 \\ \times 4 \\ \hline \end{array} \qquad \begin{array}{r} 25 \\ \times .04 \\ \hline \end{array} \qquad \begin{array}{r} 1.6 \\ \times 3.7 \\ \hline \end{array} \qquad \begin{array}{r} .02 \\ \times .004 \\ \hline \end{array}$$

12. Change each entry in problem 11 to decimal-fraction form with denominator ten or a power of ten and work out the answer. For example,

$$\frac{4}{100} \times 25 = \frac{100}{100} = 1.00 = 1.$$

13. Show by addition that $4 \times .23 = .92$ and that $7 \times .13 = .91$.

14. Work out each of the following products:

$$\begin{array}{r} 75 \\ \times .04\frac{1}{2} \\ \hline \end{array} \qquad \begin{array}{r} 128 \\ \times .023 \\ \hline \end{array} \qquad \begin{array}{r} 37.50 \\ \times .15 \\ \hline \end{array} \qquad \begin{array}{r} 26.4 \\ \times .05 \\ \hline \end{array}$$

15. Work out each of the following quotients:

(*a*) $3 \div 20$ (*b*) $8 \div 1.6$ (*c*) $2 \div 25$ (*d*) $7 \div .04$.

16. Check your answers in problem 15 by multiplying the quotient by the divisor to obtain the dividend.

17. Obtain the decimal-point form of the decimal fraction equivalent to each given common fraction. (Perform the divisions.)

(*a*) $\frac{3}{8}$ (*b*) $\frac{1}{16}$ (*c*) $\frac{7}{25}$ (*d*) $\frac{23}{50}$.

18. Check your work in problem 17 by finding suitable multipliers for the numerator and denominator to obtain decimal fractions; thus

$$\frac{1 \times 6\frac{1}{4}}{16 \times 6\frac{1}{4}} = \frac{6\frac{1}{4}}{100} = .0625.$$

19. Explain in terms of place value why

(*a*) $.12\frac{1}{2} = .125$ (*b*) $.06\frac{1}{4} = .0625$ (*c*) $.003\frac{2}{5} = .0034$.

20. Change each fraction to decimal-point form, giving three decimal places in the answers.

(*a*) $\frac{2}{3}$ (*b*) $\frac{2}{7}$ (*c*) $\frac{5}{9}$ (*d*) $\frac{4}{11}$.

11.8 SIGNIFICANT FIGURES—ROUNDING OFF NUMBERS

Often a number is used to express an approximation to an exact number. Thus the usual value of π, the ratio of the circumference of a circle to its diameter, is given as 3.1416. This is not an exact value. In fact, the value of π cannot be expressed exactly in such a way. The value 3.1416 is said to be accurate to five significant figures. The terminal figure may be less than 6 or greater than 6. To be more exact, 3.1416 is an approximate value of π within $\pm.00005$. The length of a line may be 21.23 inches, a measurement accurate to within $\pm.005$. The number 21.23 is then said to be accurate to four significant figures. In Chapter 15 a discussion of approximate numbers, significant digits, and rounding off numbers is given. In the present section we consider rounding off the answers found for repeating decimals. If we stop at a certain step in dividing and the answer is not exact, then we round off the answer by observing whether the remainder is one half a unit or more in the place where we round off. If the remainder is one half or more, we increase the last digit in the answer by one unit; if the remainder is less than half a unit, we leave the last digit in the answer unchanged. (This rule is modified in Chapter 15 in the example in which the remainder following the digit where we round off is exactly one half a unit in the place where the rounding is done.)

Example. Find the value of each fraction in decimal point form, correct to the third decimal place:

$$\frac{2}{3}, \frac{3}{4}, \frac{1}{7}, \frac{5}{6}, \frac{1}{16}, \frac{3}{11}.$$

Solution. Division to four decimal places yields the answers

.6666, .7500, .1428, .8333, .0625, .2718.

These answers are rounded, as follows, to the third decimal place:

.667, .750, .143, .833, .063, .272.

11.9 MORE ABOUT REPEATING DECIMALS

In section 11.4 it was found that, in changing the common fraction $\frac{1}{3}$ to a decimal fraction, .3333 · · · was obtained as one of the possible forms. A little experimentation on the part of the reader will lead him to discover that there are many other forms, such as .33 · · · , .333 · · · . It is easy to change a repeating decimal fraction to the common fraction form. For example, consider .121212 · · · . Instead of a single repeating figure, this number has two figures, 1 and 2, repeating in that order. Let x represent the value of this decimal fraction, then

$$x = .121212\cdots \qquad (1)$$

$$100x = 12.121212\cdots \qquad (2)$$

Subtracting (1) from (2) gives

$$99x = 12 \quad \text{and} \quad x = \frac{12}{99} \quad \text{or} \quad \frac{4}{33},$$

which is the desired result. As a check, we could divide 4 by 33, in which case .121212 · · · would be obtained as the answer.

Example 1. Express 4.657657 · · · as a common fraction.

Solution.

$$\begin{aligned}
4.657657\cdots &= 4 + .657657\cdots \\
1000(.657657\cdots) &= 657.657657\cdots \\
-.657657\cdots &= -.657657\cdots \\
\hline
999(.657657\cdots) &= 657 \\
(.657657\cdots) &= \frac{657}{999} = \frac{9 \times 73}{9 \times 111} = \frac{73}{111}.
\end{aligned}$$

The answer is $4\frac{73}{111}$.

Check.

$$\begin{array}{r}
.657\cdots \\
111\overline{)73.0000} \\
666 \\
\hline
640 \\
555 \\
\hline
850 \\
777 \\
\hline
73
\end{array}$$

Note. It can be proved that a number is rational (see section 10.1 and section 19.9) if and only if its decimal fraction expansion is either a terminating or a repeating decimal. The technique used in the preceding examples to construct rational numbers can be generalized to prove that any repeating decimal will yield a rational number. Conversely, the fact that any natural number yields at most as many remainder classes as the number itself, when it is used as a divisor of another natural number, can be used to prove that the decimal expansion of a rational number will either terminate or repeat. Nonterminating, nonrepeating decimal expansions of real numbers represent irrational numbers.

EXERCISE 6

1. Express the following common fractions as decimal fractions, some of which may be repeating decimal fractions:

(*a*) $\frac{1}{6}$ (*b*) $\frac{3}{13}$

(*c*) $\frac{3}{8}$ (*d*) $\frac{1}{15}$

(*e*) $\frac{3}{14}$ (*f*) $\frac{9}{16}$

(*g*) $\frac{4}{5}$ (*h*) $\frac{2}{25}$

(*i*) $\frac{7}{8}$ (*j*) $\frac{5}{41}$

2. Express the following repeating decimals as common fractions:

(*a*) .33 · · · (*b*) .212121 · · · (*c*) .621621 · · ·

(*d*) 2.666 · · · (*e*) .444 · · · (*f*) .32525 · · ·

3. By intuition alone, what sort of number should the denominator of a fraction be in order that its value may be expressed as a nonrepeating decimal fraction? Does your guess include such denominators as 4, 16, 25, 125, 32?

4. Find the decimal fractions equivalent to $\frac{1}{4}$, $\frac{1}{16}$, $\frac{1}{25}$, $\frac{1}{125}$, and $\frac{1}{32}$.

11.10 SCIENTIFIC NOTATION FOR NUMBERS

In order to express very large and very small numbers in a compact manner, people who work in physical science make consistent use of a special form for writing numbers. This form is called the *scientific notation* for numbers or the *exponent notation* for numbers; it is also called the *standard form* for writing numbers. The scientific notation involves two factors: (1) a mixed decimal fraction whose value lies between one and ten and (2) a power of ten which indicates the place value of the first digit in the mixed decimal fraction.

We have used powers of ten in writing place-value numerals in base ten, both for natural numbers and for proper decimal fractions. Thus the numeral 234 in base ten means $2(100) + 3(10) + 4(1)$. Here 100 is equivalent to 10^2, 10 is the same as 10^1, and 1 may be considered as 10^0. Similarly .1 or 1/10 may be taken as 10^{-1}, .01 or 1/100 may be taken as 10^{-2}, and so on. The following table is convenient in summarizing this notation:

$10{,}000 = 10^4$	$.1 = 10^{-1}$
$1{,}000 = 10^3$	$.01 = 10^{-2}$
$100 = 10^2$	$.001 = 10^{-3}$
$10 = 10^1$	$.0001 = 10^{-4}$
$1 = 10^0$	$.00001 = 10^{-5}$

Any number may now be thought of in terms of the place value of its first significant digit (its leftmost nonzero digit). The natural number 3462 may be read as three thousand and a fraction of one thousand, in fact it is $3 + \frac{462}{1000}$, or 3.462, thousands. Similarly, 567 is the same as 5 hundreds and $\frac{67}{100}$ of one hundred. In the decimal fraction .0354 there are 3 hundredths and $\frac{54}{100}$ of a hundredth. By using powers of ten to indicate the place value of the leading digit in these numbers, we obtain the following representations for the numbers:

$$3462 = 3.462 \times 10^3, \quad 567 = 5.67 \times 10^2, \quad .0354 = 3.54 \times 10^{-2}.$$

Example 1. Write each of the numbers 23.65 and .00748 in scientific notation.

Solution. 23.65 has a first digit, 2, in the tens place; hence

$$23.65 = 2.365 \times 10.$$

In this case 10^1 is the required power of ten, but a "1" exponent usually is not written. The answer is written in the form 2.365×10.

.00748 has a first nonzero digit, 7, in the thousandths place; thus

$$.00748 = 7.48 \times 10^{-3}.$$

In this case 10^{-3} is the required power of ten and 7.48×10^{-3} is the required scientific notation.

Example 2. Write the numbers 83,500,000,000 and .00000000000343 in scientific notation.

Solution. 83,500,000,000 begins with 8 in the ten billions place; since this place value is expressed as 10^{10}, the number is written 8.35×10^{10}, which is the required form for the answer. Similarly, .00000000000343 has a first nonzero digit of 3, which occurs in the place whose value is 10^{-12}. The answer is written 3.43×10^{-12}. In these cases and in others it is the leftmost nonzero digit in the group of significant digits that determines the place value for scientific notation.

The opposite process, that of writing a number that is given in scientific notation, in ordinary form simply calls for making proper use of the indicated power of ten.

Example 3. Express each number in ordinary notation:

$$5.28 \times 10^3 \quad \text{and} \quad 7.25 \times 10^{-6}.$$

Solution. $5.28 \times 10^3 = 5.28 \times 1000 = 5280.$

$$7.25 \times 10^{-6} = 7.25 \times \frac{1}{10^6} = \frac{7.25}{1,000,000} = .00000725.$$

Note that in this second case 10^{-6} represents one part in one million; hence the place value for the 7 is millionths.

A bit of reflection and observation will help the student to see that an indicated power of ten moves the decimal point as many places to the right as shown by the exponent, if it is positive, and as many places to the left as shown by the exponent, if it is negative. Again we have $2.3 \times 10^4 = 23,000$, with the decimal point moved four places to the right, and, in like manner, $5.9 \times 10^{-4} = .00059$, with the decimal point moved four places to the left. These exchanges are easily seen to be reversible.

EXERCISE 7

1. Write each of the following numbers in scientific notation:

(*a*) 186,000, (*b*) .000001, (*c*) 32,000,000,000,000, (*d*) .09033.

2. Write each of the following numbers in scientific notation:

(*a*) 93,000,000, (*b*) .00000000803, (*c*) 1,600,000,000, (*d*) .00345.

3. Express each of the following numbers in ordinary notation:

(*a*) 6.06×10^{23}, (*b*) 1×10^{-8}, (*c*) 6.24×10^{12}, (*d*) 1.6×10^{-24}.

4. Express each of the following numbers in ordinary notation:

(*a*) 2×10^{-13}, (*b*) 10^8, (*c*) 7.6×10^{-6}, (*d*) 18.3×10^{-1}.

5. Multiply the following, using the laws of exponents discussed in Chapter 2:

(*a*) $10^5 \times 10^7$, (*b*) $10^8 \times 10^{-3}$, (*c*) $10^{-4} \times 10^{-5}$, (*d*) $10^7 \times 10^{-12}$.

6. Multiply the following and express the answer in ordinary form:

(*a*) $2 \times 10^5 \times 3 \times 10^3$, (*b*) $4 \times 10^{-7} \times 5 \times 10^9$, (*c*) $3 \times 10^{12} \times 2 \times 10^{-8}$.

7. The number of atoms in a gram atom of matter is about 6.025×10^{23}. Write this number in ordinary notation.

8. The radius of an electron is about 2×10^{-13} centimeters. Write this number in ordinary notation.

9. The radius of the hydrogen atom is about 10^{-8} centimeters. How many of these atoms would there be if they were placed side by side along a line 1 centimeter long? Write your answer in two ways.

10. The distance that light travels in one year is given approximately by the product $3.6 \times 10^2 \times 24 \times 3.6 \times 10^3 \times 1.9 \times 10^5$, in miles. Show that this is about 6 trillion miles and write your answer in two ways.

REFERENCES

Banks, J. H., *Learning and Teaching Arithmetic*, pp. 317–336.
Brueckner, L. J., and F. E. Grossnickle, *Making Arithmetic Meaningful*, pp. 398–420.
Hooper, A., *An Arithmetic Refresher*, pp. 65–81.
Larsen, H. D., *Arithmetic for Colleges*, pp. 143–166.
Marks J. L., C. R. Purdy, and L. B. Kinney, *Teaching Arithmetic for Understanding*, pp. 227–250.
McSwain and Cooke, *Understanding and Teaching Arithmetic in the Elementary School*, pp. 180–213.
Morton, R. L., *Teaching Arithmetic in the Elementary School*, Vol. 2, pp. 317–365.
Spitzer, H. F., *The Teaching of Arithmetic*, pp. 289–298.
Taylor, E. H., and C. N. Mills, *Arithmetic for Teacher-Training Classes*, fourth edition, pp. 185–208.
Wheat, H. G., *How to Teach Arithmetic*, pp. 227–235, 252–259.

12

Per Cent and Percentage

12.1 INTRODUCTION

In Chapter 10 it was seen that the extension of the number system from the natural numbers to fractions caused a considerable amount of difficulty in the fundamental operations of addition, subtraction, multiplication, and division. This was particularly true if the common fraction notation was used. The introduction of the decimal fraction and the decimal-point notation simplified the operations, since, with the exception of manipulation of the decimal point, decimal fractions could be treated as natural numbers. Another method of representing a fraction is considered in this chapter. This method is one in which the denominators of all fractions are restricted to the natural number 100.

12.2 PER CENTS

The term "per cent," represented by the symbol %, literally means *per hundred*. Thus 6%, read "six per cent," means six parts in a hundred parts, and it may be written $\frac{6}{100}$ or .06. In fact, a per cent is simply another way of representing a decimal fraction whose denominator is always 100 and whose numerator is the numeral preceding the words "per cent" or the symbol %.

In order to change any fraction to a per cent, it is necessary only to change the fraction to a decimal fraction with 100 as a denominator. Thus, $\frac{1}{2} = \frac{50}{100}$, or 50 per cent. Likewise, $2\frac{1}{5} = \frac{220}{100}$*, or 220 per cent. If the given fraction is already in decimal-point form, it is necessary only to

* It should be noted in this example that 220 parts are compared with 100 parts, which is equivalent to two complete wholes and twenty parts out of one hundred.

write the number of hundredths, followed by a per cent symbol. Thus

$$.035 = \frac{3.5}{100} = 3.5\%.$$

In changing per cents to decimals or common fractions, the quantities should be considered first as parts in one hundred and then changed to fractions of the required form. Thus

$$3\tfrac{1}{4}\% = \frac{3\frac{1}{4}}{100} = .03\tfrac{1}{4} \quad \text{or} \quad .0325$$

$$15\% = \frac{15}{100} = \frac{3}{20}.$$

Example 1. Explain what 10 per cent means and write it as a fraction in decimal point form, as well as a common fraction in lowest terms.

Solution. The expression 10 per cent means "ten parts in one hundred parts"; thus $10\% = \frac{10}{100}$. In decimal-point form this would be written .10, which is equivalent to .1. The common fraction form of $\frac{10}{100}$ is equivalent to $\frac{1}{10}$, in simplest form.

Example 2. Change 2.4 per cent and 130 per cent to decimal fractions or mixed decimal fractions.

Solution. $2.4\% = \dfrac{2.4}{100} = .024$

$$130\% = \frac{130}{100} = 1.30, \text{ or } 1.3.$$

Example 3. Change the common fractions $\frac{2}{5}$ and $\frac{1}{8}$ to per cents.

Solution. $\dfrac{2}{5} = \dfrac{2 \times 20}{5 \times 20} = \dfrac{40}{100} = 40\%$

$$\frac{1}{8} = \frac{1 \times 12\frac{1}{2}}{8 \times 12\frac{1}{2}} = \frac{12\frac{1}{2}}{100} = 12\tfrac{1}{2}\%.$$

Example 4. Change the quantities .0035 and 1.38 to equivalent per cents.

Solution. $.0035 = \dfrac{.35}{100} = .35\%$

$$1.38 = 1\tfrac{38}{100} = \frac{138}{100} = 138\%.$$

Note that in order to obtain the required denominator of 100 it is necessary to multiply the numerator and the denominator of the given expression by 100, where the original denominator is understood to be 1. Thus

$$\frac{.0035}{1} = \frac{.0035 \times 100}{1 \times 100} = \frac{.35}{100} = .35\%.$$

Example 5. Change 18 per cent and $2\frac{1}{3}$ per cent to common fractions in simplest form.

Solution. $18\% = \dfrac{18}{100} = \dfrac{9}{50}$ $\qquad$ $2\tfrac{1}{3}\% = \dfrac{2\frac{1}{3}}{100} = \dfrac{7}{3} \times \dfrac{1}{100} = \dfrac{7}{300}.$

EXERCISE 1

1. Change the following per cents to decimal fractions:

(*a*) 20% (*b*) 32% (*c*) 2% (*d*) $4\frac{1}{2}$% (*e*) $87\frac{1}{2}$%
(*f*) 40% (*g*) $1\frac{1}{2}$% (*h*) 130% (*i*) 205% (*j*) $16\frac{2}{3}$%

2. Change the following per cents to common fractions:

(*a*) 25% (*b*) 30% (*c*) 75% (*d*) $83\frac{1}{3}$% (*e*) 150%
(*f*) $16\frac{2}{3}$% (*g*) $12\frac{1}{2}$% (*h*) $\frac{3}{4}$% (*i*) 175% (*j*) $\frac{2}{3}$%

3. Change the following decimal fractions to per cents:

(*a*) .3 (*b*) 1.12 (*c*) .234 (*d*) $.08\frac{1}{3}$ (*e*) .011
(*f*) $.04\frac{1}{2}$ (*g*) 1.25 (*h*) $.87\frac{1}{2}$ (*i*) .055 (*j*) .0045

4. Change the following fractions to per cents:

(*a*) $\frac{1}{5}$ (*b*) $\frac{3}{4}$ (*c*) $\frac{3}{8}$ (*d*) $\frac{1}{3}$ (*e*) $\frac{3}{200}$

(*f*) $\frac{5}{6}$ (*g*) $1\frac{1}{2}$ (*h*) $\frac{1}{50}$ (*i*) $\frac{4}{25}$ (*j*) $3\frac{1}{3}$

5. Give at least five ways that per cents are used in everyday life.

6. Cut out samples from newspaper advertisements and articles showing uses of per cents.

12.3 THE FUNDAMENTAL USES OF PER CENT

Per cent problems are usually classified as follows:

TYPE 1

Given a whole (called the *base*), to find a specified part of this whole. The specified part of this whole is called the *percentage*. Thus, to find 6 per cent of 200, multiply 200 by $\frac{6}{100}$ (or .06) to obtain 12, the percentage.

TYPE 2

Given the base (whole) and the percentage (part of the whole), to find the per cent. Another way of stating this is to ask what per cent one number is of another. Thus, to find what part 60 is of 240, we are concerned with the ratio $\frac{60}{240}$, or $\frac{1}{4}$, which is 25 per cent.

TYPE 3

Given the percentage (part of the whole) and the per cent, to find the base (whole). Perhaps this is the most difficult of the three types. A method called *unit analysis* is used to work such problems. Consider the problem of finding a number if 15 per cent of the number is 45.

If 15 per cent of the number is 45, then by dividing both numbers by 15,

1 per cent of the number is 3. Hence 100 per cent of the number (the whole) is 300.

Many teachers prefer to set up formulas for each of these types. Thus, if

b = base

p = percentage

r = per cent (expressed as a decimal or common fraction),

then

$$p = br \qquad \text{(Type 1)}$$

$$r = \frac{p}{b} \qquad \text{(Type 2)}$$

$$b = \frac{p}{r} \qquad \text{(Type 3)}$$

Later, when the student has learned some of the operations of algebra, it will become evident that the one formula, $p = br$, is sufficient. The following illustrative examples show the use of these formulas:

Example 1. Find 5 per cent of 284. (This is a Type 1 per cent problem.)

Solution. The part of the whole, or the percentage, is given by $p = br$.

$$p = 284 \times .05 = 14.20.$$

Example 2. What part of 24 is 16? (This is a Type 2 per cent problem.)

Solution. The per cent rate is given by $r = p/b$.

$$r = \frac{16}{24} = \frac{2}{3} = .66\tfrac{2}{3}, \quad \text{which is } 66\tfrac{2}{3}\%.$$

Example 3. Three per cent of a given number is 7.77. Find the number. (This is a Type 3 per cent problem.)

Solution. The whole, called the base, is given by $b = p/r$.

$$b = \frac{7.77}{.03} = 259.$$

Example 4. The dimensions of a rectangle are 24.00 by 12.00 centimeters. If each side is increased by 6 per cent, find the lengths of the new sides. By what per cent is the area of the new rectangle increased over the old rectangle?

Solution. To find 6 per cent of 24.00, use the Type 1 formula. Thus $p = 24.00 \times .06 = 1.44$. Hence the side is increased to $24.00 + 1.44 = 25.44$ centimeters. Likewise, the other side is increased to $12.00 + 12.00 \times .06 = 12.72$ centimeters. The area of the new rectangle is $25.44 \times 12.72 = 323.5968$ square centimeters. This answer should be rounded to four digits, 323.6 square centimeters. The area of the old rectangle is $24.00 \times 12.00 = 288.0$ square centimeters. The increase in area is $323.6 - 288.0 = 35.6$ square centimeters. Using the Type 2 formula, $r = \frac{35.6}{288} = .124$, or the new area is 12.4 per cent larger than the old area.

EXERCISE 2

1. Find the following:

(*a*) 7% of 135 (*b*) 15% of 237 (*c*) $\frac{1}{2}$% of 44
(*d*) 130% of 12 (*e*) 1.2% of 66 (*f*) $12\frac{1}{2}$% of 88.

2. What per cent of the first number is the second?

(*a*) 14, 7 (what per cent of 14 is 7?) (*b*) 32, 28
(*c*) 100, 150 (*d*) 3 feet, 8 inches (*e*) $55, 95 cents.

3. Find the number if

(*a*) 6% of the number is 30, (*b*) 15% of the number is 20,
(*c*) 120% of the number is 80, (*d*) $33\frac{1}{3}$% of the number is 60,
(*e*) $\frac{1}{4}$% of the number is 12, (*f*) 300% of the number is 15.

4. One way of finding $33\frac{1}{3}$ per cent of 489 is to multiply 489 by $.33\frac{1}{3}$. Do you know an easier way? *Hint.* $.33\frac{1}{3} = \frac{1}{3}$.

5. Find 25 per cent of 288 by a method similar to the one you developed in problem 4.

6. What are the common fractional equivalents of $12\frac{1}{2}$, $16\frac{2}{3}$, $37\frac{1}{2}$, 50, $66\frac{2}{3}$ per cent?

7. A sample of sugar beets tests $16\frac{2}{3}$ per cent sugar. How many pounds of these beets are needed to make 50 pounds of sugar? Use the unit analysis method.

8. Use the formula given for Type 3 per cent to work problem 7.

9. Many states have sales taxes on goods purchased in retail stores. If a state has a 4 per cent sales tax, what total amount must be paid for a radio costing $98.50?

10. A salt lake tests 3.5 per cent salt. How much of this water must be evaporated to make 50 pounds of salt? Give answer to the nearest pound.

11. A man sold two houses for $18,000 each. On one house he lost 15 per cent and on the other he gained 15 per cent. Did he gain or lose on the combined transaction and how much?

12. What would be the equivalent of "per cent" in a base twelve system?

12.4 PER CENT INCREASE AND PER CENT DECREASE

Closely related to the basic types of per cent problems are those in which a quantity is increased or decreased by a per cent of itself. In these instances *the per cent change is always related to the first given quantity as the base.* These problems should be read carefully; diagrams are always helpful in discussing them.

Example 1. The price of a loaf of bread was increased from 31 to 33 cents. What per cent increase was there in the price of the bread?

Solution. An increase of 2 cents, is to be compared with an original amount of 31 cents. The per cent increase in the price is

$$\frac{2}{31} = .0645^{+} = 6.45\% \text{ or about } 6\tfrac{1}{2}\%.$$

Fig. 1

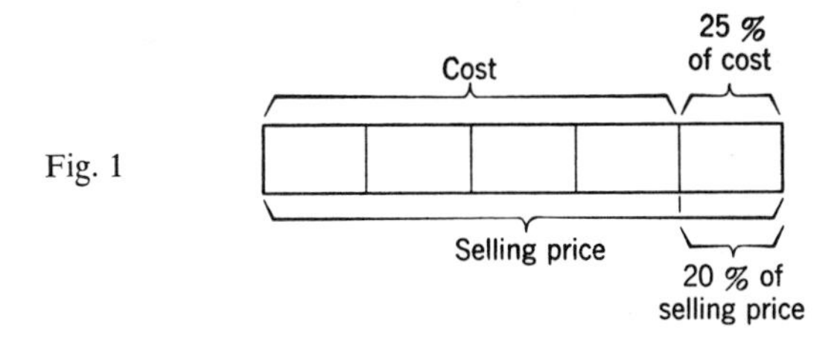

Example 2. The rent asked for a certain apartment this year is \$88, which is 10 per cent more than asked last year. What amount of rent was asked last year?

Solution. Last year's rent plus 10 per cent of last year's rent is \$88; hence

$$100\% \text{ of last year's rent } + 10\% \text{ of last year's rent} = \$88$$

$$110\% \text{ of last year's rent} = \$88$$

$$\frac{1}{11} \times 110\% = 10\%; \quad \frac{1}{11} \times 88 = 8$$

$$10\% \text{ of last year's rent} = \$8$$

Subtracting,

$$100\% \text{ of last year's rent} = \$80$$

Check. $\$80 + 10\% \text{ of } \$80 = \$80 + \$8 = \$88.$

Example 3. A man's salary of \$500 per month was decreased 15 per cent. By what per cent should his new salary be increased to restore his old salary?

Solution. The decrease in salary is 15 per cent of \$500, which is \$75. The new salary is \$500 − \$75, or \$425. The required increase in salary is \$75 and the per cent increase is $\frac{75}{425}$, which is $.176^{+}$, or about 17.6 per cent.

Example 4. An article costing \$100 is marked up (increased) 25 per cent of cost to determine the selling price (Fig. 1). What per cent of the selling price is this mark up?

Solution. The selling price is \$100 + \$25, or \$125. The mark up compared with selling price is

$$\frac{25}{125} = \frac{1}{5} = \frac{20}{100} = 20\%.$$

If the selling price is $\frac{5}{4}$ of cost, then cost is $\frac{4}{5}$ of the selling price.

EXERCISE 3

1. Find the per cent increase or decrease in each case.
   (*a*) \$300 increased to \$325, (*b*) 29 cents decreased to 24 cents, (*c*) 130 pounds increased to 150 pounds, (*d*) \$5000 decreased to \$4300.
2. Find the per cent increase or decrease in each case.
   (*a*) 19 cents increased to 23 cents, (*b*) 55 cents decreased to 39 cents, (*c*) \$2100 increased to \$2300, (*d*) \$8500 decreased to \$8000.
3. Find the new amount in each case.
   (*a*) \$125 increased by 12%, (*b*) \$95 decreased by 15%, (*c*) 28 cents decreased by 30%, (*d*) 39 cents increased by 40%.

4. Find the new amount in each case.
(*a*) 55 cents decreased by 20%, (*b*) 45 cents increased by 12%,
(*c*) $2000 increased by 15%, (*d*) $150 decreased by 7%.

5. Mr. May's salary is 10 per cent more than Mr. Ben's salary. If Mr. May's salary is $550, what is Mr. Ben's salary?

6. If, in problem 5, Mr. Ben's salary is $400, what is Mr. May's salary?

7. Mr. Gray paid $78.40 per month for rent this year. If he paid 12 per cent more than he did last year, what was his rent last year?

8. A man receives a salary that is 10 per cent more than he received last year. By what per cent should his present salary be decreased to make it equal to last year's salary?

9. What number increased by 20 per cent of itself is equal to 180?

10. What number decreased by 15 per cent of itself is equal to 102?

11. What number is 15 per cent more than 80?

12. What number is 15 per cent less than 80?

13. An article selling for $100 is discounted 20 per cent to obtain a sale price, and then the sale price is discounted 15 per cent. What single discount per cent on the selling price would be equivalent to these two successive discounts?

14. An asking price of $15,000 on a house is increased by 10 per cent, and then after a time the new price is reduced 10 per cent. What is the final asking price?

15. A family budgets and spends $80.00 per month for household necessities (exclusive of food). If this expenditure includes a 4 per cent state sales tax, what is the amount of tax paid per year?

16. If a stock quoted at $67\frac{3}{4}$ changes to a new quotation of $68\frac{1}{4}$, what is the per cent increase?

12.5 PER CENT EQUIVALENTS OF COMMON FRACTIONS

In our work with fractions the equivalents of several lists of common fractions in terms of parts in one hundred were studied. These are called aliquot parts of one hundred and can be readily transcribed as per cents:

$$\frac{1}{8} = \frac{12\frac{1}{2}}{100} = 12\tfrac{1}{2}\%, \qquad \frac{5}{8} = \frac{62\frac{1}{2}}{100} = 62\tfrac{1}{2}\%,$$

$$\frac{2}{8} = \frac{25}{100} = 25\%, \qquad \frac{6}{8} = \frac{75}{100} = 75\%,$$

$$\frac{3}{8} = \frac{37\frac{1}{2}}{100} = 37\tfrac{1}{2}\%, \qquad \frac{7}{8} = \frac{87\frac{1}{2}}{100} = 87\tfrac{1}{2}\%,$$

$$\frac{4}{8} = \frac{50}{100} = 50\%, \qquad \frac{8}{8} = \frac{100}{100} = 100\%.$$

In a similar manner we can obtain the per cent equivalents of sets of common fractions, such as thirds, sevenths, fourths, fifths, sixths, and so on. The student should become familiar with these equivalents and make use of them as occasion demands. In obtaining equivalents in per cent form, the decimal divisions should be carried to the hundredths place and the remainder should be written as a common fraction. Thirds and sevenths would be expressed as follows:

$$\frac{1}{3} = 33\tfrac{1}{3}\%, \qquad \frac{3}{7} = 42\tfrac{6}{7}\%,$$

$$\frac{2}{3} = 66\tfrac{2}{3}\%, \qquad \frac{4}{7} = 57\tfrac{1}{7}\%,$$

$$\frac{3}{3} = 100\%, \qquad \frac{5}{7} = 71\tfrac{3}{7}\%,$$

$$\frac{1}{7} = 14\tfrac{2}{7}\%, \qquad \frac{6}{7} = 85\tfrac{5}{7}\%,$$

$$\frac{2}{7} = 28\tfrac{4}{7}\%, \qquad \frac{7}{7} = 100\%.$$

EXERCISE 4

1. Write the per cent equivalents for fourths ($\frac{1}{4}$, $\frac{2}{4}$, $\frac{3}{4}$, $\frac{4}{4}$) and sixths.

2. Write the per cent equivalents for fifths and ninths.

3. Write the per cent equivalents for twelfths and fifteenths.

4. Write the per cent equivalents for elevenths and sixteenths.

5. What are the common fraction equivalents of the following per cents?
(*a*) $37\frac{1}{2}\%$ (*b*) $83\frac{1}{3}\%$ (*c*) $8\frac{1}{3}\%$ (*d*) $6\frac{1}{4}\%$.

6. What are the common fraction equivalents of the following per cents?
(*a*) $28\frac{4}{7}\%$ (*b*) $11\frac{1}{9}\%$ (*c*) $16\frac{2}{3}\%$ (*d*) $56\frac{1}{4}\%$.

12.6 LARGE AND SMALL PER CENTS

One hundred per cent of any quantity is all of the quantity, or 1.00 times the quantity, and 1 per cent of any quantity is $\frac{1}{100}$, or .01 times the quantity. In practice, a great many per cents will fall between these two limits, but there are occasions when larger per cents involving more than one of the quantity and smaller per cents involving less than $\frac{1}{100}$ of the quantity will be used. Care must be exercised in using and interpreting these large and small per cents.

Example 1. Express $2\frac{1}{2}$ times a quantity, Q, as a per cent of the quantity.
Solution. $2\frac{1}{2} \times Q = 2\frac{1}{2} \times 100\%$ of $Q = 250\%$ of Q.

Example 2. During a period of five years the value of a stock increased from $35 to $120. What per cent of increase was this?

Solution. The increase in value was $120 − $35, or $85. The per cent of increase was

$$\frac{85}{35} = 2.42\tfrac{6}{7} = 242\tfrac{6}{7}\%, \quad \text{or nearly } 243\%.$$

Example 3. Certain impurities in distilled water are listed as 2 parts in 1000, 3 parts in 2000, and 5 parts in 10,000, respectively. What are these ratios as per cents?

Solution.
$$\frac{2}{1000} = \frac{.2}{100} = .2\%$$
$$\frac{3}{2000} = \frac{3}{20} \times \frac{1}{100} = \frac{3}{20} \times 1\% = .15 \times 1\% = .15\%$$
$$\frac{5}{10000} = \frac{5}{100} \times \frac{1}{100} = \frac{1}{20} \times 1\% = .05 \times 1\% = .05\%.$$

Example 4. What are the equivalent common fractions for $\frac{1}{4}$, $\frac{1}{2}$, and $\frac{2}{3}$ per cent. Express each by a decimal fraction.

Solution.
$$\tfrac{1}{4}\% = \frac{1}{4} \times \frac{1}{100} = \frac{1}{400},$$
$$\tfrac{1}{2}\% = \frac{1}{2} \times \frac{1}{100} = \frac{1}{200},$$
$$\tfrac{2}{3}\% = \frac{2}{3} \times \frac{1}{100} = \frac{2}{300}.$$

As decimal fractions, these are equivalent to

$$\frac{1}{4} \times .01, \text{ or } .0025; \quad \frac{1}{2} \times .01, \text{ or } .005; \text{ and } \frac{2}{3} \times .01, \text{ or } .0066\tfrac{2}{3}.$$

EXERCISE 5

1. Express the following ratios as per cents:
(*a*) $3\frac{1}{4}:1$ (*b*) 7:2 (*c*) 8:1 (*d*) $1\frac{1}{2}:1$
(*e*) 2:3 (*f*) 5:8 (*g*) 8:5 (*h*) $1:1\frac{1}{2}$
(*i*) 2:300 (*j*) 2:500 (*k*) 3:800 (*l*) 1:1000.

2. Write the following per cents as decimal fractions or mixed decimals:
(*a*) 380% (*b*) 175% (*c*) 2000% (*d*) 88%
(*e*) $\frac{1}{2}$% (*f*) $6\frac{1}{2}$% (*g*) .35% (*h*) .04%.

3. Write the answers to problem 2 as common fractions or mixed numbers.

4. Find the per cent increase or decrease of each quantity:
(*a*) 285 changed to 280, (*b*) 1.76 changed to 1.88,
(*c*) 200.2 changed to 200.1, (*d*) 3.75 changed to 8.75.

12.7 ESTIMATING AND COMPARING PER CENTS

Before returning to some exercises in identifying the three types of per cent problems, we shall consider per cents as fractions having a common denominator. Per cents are similar fractions with a common denominator of 100. For this reason they can be compared directly. Suppose, for example, that in the analysis of expenditures from gross income of a business for one year it is found that 12 per cent of income is spent for plant maintenance, whereas for a second year 15 per cent of income is spent for this same maintenance. These figures show immediately that more of the gross income is going toward maintenance for the second year. In many businesses per cent analyses of expenditures and operations are made annually. Comparisons of these analyses for successive years yield a trend analysis showing readily the items of expense or operation that have varied considerably from year to year. The trend analysis reveals items that should be checked further.

Per cents are fractions or ratios, and they should be looked upon and used as such. A per cent nearly equal to 50 per cent should be considered about equal to one half; a per cent close to 25 per cent is about equal to one fourth, and so on. The student should attempt to gain some facility in dealing with per cents in this way. Note the following exercises.

EXERCISE 6

In the following examples try to choose the correct answer by estimating its size, then check:

1. 23% of 380 is (*a*) 144, (*b*) 87.4, (*c*) 38.4, (*d*) 784.

2. $\frac{1}{2}$% of 75 is (*a*) $3\frac{3}{4}$, (*b*) $37\frac{1}{2}$, (*c*) $\frac{3}{8}$, (*d*) 150.

3. $\frac{15}{38}$ is (*a*) 395%, (*b*) $253\frac{1}{3}$%, (*c*) 3.9%, (*d*) $39\frac{1}{2}$%.

4. $\frac{8}{2000}$ is (*a*) .4%, (*b*) 4%, (*c*) 40%, (*d*) 250%.

5. 12 is 15% of (*a*) 30, (*b*) 80, (*c*) 1.8, (*d*) 300.

6. 300 is 6% of (*a*) 5000, (*b*) 500, (*c*) 1800, (*d*) 18.

7. 5 is 200% of (*a*) 10, (*b*) $2\frac{1}{2}$, (*c*) 25, (*d*) 2.

8. $\frac{1}{2}$ is 10% of (*a*) 20, (*b*) 10, (*c*) 5, (*d*) 100.

9. 150% of 38 is (*a*) 570, (*b*) $253\frac{1}{3}$, (*c*) 5.7, (*d*) 57.

10. $\frac{85}{300}$ is (*a*) 283%, (*b*) 28.3%, (*c*) $2\frac{5}{6}$%, (*d*) 38%.

12.8 DIFFICULTIES WITH PER CENT PROBLEMS

A student usually has some difficulty at first in deciding which type of per cent problem is involved in a given problem. A careful reading of the problem will help him to determine which of the three elements of a per cent problem are given and which is the required element to find. Comparison with worked-out illustrative problems should be an added aid in problem solving. The following problems are given to help the student overcome such difficulties.

EXERCISE 7

Determine the type of per cent problem involved in each of the following problems. Complete the solutions.

1. In a given town of population 6250, 60 per cent of the people own cars. How many people in this town own cars?

2. At a clearance sale a certain make of radio sold at 80 per cent of its marked price. What was the original marked price if the radio sold for $56?

3. A certain grade of milk tested $3\frac{3}{4}$ per cent butterfat. How many pounds of butterfat are contained in a ton of this milk?

4. How much milk, testing 3 per cent butterfat, is needed to make 60 pounds of butter?

5. In order to make a certain grade of concrete, one part cement, three parts sand, and five parts gravel are used. Find the per cent of each of these dry components in the mixture.

6. At a certain time during the season a baseball player had made 23 hits for 84 times at bat. Compute his batting per cent to the nearest one tenth of a per cent. How is a batting ratio usually expressed in the sport section of a newspaper and what is it called?

7. The workers in a certain factory were earning $2.10 per hour. A strike settlement granted a 15-cent per hour increase in wages. What per cent increase was this?

8. A secretary's salary was decreased by 15 per cent. By what per cent must her new salary be increased in order to restore the old?

9. What number decreased by 20 per cent of itself is 20?

10. A one-inch cube is made by using fine wire for its edges. Heated uniformly, each edge increases to 1.003 inches. By what per cent do the edges increase? By what per cent does the area of the faces of the cube increase? By what per cent does the volume of the cube increase?

11. If 5 per cent of the eggs placed in an incubator will not hatch, how many eggs (nearest whole number) should be placed in an incubator to obtain 1500 live chicks?

12. The price of a car was increased by 12 per cent to a new price of $1560. What was the old price?

13. If $1500 earns interest at $4\frac{1}{2}$ per cent per year, how much is the interest for one fourth of a year?

14. If a man's salary was decreased 20 per cent to an amount of $6800, what was his original salary?

15. If 8 per cent of a crop of walnuts will be bad, how many pounds of good walnuts will there be in 250 pounds of this crop?

16. What per cent of error is there in a measurement of $16\frac{1}{2}$ feet if the error is $\frac{1}{4}$ foot?

REFERENCES

Hooper, A., *An Arithmetic Refresher*, pp. 97–105.

Larsen, H. D., *Arithmetic for Colleges*, pp. 167–173.

Layton, W. I., *College Arithmetic*, pp. 97–110.

Marks, J. L., C. R. Purdy, and L. B. Kinney, *Teaching Arithmetic for Understanding*, pp. 251–272.

McSwain and Cooke, *Understanding and Teaching Arithmetic in the Elementary School*, pp. 214–219.

Morton, R. L., *Teaching Arithmetic in the Elementary School*, Vol. 2, pp. 366–393.

Price and Knowler, *Basic Skills*, pp. 158–170.

Taylor, E. H., and C. N. Mills, *Arithmetic for Teacher-Training Classes*, fourth edition, pp. 249–267.

13

Further Applications of Per Cent

13.1 TRADE DISCOUNT

Retail and other stores sometimes offer a reduction in the price of the goods they have for sale. This reduction is known as a *trade discount* or *discount* and is often advertised as a certain per cent of the original or listed price of the article involved. The per cent indicated is called the *discount per cent*, which, when expressed in hundredths, is called the *discount rate*. In common practice, the term discount may be used to mean the actual reduction in price, the discount per cent, or the discount rate. Teachers should be careful to distinguish between these terms when they are introduced in an arithmetic class for the first time.

Example 1. A store offers a 20 per cent discount on a television set, which is listed at \$162.50. What is the discount and what is the new selling price of the television set?

Solution. Discount per cent = 20%.
Discount rate = .20.
Discount: .20 × \$162.50 = \$32.50.
New selling price: \$162.50 − \$32.50 = \$130.00.

An alternate method of finding the selling price is by multiplying \$162.50 by (1 − .20), which is .80 × \$162.50 = \$130.00. This method is desirable if only the new selling price is needed.

Occasionally more than one discount is allowed on an article, in which case each discount is deducted in succession.

Example 2. A lumber company offers builders a discount of 15 per cent on all the lumber they purchase. A further discount of 2 per cent is offered for cash payments with the purchase. What does a builder pay for an order of lumber amounting to \$858.20 if he pays cash?

Solution. Builders' discount: $.15 \times \$858.20 = \$128.73$.
Discount amount of bill: $\$858.20 - \$128.73 = \$729.47$.
Cash discount: $.02 \times \$729.47 = \$14.59$.
Cash payment: $\$729.47 - \$14.59 = \$714.88$.

An alternate solution is as follows:

Discounted amount of bill due to builders' discount: $(1 - .15)\ \$858.20 = .85(\$858.20)$.

Cash payment will then be $(1 - .02)(.85)(\$858.20) = .98 \times .85 \times \$858.20 = \$714.88$.

Note. Both orders of deducting the two discounts give the same result. Verify this for the foregoing example.

EXERCISE 1

Find the discount and selling price of each of the articles whose list discount per cent is shown.

	List Price	Discount Per Cent	Net Selling Price
1.	\$34.80	33%	________
2.	\$165.50	20%, 10%	________
3.	\$845.00	15%, 10%, 2%	________
4.	\$94.00	$12\frac{1}{2}$%, 4%	________
5.	\$230.70	18%, 22%, 13%	________

6. Show that a discount per cent of 20 per cent followed by one of 10 per cent is not the same as a single discount per cent of 30 per cent.

7. Which is better, a $14\frac{1}{2}$ per cent discount or two successive discounts of 10 and 5 per cent?

8. Show that successive discount rates of r_1 and r_2 are equivalent to a single discount rate of $r_1 + r_2 - r_1r_2$.

9. Show that a discount of x per cent followed by one of y per cent is the same as a discount of y per cent followed by one of x per cent.

13.2 COMMISSION

The money received by one person for buying or selling for another is called a *commission.* A newsboy may receive 3 cents for each paper sold for 10 cents. A stock broker may ask 17 cents per share for buying stock for a customer. The commission rate is usually given as a per cent. A real estate broker may charge the seller 5 per cent for the sale of the seller's property.

Example 1. If a newsboy receives 2 cents for each paper sold at 7 cents, what is his commission if he sells 87 papers?

Solution. At 2 cents per paper, he makes a total of $87 \times \$.02 = \$1.74$.

Example 2. A real estate broker charges a 5 per cent commission. What is the commission on a house that is sold for $16,500? What does the seller receive?

Solution. The commission is .05 × $16,500 = $825. The seller receives $16,500 − $825 = $15,675.

EXERCISE 2

1. A newsboy receives 5 cents for every two papers he sells at 10 cents each. How much money does he collect if he sells 36 papers? What is his commission?

2. A real estate broker sells a piece of property for $13,500. He charges the seller a commission figured at a 5 per cent rate. What commission does the real estate broker make on this transaction?

3. A retail market orders 250 dozen ears of corn at 20 cents per dozen from a produce broker who charges 15 per cent as a commission. What was the cost of the corn, the commission, and the total bill?

4. If the retailer in problem 3 had spent $79.35, how many ears of corn would he have bought?

5. A salesman has a regular salary of $200 per month but he also receives 10 per cent of the amount of all sales he makes if they are $500 per week or more. During February his sales for the first, second, third, and fourth weeks were $400, $700, $650, and $550. What were his total earnings for that month?

13.3 PROFIT AND LOSS

In the buying and selling of goods by retailers and others, the excess of the *selling price* over the *buying cost* is called the *margin.* In addition to the buying cost or *cost* of the goods, such items as cost of selling, rental of store, and delivery must be considered. The sum of all of these items is usually called *overhead.* The difference between the selling price and the sum of the cost and overhead is called the *profit* if the selling price is greater than this sum. Otherwise the differences between this sum and the selling price is called the *loss.*

Example 1. A wood dealer buys wood at $15.50 per cord. He figures that his delivery will be $2.75 per cord and that a fair share of the cost of selling, rental on his warehouse, and other items would amount to $1.50 per cord. He sells the wood at $22 per cord. Find the margin, the overhead, and the profit or loss per cord.

Solution. Margin = $22 − $15.50 = $6.50.
Overhead = $2.75 + $1.50 = $4.25.
Profit = $22 − ($15.50 + $4.25) = $22 − $19.75 = $2.25 per cord.

Example 2. The wood dealer in Example 1 finds that he has a few cords of wood of low quality which he wishes to sell at a reduced price. If he sells this wood at $18.50 per cord, what is his profit or loss?

Solution. Since the sum of the overhead and the cost is greater than the selling price, the loss is $19.75 − $18.50 = $1.25 per cord.

It is customary in modern business to express profit or loss, margin, cost, selling price, and overhead in terms of per cent, using the selling price as base.

Example 3. Express as per cents the cost, margin, overhead, profit, and selling price of a cord of wood in Example 1.

Cost per cent $\frac{\$15.50}{\$22} = .705$ or 70.5%.

Margin per cent $\frac{\$650}{\$22} = .295$ or 29.5%.

Overhead per cent $\frac{\$4.25}{\$22} = .193$ or 19.3%.

Profit per cent $\frac{\$2.25}{\$22} = .102$ or 10.2%.

Selling price per cent $\frac{\$22}{\$22} = 1.000$ or 100.0%.

It should be noted that the cost per cent plus the margin per cent equals 100 per cent, or the selling price per cent. What can be said about the sum of the overhead and profit per cents? What is this relation if the article sells at a loss?

Example 4. An article sells for \$56.60. The margin per cent is 45 per cent. What is the cost per cent? What is the margin? What is the cost?

Solution. Cost per cent: $100\% - 45\% = 55\%$.
Margin: $.45 \times \$56.60 = \$25.47$.
Cost: $.55 \times \$56.60 = \$31.13$.

Example 5. A radio costs \$36. At what price should a retailer sell this radio if his margin is 40 per cent?

Solution. Since the margin is 40 per cent, the cost is $100 - 40 = 60$ per cent. Hence 60 per cent of the selling price is equivalent to \$36, or 1 per cent of the selling price is equivalent to \$.60. Therefore, 100 per cent of the selling price is \$60. This solution can be outlined as follows:

40% of selling price = margin; hence
60% of selling price = cost, or \$36; thus, dividing by 6,
10% of selling price = \$6.00; therefore,
100% of selling price = \$60.00.

Note that either $\frac{1}{60}$ of 60 per cent or $\frac{1}{6}$ of 60 per cent can be used at step 3 of the solution to find a suitable portion of 60 per cent with which to work.

EXERCISE 3

Find the missing quantities in the following problems:

	Cost	Overhead	Profit	Margin	Selling Price
1.	\$40	—	\$5	—	\$60
2.	\$165	\$25	\$50	—	—
3.	—	\$10	\$15	—	\$80
4.	—	—	\$55	\$90	\$250
5.	\$67	\$22	—	—	\$100

6. The margin on a certain make of television set selling for $225 is 52 per cent. The overhead is 35 per cent. Find the cost, the margin, and the profit on one of these sets.

7. The dealer who sells the television sets in problem 6 decides to give a 10 per cent discount on the selling price of his sets in order to speed up sales. What profit or loss is there on each set at this discounted price?

8. If the dealer in problem 7 has advertised a 20 per cent discount, what profit or loss is there on each set? At what per cent discount would he break even?

9. A dealer buys shoes at $8.50. If he wishes to maintain a margin of 34 per cent, at what price should he sell the shoes?

10. Radios are purchased at a price of 3 for $200. At what price should they be sold in order to maintain a margin per cent of $33\frac{1}{3}$ per cent?

11. Some sets of furniture are marked to sell at an increase of 50 per cent on cost. If these sets cost $280, what is their selling price? What is the margin per cent?

12. Boxes of stationery are purchased for $1.30 each and are marked to sell at 60 per cent increase on cost. What is the selling price? What is the margin per cent?

13.3.1. Per cent increase on cost. The last two problems in Exercise 3 suggest one other important per cent rate in business problems. This is the *per cent of increase on cost.* If the margin is the amount by which the cost is increased to obtain the selling price, then the ratio of the *margin compared with the cost as the base is called the per cent of increase on cost.*

Example 1. If an article costing $3.40 is sold at a price of $6.00, what is the per cent of increase on cost?

Solution. The margin is $6.00 − $3.40 or $2.60; hence

$$\text{per cent of increase on cost} = \frac{\text{increase}}{\text{cost}} \times 100\% = \frac{2.60}{3.40} \times 100\% = 76\tfrac{8}{17}\%,$$ or about 76.5%.

Note that the margin per cent is $\frac{2.60}{6.00} \times 100\% = 43\frac{1}{3}\%$, in this example, where the base is the selling price.

Example 2. What is the per cent of increase on cost equivalent to a margin per cent of 35 per cent?

Solution. The margin is 35 per cent of the selling price, and therefore the cost is 65 per cent of the selling price; hence

$$\text{per cent of increase} = \frac{.35 \text{ selling price}}{.65 \text{ selling price}} \times 100\% = 53\tfrac{11}{13}\%, \quad \text{or } 53.8\%.$$

In general, the per cent of increase corresponding to a given margin per cent would be given by the formula

$$\text{per cent of increase} = \frac{\text{margin}\,\%}{100\% - \text{margin}\,\%} \times 100\%.$$

13.3.2. Summary of business per cents. Let the number of dollars for each item be given as follows:

$$\begin{aligned} C &= \text{number of dollars cost,} \\ M &= \text{number of dollars margin,} \\ E &= \text{number of dollars overhead expense,} \\ S &= \text{number of dollars selling price,} \\ P &= \text{number of dollars profit.} \end{aligned}$$

The formulas connecting these quantities are

$$C + M = S \quad \text{or} \quad M = S - C.$$
$$E + P = M \quad \text{or} \quad P = M - E.$$

The important per cent rates are defined as follows:

$$\text{margin per cent} = \frac{M}{S} \times 100\%, \quad \text{profit per cent} = \frac{P}{S} \times 100\%,$$

$$\text{overhead per cent} = \frac{E}{S} \times 100\%, \quad \text{cost per cent} = \frac{C}{S} \times 100\%,$$

$$\text{per cent increase on cost} = \frac{M}{C} \times 100\%.$$

EXERCISE 4

1. Given the following items, find the per cent increase on cost:

Cost, \$:	25.00,	3.50,	85.00,	.35,	2.20,	.02.
Selling Price, \$:	35.00,	6.00,	110.00,	1.00,	3.00,	.05.

2. Given the following items, find the selling price:

Cost, \$:	32.00,	1.80,	.60,	.02,	250.00,	7.50.
Per cent increase:	30%,	100%,	$66\frac{2}{3}$%,	150%,	50%,	60%.

3. In each part of problem 1 find the margin per cent.

4. In each part of problem 2 find the margin per cent.

5. Find the margin per cent that corresponds to each of the following per cents of increase on cost:

20%, 80%, 40%, $66\frac{2}{3}$%, 35%, 50%, 100%.

6. Find the per cent margin, per cent profit, and per cent overhead in each of the following cases:

Cost, \$:	20.00	6.50	.02	156.00.
Overhead, \$:	8.00	3.00	.01	24.00.
Selling Price, \$:	35.00	12.00	.05	200.00.

7. Find the per cent cost and the per cent increase on cost in each of the four parts of problem 6.

8. Find the per cents of increase on cost that correspond to the following margin per cents:

30%, 25%, 45%, 12%, 50%, 40%.

13.4 INCOME TAXES

At various times in the early history of the United States income taxes were imposed by the Federal Government. In 1895 the U.S. Supreme Court declared such a tax unconstitutional. It was not until 1913 that an income tax was made legal by the passing of an amendment to the Constitution. Since that time the income tax on individuals and corporations has become the main source of national income.

According to the schedules of income taxes for 1960, every citizen or resident of the United States, whether an adult or a minor, except for those aged 65 or over, must file a return if his income is $600 or more a year. A citizen or resident aged 65 or over must file a return if his income is $1200 or more. Furthermore, since the government has been withholding taxes on income, through employers, a person must file a return even if his income is less than the above amounts in order to receive a refund of taxes withheld.

In general, the amount of tax an individual or a married couple must pay is dependent upon what is called an adjusted gross income. To determine the adjusted gross income, the total of all income received from salary or salaries, profit from business, dividends, rents, interest, pensions, and so on, received by the person (or married couple) during the year, must be declared. This amount is then decreased by various kinds of allowable deductions. The difference between the total income and the deductions is the adjusted gross income.

Since 1958 a new simplified card form (Form 1040A) has been available for use by persons whose gross income consists of wages reported on withholding statements (Forms W-2) totaling $5000 or less, with not more than $200 coming from other wages, interest, and dividends. Such a card can be filed if the person so reporting wishes to take the standard deduction (about 10 per cent of his income) instead of itemizing his deductions. Furthermore, when a person's income is less than $5000, he may choose to have the Internal Revenue Service figure his tax.

A large number of taxpayers, both individuals and married couples, must file what is called Form 1040. For taxpayers having an adjusted gross income of $5000 or less, a tax table may be used if the taxpayer is willing to take a standard deduction of about 10 per cent of his income in place of itemized deductions for such things as taxes paid to the state, contributions to churches or charitable institutions, and other allowable expenses. This tax table gives the exact amount of tax to be paid. The following examples illustrate how the number of dependents affects the tax when the tax table is used.

Example 1. Find the tax a single person must pay if his adjusted gross income is $4500.

Solution. Using the tax table* for 1960, the tax is found to be $724. The reader should obtain a current tax table and compare this answer with that obtained from the table.

Example 2. Find the tax a married couple with no dependents must pay on an adjusted gross income of $4500.

Solution. The tax will be found in the column headed "2 exemptions, married couple filing jointly" in the tax table. The amount of tax is $575.

Example 3. Compare the tax for the married couple in Example 2 if (*a*) they had one dependent child, (*b*) two dependent children, (*c*) three dependent children, (*d*) four dependent children, (*e*) five dependent children, (*f*) six or more dependent children.

Solution. The tax paid in each case is as follows, using the 1960 tax table:

1 child (3 exemptions)	$455
2 children (4 exemptions)	$335
3 children (5 exemptions)	$215
4 children (6 exemptions)	$95
5 or more children (7 or more exemptions)	$0.

(Note the remark made at the end of the solution of Example 1.)

For those with adjusted gross incomes greater than $5000 and those with incomes of $5000 or less who wish to itemize their deductions, the tax is computed from special tax schedules. These schedules are (1) Schedule I (A) for single taxpayers who do not qualify for rates in Schedules II and III and (B) married persons filing separate returns; (2) Schedule II for (A) married taxpayers filing joint returns or (B) for certain widows or widowers; and (3) Schedule III for unmarried (or legally separated) taxpayers qualifying as "head of a household."

In order to use these schedules, a taxable income is determined by subtracting from the adjusted gross income the allowable deductions, itemized or otherwise, and the allowances for exemptions. These exemptions include one for each person and one for each dependent. Taxpayers over age 65 or taxpayers who are blind are given an extra exemption for each such condition.

Since these schedules are too extensive to print in a book of the present scope, the following illustrations are given to show how the tax increases with the amount of adjusted gross income, less allowed deductions; this difference is called the taxable income. Since the taxes are based on taxable income, donations to nonprofit organizations, up to a legal maximum per cent deduction, are often made by persons with large incomes.

* Such tables may be obtained from the nearest office of the Internal Revenue Service. A teacher may wish to write to the Internal Revenue Service, Washington, D.C., for a special teacher's kit to aid in teaching income taxes. Two excellent publications have appeared: Publication No. 19, *Teaching Federal Income Taxes*, and Publication No. 27, *Federal Income Tax Students Handbook*.

In effect, this transfers a portion of the person's income to the organization rather than to the Federal Government.

Taxable Income (Gross − Deductions)	Schedule I Individual	Schedule II Married Couple
$ 20,000	$ 7,260	$ 5,280
$ 40,000	$ 19,740	$ 14,520
$ 60,000	$ 34,320	$ 26,440
$ 80,000	$ 50,220	$ 39,480
$100,000	$ 67,320	$ 53,640
$200,000	$156,820	$134,640
$300,000	$247,820	$223,640

13.5 REAL ESTATE AND PERSONAL PROPERTY TAX

In order to support city and county government, a real estate and personal property tax is usually levied. This tax is set by having an assessor make evaluations of all property within the governmental unit for which the tax is needed. Such things as payment of salaries of city and county officers and employees, fire protection, police protection, and school maintenance, are a few of the services which must be supported. A budget is made up as an estimate of the amount of money needed to run the governmental unit efficiently. This amount divided by the total assessed valuation gives the amount each taxpayer must pay per dollar of assessed valuation. The tax rate may be expressed as a per cent, but often it is given as the number of dollars per $100 of assessed valuation.

Example 1. A small city has an assessed valuation of $11,000,000. What is its tax rate if $650,000 per year is needed for schools and other services?
Solution. $650,000 divided by $11,000,000 is the amount needed per dollar of assessed valuation. $650{,}000 \div 11{,}000{,}000 = .05909$. This tax rate is 5.909 per cent, or $.05909 per dollar of assessed valuation or $5.909 per $100.

Example 2. A property owner in the city mentioned in Example 1 has a house and personal property which is assessed at $9500. What is the amount of his tax?
Solution. The tax is $9500 \times .05909$, or $561.36.

EXERCISE 5

1. The tax rate in a certain city is $7.2345 per one hundred dollars of assessed valuation. What is the real estate and personal property tax on an assessed valuation of $8235?

2. A school district needs $500,000 for a new school in a city of $750,000,000 assessed valuation. If cash is paid for this new school, how much will it raise the tax per hundred dollars of valuation?

3. A certain county has a fixed rate of 5 per cent of the assessed valuation of property, both real estate and personal, in the county. The assessed valuation during a given year was $800,000,000. This provided $40,000,000 for county expenses. It was found that during the following year that $45,000,000 would be needed to run the county government. How much would the assessed valuation of the county have to be raised to meet this increased cost if the tax rate remained fixed at 5 per cent?

4. A small business in the county of problem 3 had an assessed valuation of $50,000. How much was its valuation raised? How much did the tax on this property increase?

5. Obtain copies of Form 1040 from your local office of the Internal Revenue Service and use the tax schedules to compute the amount of tax paid, assuming in each case that the standard 10% deduction is taken.

(*a*) A single person, total gross income $2000, no dependents except self.
(*b*) A single person, total gross income $3500, one dependent (mother).
(*c*) A married couple, total gross income $9000, two dependent children.
(*d*) A married couple, total gross income $15,000, one dependent child.

13.6 OTHER APPLICATIONS OF PER CENT

The well-known sales tax which is applied in a majority of states is a tax on the selling price of various sorts of goods, not even excluding food. Although some authorities feel that perhaps this sort of tax is unfair to the person with a small income, it has become very popular with governmental agencies because of its ease of collection. It is levied for various services in the states, and in some areas, for schools. The tax is stated as a per cent so that the amount can be computed easily. The tax is collected by the seller and is determined, to within one cent for small purchases, by means of a table. Thus in a state with a 4% sales tax rate the sales tax on a purchase of $25.50 is $.04 \times 25.50 = \$1.02$.

Other taxes which are usually computed by using a per cent are travel, inheritance, and estate taxes, fees, and licenses. Per cents are also used to compute various forms of insurance, such as fire, automobile, and life. Each of these topics might well serve as project material in a class in junior high school mathematics when per cents and consumer arithmetic are being studied.

EXERCISE 6

Review of Problems in Per Cent

1. What is the amount of the tax on an article selling for $84.50 if the sales tax rate is 4 per cent?

2. What is the amount of commission paid on the sale of a house if it sells for $12,750 and the commission rate is 5 per cent?

3. What are the per cents of *A* grades, *B* grades, and *C* grades in each group of students if the grades are given as follows:

	A	*B*	*C*	*D*	*E*	*F*
(*a*)	3	13	27	12	0	5
(*b*)	5	12	18	10	2	3

4. The price of a loaf of bread was increased from 31 to 35 cents. What was the per cent of increase?

5. The number of traffic fatalities in April was 183 and in May it was 168. What was the per cent of decrease in traffic fatalities from April to May?

6. The list price of a console radio is $85. If a dealer buys three of these sets and receives trade discounts of 20 and 10 per cent, how much does he pay for each set?

7. What single discount rate is equivalent to a discount series of 20, 15, and 10 per cent?

8. If 18 per cent of a magnesium ore is pure magnesium compound, how many tons of ore must be processed to obtain 36 tons of pure magnesium compound?

9. In a batch of light bulbs 4 per cent will probably be defective. How many bulbs should be purchased to be sure to get 3000 nondefective bulbs?

10. In hatching eggs of a certain variety, it is found that 7 per cent will normally fail to hatch. How many live chicks will 1200 eggs produce?

11. In problem 10 how many eggs must be incubated to produce 1860 live chicks?

12. After a man's salary is cut 15 per cent, he receives $467.50 per month. What was his former salary?

REFERENCES

Hooper, A., *An Arithmetic Refresher*, pp. 105–107.
Layton, W. I., *College Arithmetic*, pp. 106–110.
McSwain and Cooke, *Understanding and Teaching Arithmetic in the Elementary School*, pp. 221–243.
Morton, R. L., *Teaching Arithmetic in the Elementary School*, Vol. 2, pp. 393–407.
Price and Knowler, *Basic Skills*, pp. 166–190.
Taylor, E. H. and C. N. Mills, *Arithmetic for Teacher-Training Classes*, fourth edition, pp. 268–295.

14

Mental Arithmetic

14.1 MENTAL ARITHMETIC IN THE CLASSROOM

Children like problems they can work without the use of pencil and paper, and it is always well to have a supply on hand to assign whenever there are spare moments. The opening of the class period is often a good time for a few mental arithmetic problems. This preliminary work helps the children to get settled and in the mood and spirit for the regular lesson. Five problems may be written on the board, with instructions to do the calculations mentally and to write only the answers. The teacher need not wait until all students have worked the problems before calling on one to read a problem, to tell how he worked it, and to give the answer.

Problems selected for the work in mental arithmetic should include examples that deal with the four fundamental arithmetical operations as well as those calling for the use of concepts. Multiples of 10, 100, and 1000 might be simpler to handle in most of the multiplication and division problems. Consider the following examples.

14.1.1. Sample problems. Decide which of the fundamental operations should be used in each problem and solve without pencil and paper:

1. A pump can deliver five gallons per minute. How long will it take this pump to fill a thirty-gallon tank?
2. If it costs $5000 to resurface a mile of highway, what would the cost be of resurfacing a fifty-mile strip at the same rate?
3. One year the students in a graduating class received one hundred scholarships. If the amount for scholarships totaled $50,000, what was the average value of these scholarships received?
4. Almost 15,000 relatives and friends witnessed the graduation ceremonies in the Rose Bowl with the following number of graduates: 1300 from Pasadena City College, 800 from Pasadena High School, and 725

from John Muir High School. What was the total number of graduates from the three schools?

5. The elevation of Mt. Shasta is 14,160 feet and that of Mt. Lassen, 10,450 feet. How much higher is Mt. Shasta than Mt. Lassen?

14.2 TYPES OF PROBLEMS TO BE SOLVED MENTALLY

Problems to meet the individual needs of the class can be adapted from newspaper articles or from statistics in the world almanac. Those involving relatively easy calculation with only one step can be done mentally. In two-step problems of one or two digit numbers care should be taken to choose the numbers for ease of calculation. Most processes in arithmetic can be illustrated by simple examples calling for little computation. Problems based on such examples should be used for work in mental arithmetic.

14.3 SHORT CUTS

Many short cuts in computation can be performed mentally. Some were given in other chapters, but a few are added here.

(*a*) *Addition by grouping for ten.* In examples such as those shown

8	6	5	3
7	4	8	7
2	3	5	6

the student can improve not only his speed but also his accuracy by first grouping two numbers whose sum is ten and then adding the other number.

(*b*) *Addition by the complementary method.* In these problems a modified method of complements can be used. In adding 18 and 17, the student calculates "18 and 17 are short 2 and 3 respectively, of being 20 and 20; hence the sum is 40 minus 5, or 35." Similarly, "39 and 57 are short 1 and 3 respectively, of being 40 and 60, hence, the sum is 100 minus 4, or 96."

18	39	26
17	57	88

(*c*) *Addition of products with common factors.* Consider the addition of multiples of the same number.

$$\begin{array}{r} 6 \times 8 \\ +3 \times 8 \\ \hline 9 \times 8 = 72 \end{array} \qquad \begin{array}{r} 7 \times 3 \\ +4 \times 3 \\ \hline 11 \times 3 = 33. \end{array}$$

Instead of multiplying separately and then adding, perform the addition and then the multiplication. This makes use of one form of the distributive law.

$$\begin{array}{r} 6 \times 8 = 48 \\ 3 \times 8 = 24 \\ \hline (6 + 3) \times 8 \quad \\ 9 \times 8 = 72 \end{array} \qquad \begin{array}{r} 7 \times 3 = 21 \\ 4 \times 3 = 12 \\ \hline (7 + 4) \times 3 \quad \\ 11 \times 3 = 33. \end{array}$$

A few problems of this kind will also prepare the student for the addition of algebraic terms such as $6x + 3x = 9x$; $7x + 4x = 11x$. In the foregoing examples, we can also say "6 eights and 3 eights are 9 eights" and "7 threes and 4 threes are 11 threes."

(*d*) *Addition with place value.* In adding 456 and 279, we have

$$\begin{array}{rl} & 456 = 400 + \ \ 50 + \ \ 6 \\ & 279 = 200 + \ \ 70 + \ \ 9 \\ \hline \text{The sum is} & \qquad 600 + 120 + 15 \quad \text{or} \quad 735. \end{array}$$

(*e*) *Multiplication involving a sum and difference.* To find the products of

$$31 \times 29, \qquad 98 \times 102, \qquad 67 \times 73,$$

think of these examples as being made up of a sum and difference:

$$(30 + 1)(30 - 1), \qquad (100 - 2)(100 + 2), \qquad (70 - 3)(70 + 3).$$

The products are then found to be

$$(900 - 1), \text{ or } 899, \qquad (10000 - 4), \text{ or } 9{,}996, \qquad (4900 - 9), \text{ or } 4891.$$

(*f*) *Multiplication involving two-digit numbers.* In multiplying two 2-digit numbers a short cut based on the use of place value can be developed. Consider the product of 24 × 47. The steps are

$$\begin{array}{r} 47 \\ \times 24 \\ \hline \end{array} \text{ is equal to } \begin{array}{r} (40 + 7) \\ \times(20 + 4) \\ \hline \end{array} \text{ or } \begin{array}{r} 40 + \\ \times 20 \\ \hline \end{array} \quad \begin{array}{r} 40 + \\ \times 4 \\ \hline \end{array} \quad \begin{array}{r} 7 + \\ \times 20 \\ \hline \end{array} \quad \begin{array}{r} 7 \\ \times 4 \\ \hline \end{array}$$

$$\begin{aligned} 24 \times 47 &= 800 + 160 + 140 + 28, \\ &= 8 \times 100 + (16 + 14 + 2) \times 10 + 8, \\ &= 8 \times 100 + 32 \times 10 + 8, \\ &= 11 \times 100 + 2 \times 10 + 8, \\ &= 1128. \end{aligned}$$

The student can develop his own technique for combining these terms, by writing the answer from left to right or from right to left.

In practice, "4 sevens are 28, write 8 and carry 2 (tens); 4 fours are 16, 2 sevens are 14, 16 and 14 and 2 are 32, write 2 (tens) and carry 3 (hundreds); 2 fours are 8, 8 and 3 are 11 (hundreds). The answer is 1128."

In a second example of finding the product of 56 × 38, we calculate as shown in the parentheses, but we write only the digits of the answer.

$$\begin{array}{r} 3 \quad 8 \\ \times 5 \ \times \ 6 \\ \hline (4)8 \\ (40) \\ (18) \\ 1(5) \\ \hline 2\ 12\ 8 \end{array} \qquad \begin{array}{l} \\ \\ 6 \times 8 \\ 5 \times 8 \\ 6 \times 3 \\ 5 \times 3 \\ \\ \end{array} \qquad \begin{array}{r} 38 \\ \times 56 \\ \hline 2128 \\ \\ (58 + 4 = 62) \quad (15 + 6 = 21) \\ \\ \\ \end{array}$$

(*g*) *Multiplication in terms of place value.* Consider the following example:

$$\begin{array}{r} 264 \\ \times 3 \\ \hline \end{array} \qquad 264 \text{ is } \begin{array}{r} 200 \\ \times 3 \\ \hline 600 \end{array} + \begin{array}{r} 60 \\ \times 3 \\ \hline 180 \end{array} + \begin{array}{r} 4 \\ \times 3 \\ \hline 12 \end{array} \text{ or } 792.$$

The product is

(*h*) *Multiplication involving fractional or aliquot parts.* Many short cuts in multiplication and division can be found by using aliquot parts. Review the item in Chapter 10 on operations with fractions. One example is repeated here. Since 25 is $\frac{1}{4}$ of 100, to multiply by 25, multiply first by 100 and then divide by 4. To divide by 25, divide first by 100 and then multiply by 4, or multiply first by 4 and then divide by 100.

$$850 \times 25 = \frac{850 \times 100}{4} = \frac{85{,}000}{4} = 21{,}250$$

$$850 \div 25 = \frac{850}{100} \times 4 = 8.50 \times 4 = 34.00, \quad \text{or} \quad 34.$$

(*i*) *Multiplication by* 11. To multiply by 11, add ten times the number to the number itself.

$$\begin{array}{r} 2765 \\ \times 11 \\ \hline 2765 \\ 2765 \\ \hline 30415 \end{array}$$

short cut: 2765 × 11 (with *d*, *b* marked above and *e*, *c*, *a* marked below the digits)

Write 5, the last digit in the answer, (*a*). This is the last digit in the multiplicand. To the left of 5 write 1, the units digit in the sum of 6 and 5, (*b*). To the left of 1 write 4, the units digit in the sum of 7 and 6 and 1 carried, (*c*). Next add mentally 7 and 2 and 1 carried from the preceding sum of 14, (*d*); and write 0 and carry 1. Next write 3 as the sum of 2 and 1 carried from the preceding sum, (*e*). The answer is 30,415.

EXERCISE 1

1. Write six problems suitable for use in mental arithmetic practice. Include at least one word problem for each of the different operations in arithmetic.

2. Write two word problems on the concepts of fractions for use in mental arithmetic.

3. Add, using groups of tens, place value or complements.

$$\begin{array}{ccc} 2 & 6 & 5 \\ 3 & 0 & 3 \\ 4 & 9 & 8 \\ 7 & 8 & 5 \\ 5 & 3 & 2 \\ \hline \end{array} \qquad \begin{array}{r} 16 \\ 19 \\ \hline \end{array} \quad \begin{array}{r} 37 \\ 28 \\ \hline \end{array} \quad \begin{array}{r} 69 \\ 59 \\ \hline \end{array} \quad \begin{array}{r} 18 \\ 16 \\ \hline \end{array}$$

$$\begin{array}{r} 298 \\ 696 \\ \hline \end{array} \quad \begin{array}{r} 395 \\ 495 \\ \hline \end{array} \quad \begin{array}{r} 28 \\ 78 \\ \hline \end{array} \quad \begin{array}{r} 65 \\ 75 \\ \hline \end{array}$$

4. Multiply, making use of place value and/or short cuts,

$$\begin{array}{r} 64 \\ \times 23 \\ \hline \end{array} \quad \begin{array}{r} 72 \\ \times 68 \\ \hline \end{array} \quad \begin{array}{r} 102 \\ \times 98 \\ \hline \end{array} \quad \begin{array}{r} 13 \\ \times 17 \\ \hline \end{array} \quad \begin{array}{r} 58 \\ \times 27 \\ \hline \end{array} \quad \begin{array}{r} 42 \\ \times 38 \\ \hline \end{array}$$

5. Multiply, using place value or short cuts,

$$\begin{array}{r} 264 \\ \times 3 \\ \hline \end{array} \quad \begin{array}{r} 96 \\ \times 104 \\ \hline \end{array} \quad \begin{array}{r} 205 \\ \times 195 \\ \hline \end{array} \quad \begin{array}{r} 234 \\ \times 11 \\ \hline \end{array} \quad \begin{array}{r} 687 \\ \times 11 \\ \hline \end{array} \quad \begin{array}{r} 4567 \\ \times 11 \\ \hline \end{array}$$

6. Work out each example two ways.

$$\begin{array}{r} 4 \times 8 \\ +7 \times 8 \\ \hline \end{array} \quad \begin{array}{r} 6 \times 7 \\ +5 \times 7 \\ \hline \end{array} \quad \begin{array}{r} 13 \times 8 \\ +7 \times 8 \\ \hline \end{array} \quad \begin{array}{r} 7 \times 5 \\ +8 \times 5 \\ \hline \end{array}$$

7. Explain the solutions given for the following examples.

$$23 \times 19 = 460 - 23 = 437, \quad 23 \times 21 = 460 + 23 = 483.$$

8. Work out each example, and check by casting out nines.

$$\begin{array}{r} 325 \\ \times 29 \\ \hline \end{array} \quad \begin{array}{r} 642 \\ \times 25 \\ \hline \end{array} \quad \begin{array}{r} 478 \\ \times 50 \\ \hline \end{array} \quad \begin{array}{r} 525 \\ \times 31 \\ \hline \end{array} \quad \begin{array}{r} 320 \\ \times 99 \\ \hline \end{array} \quad \begin{array}{r} 75 \\ \times 18 \\ \hline \end{array} \quad \begin{array}{r} 444 \\ \times 25 \\ \hline \end{array}$$

14.4 ORAL PROBLEMS TO REVIEW FUNDAMENTAL OPERATIONS

These problems are to be done orally and in the order given.

1. To 7, add, 3, divide by 2, multiply by 3, add 10, divide by 5, multiply by 2, add 4, divide by 7, add 5, divide by 7. The answer is 1.
2. Begin with 6, add 5, subtract 2, divide by 3, multiply by 2, add 8, divide by 7, add 9, subtract 4, divide by 7, add 9. The answer is 10.
3. Take 5, multiply by 6, subtract 6, divide by 2, add 3, divide by 5, add 15, divide by 6, multiply by 9, add 3, divide by 10. The answer is 3.
4. Take 4, multiply by 5, subtract 2, divide by 6, multiply by 4, add 9, divide by 7, multiply by 10, subtract 3, divide by 9, multiply by 4. The answer is 12.
5. Begin with 3, add 9, add 10, subtract 2, divide by 5, multiply by 6, divide by 12, multiply by 5, multiply by 6, divide by 5, multiply by 12. The answer is 144.

A series of problems can be prepared in advance. At first the problems must be given rather slowly but increasing the speed as the students progress. The students themselves enjoy making up problems of five to ten operations, to be completed without use of a pencil.

14.5 COMPUTING CONTESTS

Computing contests similar to spelling contests can be conducted if the teacher has prepared a set of three or four dozen questions. Here are thirty sample questions which may be used for such contests or events.

1. In one aircraft company 20 per cent of the personnel make the blueprints and 80 per cent read and use them. What is the ratio of the number of those who read and use the blueprints to the number who make them?
2. Statistics show that 55 per cent of all high school graduates in California go to junior colleges. What per cent would represent those who do do not go to junior college?
3. If a person accumulates $95,000 during a ten-year period, what would his average yearly earning be for this period?
4. The *Cleveland Plain Dealer* at one time increased its single copy price from 7 to 10 cents. What was the per cent increase?
5. The submarine *Skate* remained under ice twelve days and logged 3090 miles on her second trip to the North Pole. What was the average number of miles logged per day?
6. The average life of a 70-watt light bulb is 1000 hours. How many months would a light bulb last if it were used only four hours per day?
7. It is said that for every 2.5 persons in Los Angeles county there is one car. How many cars are there then for every 100 persons in the county?
8. For every one hundred persons in Los Angeles there are sixty-one telephones. At that rate, how many telephones for every million people?
9. Express $100,000.00 in pennies.
10. Last year one company spent four million dollars on research. That was five times the amount it spent ten years before. What was the amount the company spent on research ten years before?
11. Of the 16,000 students at one university, 5000 are graduate students. Is that more or less than $33\frac{1}{3}$ per cent?
12. A high-speed drill used in dentistry makes 300,000 revolutions per minute. How many revolutions per second does this drill make?
13. What is the interest on $1000 for three months at 6 per cent?
14. Americans owe about one trillion dollars in public and private debts. If the average rate of interest on this amount is 4 per cent, how many billion dollars are paid per year in interest?
15. The State of Hawaii has a population of about 600,000 (1961), of which only 12,000 are pure-blood Hawaiians. What per cent of the population is pure-blood Hawaiian?
16. The year 1959 was the seventy-fifth anniversary of the use of standard time. In what year did standard time originate?

17. If in 1958 about 5000 Americans visited Russia, twice the number that had visited Russia the year before, how many Americans visited Russia in 1957?

18. At one time the Red Cross Fund Drive had reached 67 per cent of its goal. What part had still to be reached?

19. A sturdy stool is guaranteed to hold one half ton. How many fifty pound blocks could be stacked on it?

20. If the population of the metropolitan area of Los Angeles was 4,367,911 in 1950 and that of the city of Los Angeles was 1,970,358, was the population of the city more or less than 50 per cent of the metropolitan population?

21. The United States today uses more than ten trillion cubic feet of natural gas each year. How is ten trillion written, a one followed by how many zeros?

22. The United States uses about 650 billion kilowatt hours of electricity a year. What is the monthly average?

23. Every day the sun drenches the earth with energy equal to the output of 120 trillion tons of soft coal. What is the equivalent output for one month?

24. Before World War II Great Britain imported 66 per cent of its food. Beginning in 1958 only 50 per cent of its food was imported. This reduction represents what fractional part of Great Britain's food?

25. The Treasury Department has reported that no silver dollars have been minted since 1935. For how many years since 1935 have no silver dollars been minted?

26. The city of San Diego reports an increase of 60,000 in population in two years. What is the average increase per year?

27. To advertise the Equestrian Trail Convention, Los Angeles horsemen started a 350-mile trail ride. If eleven days were planned for the trip, how many miles, to the nearest whole mile, would have to be covered each day?

28. According to the Automobile Manufacturing Association, 24 cents in every dollar of the cost of a new car goes for taxes. At that rate, what amount would go for taxes on a car costing $3000?

29. A judge resigned his office to accept a postmastership because it paid $1500 a year more than his former yearly salary of $3300. What is his new monthly salary?

30. If a bicycle racing champion travels from Los Angeles to Bakersfield, a distance of 105 miles, in seven hours, what is his average rate of speed?

Although the foregoing problems were suggested for use in contests, they could be adapted to any purpose desired. In one method the students draw numbers; the numbers drawn indicate problems to be worked out orally.

14.6 ESTIMATING AND CHECKING ANSWERS

An important application of mental arithmetic is its use in estimating the size or approximate value of the answer to a problem. By this is meant the use of round numbers in place of the entries in a given problem to obtain mentally a round number for the answer. Estimates of this kind can be very useful in checking answers found by longer calculations. It is worthwhile for teachers and pupils to develop the habit of mentally checking all their work. The following examples illustrate this concept:

Example 1. Estimate the size of the answer for 23.6×16.4.

Solution. For purposes of checking, each entry in the problem is replaced by 20. Since 20×20 is 400, the answer should be about 400. It should be observed that it could not possibly be so small as 40 nor so large as 4000. When the answer is worked out, it is found to be 387.04. This number should be rounded off to 387 if the entries for the example are approximate.

Example 2. Estimate the size of the answer for $37\frac{3}{8} \div 4\frac{3}{8}$.

Solution. For purposes of checking, 40 and 5, respectively, are substituted for the entries. Since the quotient of $40 \div 5$ is 8, the answer to the example should be about 8. It could not possibly be so large as 100 nor so small as one unit. The answer is $8\frac{19}{35}$.

Example 3. Estimate the answer to this problem. In a class of 825 students 53 were English majors. What per cent of the class did this represent?

Solution. Per cent means parts in one hundred. Since about 800 students are in the total group, the parts in 100 will be $\frac{1}{8}$ of 53 and will lie between 6 and 7. The answer, rounded to the nearest .1 per cent, is 6.4 per cent.

Example 4. Estimate the answer to this problem. The speed of sound is about 1060 feet per second. How long—to the nearest .1 second—will it take sound to travel ten miles?

Solution. For purposes of estimating, 10 miles are about 50,000 feet, and the speed of sound is about 1000 feet per second. The quotient of $50{,}000 \div 1000$ is 50, which means that it takes sound about 50 seconds to travel 10 miles. Using 5280 feet in one mile and 1060 feet per second for the speed of sound, the answer is 49.8 seconds.

EXERCISE 2

Choose the number that is nearest to the correct answer for the given example in each case.

	(*a*)	(*b*)	(*c*)	(*d*)
1. 473×1.7	90	230	10,000	900
2. 12% of 8300	900	10,000	98	750
3. $18 \div 1200$	15%	1.5%	$\frac{2}{3}$ of 1%	67%

4. $23\frac{1}{2} \div 7\frac{1}{8}$	185	$2\frac{1}{8}$	$3\frac{1}{8}$	$33\frac{1}{3}$
5. $45 \times \$.35$	$15.00	$120	$1.50	$1500
6. $\frac{1}{3} \times 6\frac{3}{8}$	$19\frac{1}{8}$	$3\frac{1}{8}$	$2\frac{1}{8}$	21
7. $18\frac{1}{3} \div 2\frac{2}{3}$	$72\frac{1}{2}$	7	$\frac{1}{6}$	$48\frac{1}{3}$
8. $32 \times \$3.98$	$8	$13	$1280	$130
9. $62.7 \div .032$	2000	1.8	198	.21
10. 17 is 9% of	1.6	190	19	1600

Work out each of the following examples, correct to three significant figures, *first estimating* the size of the answer.

11. If 1850 persons in 100,000 are 31 years of age, what per cent of the population is 31 years of age?

12. What is the cost of 250 towels at 23 cents each?

13. How far does sound travel in 35 seconds if it travels 1060 feet per second?

14. Find the answer to problem 13 in terms of miles.

15. How many miles above sea level is the top of Mount Everest if its elevation is 29,000 feet?

16. How long will a jet airplane take to travel 2200 miles at a rate of 620 miles per hour?

17. A tank has dimensions of 4 by $3\frac{1}{2}$ by 6 feet. How many gallons will it hold if $7\frac{1}{2}$ gallons equal 1 cubic foot?

18. A tank has a volume of 50,000 cubic inches. How many gallons will the tank hold if there are 231 cubic inches in 1 gallon?

19. A car uses 18.4 gallons of gasoline for a trip of 235 miles. What is the average number of miles per gallon traveled by this car, to the nearest .1 mile per gallon?

20. Some handkerchiefs are bought at a cost of $1.00 per dozen and sold at 19 cents each. What is the total gain (margin) on 60 of these handkerchiefs?

21. What is the per cent margin, and the per cent increase on cost, in problem 20?

22. If pencils are bought at $2.50 per dozen dozen (or gross) and are sold at 4 cents each, what is the total gain if 432 of these pencils are sold?

REFERENCES

Bakst, A., *Mathematical Puzzles and Pastimes.*

Gamow, G., M. Stern, *Puzzle-Math: A Book of Brain Twisters.*

Huberich, P. G., *Short Method Arithmetic*, pp. 6–63.

Kraitchik, M., *Mathematical Recreations.*

Marks, J. L., C. R. Purdy, and L. B. Kinney, *Teaching Arithmetic for Understanding*, pp. 310–341.

Mott-Smith, G., *Mathematical Puzzles*, pp. 1–94.

Schaaf, W. L., *Recreational Mathematics: A Guide to the Literature.* National Council of Teachers of Mathematics, 1955, pp. 18–23, 59–78.

15

Approximate Numbers

15.1 INTRODUCTION

In counting the number of people in a small class, the teacher is usually confident that the number he obtains is exact; that is, if his count is 29, he knows that it is not 28 or 30 or any other number. If in the process of counting—such as a teacher counting his class—a correct count is made, then the number obtained is called an *exact number*. A count of a large number of people may very well be inaccurate. Thus in making a census count, the total number reported may be inexact because of the omission of some people from the count, the counting of some people more than once, or because of tabulation errors. If a number is reported as the total population it may be in error by several tens or several hundreds. A total such as that reported to represent a population count is an example of an *approximate number*.

Approximate numbers arise in measurements of all kinds. For example, in measuring the width of a table with a one-foot ruler, the number obtained is approximate because (1) the one-foot ruler may be in error, (2) the placing of the ruler after each measurement of one foot is subject to error, and (3) the reading of the scale on the ruler introduces another error. It is apparent that an exact reading cannot be made, hence the recorded distance is in general an approximate number. Another way in which approximate numbers arise is in the process of *rounding off* either exact numbers or irrational numbers. Thus, if 56,735 people attended a football game, the attendance could be reported as 56,700, an approximate number accurate to within plus or minus 50 of the exact number. In like manner, the exact irrational number $\sqrt{2}$ can be expressed as the approximate number 1.4142. This number can be rounded off to give still another approximate number, 1.41.

15.2 SIGNIFICANT DIGITS—ROUNDING OFF NUMBERS

If a number is written in decimal-point form, with one or more digits following the decimal point, and it is assumed that the last digit is in error by not more than $+.5$ of its place value nor less than $-.5$ of its place value, then the *significant digits* of the number are those beginning with the first nonzero digit and ending with the last digit, including all zeros. Thus .0025 has two significant digits. It may be said that this number is accurate to two significant places. Likewise, 76.021 has five significant places. Since a terminal zero counts, 42.3480 has six significant places.

If a measurement is expressed as a natural number, it is not always possible to determine the number of significant digits. Therefore, if the distance between two cities is given as 860 miles, the mileage may be expressed within the nearest ten miles; that is, the distance may be as small as 855 or as large as 865 miles. In this case 860 has only two significant digits. If the distance is measured within the nearest mile, the actual distance would be somewhere between 859.5 and 860.5 miles. In this case the number 860 has three significant digits. It is seen that the terminal zero in a number such as 860 may or may not be significant. In a similar way the two zeros in 800 may or may not be significant.

If there are no terminal zeros in an approximate number, which is expressed as a natural number, it will be assumed that the number of significant digits, including nonterminal zeros, is equal to the total number of digits in the number. Thus the approximate number 2583 has four significant digits. The approximate number 8007 has four significant digits. The approximate number 7300 could have four, three, or two significant digits. If this number is accurate to the nearest hundred, then it has two significant digits. How many significant digits has it if it is accurate to the nearest ten? to the nearest one?

If an approximate number represented by a natural number has terminal zeros, the need for a better way of representing it becomes imperative. The exponential form (usually called scientific notation) is desirable for this purpose. (See section 11.10.) Thus 7300 may be written as 7.300×10^3. When the number is written in this form, four significant digits are implied. Likewise, the form 7.30×10^3 implies three significant digits and 7.3×10^3 implies two.

For computational purposes, and for other reasons, it becomes desirable to round off numbers. To start the rounding process, any natural number containing more than one digit should be expressed in scientific form. Then all digits lying to the right of the place to be retained should be dropped. The digit in that place is increased by one if the digits dropped amount to more than five in the following place; if this value is less than five, the last digit retained is unchanged. If the amount dropped is exactly five in the place following the last digit retained, this last digit could either be increased by one or left unchanged. The method used depends on the situation under consideration. If a customer buys an article marked 8.5 cents, he expects to pay 9 cents for it rather than 8 cents. He would pay exactly 17 cents for two of these articles, 26 cents for three and so on. This sort of usage gives rise to the rounding *up* procedure when the terminal digit is exactly five. Thus 2.65 rounded off to two significant places is 2.7; 873.5 rounded off to three significant places is 874.

Table 11
Numbers Rounded Off to Fewer Significant Places

Number	Four Places	Three Places	Two Places
26.035	26.04	26.0	26
150.48	150.5	1.50×10^2	1.5×10^2
4.9999	5.000	5.00	5.0
8.3494	8.349	8.35	8.3
50,000	5.000×10^4	5.00×10^4	5.0×10^4
340.65	340.6	341	3.4×10^2

This method is not good practice in general computing, since rounding up when the terminal digit to be dropped is exactly five will tend to make the rounding-off errors cumulative. A rule generally followed by computers (called the computer's rule) is as follows:

If a number is to be rounded off by one place and the terminal digit is exactly five, then the five is dropped if the preceding digit is even; if the preceding digit is odd, this digit is increased by one, and the five is dropped. Note that this rule will make the terminal digit retained *even* in each case. For example, the four-digit numbers 23.45 and 68.75 would be rounded off to 23.4 and 68.8, respectively, as three-digit numbers.

The examples in Table 11 show the proper rounding off of numbers to a given number of places. Exponent notation and the computer's rule are used when necessary.

It should be noted that in some cases it is necessary, in successive rounding, to go back to the original number. The second, third, and fourth entries in Table 11 illustrate this point.

EXERCISE 1

Determine the number of significant figures in each of the following approximate numbers.

1. 28.45 **2.** .0213

3. 40.002

4. .00004

5. 672

6. 8.00×10^2

7. 8.0×10^2

8. 9.2×10^5

9. 2.01×10^{-4}

10. 700.1

Round off each of the following numbers to the required number of significant figures:

11. 8.248, round off to 3 significant figures.

12. 10.45, round off to 3 significant figures.

13. .00499, round off to 2 significant figures.

14. 1.700×10^3, round off to 3 significant figures.

15. 3.1416, round off to 4 significant figures.

16-20. Round off each number in problems 11 to 15 to one less significant figure (2 instead of 3, etc.) than requested in the problem.

21. State a rule that would be as good as the computer's rule for rounding off a number one place when the terminal digit is exactly five.

Write each of the following numbers in exponent notation, showing each with four significant figures:

22. 5280

23. 186,000

24. 92,900,000

25. .012345

26. 24.75

27. 80,000

28. .003300

29. 57,555,000

30. Write problems 22 to 25 with three significant figures.

15.3 NUMERICAL OPERATIONS WITH APPROXIMATE NUMBERS

Consider the problem of finding the area of a rectangle for which the sides are 24.02 and 35.56 feet. Suppose the lengths of these sides are measured to an accuracy of $\pm .005$ foot. The area, using the digits given, is then

$$A = (35.56)(24.02) = 854.1512 \text{ square feet.}$$

The following question arises: how many of the digits in the product should be retained in the answer? If the sides were in error as much as $+.005$ foot, then the number of square feet in the area could be as large as

$$(35.565)(24.025) = 854.449125 \text{ square feet,}$$

or, if the sides were in error as much as $-.005$ foot, the number of square feet in the area could be as small as

$$(35.555)(24.015) = 853.853325 \text{ square feet.}$$

It is evident that not all seven digits of the original product should be retained in reporting the area of the rectangle. Suppose the area is indicated as 854.2 square feet, the value obtained by rounding off the first product obtained. This value is reasonable, for if the maximum and minimum areas are averaged and rounded-off to four figures, the same result is obtained. Thus

$$\frac{854.449125 + 853.853325}{2}$$

equals 854.151225, which is equal to 854.2 when rounded off to four figures. The value 854.2 appears to be a good answer to report. It is considered as a more probable value than either of the extreme values. A value such as this, obtained as an average of a maximum and a minimum value, is called the *probable value* of the product. It should be noted that the number of significant digits in this probable value is the same as the number of significant digits in each of the factors.

Consider a second example of a product, for which the number of significant digits in the factors is different: Find the product of 24.3 and 37.82 where 24.3 is accurate to within $\pm.05$ and 37.82 is accurate to within $\pm.005$. Let P represent the product; then we have

$$P = (24.3)(37.82) = 919.026.$$

Using the maximum possible values of the entries, we find that the product is

$$(24.35)(37.825) = 921.03875.$$

Using the minimum possible values of the entries, we find that the product is

$$(24.25)(37.815) = 917.01375.$$

In this example it becomes apparent that not more than three figures should be indicated in the probable product. This value, 919, is again the average of the maximum and minimum possible values of the product. The two foregoing examples indicate a basis for the usual rule given for finding the product of two approximate numbers.

The product of two approximate numbers should be rounded off to the number of significant digits occurring in the factor with the smaller number of significant digits.

The same rule also applies to the division of one approximate number by another. The entry with fewer digits limits the number of significant digits that can be reported in the quotient. *If the two numbers used in multiplication or division differ by more than one significant digit, it is desirable to round off the one with the greater number of significant digits within one place more than the other* before performing the operation of multiplication or division.

The rules for adding and subtracting approximate numbers are different from those for multiplying and dividing. For convenience in discussing addition and subtraction, it is desirable to define the *terminal place* of an approximate number as *the last place occupied by a significant digit in the number*, reading from left to right; the terminal place is characterized by its place value. Thus the terminal place in 34.52 is the place occupied by the "2," and its place value is hundredths. The rule for adding approximate numbers is the following:

The sum of two or more approximate numbers should be rounded off so that its terminal place corresponds, in position relative to the decimal point, to that addend (or addends) with a terminal place farthest to the left. All entries should first be rounded off within one decimal place to the right of the number(s) terminating farthest to the left.

This rule also applies to the subtraction of approximate numbers. The following examples illustrate the application of the rules.

Example 1. Add 2.613 and 781.6 as approximate numbers.

Solution.

$$\begin{array}{r} 2.61\not{3} \\ +781.6 \\ \hline 784.21 \end{array} \rightarrow 784.2.$$

The answer is rounded off to 784.2, since 781.6 terminates in the "tenths" place.

Example 2. Add the approximate numbers 432.38 and 71.2.

Solution.

$$\begin{array}{r} 432.38 \\ +71.2 \\ \hline 503.58 \end{array} \rightarrow 503.6.$$

Again the answer is rounded off to the "tenths" place, to give 503.6.

Example 3. Subtract 8.74 from 34.7356, if both are approximate numbers.

Solution.

$$\begin{array}{r} 34.736 \\ -8.74 \\ \hline 25.996 \end{array} \rightarrow 26.00.$$

The answer is rounded off to the "hundredths" place.

Example 4. Subtract 1.62×10^4 from 93.24×10^3.

Solution. The entries should be rewritten as shown; the digits underscored are terminal places.

$$\begin{array}{r} 932\underline{4}0 \\ -16\underline{2}00 \\ \hline 77040 \end{array} \rightarrow 77\underline{0}00$$

The answer is 7.70×10^4. A better method of solving this example is to rewrite

93.24×10^3 as 9.324×10^4; the problem is then written

$$\begin{array}{r} 9.324 \times 10^4 \\ -1.62 \quad \times 10^4 \\ \hline 7.704 \times 10^4 \end{array} \rightarrow 7.70 \times 10^4.$$

Example 5. Find the product of 3.864 and 2.7.*

Solution. Instead of using all digits as shown, round off

$$\begin{array}{r} 3.864 \\ \times 2.7 \\ \hline 2.7048 \\ 7.728 \\ \hline 10.43\not{2}\not{8} \end{array} \qquad \begin{array}{r} 3.86 \\ \times 2.7 \\ \hline 2.702 \\ 7.72 \\ \hline 10.42\not{2} \end{array} \rightarrow 10.4$$

EXERCISE 2

The numbers given in the following examples are approximate numbers. Perform the indicated operations by making use of the rules given in the preceding section.

1. $37.213 + 485.73 =$

2. $43.81 + .008 =$

3. $34.078 + 9.33 =$

4. $8.92 \times 10^4 + 3.10 \times 10^3 =$

5. $47.321 - 9.58 =$

6. $7.82 \times 10^3 - 3.25 \times 10^2 =$

7. $7.938 \times 2.45 =$

8. $35.007 \times 48.3 =$

9. $(1.741 \times 10^3) \div (2.47 \times 10^2) =$

10. $7.25 \div 3.1416 =$

11. $6.734 \div 8.925 =$

12. $7344 \div .0009 =$

13. The dimensions of a rectangular box are 37.2 by 18.3 by 123.9 centimeters, accurate to $\pm .05$ centimeter. Find the probable value of the volume of the box.

14. The dimensions of a rectangle are 23.06 and 83.2 feet, and each dimension is an approximate number. Find approximate values for the area and the perimeter. How many digits should be in the answers?

15. Sound travels at a rate of about 1.09×10^3 feet per second. Find, to three significant figures, the number of seconds it takes sound to travel one mile (5.280×10^3 feet).

16. There are 39.37 inches in the standard meter. What is the number of feet, to three significant figures, in the standard meter?

17. How many seconds are there in one day of 24 hours? How many days, to three significant figures, are there in 1,000,000 seconds?

18. The standard liter is equal to about 1.0567 liquid quarts. What fraction of a liter is there in one liquid quart? (Obtain four significant figures.)

19. The distance from the earth to the sun is about 9.3×10^7 miles. How long does it take light, which travels at about 1.86×10^5 miles per second, to come from the sun to the earth?

* It might be noted that the answer to this example appears to contradict the rule for rounding off products. We have retained three digits in the answer instead of two. Such exceptions can occur in a product if the leading digit is a 1. The reader may wish to verify this with further examples.

20. If the equatorial diameter of the earth is 7.960×10^3 miles, and the value of π is 3.1416, what is the length of the circumference of the earth along the equator, to the nearest 10 miles?

21. Archimedes proved that the value of π lies between $3\frac{1}{7}$ and $3\frac{10}{71}$. Work out each of these values to six significant figures and compare them with 3.14159, which is a six-figure value of π.

22. A velocity of exactly 60 miles per hour is equivalent to exactly 88 feet per second. The term Mach 1 is applied to a velocity equal to that of sound, which is 1.09×10^3 feet per second at a given altitude. Express Mach 1 in miles per hour, to three significant figures. Express Mach 2 (twice Mach 1) in miles per hour.

23. Compute an approximate value of π from the ratio of 355 to 113.

24. Compare your answer in problem 23 with the answers in problem 21.

REFERENCES

Buckingham, B. R., *Elementary Arithmetic, Its Meaning and Practice*, pp. 456–480, 653–735.

Larsen, H. D., *Arithmetic for Colleges*, pp. 200–219.

Layton, W. I., *College Arithmetic*, pp. 113–129.

Marks, J. L., C. R. Purdy, and L. B. Kinney, *Teaching Arithmetic for Understanding*, pp. 273–309.

National Council of Teachers of Mathematics, *Twelfth Yearbook, Approximate Computation.*

Swain, R. L., *Understanding Arithmetic*, pp. 231–249.

16

Denominate Numbers

16.1 INTRODUCTION

Glancing over the front page of a metropolitan daily newspaper, we would find items such as the following: a royal couple was celebrating their twentieth wedding anniversary; the temperature that day was 57° F; the storm of the preceding day left 1.01 inches of rain; a landslide deposited forty cubic yards of earth in one person's backyard; the airline distance from Peiping to Moscow was quoted as 3600 miles; one country cut its armed forces by 1,840,000 men. These are only six of the many uses of numbers with different units that give more precision to the articles. In this edition of the paper there were eighteen articles on the front page, and everyone of them made some use of numbers.

A number by itself is often incomplete. The *number* tells *how many* units of some kind are being considered, but a *name* is needed to denote the *kind of unit* or *denomination*. Such numbers and units are referred to as *denominate numbers*, with the *number* giving the amount of the standard unit of measure and the *name*, the kind of unit. A *simple* denominate number, such as *twenty years*, is one employing a single kind of unit. A *compound* denominate number, such as *three years*, *seven months*, and *ten days*, is one employing more than one kind of unit. The quantities and the country of the world in which they are being measured will determine the units to be used. In the United States weights are often given in terms of pounds and ounces, whereas in Australia weights are given in terms of stones and pounds. For example, an American boy might give his weight as 130 pounds; an Australian boy of equal weight would give his weight as 9 stones 4, meaning 9 stones 4 pounds. A *stone* is equivalent to 14 pounds. Again, most Americans measure a ton as 2000 pounds, but in England a ton is 2240 pounds. The *metric ton*, used in France, Germany, and other countries is 2204.6 pounds. The ton of 2000 pounds is sometimes called the *short ton*, and the ton of 2240 pounds is sometimes called the *long ton.*

16.2 TABLES OF COMMON MEASURE

To measure various quantities, groups of different kinds of units are employed; hence, in studying denominate numbers, it is convenient to have

Table 12
Tables of Measure, English System

Counting
12 items = 1 dozen
12 dozen = 1 gross
20 items = 1 score
500 sheets = 1 ream

Linear Measure
12 inches = 1 foot
3 feet = 1 yard
$16\frac{1}{2}$ feet = $5\frac{1}{2}$ yards = 1 rod
5280 feet = 1760 yards = 320 rods = 1 mile

Square Measure (surface area)
144 square inches = 1 square foot
9 square feet = 1 square yard
$30\frac{1}{4}$ square yards = 1 square rod
160 square rods = 1 acre
43,560 square feet = 1 acre
640 acres = 1 square mile

Cubic Measure (volume or capacity)
1728 cubic inches = 1 cubic foot
27 cubic feet = 1 cubic yard
128 cubic feet = 1 cord

Liquid Measure
4 gills = 1 pint
2 pints = 1 quart
4 quarts = 1 gallon
231 cubic inches = 1 gallon
$31\frac{1}{2}$ gallons (approximately) = 1 barrel

Dry Measure
2 pints = 1 quart
8 quarts = 1 peck
4 pecks = 1 bushel

Avoirdupois Weight
16 ounces = 1 pound
100 pounds = 1 hundredweight
2000 pounds = 1 ton

Apothecaries' Fluid Measure
16 fluid ounces = 1 pint

Angles and Arcs
60 seconds (″) = 1 minute (′)
60 minutes = 1 degree (°)
90° = 1 right angle
90° = 1 quadrant
360° of arc = 1 circumference
360° of angle = 1 complete rotation
π radians = 180°, exactly
1 radian = 57.3°, approximately

Time
60 seconds = 1 minute
60 minutes = 1 hour
24 hours = 1 day
7 days = 1 week
365 days = 1 year
366 days = 1 leap year
12 months = 1 year
360 days = 1 commercial year

tables of common measure available for ready reference. The items in Table 12 show some of the common units of measure in the *English system* of measurement. The other principal system of measurement is the *metric system* which is discussed in some of the sections to follow. Many of the units in the English system are haphazard, since they have come from various sources, but because these units are in constant use it is important to know them. It should be observed that some of the groups of units are *primary*, that is, they are matters of definition or convention. For example, the units of linear measure are primary. Other groups of units, such as those for square and cubic measure, are *derived*; that is, they depend on the primary units and the relations between the quantities being measured. For example, 1 foot = 12 inches is a relation between primary units and is a matter of definition, whereas 1 square foot = 144 square inches is a derived relation since 1 square foot = 12×12 square inches. (See Chapter 8 on introduction to measurement.)

16.3 MISCELLANEOUS UNITS OF MEASURE

Few people realize how complicated our units of measure have become. A trip to the supermarket or grocery store will be revealing. Some items are sold by the pound. Can you name five such items? Some are sold by the dozen whereas others are sold by the quart, pint, or half gallon. Can you name three items of each kind? Some articles are sold in packages containing a certain number of items; for example, a roll of paper towels contains 150 towels and a box of cleansing tissues contains 200 tissues. Many items are sold by the can. Cans are classified by size as No. 00, No. $\frac{1}{2}$, No. 303, No. $2\frac{1}{2}$, and so on, whereas others contain a certain number of liquid ounces, such as 10, 12, or 46 ounces. Note that in liquid-ounce measure 32 ounces = 1 quart. Can you name three products that are sold by the liquid ounce? Can you name two or three items, each of which is sold by the pair, by the sack, or by the square yard?

Here is a quiz on some everyday items. If you can get all of them right, you are more observant than the average person. Which of the following statements are true and which are false?

1. A quart of water will fill about 4 cups.
2. A loaf of bread weighs nearly 1 pound or else $1\frac{1}{2}$ pounds.
3. A regulation tennis ball weighs 8 ounces.
4. Fire hydrants are usually 4 feet high.
5. A pound of flour will fill about 4 cups.
6. A drinking fountain is about 3 feet high.
7. Steps on stairs are about 12 inches high.
8. This book would weigh more if the pages were shortened one third in length and were made one third wider.
9. Streets marked off for parallel parking have car spaces about 15 feet long.

10. When 10 adults enter an elevator at the same time, the elevator should have a capacity of at least 1 ton.

EXERCISE 1

1. What unit of measure is used in specifying quantities of the following items: butter, doughnuts, milk, cloth, carpeting, gasoline, speed of a car, elevation above sea level, coal, temperature, size of a farm, pressure in a tire, capacity of a tank.

2. Complete as many of these as possible without using the reference table. If you do not get all of them, use the tables, but check each answer with an "R" to indicate the need for more work with the particular unit.

(*a*) $3\frac{1}{2}$ feet = ___ inches. (*b*) 48 inches = ___ feet.
(*c*) 5 yards = ___ feet. (*d*) 2 yards = ___ inches.
(*e*) 6 hours = ___ minutes. (*f*) 4 square yards = ___ square feet.
(*g*) 7 quarts = ___ pints. (*h*) 10 quarts = ___ gallons.
(*i*) 6 pounds = ___ ounces. (*j*) 150 minutes = ___ hours.
(*k*) 3 tons = ___ pounds. (*l*) 300 square inches = ___ square feet.

3. Use the tables if needed to complete the following:

(*a*) $\frac{1}{2}$ gallon = ___ quarts. (*b*) $\frac{1}{4}$ foot = ___ inches.
(*c*) $\frac{1}{2}$ yard = ___ inches. (*d*) $\frac{1}{6}$ square foot = ___ square inches.
(*e*) $\frac{5}{8}$ pound = ___ ounces. (*f*) 3456 cubic inches = ___ cubic feet.
(*g*) $\frac{5}{6}$ hour = ___ minutes. (*h*) 1 gross = ___ items.
(*i*) $\frac{3}{4}$ mile = ___ feet. (*j*) $\frac{4}{5}$ ton = ___ pounds.
(*k*) $\frac{3}{4}$ gallon = ___ pints. (*l*) 54 cubic feet = ___ cubic yards.

16.4 OPERATIONS WITH DENOMINATE NUMBERS

Denominate numbers can be added and subtracted in the same way as ordinary numbers, except that sometimes it is necessary to change the units from one denomination to another; that is, if 1 yard, 2 feet, 5 inches are to be added to 1 yard, 2 feet, 9 inches, the first answer can be 2 yards, 4 feet, 14 inches, although this is not considered the best form.

Add	1 yard, 2 feet, 5 inches
	1 yard, 2 feet, 9 inches
	2 yards, 4 feet, 14 inches
Answer.	3 yards, 2 feet, 2 inches

This answer is derived when 14 inches are converted to 1 foot, 2 inches, and 5 feet become 1 yard, 2 feet.

If 2 minutes, 50 seconds are to be subtracted from 12 minutes, 40 seconds, some regrouping is necessary. The 12 minutes 40 seconds should be converted to 11 minutes plus 1 minute and 40 seconds or 11 minutes and 100 seconds.

Subtract	12 minutes, 40 seconds	=	11 minutes, 100 seconds
	2 minutes, 50 seconds	=	2 minutes, 50 seconds
Answer.			9 minutes, 50 seconds

EXERCISE 2

1. Add (give answers in simplest form)

(*a*) 3 yards, 2 feet, 7 inches
6 yards, 1 foot, 4 inches
1 yard, 2 feet, 9 inches

(*b*) 4 hours, 4 minutes, 30 seconds
5 hours, 55 minutes, 10 seconds
2 hours, 10 minutes, 25 seconds

(*c*) 3 years, 8 months, 24 days
2 years, 3 months, 10 days
4 years, 2 months, 16 days

(*d*) 4 ton, 1250 pounds
5 ton, 1200 pounds
3 ton, 800 pounds

(*e*) 4 gallons, 2 quarts, 1 pint
5 gallons, 3 quarts, 0 pint
6 gallons, 1 quart, 1 pint

(*f*) 5 pounds, 13 ounces
12 pounds, 10 ounces
6 pounds, 7 ounces

2. Subtract

(*a*) 40 minutes, 20 seconds
30 minutes, 30 seconds

(*b*) 5 hours, 40 minutes
2 hours, 25 minutes

(*c*) 5 gallons, 1 quart
2 gallons, 2 quarts, 1 pint

(*d*) 10 pounds, 4 ounces
6 pounds, 10 ounces

(*e*) 5 yards, 2 feet, 4 inches
3 yards, 2 feet, 10 inches

(*f*) 7 years, 3 months, 10 days
4 years, 7 months, 17 days

The operations of multiplication and division are also applied to denominate numbers, but great care must be exercised in changing from one unit to another.

Multiply 3 yards, 2 feet by 4.

Solution.
3 yards, 2 feet
×4
12 yards, 8 feet, but 8 feet are 2 yards, 2 feet.

Answer. 14 yards, 2 feet.

Divide 9 feet, 4 inches by 2.

Solution. 2 ⟌ 9 feet, 4 inches becomes 2 ⟌ 8 feet, 16 inches (quotient: 4 feet, 8 inches)

Answer. 4 feet, 8 inches.

Another method gives

2 ⟌ 9 feet, 4 inches (quotient: $4\frac{1}{2}$ feet, 2 inches) but $4\frac{1}{2}$ feet, 2 inches = 4 feet, 8 inches.

EXERCISE 3

1. Multiply (give answers in simplest form)

(*a*) 3 yards, 2 feet, 7 inches × 4

(*b*) 4 pounds, 7 ounces × 5

(*c*) 9 hours, 12 minutes × 6

(*d*) 3 quarts, 1 pint × 9

2. Divide (give the answers in the simplest form)

(*a*) 3 ⟌ 7 feet, 9 inches

(*b*) 4 ⟌ 22 pounds, 12 ounces

(*c*) 6 ⟌ 19 hours, 24 minutes

(*d*) 9 ⟌ 29 square yards, 7 square feet, 108 square inches

3. Summary and review; complete as indicated:

(*a*) 17 inches = ____ feet ____ inches.

(*b*) 132 inches = ____ yards ____ feet ____ inches.

(*c*) 37 yards, 2 feet, 6 inches = ____ feet.

(*d*) 4 miles = ____ rods.

(*e*) 3 miles = ____ feet.

(*f*) 3 gallons, 2 quarts, 1 pint = ____ pints.

(*g*) 5 pounds, 10 ounces = ____ ounces.

(*h*) 78 ounces = ____ pounds ____ ounces.

(*i*) 8400 pounds = ____ tons ____ pounds.

(*j*) 2 years, 6 months, 12 days = ____ days.

(*k*) 14 yards, 1 foot, 6 inches − 3 yards, 1 foot, 9 inches

(*l*) 4 ⟌ 15 pounds, 12 ounces

(*m*) 7 gallons, 2 quarts, 1 pint × 8

(*n*) 22 hours, 10 minutes, 14 seconds − 21 hours, 55 minutes, 50 seconds

(*o*) 7 rods, 4 yards, 2 feet × 7

(*p*) 4 rods, 5 yards, 2 feet + 6 rods, 4 yards, 2 feet

16.5 THE METRIC SYSTEM

Many of the common units of measurement in the English system have been collected from various sources; hence some are logically related and others are not. The interrelations are thus rather haphazard: sixteen ounces in one pound, two thousand pounds in one ton, three feet in one yard, five and one half yards in one rod, and so on. A decimal system of weights, distances, and capacities, called the *metric system*, was adopted by the French government in 1799. It was developed on a logical and scientific basis and is generally applied in all scientific work. It is the official system of weights and measures in almost all countries of the world except the United Kingdom and the United States. However, the metric system is also a legal system of measurement in the United States and has been for nearly 100 years, but it is not in common use.

In the metric system the basic unit of length is the *meter* (39.37 inches), which is about 10 per cent longer than the English yard. The basic unit of weight is the *gram*, which is about $\frac{1}{28}$ of one ounce; there are about 454 grams in one pound. The basic unit of capacity is the *liter*, which is about 1.057 quarts. All multiples and submultiples* of these basic units are given in terms of powers of ten. The prefixes *deka* (ten), *hecto* (hundred), *kilo* (thousand) denote the multiples of the standard unit, and the prefixes *deci* (tenth), *centi* (hundredth), and *milli* (thousandth) represent the submultiples. (The prefix *mega* is used for one million, the prefix *micro*, for one millionth.)

	kilometer	1000	kilogram	kiloliter
	hectometer	100	hectogram	hectoliter
	dekameter	10 ↑	dekagram	dekaliter
Standard unit	*meter*	1	*gram*	*liter*
	decimeter	.1 ↓	decigram	deciliter
	centimeter	.01	centigram	centiliter
	millimeter	.001	milligram	milliliter

Note that each unit immediately below the other is one tenth as large, and each one immediately above is ten times as large. Similarly, items two rows apart are related by a ratio of 100 to 1.

Not only is there a relation among the units of a given group in the metric system in terms of powers of ten, but there are relations among the groups of units. A length of one centimeter, or .01 meter, is about $\frac{2}{5}$ of one inch. A small cube with each edge one centimeter long holds one cubic centimeter of material. *A liter is a measure of capacity equal to* 1000 *cubic centimeters.* A liter is also equivalent to a cubic decimeter, that is, a cubical container one decimeter or ten centimeters on each edge. A cube 10 by 10 by 10 centimeters has a volume equal to 1000 cubic centimeters, or one liter. A cubic meter, one meter on each edge, or 10 by 10 by 10 decimeters, has a volume equal to 1000 liters, or one kiloliter. There is a close relation between mass, or quantity of matter, and volume in the metric system.

The unit of mass in the metric system is the gram. *One gram of matter is the quantity of matter equivalent to one cubic centimeter of pure water at a temperature of* 4° *Centigrade.* A cubic centimeter of water thus has a mass of one gram, and a liter of water has a mass of one kilogram. Other substances, such as iron and lead, are denser than water; hence a cubic centimeter of either one would have a mass of several grams. One cubic

* A submultiple of a number is the number divided by a natural number, in this case ten or a power of ten.

centimeter of iron has a mass of about 7.80 grams, and one cubic centimeter of lead has a mass of about 11.0 grams.

Temperature in the metric system is measured in degrees Centigrade; 0° C is the freezing point of water and 100°C is the boiling point. A one-degree change in temperature in the Centigrade scale is thus 1/100 of the difference between the temperatures of freezing and boiling water. In the English system the Fahrenheit scale, in which the freezing point of water is 32° F, the boiling point, 212° F, is used.

The unit of time in the metric system is the same as that of the English system, namely the *second*; sixty seconds equal one minute, sixty minutes equal one hour, and twenty-four hours equal one mean solar day; 365 days equal one calendar year. The metric system of units is often referred to as the c.g.s. system for centimeter-gram-second. The English system of units is similarly referred to as the foot-pound-second system.

16.6 CONVERSION FACTORS FOR THE ENGLISH AND METRIC SYSTEMS

In practical problems it is often necessary to change denominate numbers from units in one system to units in the other. A list of some of the more important conversion factors is given in Table 13.

Table 13
Conversion Factors, Metric ↔ English Systems
(Approximate Equivalents)

1 meter = 39.37 inches = 3.281 feet	1 foot = 30.48 centimeters
1 kilometer = .6215 mile or $\frac{5}{8}$ mile	1 mile = 1.609 kilometers
1 liter = 1.057 quarts	1 quart = .9461 liter
1 kilogram = 2.205 pounds	1 pound = 453.6 grams
1 centimeter = .3937 or nearly $\frac{2}{5}$ inch	1 inch = 2.540 centimeters

If we travel south of the border of the continental United States into Mexico we would find distances between towns stated in kilometers. Since one kilometer is .62 mile, a distance of one hundred kilometers would be about sixty-two miles. Gasoline is sold by the liter, and since a liter is about 1.06 quarts, four liters of gasoline would be about one gallon plus a half pint of gasoline. Fruit and other commodities ordinarily sold by weight are measured by the kilo (kilogram), which would be about $2\frac{1}{5}$ pounds. To buy about one pound of produce we should have to order one half kilo.

A little arithmetic, using place value in the metric system and the common equivalents in the English system, will enable us to scale the conversion factors in Table 13 upward or downward as required in converting quantities from one system to the other.

Example 1. Two standard widths of film are 16 and 35 millimeters. Express these widths in inches.

Solution. Since 1 inch equals 2.54 centimeters, 1 inch also equals 25.4 millimeters, or about 25 millimeters.

$$16 \text{ millimeters} = \frac{16}{25} \text{ inch, or slightly more than } \frac{3}{5} \text{ inch.}$$

$$35 \text{ millimeters} = \frac{35}{25} \text{ inch, or about } 1\tfrac{2}{5} \text{ inches.}$$

Example 2. What is the difference between the distances of a 220-yard race and a 200-meter race?

Solution. One yard equals 36 inches and 1 meter equals 39.37 inches. Hence we have

$$220 \text{ yards} = 220 \times 36 \text{ inches} = 7920 \text{ inches}$$
$$200 \text{ meters} = 200 \times 39.37 \text{ inches} = 7874 \text{ inches.}$$

The difference is 46 inches, or 1 yard, 10 inches.

Example 3. How many grams does a $\frac{1}{4}$ pound of butter weigh?
Solution. Since 1 pound equals 454 grams, $\frac{1}{4}$ pound will equal $113\frac{1}{2}$ grams.

Example 4. How much does 1 quart of water weigh?

Solution. One quart equals .946 liter or 946 cubic centimeters. Since 1 cubic centimeter of water weighs 1 gram, 1 quart of water weighs 946 grams; 946 grams is about 2 pounds, $1\frac{1}{3}$ ounces, since 454 grams equal 1 pound.

EXERCISE 4

1. Change the following denominate numbers to new units as indicated.

(*a*) 35 centimeters = ____ meters.
(*b*) 28.35 grams = ____ kilograms.
(*c*) 1.609 kilometers = ____ centimeters.
(*d*) 1 hectoliter = ____ liters.
(*e*) 75 millimeters = ____ centimeters.
(*f*) 100 cubic centimeters = ____ liters.
(*g*) 2.5 decimeters = ____ centimeters.
(*h*) 10 liters = ____ cubic centimeters.

2. Use the definitions of units and the conversion factors to show the following equivalences:

(*a*) 1 yard = .9144 meter,
(*b*) 1 meter = 3.28 feet, (1 meter = 39.37 inches, 1 foot = 12 inches)
(*c*) 1 ounce = 28.35 grams,
(*d*) 1 gallon = 3.78 liters,
(*e*) 1 centimeter = .394 inch,
(*f*) 1 metric ton = 2205 pounds, (1 metric ton equals 1000 kilograms)
(*g*) 1 foot = .305 meter,
(*h*) 1 meter = 1.093 yards.

3. How many square centimeters are equivalent to 1 square foot? Answer to the nearest square centimeter.

4. The distance from Nogales, Mexico, to Tucson, Arizona, is about 120 kilometers. Express this distance in miles.

5. Light travels at a rate of 186,000 miles per second. What is the equivalent of this rate in kilometers per second? How many centimeters per second?

6. How many gallons are equivalent to 1 hectoliter?

7. Mount Everest is 29,008 feet high. Express this height in meters. Express it also in kilometers.

8. The Eiffel Tower in Paris, France, is 300 meters high. Express this height in feet.

9. A dealer buys 300 kilograms of dried fruit at $1.25 per kilogram. If he sells this fruit in half-pound packages, at 75 cents a package, what is his gross gain on the transaction?

10. A small foreign car weighs about 770 kilograms. What is the weight of this car in pounds?

11. The specific gravity (mass of a given volume of the substance compared with the same volume of water) for some common substances is given as follows:

Substance	Specific Gravity	Substance	Specific Gravity
Water	1.000	Iron	7.75
Ice	.92	Cork	.25
Milk	1.033	Mercury	13.60

(*a*) If water weighs 1 kilogram per liter, how many grams does 1 liter of ice weigh?

(*b*) How many grams does 1 liter of milk weigh?

(*c*) How many grams does 1 liter of mercury weigh?

12. Use the data of problem 11 and a suitable conversion factor to find the weight of 1 quart of water in grams. What is the weight of 1 quart of water in pounds, to the nearest .01 pound?

13. How many pounds would a quantity of iron having a volume of 1 liter weigh? (See data in problem 11.)

14. What volume would 1 kilogram of cork occupy?

15. How many pounds does 1 pint of milk weigh?

REFERENCES

Bowman, M. E., *Romance in Arithmetic: Currency, Weights and Measures.*

Buckingham, B. R., *Elementary Arithmetic, Its Meaning and Practice*, pp. 480–501.

Hallock, W., *The Evolution of Weights and Measures.*

Layton, W. I., *College Arithmetic*, pp. 71–94.

Morton, R. L., *Teaching Arithmetic in the Elementary School*, Vol. 2, pp. 411–431.

National Council of Teachers of Mathematics, *Twentieth Yearbook, The Metric System.*

Swain, R. L., *Understanding Arithmetic*, pp. 192–216.

17

Simple and Compound Interest

17.1 SIMPLE INTEREST

The following definitions and symbols are used in the discussion of simple interest:

1. *Interest* is the money received (or paid) for the use of capital. It is assumed that both interest and capital are expressed in the same units of money.
2. The *principal* is the money borrowed or loaned.
3. The *time* is the number of years (which may involve fractional parts of a year) for which the principal is borrowed or loaned. Therefore, the unit of time is one year.
4. The *rate of interest per unit of time* is the quotient obtained by dividing the interest for one unit of time by the principal. Unless stated otherwise, the unit of time is one year. The rate of interest may be expressed as a per cent or as a decimal fraction.
5. The *amount* of principal accruing interest is the sum of the principal and the interest.

Example 1. John borrows \$150, for five years at 4 per cent. What is the principal, the time, and the interest rate?

Solution. The principal is \$150, the time is 5 years, the interest rate is 4 per cent.

The quantities defined are represented by the following symbols:

P = principal in dollars or other units of money.
n = time in years.
i = rate of interest per year, expressed as a decimal fraction.
I = interest in dollars or other units of money of a principal, P, at interest for n years if the interest rate is i.
S = amount in dollars or other units of money of a principal, P, at interest for n years if the interest rate is i.

Hence it follows that

$$I = Pni \tag{1}$$

$$S = P + I. \tag{2}$$

Since $I = Pni$, formula 2 may be written

$$S = P + Pni,$$

or

$$S = P(1 + ni). \tag{3}$$

Example 2. Find the interest and amount in Example 1.

Solution. $I = 150\,(5)\,(.04) = \$30$* (by use of formula 1),

$S = 150 + 30 = \$180$ (by use of formula 2).

The amount may be obtained in another way by the use of formula 3. Thus

$$S = 150[1 + (5)\,(.04)] = 150(1.2) = \$180.$$

Interest computed in this manner is called *simple interest*, in contrast with compound interest, which is discussed later.

Example 3. Find the simple interest on \$500 for three months at 8 per cent and give the amount.

Solution. $P = \$500$, $n = \frac{3}{12}$ or $\frac{1}{4}$ year, $i = .08$.

Hence

$$I = 500(\tfrac{1}{4})(.08) = \$10.$$

The amount is

$$S = 500 + 10 = \$510,$$

or, by formula 3,

$$S = 500[1 + \tfrac{1}{4}(.08)] = 500(1.02) = \$510.$$

Example 4. Find the simple interest and the amount if \$200 is invested for two months at 6 per cent. Also find the amount at the end of one year.

Solution. In working interest problems, it is sometimes helpful to have what is called a line diagram. For this example the time is only two months (see Fig. 1).

For the amount at the end of two months, $n = \frac{2}{12}$, or $\frac{1}{6}$ year. The amount is

$$S = 200[1 + \tfrac{1}{6}(.06)] = \$202, \text{ and the interest is}$$

$$I = 200(\tfrac{1}{6})(.06) = 200(.01) = \$2.$$

Similarly, for the period of one year,

$$S = 200[1 + .06] = \$212.$$

In the foregoing example it should be noted that finding the interest on \$200 for two months at 6 per cent involves moving the decimal point in

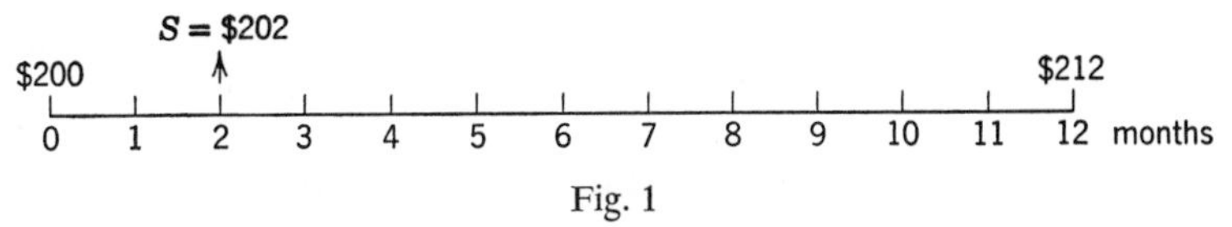

Fig. 1

* In this chapter the units in which the quantities are expressed are omitted in working out the examples. The proper unit is expressed in the final answer only.

the principal two places to the left, since the time is $\frac{1}{6}$ and the interest rate is .06. Thus $\frac{1}{6} \times .06 = .01$, which, when used as a multiplier, simply moves the decimal point two places to the left. This method is sometimes called the *sixty-day, 6 per cent method* for simple interest. A 360-day year is implied in the use of this method.

Example 5. Use the sixty-day, 6 per cent method to find the interest on \$237 for 82 days at 6 per cent.

Solution.

Interest on \$237 for 60 days at 6 per cent	2.370
Interest on \$237 for 20 days at 6 per cent	.790
Interest on \$237 for 2 days at 6 per cent	.079
	\$3.239 or \$3.24

It should be noted that the interest for 20 days is $\frac{1}{3}$ of that for 60 days and that the interest for 2 days is $\frac{1}{10}$ of that for 20 days. The reader should check the answer by using formula 1.

The sixty-day, 6 per cent method may be used when the rate is not 6 per cent. The following example illustrates a technique for carrying out this computation.

Example 6. Find the interest on \$540 for 60 days at 4 per cent.

Solution.

Interest on \$540 for 60 days at 6 per cent	5.40
Interest on \$540 for 60 days at 2 per cent	1.80
Interest on \$540 for 60 days at 4 per cent	\$3.60

The interest at 2 per cent is $\frac{1}{3}$ of the interest at 6 per cent. The answer is obtained by subtraction, since 4 per cent equals 6 per cent minus 2 per cent, or it could be obtained by doubling the interest at 2 per cent.

EXERCISE 1

1. Find the amount and simple interest on \$635 for three years if the interest rate is 5 per cent.

2. W. C. Brown borrows \$500 from A. L. George for eight months and agrees to pay 7 per cent simple interest. How much must Brown pay George at the end of eight months?

3. Using the sixty-day, 6 per cent method, find the interest on

(*a*) \$783.50 for 60 days at 6 per cent.
(*b*) \$813.60 for 90 days at 6 per cent.
(*c*) \$935.40 for 96 days at 6 per cent.
(*d*) \$435.90 for 60 days at 4 per cent.
(*e*) \$238.50 for 82 days at 4 per cent.

4. \$1700 is invested at 5 per cent simple interest for five years. At what interest rate must this be invested to earn just as much in four years?

17.2 ORDINARY AND EXACT SIMPLE INTEREST

In figuring simple interest, the question of the number of days counted in the year is important. If 360 days are counted, then *ordinary simple interest* is used. If 365 days are counted, then *exact simple interest* is computed.

There are variations in practice in counting the number of days between dates in computing simple interest. In the following sections the exact elapsed time is used unless it is given in months, in which case each month is considered as having thirty days.

Example 1. Find the ordinary simple interest on $235 loaned from March 23, 1961, to August 2, 1961, at 4 per cent.

The total time for the loan is figured as follows

March	has	8 days	(31 − 23)
April	has	30 days	
May	has	31 days	
June	has	30 days	
July	has	31 days	
August	has	2 days	
Total		132 days.	

Hence $I = 235(\frac{132}{360})(.04) = \$3.45$.

Some calendars number each day of the year. Thus March 23 is the eighty-second day of the year (one more in a leap year) and August 2 is the two-hundred fourteenth day (one more in a leap year). The exact number of days is 214 − 82 = 132 days, which was the answer obtained by direct count. For convenience a table is given on page 252, in which each day of the year is numbered.

Example 2. Find the ordinary and the exact simple interest on $400 from May 10 to October 5 if interest is computed at 5 per cent.

Solution. As listed in the table of day numbers, May 10 is the one hundred thirtieth day of the year and October 15 is the two hundred eighty-eighth. Hence the time is 288 − 130 = 158 days. The ordinary simple interest is $400(\frac{158}{360})(.05) = \$8.78$. The exact simple interest is $400(\frac{158}{365})(.05) = \$8.66$.

Example 3. Find the ordinary simple interest on $1200 from February 5, 1959, to August 23, 1960, at 3 per cent.

Solution. Since 1960 is a leap year, one day should be added to the entry in the time table after February 28. February 5 is the thirty-sixth day and August 23, 1960, is the two hundred thirty-sixth day. Thus the time is 236 − 36 = 200 days. The ordinary simple interest is $1200(\frac{200}{360})(.03) = \$20.00$.

EXERCISE 2

1. Find the ordinary simple interest on $250 from May 15, 1962, to July 2, 1962, at 8 per cent.

2. Find the exact simple interest on $600 from January 29, 1960, to August 5, 1960 at 7 per cent.

3. Find the ordinary simple interest on $900 from June 24, 1958, to March 31, 1959, at 8 per cent.

Table 14 The Number of Each Day of the Year

Day of Month	Jan.	Feb.	Mar.	Apr.	May	June	July	Aug.	Sept.	Oct.	Nov.	Dec.	Day of Month
1	1	32	60	91	121	152	182	213	244	274	305	335	1
2	2	33	61	92	122	153	183	214	245	275	306	336	2
3	3	34	62	93	123	154	184	215	246	276	307	337	3
4	4	35	63	94	124	155	185	216	247	277	308	338	4
5	5	36	64	95	125	156	186	217	248	278	309	339	5
6	6	37	65	96	126	157	187	218	249	279	310	340	6
7	7	38	66	97	127	158	188	219	250	280	311	341	7
8	8	39	67	98	128	159	189	220	251	281	312	342	8
9	9	40	68	99	129	160	190	221	252	282	313	343	9
10	10	41	69	100	130	161	191	222	253	283	314	344	10
11	11	42	70	101	131	162	192	223	254	284	315	345	11
12	12	43	71	102	132	163	193	224	255	285	316	346	12
13	13	44	72	103	133	164	194	225	256	286	317	347	13
14	14	45	73	104	134	165	195	226	257	287	318	348	14
15	15	46	74	105	135	166	196	227	258	288	319	349	15
16	16	47	75	106	136	167	197	228	259	289	320	350	16
17	17	48	76	107	137	168	198	229	260	290	321	351	17
18	18	49	77	108	138	169	199	230	261	291	322	352	18
19	19	50	78	109	139	170	200	231	262	292	323	353	19
20	20	51	79	110	140	171	201	232	263	293	324	354	20
21	21	52	80	111	141	172	202	233	264	294	325	355	21
22	22	53	81	112	142	173	203	234	265	295	326	356	22
23	23	54	82	113	143	174	204	235	266	296	327	357	23
24	24	55	83	114	144	175	205	236	267	297	328	358	24
25	25	56	84	115	145	176	206	237	268	298	329	359	25
26	26	57	85	116	146	177	207	238	269	299	330	360	26
27	27	58	86	117	147	178	208	239	270	300	331	361	27
28	28	59	87	118	148	179	209	240	271	301	332	362	28
29	29	...	88	119	149	180	210	241	272	302	333	363	29
30	30	...	89	120	150	181	211	242	273	303	334	364	30
31	31	...	90	...	151	...	212	243	...	304	...	365	31

Note. After February 28, in leap years, the number of the day is one greater than that given in the table.

4. Use the sixty-day, 6 per cent method to figure the ordinary simple interest on \$456.30 from May 15, 1963, to July 29, 1963, at 6 per cent.

5. Use the same method indicated in problem 4 to find the interest on \$635.60 from October 17, 1962, to December 1, 1962, at 4 per cent.

17.3 FURTHER USES OF THE INTEREST FORMULA

We have used the interest formula to find the interest when the time, interest rate, and principal are given. Additional uses may result from solving the formula, $I = Pni$, in turn for P, n, i. We obtain the following:

$$P = \frac{I}{ni}, \quad n = \frac{I}{Pi}, \quad i = \frac{I}{Pn}. \tag{4}$$

The following examples illustrate some of the possible applications of these formulas:

Example 1. Find the amount of money needed to earn \$240 in simple interest in 4 years at an interest rate of 6 per cent.

Solution. From the first of the three formulas,

$$P = \frac{240}{4(.06)} = \$1000.$$

Some may prefer to substitute in formula 1 and solve. Thus $I = Pni$, or $240 = P(4)(.06)$. Hence $60 = P(.06)$, or $P = \$1000$.

Example 2. How long will it take \$500 to double itself if a simple interest rate of 8 per cent is used?

Solution. The second of the formulas in (4) gives $n = I/Pi$. Since \$500 is to double itself, it must earn \$500. Thus

$$n = \frac{500}{500(.08)} = \frac{1}{.08} = 12\tfrac{1}{2} \text{ years.}$$

Example 3. At one time a certain issue of U.S. Savings Bonds could be purchased for \$75. The repayment value after ten years was \$100. What simple interest was earned on such bonds? Using the third of the formulas (4), $i = I/Pn$. Substituting,

$$i = \frac{25}{75 \times 10} = \frac{1}{30} = .03\tfrac{1}{3} \quad \text{or} \quad 3\tfrac{1}{3}\%.$$

EXERCISE 3

1. At the end of $1\frac{1}{2}$ years the interest on a given principal is \$38.22. If the interest rate is 4 per cent, find the principal.
2. An investment of \$1000 paid \$130 the first year and \$155 the second year. What average simple interest rate was earned on this investment over the two-year period? (Give your answer with three significant figures.)
3. How long will it take \$100 to increase threefold at simple interest of 4 per cent? Would the answer be changed if \$200 was used instead of \$100?
4. In what time will \$600 earn \$5 if the simple interest is 5 per cent?
5. \$800 was invested at 6 per cent on May 15. At what time (month and day) will this investment have earned \$24, using ordinary simple interest?
6. \$1200 was invested at 5 per cent on June 30. At what time (month and day) will this investment have earned \$27?

17.4 PRESENT VALUE AND DISCOUNT

An amount of money S, due at some future date, has a value now called its *present value*, P. If the interest rate is i, then by formula in (3)

$$S = P(1 + ni).$$

This formula may be solved for P, giving

$$P = \frac{S}{1 + ni}. \qquad (5)$$

The difference, $S - P$, is called the *simple discount* on S, using a *simple interest rate* (see Chapter 18, section 18.1 for a discussion of discount at a discount rate).

Example. What is the present value of \$500 due in two years if money can be invested at a simple interest rate of 4 per cent? What is the simple discount?

Solution. $P = \dfrac{500}{1 + 2(.04)} = \dfrac{500}{1.08} = \$462.96.$

As a check, compute the simple interest on \$462.96 for two years. Add it to \$462.96. The result should be \$500. The simple discount is $500 - 462.96 =$ \$37.04.

EXERCISE 4

1. (*a*) Find the present value of \$300 due in $1\frac{1}{2}$ years at an interest rate of 4 per cent. (*b*) What is the simple discount on \$300?

2. An investor expects to receive a dividend of \$750 in six months. If money can be invested at 5 per cent, what is the present value of the dividend?

3. A lot may be purchased for \$1000 down and \$4000 at the end of the first year. If money can be invested at 5 per cent, what is the equivalent cash price of this lot?

4. What is the present value of \$800 due in two years at $3\frac{1}{2}$ per cent interest?

17.5 COMPOUND INTEREST

An examination of the formula in (1) indicates that simple interest is directly proportional to the time. Thus, if the simple interest on a given sum of money for one year is \$12, then the interest for two years is \$24; for three years it is \$36, and so on. Instead of simple interest, the lending industry usually uses what is called compound interest if the period is over a year. In computing interest by this method, interest is added to the principal at the end of each period. Suppose \$600 is loaned for three years at a compound interest rate of 5 per cent per year. The interest is computed as follows:

At the end of the first year the interest is $600 \times .05 = \$30$. The new principal is

$$600 + 30 = \$630,$$

which may be called the amount S_1 at the end of one year. Let S_2 represent the amount at the end of two years; then

$$S_2 = 630 + 630(.05) = \$661.50.$$

Hence

$$S_3 = 661.50 + 661.50(.05) = 661.50(1.05) = \$694.58.$$

The compound interest is $694.58 - 600 = \$94.58$ on \$600 for three years at 5 per cent. If simple interest had been used, the interest would have been

$$I = 600 \times 3 \times .05 = \$90.$$

In this example it is seen that the compound interest is \$4.58 greater than the simple interest.

The following symbols are used later in compound interest formulas. Note that these symbols have slight variations from the similar ones given for simple interest.

P = principal in dollars or other units of money,
i = interest rate per period,
n = number of periods,
S_n = compound amount at the end of the first n periods,
I_n = compound interest at the end of n periods.

The amount, S_1, of P at the end of the first period is

$$S_1 = P + Pi = P(1 + i),$$
$$S_2 = P(1 + i) + P(1 + i)i = P(1 + i)(1 + i) = P(1 + i)^2,$$

and

$$S_3 = P(1 + i)^2 + P(1 + i)^2 i = P(1 + i)^3.$$

It would appear that the amount of P for n periods is

$$S_n = P(1 + i)^n. \tag{6}$$

This formula is indeed true and can be proved by mathematical induction.

The period indicated may be one of many possible time limits, such as one year, one month, one quarter year, or one half year. The interest rate, i, in the foregoing formula is for the period indicated, but it is customary to express it on a yearly basis simply by multiplying the period rate by the number of periods in a year. A rate of 2 per cent per quarter would be expressed as 8 per cent per year compounded quarterly, which is technically

Table 15 I
Values of $(1 + i)^n$

n	$i = \frac{1}{2}\%$	$i = 1\%$	$i = 1\frac{1}{4}\%$	$i = 1\frac{1}{2}\%$	$i = 2\%$
1	1.0050000	1.0100000	1.0125000	1.0150000	1.0200000
2	1.0100250	1.0201000	1.0251563	1.0302250	1.0404000
3	1.0150751	1.0303010	1.0379707	1.0456784	1.0612080
4	1.0201505	1.0406040	1.0509453	1.0613636	1.0824322
5	1.0252513	1.0510101	1.0640822	1.0772840	1.1040808
6	1.0303775	1.0615202	1.0773832	1.0934433	1.1261624
7	1.0355294	1.0721354	1.0908505	1.1098449	1.1486857
8	1.0407070	1.0828567	1.1044861	1.1264926	1.1716594
9	1.0459106	1.0936853	1.1182922	1.1433900	1.1950926
10	1.0511401	1.1046221	1.1322708	1.1605408	1.2189944
11	1.0563958	1.1156683	1.1464242	1.1779489	1.2433743
12	1.0616778	1.1268250	1.1607545	1.1956182	1.2682418
13	1.0669862	1.1380933	1.1752639	1.2135524	1.2936066
14	1.0723211	1.1494742	1.1899547	1.2317557	1.3194788
15	1.0776827	1.1609690	1.2048292	1.2502321	1.3458683
16	1.0830712	1.1725786	1.2198895	1.2689855	1.3727857
17	1.0884865	1.1843044	1.2351382	1.2880203	1.4002414
18	1.0939289	1.1961475	1.2505774	1.3073406	1.4282462
19	1.0993986	1.2081090	1.2662096	1.3269507	1.4568112
20	1.1048956	1.2201900	1.2820372	1.3468550	1.4859474
21	1.1104201	1.2323919	1.2980627	1.3670578	1.5156663
22	1.1159722	1.2447159	1.3142885	1.3875637	1.5459797
23	1.1215520	1.2571630	1.3307171	1.4083772	1.5768993
24	1.1271598	1.2697346	1.3473511	1.4295028	1.6084372
25	1.1327956	1.2824320	1.3641929	1.4509454	1.6406060
26	1.1384596	1.2952563	1.3812454	1.4727095	1.6734181
27	1.1441519	1.3082089	1.3985109	1.4948002	1.7068865
28	1.1498726	1.3212910	1.4159923	1.5172222	1.7410242
29	1.1556220	1.3345039	1.4336922	1.5399805	1.7758447
30	1.1614001	1.3478489	1.4516134	1.5630802	1.8113616
31	1.1672071	1.3613274	1.4697585	1.5865264	1.8475888
32	1.1730431	1.3749407	1.4881305	1.6103243	1.8845406
33	1.1789083	1.3886901	1.5067321	1.6344792	1.9222314
34	1.1848029	1.4025770	1.5255663	1.6589964	1.9606760
35	1.1907269	1.4166028	1.5446359	1.6838813	1.9998896
36	1.1966805	1.4307688	1.5639438	1.7091395	2.0398873
37	1.2026639	1.4450765	1.5834931	1.7347766	2.0806851
38	1.2086772	1.4595272	1.6032868	1.7607983	2.1222988
39	1.2147206	1.4741225	1.6233279	1.7872103	2.1647448
40	1.2207942	1.4888637	1.6436195	1.8140184	2.2080397
41	1.2268982	1.5037524	1.6641647	1.8412287	2.2522005
42	1.2330327	1.5187899	1.6849668	1.8688471	2.2972445
43	1.2391979	1.5339778	1.7060289	1.8968798	2.3431894
44	1.2453939	1.5493176	1.7273542	1.9253330	2.3900531
45	1.2516208	1.5648107	1.7489461	1.9542130	2.4378542
46	1.2578789	1.5804589	1.7708080	1.9835262	2.4866113
47	1.2641683	1.5962634	1.7929431	2.0132791	2.5363435
48	1.2704892	1.6122261	1.8153549	2.0434783	2.5870704
49	1.2768416	1.6283483	1.8380468	2.0741305	2.6388118
50	1.2832258	1.6446318	1.8610224	2.1052424	2.6915830

Table 15 II

Values of $(1 + i)^n$.

n	$i = 2\frac{1}{2}\%$	$i = 3\%$	$i = 4\%$	$i = 5\%$	$i = 6\%$
1	1.0250000	1.0300000	1.0400000	1.0500000	1.0600000
2	1.0506250	1.0609000	1.0816000	1.1025000	1.1236000
3	1.0768906	1.0927270	1.1248640	1.1576250	1.1910160
4	1.1038129	1.1255088	1.1698586	1.2155063	1.2624770
5	1.1314082	1.1592741	1.2166529	1.2762816	1.3382256
6	1.1596934	1.1940523	1.2653190	1.3400956	1.4185191
7	1.1886858	1.2298739	1.3159318	1.4071004	1.5036303
8	1.2184029	1.2667701	1.3685691	1.4774554	1.5938481
9	1.2488630	1.3047732	1.4233118	1.5513282	1.6894790
10	1.2800845	1.3439164	1.4802443	1.6288946	1.7908477
11	1.3120867	1.3842339	1.5394541	1.7103394	1.8982986
12	1.3448888	1.4257609	1.6010322	1.7958563	2.0121965
13	1.3785110	1.4685337	1.6650735	1.8856491	2.1329283
14	1.4129738	1.5125897	1.7316764	1.9799316	2.2609040
15	1.4482982	1.5579674	1.8009435	2.0789282	2.3965582
16	1.4845056	1.6047064	1.8729812	2.1828746	2.5403517
17	1.5216183	1.6528476	1.9479005	2.2920183	2.6927728
18	1.5596587	1.7024331	2.0258165	2.4066192	2.8543392
19	1.5986502	1.7535061	2.1068492	2.5269502	3.0255995
20	1.6386164	1.8061112	2.1911231	2.6532977	3.2071355
21	1.6795819	1.8602946	2.2787681	2.7859626	3.3995636
22	1.7215714	1.9161034	2.3699188	2.9252607	3.6035374
23	1.7646107	1.9735865	2.4647155	3.0715238	3.8197497
24	1.8087259	2.0327941	2.5633042	3.2250999	4.0489346
25	1.8539441	2.0937779	2.6658363	3.3863549	4.2918707
26	1.9002927	2.1565913	2.7724698	3.5556727	4.5493830
27	1.9478000	2.2212890	2.8833686	3.7334563	4.8223459
28	1.9964950	2.2879277	2.9987033	3.9201291	5.1116867
29	2.0464074	2.3565655	3.1186515	4.1161356	5.4183879
30	2.0975676	2.4272625	3.2433975	4.3219424	5.7434912
31	2.1500068	2.5000803	3.3731334	4.5380395	6.0881006
32	2.2037569	2.5750828	3.5080587	4.7649415	6.4533867
33	2.2588509	2.6523352	3.6483811	5.0031885	6.8405899
34	2.3153221	2.7319053	3.7943163	5.2533480	7.2510253
35	2.3732052	2.8138625	3.9460890	5.5160154	7.6860868
36	2.4325353	2.8982783	4.1039326	5.7918161	8.1472520
37	2.4933487	2.9852267	4.2680899	6.0814069	8.6360871
38	2.5556824	3.0747835	4.4388135	6.3854773	9.1542523
39	2.6195745	3.1670270	4.6163660	6.7047512	9.7035075
40	2.6850638	3.2620378	4.8010206	7.0399887	10.2857179
41	2.7521904	3.3598989	4.9930615	7.3919881	10.9028610
42	2.8209952	3.4606959	5.1927839	7.7615876	11.5570327
43	2.8915201	3.5645168	5.4004953	8.1496669	12.2504546
44	2.9638081	3.6714523	5.6165151	8.5571503	12.9854819
45	3.0379033	3.7815958	5.8411757	8.9850078	13.7646108
46	3.1138509	3.8950437	6.0748227	9.4342582	14.5904875
47	3.1916971	4.0118950	6.3178156	9.9059711	15.4659167
48	3.2714896	4.1322519	6.5705282	10.4012696	16.3938717
49	3.3532768	4.2562194	6.8333494	10.9213331	17.3775040
50	3.4371087	4.3839060	7.1066833	11.4673998	18.4201543

called a *nominal rate* of 8 per cent compounded quarterly. A rate of 6 per cent compounded semiannually means that the interest rate is 3 per cent each half year.

Example. Find the compound interest on \$800 for four years if the interest rate is 4 per cent compounded semiannually.

Solution. Since the interest is compounded semiannually, there are two periods per year. Hence in four years there are eight periods, and the interest rate per period is .02. By formula in (6),

$$S_8 = \$800(1.02)^8.$$

Raising 1.02 to the eighth power gives 1.17166, to six significant figures; hence

$$S_8 = \$800(1.17166)$$
$$= \$937.33.$$

The compound interest is \$937.33 − \$800.00 = \$137.33.

Normally the labor involved in computing $(1 + i)^n$ is too great for easy computation, even for relatively small values of n. A table of powers of $(1 + i)$ is of great value in computing compound interest. Such a table is given on page 256. To evaluate $(1.02)^8$, consult the column headed by 2 per cent and the row marked 8. The value read is 1.1716594. If accuracy to the nearest cent is desired in an example such as the foregoing, this number can be rounded off to 1.17166.

EXERCISE 5

Find the compound amount and the compound interest for each of the following problems:

	Principal	*Interest Rate*	*Compounded*	*Years*
1.	\$ 500	5%	annually	6
2.	\$ 1,200	4%	semiannually	3
3.	\$ 1,500	6%	quarterly	10
4.	\$ 200	8%	semiannually	25
5.	\$ 895	4%	quarterly	12
6.	\$10,000	6%	monthly	4

7. A man invested \$4000 for his son, at age 10 years, in a savings association which paid 4 per cent compounded quarterly. How much was there on deposit in the account when the boy reached age 18?

8. One investment pays interest at the rate of 5 per cent compounded semiannually. Another pays interest at the rate of 5 per cent compounded annually. Which is the better investment if funds are invested for four years? Is the answer changed if the period is five years?

9. Suppose a \$15,000 investment is made in each of the investment companies mentioned in problem 8. What is the difference between the earnings after four years? What is the difference after five years?

10. Write an equation from which it can be determined how long it will take money to double itself at 6 per cent compounded annually; at 4 per cent compounded annually; at 3 per cent; at 2 per cent. Use the compound interest table to obtain an approximate answer.

17.6 PRESENT VALUE

Another important application of the compound interest formula determines the sum of money needed now to provide a given amount at a future date, if money can be invested at compound interest. The sum of money needed now is called the *present value* of the given amount at a future date. This value is found by solving the compound interest formula for P. Thus

$$S_n = P(1 + i)^n;$$

hence

$$P = \frac{S_n}{(1 + i)^n}, \tag{7}$$

where P is the present value of S_n due in n periods.

Example. What sum of money must be invested now in a bank paying interest at the rate of 3 per cent compounded semiannually to provide \$4000 in twenty years?

Solution.

$$P = \frac{\$4000}{(1.015)^{40}},$$

$$= \frac{\$4000}{1.814018}, \quad \text{using Table 15I,}$$

$$= \$2205.05.$$

If the present value formula is written $P = S_n(1 + i)^{-n}$, then a table giving values of $(1 + i)^{-n}$ for various values of i and n would be valuable for computational purposes, since only a multiplication would be needed. Such tables may be found in various mathematics of finance books.*

EXERCISE 6

Find the present value P of S_n due in n periods in problems 1 to 6 below.

	S_n	*Number of years to Due Date*	*Interest Rate*	*Compounded*
1.	\$ 500	4	6%	semiannually
2.	\$ 1,000	50	5%	annually
3.	\$ 350	12	4%	quarterly
4.	\$ 2,000	4	6%	monthly
5.	\$ 350	48	1%	annually
6.	\$15,000	50	3%	annually

* See Bell and Adams, *Mathematics of Finance*, combined edition, Holt, New York, 1949.

7. Which is larger, the present value of $1000 due in 25 years if money earns 6 per cent compounded annually or $1000 due in twenty-five years if money earns 6 per cent compounded semiannually? Find the difference in the present values.

8. Write an expression to indicate the present value of $1000 due in fifty years with interest computed at 6 per cent compounded quarterly. Can you use the table given in the book directly? If not, how would you compute the present value?

REFERENCES

Bell, C. and L. J. Adams, *Mathematics of Finance*, combined edition, pp. 105–130 140–147, 247–268.

Simpson, T. M., Z. M. Pirenian, and B. H. Crenshaw, *Mathematics of Finance*, third edition, pp. 46–70.

Taylor, E. H., and C. N. Mills, *Arithmetic for Teacher-Training Classes*, fourth edition, pp. 285–298.

18

General Monetary Applications

18.1 NOTES AND BANK DISCOUNT

Usually, when short-term loans are made, the borrower is required to sign a written agreement promising to pay a fixed sum at some future date. Such an agreement is called a *note*. The money to be repaid by the borrower is called the *face* of the note. The amount of money received by the borrower upon signing the note is called the *proceeds* or the *present value* of the note. The difference between the face of the note and the proceeds is called the *discount*. (See Chapter 17, section 17.4.) A certain per cent of the face of the note is used to figure the discount. This is called the *discount rate*, and it is commonly expressed as a per cent for the year. The time the note is to run before the due date is called the *term* of the note. The discount figured by using a discount rate is sometimes called a *bank discount*.

These quantities are generally represented as follows:

D = bank discount,
S = maturity value of note (or the face value if the note carries no interest),
n = term in years,
d = discount rate,
P = proceeds (present value).

They are related by the following equations:

$$D = Snd \qquad \text{and} \qquad P = S - D, \tag{1}$$

which in turn can be expressed as

$$P = S - Snd = S(1 - nd). \tag{2}$$

$300.00 Spingfield, Ill., Oct. 6 19__

Three months ---------------- after date I promise to pay to

the order of James Davidson --

Three hundred and no/100 ------------------------------------ Dollars

VALUE RECEIVED

Charles Fraser

$1655.00 Boston, Mass., April 30 19__

Ninety days ------------------- after date I promise to pay to

the order of Beckman Instrument Co. --------------------------------

Sixteen hundred fifty-five and no/100 ----------------------- Dollars

for value received, with interest at 6 %.

Arthur James

Fig. 1

Example .1 A man needs at least \$175. His banker agrees to lend him the proceeds of a \$200 note due in one year for which a 7 per cent discount rate is charged. (*a*) What is the discount? (*b*) What are the proceeds?

Solution. The discount is 7 per cent of \$200, or \$14. The proceeds are $200 - 14 = \$186$, which is sufficient to meet the needs of the borrower.

Many notes are written to call for the repayment of the face value with interest at a given rate. Such notes may be discounted by the bank immediately or sold on the market at any time after the note is made and before it is due. Illustrations of the two types of notes are given in Fig. 1.

Example 2. A note calls for the repayment of \$500 in nine months with interest at 6 per cent. The note was sold after three months at a discount rate of 5 per cent. Find (*a*) the maturity value of the note and (*b*) the selling price (proceeds) of the note.

Solution. (*a*) It is helpful to make a line diagram of the time for problems of this sort (Fig. 2).

The maturity value of the note is $500\,[1 + \frac{9}{12}(.06)] = \$522.50$.

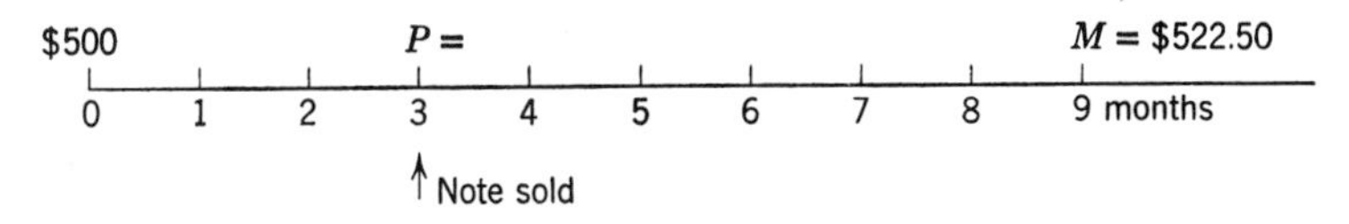

Fig. 2

(*b*) The proceeds, P, are obtained by discounting \$522.50 for six months at 5 per cent. $D = 522.50 \times \frac{1}{2} \times .05 = \$13.06$. The proceeds are $522.50 - 13.06 = \$509.44$. This amount is the selling price of the note. Note that *the term for the discount of a note is the time, in years, elapsing between the discount date and the maturity date.*

Example 3. (*a*) What interest rate was earned by the original holder of the note? (*b*) What interest rate was earned by the buyer? (*c*) What interest rate was paid by the borrower?

Solution. (*a*) The original holder of the note loaned \$500, for which he received \$509.44 after three months. Hence the interest rate for the three-month period is $9.44 \div 500 = .01888$; $4(.01888) = .07552$, or 7.552 per cent is the yearly rate.

(*b*) The buyer pays \$509.44 for the note and after six months receives \$522.50. Hence he earns \$13.06 in interest during the half year he has held the note. The interest rate earned by the buyer, using the simple interest formula $I = Pni$, is

$$i = \frac{13.06}{509.44 \times \frac{1}{2}} = .05127, \quad \text{or} \quad 5.127\%.$$

(*c*) The borrower is not affected by the sale of the note. He still pays 6 per cent.

EXERCISE 1

1. Mr. James borrows money from a bank for which he signs a note for \$600 due in nine months. The bank uses a discount rate of 5 per cent. How much does Mr. James receive? What is this called? What is the discount?

2. An interest-bearing note requires the repayment of \$5000 after one year with interest at 4 per cent. This note is sold immediately after it is made at a discount rate of 5 per cent.

(*a*) Find the maturity value of the note.
(*b*) Find the discount on the note.
(*c*) Find the proceeds of the note.

3. Mr. White lends Mr. Eagle \$950 and receives a note from Mr. Eagle calling for the repayment of \$950 in eight months with interest at 8 per cent. After two months Mr. White sells his note to a bank at a discount rate of 6 per cent.

(*a*) Find the maturity value of the note.
(*b*) Find the discount on the note.
(*c*) What did Mr. White receive for the note when he sold it?
(*d*) What interest rate did Mr. White earn on his investment?
(*e*) What interest rate did the bank earn on its investment?
(*f*) Did the sale of the note change the interest rate paid by Mr. Eagle?

4. A note calls for the repayment of $1000 in eighteen months with interest at 7 per cent. The note was immediately sold at a discount rate of 7 per cent. What were the proceeds?

5. Which is better for the borrower, a discount rate of 4 per cent or an interest rate of 4 per cent? Why?

6. Compare the bank proceeds on a note for $600 due in six months without interest, if the discount rate is 6 per cent, with the present value of $600 six months from now if the simple interest rate is 6 per cent.

7. What is the maturity value of a note for $450 for nine months with interest at 5 per cent? What are the proceeds on this note if it is discounted after six months at a discount rate of 6 per cent?

18.2 INSTALLMENT BUYING

Many people buy furniture, automobiles, and other things on the installment plan. The usual plan is to make a down payment on the purchase and then pay the balance, including a *carrying charge*, in monthly payments for six, twelve, eighteen, or twenty-four payments. The following symbols are used in setting up the formulas given below.

c = carrying-charge rate per year,
C = carrying charge,
B = unpaid balance (cash price less the down payment),
n = number of monthly payments,
R = equal monthly payment,
i = simple interest rate per year.

The carrying charge is given by the formula*

$$C = \frac{Bnc}{12}. \tag{3}$$

The monthly payment at the end of each month for n months is

$$R = \frac{C + B}{n}. \tag{4}$$

It should be noted that the carrying-charge rate is not an interest rate, since it is computed on the outstanding balance rather than on the partial balances after each monthly payment is made. The interest rate actually is much higher. Various formulas are given in arithmetic books for approximating the interest rate involved in installment buying. One of the

* Occasionally the carrying charge is determined without reference to a carrying-charge rate.

more common formulas is (5).

$$i = \frac{24C}{n(n + 1)R}. \tag{5}$$

$$i = \frac{24C}{n(B - C + R)}. \tag{6}$$

$$i = \frac{24C}{(n + 1)B}. \tag{7}$$

The derivations of these formulas may be found in an article by Adams and Bell in *Mathematics Teacher.** It is interesting to note that the commonly used formula (5) does not give a simple interest rate at all but a simple discount rate. Formula 6 gives an actual simple interest rate, and (7) gives neither a simple interest rate nor a simple discount rate, but it does give an approximate average of the rates obtained by (5) and (6).

Since, for most purposes, an approximate value of the interest rate is adequate in installment buying, any one of these formulas can be used. The following illustrative problem shows how the various values of i compare:

Example. A gas range selling for \$450 cash may be bought for \$50 and the balance; the carrying charge is computed at 6 per cent per year paid in eighteen monthly payments. Find the outstanding balance, the carrying charge, the monthly payment, and the interest rates involved, using each of the three formulas for the interest.

Solution. The outstanding balance from (3) is

$$B = \$450 - \$50 = \$400.$$

The carrying charge is

$$C = \frac{(400)(18)(.06)}{12} = \$36.$$

The monthly payment, computed from (4), is

$$R = \frac{\$36 + \$400}{18} = \$24.22.$$

The interest rates computed by each of the formulas (5), (6), and (7) are as follows:

From (5), $$i = \frac{24(36)}{18(19)(24.22)} = .104 \quad \text{or} \quad 10.4\%.$$

From (6), $$i = \frac{24(36)}{18(400 - 36 + 24.22)} = .124 \quad \text{or} \quad 12.4\%.$$

From (7), $$i = \frac{24(36)}{19(400)} = .114 \quad \text{or} \quad 11.4\%.$$

* Vol. XLIII, No. 8, December, 1950.

Thus the actual simple discount rate is 10.4 per cent, the actual simple interest rate is 12.4 per cent, and the approximate average, by use of (7), is 11.4 per cent. In this case the last is the actual average of the two preceding values, to three significant figures.

EXERCISE 2

1. A car may be bought for $2500 cash. It can be bought on the installment plan for $500 down and the balance in twenty-four equal monthly payments, including a carrying charge computed by using a rate of 7 per cent per year. Find

(*a*) the outstanding balance,
(*b*) the carrying charge,
(*c*) the equal monthly payment,
(*d*) the simple interest rate involved to three significant figures.

2. Find the simple discount rate in problem 1 to three significant figures.

3. Use (7) to compute the interest rate in problem 1 to three significant figures. Is this the exact average of the simple interest obtained in problem 1 and the simple discount rate obtained in problem 2? If it is, then compute each of the answers for i obtained in problems 1, 2, and 3 to four significant places, average again, and compare.

4. A television set sells for $250 cash or for $50 down and $18 payable at the end of each month for twelve months. If the set is bought on the installment plan, what is the simple interest rate paid?

5. Rewrite (7) by replacing C by its value obtained from (4).

6. Find the approximate interest rate involved, by the use of (7), on a twenty-four month installment payment of $25 on an unpaid balance of $500.

18.3 STOCKS AND BONDS

When corporations are formed to produce airplanes, automobiles, and many other commodities connected with the general business of the country, money is raised by selling shares of stock in the corporation. Such shares are called *common stock* and the owner of the stock is actually a part owner of the corporation; as a part owner he is entitled to a share of its earnings. When payments are made on stocks from corporation earnings they are called *dividends*.

A corporation may need money for expansion at various times after it is formed. This money may be provided by issuing *preferred stock*, which carries a fixed dividend, or by issuing *bonds*, which are notes usually secured by a mortgage on the property of the corporation. The bonds carry a fixed interest rate based on their face value.

Interest on the bonds of a corporation must be paid first as an expense of the company. Next, the holders of preferred stock must be paid their dividends. If there is any profit remaining from the earnings of the corporation, then the holders of common stock may be paid dividends.

Since holders of common stock are actual owners of the corporation, they are entitled to vote on important decisions made by the directors of the corporation. In fact they have a voice in selecting such directors, a privilege very rarely given to holders of preferred stock and never to bond holders. The holders of preferred stock have certain other privileges which distinguish them from bond holders. Often there is a provision that after a certain number of years preferred stock may be exchanged for common stock at the rate of a fixed number of shares of common stock for one share of preferred stock.

18.4 BUYING AND SELLING STOCK

The buying and selling of shares of stock is done, in general, through stock exchanges. The New York Stock Exchange and the American Stock Exchange are the largest exchanges through which stocks are bought and sold. Other principal exchanges are located in Boston, Philadelphia, Chicago, and on the Pacific Coast. Any city of reasonable size throughout the country will have at least one brokerage firm through which orders can be placed to the various exchanges. The customer who wishes to buy or sell stock places his order with such a firm.

Many daily newspapers throughout the country list the transactions on the various stock exchanges. The actual numbers of shares exchanging hands are listed for each of the corporations, with the high, low, and closing quotations. These quotations, and other information about the standings of the corporations, their earnings, and so on, provide a means by which the prospective buyer or seller can make his decisions. If the reader is not familiar with such items on the financial pages of his newspaper, he should examine them to note the kind of information listed.

A person wishing to buy or sell stock must open an account with a brokerage firm. Having done this, he is assigned to one of the account executives in the firm who takes care of all of his buying and selling orders. For this service the brokerage house will charge a fee. The amount of the brokerage fee is determined by the stock exchange or exchanges through which the brokerage house deals. A federal transfer tax is also charged to the seller. In addition, some states, such as New York, impose stock transfer taxes.

It should be noted that the prices quoted on the exchanges and in the newspapers are in dollars and in eighths or sixteenths of dollars. For a few extremely low-priced stocks the price quoted is in cents, but in all such cases this is clearly indicated. It has been said that the reason for using an eighth of a dollar as the fractional unit in quoting stocks is that in the early days of this country a *bit* was a piece of money worth one eighth of a dollar. Furthermore, a bit was charged as the brokerage fee for each share bought or sold. The amount charged today is based upon the value of the stock as well as the number of shares traded. For the purpose of simplifying the statement of problems and examples, a fixed amount per share is given as the brokerage fee. This includes all of the charges necessary to buy or sell the particular stock.

Example 1. Mr. Smith ordered 100 shares of Seaside Electric for which he specified a price of $91\frac{3}{8}$. The broker charged a commission of 48 cents per share. What did Mr. Smith pay for this stock if the broker bought it at the specified price?

Solution. The cost of 100 shares at $91\frac{3}{8}$ is

$$100 \times 91.375 = \$9137.50.$$

The commission is $100 \times .48 = \$48.00.$

Thus the cost of 100 shares is $9137.50 + 48.00 = \$9185.50.$

Note. In general, a lot of 100 shares of a stock is called a *trading unit* or *round lot*, for which the usual brokerage fee applies. On odd lots (less than a unit of trading) a larger brokerage fee per share may be charged.

Example 2. Mr. Brown asked his broker to sell 200 shares of Almafo Manufacturing at 89 or better. His broker sold the shares at $89\frac{7}{8}$. The brokerage charge was 48 cents per share. How much did Mr. Brown receive for his stock?

Solution. The selling price received for the stock was

$$200 \times 89.875 = \$17,975.00.$$

The brokerage charge was $200 \times .48 = \$96.00.$

Hence Mr. Brown received $17,975 - 96 = \$17,879.$

In buying or selling stock the total gained or lost on any investment program is dependent on the dividends paid as well as on the buying and selling prices. Actually, in a careful analysis of gain or loss on an investment program the income tax should be considered. However, since the income tax is dependent on the total income of the person concerned, it is neglected in the problems and examples.

Example 3. Mr. Smith bought 100 shares of Intermountain Water and Telephone at $38\frac{1}{2}$, paying a brokerage charge of 37 cents per share. The stock paid dividends of \$1.40 per year for the first nine years that Mr. Smith held the stock. During the following year it paid only \$1.00. Mr. Smith immediately sold his stock at $37\frac{3}{4}$, paying a brokerage charge of 36 cents per share. What amount did Mr. Smith gain or lose on this investment program?

Solution.

Cost of shares:	$100 \times 38.50 =$	\$3850
Brokerage charge:	$100 \times .37 =$	37
Total cost:		\$3887
Dividends for first nine years:	$9 \times 100 \times 1.40 =$	\$1260
Dividend for the tenth year:	$1 \times 100 \times 1.00 =$	100
Total amount of dividends:		\$1360
Selling price of stock:	$100 \times 37.75 =$	\$3775
Brokerage charge:	$100 \times .36 =$	36
Amount received for stock:		\$3739

Total realized:	\$1360 + \$3739 = \$5099
Total cost:	3887
Net gain:	\$1212

It should be noted that a capital loss of \$3887 − \$3739 = \$148 was suffered in this investment program. The net gain was the result of dividends earned.

EXERCISE 3

Find the cost, brokerage, and total cost if the following stocks are bought.

	Number of Shares	*Purchase Price*	*Brokerage per Share*
1.	100	$24\frac{3}{8}$	32 cents
2.	150	10	17 cents
3.	200	$36\frac{1}{2}$	37 cents
4.	20	$74\frac{1}{4}$	58 cents
5.	100	$34\frac{1}{8}$	36 cents
6.	200	$23\frac{7}{8}$	31 cents
7.	80	$47\frac{5}{8}$	56 cents
8.	100	$118\frac{3}{4}$	50 cents
9.	300	$1\frac{3}{8}$	6 cents
10.	10	$444\frac{1}{2}$	527 cents

Find the selling price, brokerage, and the total amount realized by the seller upon sale of the following stocks.

	Number of Shares	*Selling Price*	*Brokerage per Share*
11.	100	26	32 cents
12.	150	$14\frac{3}{4}$	22 cents
13.	300	$48\frac{3}{4}$	44 cents
14.	100	$5\frac{1}{8}$	12 cents
15.	50	$46\frac{1}{2}$	54 cents
16.	30	$13\frac{1}{8}$	33 cents
17.	110	$41\frac{1}{2}$	39 cents
18.	100	$57\frac{3}{4}$	45 cents
19.	200	$3\frac{7}{8}$	11 cents
20.	130	109	50 cents

21. Mrs. Hansen bought 100 shares of Oswego Gas at $31\frac{1}{2}$, for which she paid 34 cents per share brokerage. This stock paid \$1.60 per share dividend for the next ten years. At the end of the period she sold the stock at $47\frac{3}{4}$, paying a brokerage fee of 42 cents per share. What was her gain or loss on this investment program?

22. Mr. Rogers bought 200 shares of Bonanza Gold at $2\frac{7}{8}$, paying a brokerage charge of 9 cents per share. The stock's dividend record was as follows:

First year	0 per share
Second year	$ .05 per share
Third year	$1.10 per share
Fourth year	$1.50 per share
Fifth year	$ .01 per share

At the end of five years he sold the stock at $1\frac{1}{8}$ per share, paying a brokerage charge of 6 cents per share. What was his gain or loss on the investment program?

23. Mr. Peters bought 100 shares of R.S.T. at $118\frac{1}{8}$, paying 50 cents per share brokerage. This stock paid $4.00 per share for the first eight years, followed by $1.00 for the ninth year and nothing for the tenth year. He then sold the stock at $80\frac{7}{8}$, paying a brokerage charge of 47 cents per share. What was Mr. Peter's gain or loss on this investment program?

24. Find the interest yield for the following stock:

(*a*) Stock bought at $47\frac{1}{2}$, brokerage 42 cents per share, dividends $2.00 per share.

(*b*) Stock bought at $89\frac{1}{2}$, brokerage 48 cents per share, dividends of $2.25 per share.

25. Which is the better investment from the standpoint of interest yield on the money invested?

(*a*) A purchase of 100 shares of stock at $35\frac{1}{2}$, brokerage charge of 37 cents per share, and dividends of $1.75 per share, or

(*b*) a purchase of 100 shares of stock at $89\frac{3}{4}$, brokerage charge of 48 cents per share, and dividends of $4.38 per share.

18.5 BUYING AND SELLING BONDS

Bonds are quoted on the market in terms of a per cent of the face value of the bond. Thus a 5 per cent, $5000 bond quoted at $85\frac{1}{2}$ would sell for (or could be bought for) $85\frac{1}{2}$ per cent of the $5000 face amount, or $4275 plus the necessary brokerage charge. Since this is a 5 per cent bond, it would pay $250 in interest each year. The *actual* (or *yield*) *rate* of interest involved in this transaction depends not only on what was paid for the bond, the interest and the brokerage charge, but also on its maturity date. Bond brokers quote what they call a *current interest rate*, which is defined as the annual interest divided by the selling (or purchase) price of the bond. Thus for this bond the current interest rate is $250 \div 4275$, which is .0585, or 5.85 per cent.

Since the determination of the yield rate of interest requires a knowledge of the mathematics of finance, only the current interest rate is computed in this book.

EXERCISE 4

Find the current interest rate involved for each of the following bonds:

	Face Value	*Bond Rate of Interest*	*Market Quotation*
1.	\$1000	4 per cent	90
2.	\$5000	6 per cent	105
3.	\$500	$2\frac{1}{2}$ per cent	85
4.	\$10,000	3 per cent	92
5.	\$1000	$1\frac{3}{4}$ per cent	80

6. A 2 per cent, \$1000 bond was quoted at 88.
(*a*) What was the current interest rate?
(*b*) Suppose that this bond was paid off at the end of one year after purchase at 88 and that the brokerage charge paid at the time of purchase was \$15. What was the actual interest rate earned by the purchaser on this investment program?
(*c*) Suppose that the bond had 100 years to run before maturity. Which interest rate would more closely give the yield rate—the one in (*a*) or the one in (*b*)?

7. Which bond would have the higher current interest rate?
(*a*) 3 per cent, \$500 bond quoted at 90,
(*b*) 5 per cent, \$1000 bond quoted at 140.

REFERENCES

Simpson, T. M., Z. M. Pirenian, and B. H. Crenshaw, *Mathematics of Finance*, pp. 171–187.

Taylor, E. H., and C. N. Mills, *Arithmetic for Teacher-Training Classes*, fourth edition, pp. 315–338.

19

Introduction to Algebra

19.1 INTRODUCTION

An early Arabian mathematician, Mohammed ibn Musa Abu Djebar Al-Khwarizmi, about 830 wrote a treatise, "Al-jebr we'l mukabala," from which our term algebra is derived. Al-jebr means restoration and al mukabala means the process of simplification.* Algebra is one of the branches or fields of mathematics. It is concerned largely with the structure of number systems, operations with numbers and statements involving numbers, as well as the solution of problems. Algebra is the language used to develop and express much of the scientific data of our day. Many arithmetic procedures that seem rather complicated become quite simple when treated algebraically. Some of these procedures are discussed in this chapter.

19.2 USE OF FORMULAS

In several of the sections of the text, formulas have been used to express relations between quantities. These formulas represent an extension of arithmetic into algebra. For example, the formula $I = Pni$ shows how the interest I, in dollars, can be calculated for a principal sum of P dollars, at a rate per cent i per year, for a time of n years. By substituting known values of these quantities into the formula and performing the operations of arithmetic, we find the value of the interest for the given example. A principal of \$150.00 at an interest rate of 5 per cent per year for eight months, or two thirds of a year, will earn interest $I = 150 \times (\frac{5}{100}) \times (\frac{2}{3}) =$ \$5.00. Formulas treat a collection of examples of a given kind in arithmetic by means of a generalization. They are a shorthand for representing relations between quantities. Evaluating a formula by substituting

* W. W. R. Ball, *A Short Account of the History of Mathematics*, p. 156, 1960.

numerical values for its letters requires close attention to the example in arithmetic.

Example 1. The formula giving F, the number of degrees Fahrenheit corresponding to C, the number of degrees Centigrade, is

$$F = \frac{9}{5} C + 32.$$

Find the Fahrenheit readings corresponding to the Centigrade readings 10, 20, 35, 50, and 100°.

Solution. Substituting the assigned values, we have

$$F = \frac{9}{5}(10) + 32 = 9(2) + 32 = 18 + 32 = 50,$$

$$F = \frac{9}{5}(20) + 32 = 9(4) + 32 = 36 + 32 = 68,$$

$$F = \frac{9}{5}(38) + 32 = 68\tfrac{2}{5} + 32 = 100\tfrac{2}{5} \text{ or } 100.4,$$

$$F = \frac{9}{5}(56) + 32 = 100\tfrac{4}{5} + 32 = 132\tfrac{4}{5} \text{ or } 132.8,$$

$$F = \frac{9}{5}(100) + 32 = 180 + 32 = 212.$$

In recording temperatures, the label for the temperature scale is usually affixed to the reading. Thus the answers in complete form would be 50, 68, 100.4, 132.8, and 212° F.

Example 2. The formula in Example 1 can be solved for C in terms of F. It then reads

$$C = \frac{5}{9}(F - 32).$$

Evaluate this formula when $F = 32, 50, 72, 100, 122°$.

Solution. Substituting the assigned values, we have

$$C = \frac{5}{9}(32 - 32) = \frac{5}{9}(0) = 0, \qquad C = \frac{5}{9}(50 - 32) = \frac{5}{9}(18) = 10,$$

$$C = \frac{5}{9}(72 - 32) = \frac{5}{9}(40) = 22\tfrac{2}{9}, \qquad C = \frac{5}{9}(100 - 32) = \frac{5}{9}(68) = 37\tfrac{7}{9},$$

$$C = \frac{5}{9}(122 - 32) = \frac{5}{9}(90) = 50.$$

These answers should be written 0, 10, $22\frac{2}{9}$, $37\frac{7}{9}$, and 50° C.

Example 3. The distance, s, fallen by an object starting at rest from a point near the earth's surface is given by the formula

$$s = \frac{1}{2}gt^2,$$

where g has an approximate value of 32 feet per second squared, if t is the time in seconds and s is the number of feet fallen. Find the distance fallen by a stone dropped from a bridge if the stone strikes the ground after three seconds. How much farther would the stone fall in the next half second if it were not stopped after three seconds?

Solution. Substituting in the formula the values $t = 3$ and $g = 32$, we have

$$s = \frac{1}{2}(32)(3^2) = 16(9) = 144;$$

and for $t = 3\frac{1}{2}$ we have

$$s = \frac{1}{2}(32)(3\tfrac{1}{2})^2 = 16(12\tfrac{1}{4}) = 196.$$

Thus the stone falls 144 feet during the first 3 seconds and 196 feet during the first $3\frac{1}{2}$ seconds; the difference is $196 - 144 = 52$. The stone falls 52 feet during the last half second if it is free to fall.

Example 4. The sequence of natural numbers, 2, 5, 8, 11, $\cdots$, in which each successive number is obtained by adding 3 to the preceding number is called an arithmetical progression. It is easily shown that if a represents the first term of such a progression, d represents the difference between two successive terms, n represents the number of terms, and l represents the nth term then

$$l = a + (n - 1)d.$$

In the progression 2, 5, 8, 11, $\cdots$, find a and d, and, if n is 4, find l. Also find the tenth term and check by generating the terms out to the tenth term.

Solution. Since 2 is the first term, $a = 2$, and, since $8 - 5$ or $11 - 8 = 3$, $d = 3$. Since 11 is the fourth term, it is seen that $l = 11$ when $n = 4$; but also by the formula, $l = 2 + (4 - 1)3 = 2 + 3(3) = 11$. By the formula also, if $n = 10$, then l is given by

$$l = 2 + (10 - 1)3 = 2 + 9(3) = 29.$$

This result can be checked by counting out to the tenth term:

2, 5, 8, 11, 14, 17, 20, 23, 26, 29.

Example 5. It is readily shown by writing the sum s of the first n terms of an arithmetical progression in two ways, and combining, that a formula for the sum is

$$s = \frac{n}{2}(a + l).$$

Thus

$$s = a + (a + d) + (a + 2d) + \cdots + (l - d) + l,$$

and

$$s = l + (l - d) + (l - 2d) + \cdots + (a + d) + a.$$

Hence

$$2s = (a + l) + (a + l) + (a + l) + \cdots + (a + l) + (a + l),$$

$$2s = n(a + l), \quad \text{or} \quad s = \frac{n}{2}(a + l).$$

Use this formula to find the sum of the first ten terms of the progression in Example 4. Also find the sum of the first 100 even natural numbers.

Solution. From Example 4, for the progression 2, 5, 8, 11, $\cdots$, we have $l = 29$ when $n = 10$. Thus

$$s = \frac{10}{2}(2 + 29) = 5(31) = 155.$$

Also, for the first 100 even natural numbers, $a = 2$, $d = 2$, $n = 100$. Hence

$$l = 2 + (100 - 1)2 = 2 + 198 = 200.$$

$$s = \frac{100}{2}(2 + 200) = 50(202) = 10{,}100.$$

EXERCISE 1

Find the value of the quantity for each formula when the given numerical values are substituted in the formula:

1. $p = 2l + 2w$ (perimeter of a rectangle) if $l = 15$ inches, $w = 11$ inches.

2. $i = prt$ (simple interest) if $p = \$285.00$, $r = 6$ per cent, $t = \frac{1}{3}$ year.

3. $A = \frac{1}{2}bh$ (area of a triangle) if $b = 23$ inches, $h = 10$ inches.

4. $A = \frac{h}{2}(b_1 + b_2)$ (area of a trapezoid) if $h = 13$ inches, $b_1 = 21$ inches, $b_2 = 17$ inches.

5. $V = LWH$ (volume of a box) if $L = 2\frac{1}{2}$ inches, $W = 6$ inches, $H = 5$ inches.

6. $l = a + (n - 1)d$ (nth term of a progression) if $a = 1$, $d = 2$, $n = 100$.

7. $s = \frac{n}{2}(a + l)$ (sum of n terms of a progression) if $n = 100$, $a = 1$, $l = 199$.

8. $E = IR$ (electric voltage) if $I = 6.5$, $R = 12$.

9. $s = \frac{1}{2}gt^2$ (distance fallen by object) if $g = 32.16$, $t = 3.10$.

10. $v = \pi r^2 h$ (volume of a cylinder) if $\pi = \frac{22}{7}$, $r = 3.0$, $h = 14$.

Write a formula for each of the following:

11. Express the area, A, of a rectangle in terms of its length, l, and its width, w.

12. Express the number of days, d, in w weeks.

13. Express the number of hours, h, in d days.

14. Express the number of cents, c, in n nickels.

15. Express the number of cents, c, in p pennies, n nickels, and d dimes.

16. Develop a formula for the time, t, needed to go a distance, d, traveling at a rate, r. Use your formula to find the time needed for a train to go 380 miles if it averages 50 miles per hour.

17. Develop a formula for the surface area of a box with dimensions L, W, H. Find the number of square inches of surface area for a box 12 inches long, 8 inches wide, and 6 inches high.

18. Write a formula using the letters V, B, H, for the volume of a pyramid if the volume of this pyramid is one third of the area of the base times the height. Use the formula to find the volume of a pyramid whose base is a square 6 inches on a side and whose height is 5 inches.

Use the formulas of Example 4 and Example 5 in the text to solve the following.

19. Find the fifteenth term and the sum of the first 15 terms of the progression: 7, 11, 15, 19, $\cdots$.

20. Find the sum of the first 1000 even natural numbers 2, 4, 6, $\cdots$, 2000. Also find the sum of the first 1000 odd natural numbers 1, 3, 5, $\cdots$, 1999. Find the difference between the two sums and explain it.

21. Given the following readings of temperature in the Fahrenheit scale, change them to readings in the Centigrade scale.

(*a*) 41° F (*b*) 59° F (*c*) 350° F (*d*) 800° F (*e*) 450° F (*f*) 212° F.

22. Given the following readings in the Centigrade scale, change them to readings in the Fahrenheit scale.

(*a*) 30° C (*b*) 400° C (*c*) 60° C (*d*) 5° C (*e*) 200° C (*f*) 500° C.

23. A temperature called absolute zero occurs at −273.15° C (273.15° below 0° C). Temperatures measured from this point are measured in *degrees Kelvin* (K), so that 0° C equals 273.15° K. 100° C would be 373.15° K, and so on. Convert the following temperatures to the Kelvin scale.

(*a*) 10° C (*b*) −73.15° C (*c*) 26.85° C (*d*) 95° F (*e*) 212° F (*f*) −270° C.

19.3 SETS, SOLUTION SETS, AND EQUATIONS

In Chapter 2 we discussed the concepts of sets and subsets, a set being any well-defined collection of objects (it must be possible to state whether a given object is in the set or not). A subset was defined as a set of elements taken from a given set. For our purposes in discussing equations we shall be concerned first with a set made up of the natural numbers and zero. The numbers that satisfy the statements in our equations are subsets of this set of natural numbers and zero. Later we shall consider more inclusive sets containing negative numbers and positive and negative fractions, for use when we work with the general first-degree equation.

19.3.1. Equations. The formulas we have been using are *equations*, which are statements of equality between numbers or between expressions representing numbers. The terms on the left side of the equals sign make up the left member of the equation and those on the right side make up the right member. Equations are solved by performing the operations necessary to select the number or numbers from a given set that will make the statement in the equation true. The set of numbers for which the statement in an equation is true is called a *solution set* or a solution of the equation. It is assumed or postulated that the following operations will not affect the solution set for which the statement in an equation is true.

ADDITION AXIOM

If equal quantities are added to equal quantities, the sums are equal.

SUBTRACTION AXIOM

If equal quantities are subtracted from equal quantities, the remainders are equal.

MULTIPLICATION AXIOM

If equal quantities are multiplied by equal quantities, the products are equal.

DIVISION AXIOM

If equal quantities are divided by equal quantities, except by zero, the quotients are equal.

As a rule the letters nearer the end of the alphabet, such as q, r, x, y, z, represent numbers to be selected by the equation, whereas the letters at the beginning of the alphabet, such as a, b, c, k, represent assigned or known quantities.

Example 1. Find the solution set of $x + 12 = 34$, where x is the set of natural numbers.

Solution. By subtracting 12 from both sides of the equation, we obtain

$$\begin{array}{r} x + 12 = 34 \\ 12 = 12 \\ \hline x \qquad = 22. \end{array}$$

Check. The problem is checked by showing that the statement in the equation is true when x is the number 22. Since $22 + 12 = 34$, the statement is true for $x = 22$. Since the statement is false if x is greater than 22 or if x is less than 22, the solution set is $x = 22$.

APPLICATION PROBLEMS

Example 2. If a number increased by 4 gives 17, what is the number?

Solution. Let x represent the unknown number; then $x + 4$ represents the number increased by 4, but 17 is the number increased by 4. We have the known facts in the problem expressed in two ways, and we form an equation that we solve

$$x + 4 = 17.$$

Subtract 4, $x = 13$, the unknown number.

Check. Thirteen increased by 4 is 17.

Example 3. After a \$2500 raise, a man receives a \$7500 salary. What was his original salary?

Solution. Let x be the amount in dollars of the original salary; then $x + 2500$ is the salary the man now receives, which is 7500. Therefore, the equation is

$$x + 2500 = 7500.$$

Subtract 2500, $x = 5000.$

Hence the man's original salary is \$5000.

Check. $\$5000 + \$2500 \stackrel{?}{=} \$7500,$ $\$7500 = \$7500.$ (The question mark ? is used to ask if the statement is true.)

Example 4. The equation $x - 4 = 20$ states that after four units had been taken away from an unknown quantity, there were twenty units left. The original number of units is found by solving the equation.

Solution. $x - 4 = 20.$

Add 4, $x = 24$ (the addition should be done mentally).

Check. Substitute 24 for x in the original equation.

$$x - 4 = 20, \qquad 24 - 4 \stackrel{?}{=} 20, \qquad 20 = 20.$$

Example 5. After spending \$5.80, a man had \$12.20 left. How much had he at first?

Solution. Setting up the problem, we proceed as follows. Let x be the amount of money he had at first. If he spent \$5.80, then $x -$ \$5.80 would represent the amount he had left, which is \$12.20. The equation is

$$x - \$5.80 = \$12.20.$$

Add \$5.80, $x = \$18.00,$ the amount he had at first.

Check. $\$18.00 - \$5.80 \stackrel{?}{=} \$12.20, \qquad \$12.20 = \$12.20.$

Example 6. $4x = 20$. The equation states that four times an unknown number is twenty and the solution gives the unknown number.

Solution. $4x = 20.$

Divide by 4, $x = 5$ (the division should be done mentally).

Check. Substitute the value for x in the original equation.

$$4x = 20, \qquad 4 \cdot 5 \stackrel{?}{=} 20, \qquad 20 = 20.$$

Example 7. Eight times a certain number gives 1440. What is the number?

Solution. Set up the problem. Let x be the certain number; then $8x$ represents eight times the number, which is 1440. The equation is

$$8x = 1440.$$

Divide by 8, $x = 180,$ the original number.

Check. $8(180) \stackrel{?}{=} 1440, \qquad 1440 = 1440.$

Example 8. What is the side of a square if its perimeter is 56 inches?

Solution. Set up the problem. Let x be the number of units of length of the side of the square; then $4x$ is the perimeter. But 56 is the perimeter. The equation is

$$4x = 56.$$

Divide by 4, $x = 14$ inches, the length of one side of the square.

Check. $4 \cdot 14 \stackrel{?}{=} 56,$
$56 = 56.$

Example 9. A fellow whose main hobby is bike racing traveled the distance from Los Angeles to Bakersfield, 105 miles, in seven hours. What was his average rate of speed?

Solution. Set up the problem. Let x be the rate in miles per hour, and 7 is the number of hours of racing; then $7x$ is the distance traveled in miles (distance = rate times time). But 105 is the distance traveled. The equation is

$$7x = 105,$$

Divide by 7, $x = 15$ miles per hour.

Check. Fifteen miles per hour for seven hours should give 105 miles and 15×7 is 105.

Example 10. $x/4 = 20$, or $\frac{1}{4}x = 20$. This equation is solved by using the multiplication axiom. It states that an unknown quantity has been divided into four equal parts, and each part has twenty in it. The solution would give the amount in the original quantity.

Solution. $$\frac{x}{4} = 20.$$

Multiply by 4, $x = 80$ (the multiplication should be done mentally).

Check. Substitute 80 for x in the original equation.

$$\frac{x}{4} = 20, \qquad \frac{80}{4} \stackrel{?}{=} 20, \qquad 20 = 20.$$

Example 11. A man divided his estate equally among his five sons. If each son received \$2350, what was the value of the estate?

Solution. Let x represent the number of dollars value of the estate; then $x/5$ would represent the amount in dollars each son received, which was \$2350. Therefore the equation is

$$\frac{x}{5} = 2350.$$

Multiply by 5, $x = \$11750$, the value of the estate.

Check. $\frac{\$11,750}{5} \stackrel{?}{=} \$2350, \qquad \$2350 = \$2350.$

EXERCISE 2

Find the solution set of each equation, state how it is obtained, and check.

1. $3x = 15.$
2. $x + 9 = 27.$
3. $2x = 300.$
4. $x - 4 = 44.$
5. $45 = \frac{x}{3}.$
6. $24 = x + 4.$
7. $5x = 125.$
8. $x - 5 = 57.$
9. $48 = x - 12.$
10. $\frac{1}{2}x = 28.$
11. $25x = 100.$
12. $100 = \frac{x}{4}.$
13. $60 = 4 + x.$
14. $75 = 25x.$
15. $\frac{x}{15} = 30.$

In problems 16 to 20 represent the unknown by a letter, being careful to state the quantity for which it stands. Form the equation to meet the condition stated in the problem.

16. If the perimeter of a square is 144 inches, how long is one side?

17. After reading 72 pages of a book, a student still had 234 pages to read. How many pages of reading had been assigned?

18. A student scheduled his Saturday's work so that he would complete eighteen jobs. If he planned to work six hours, how many things had he scheduled himself to do each hour (assuming all jobs took the same length of time)?

19. After a man's salary was increased \$120 per month, he received \$880 per month. What was his monthly salary before the increase?

20. If in ten years a boy will be 21 years old, what is his age now?

Check your equations in problems 16 to 20 and solve them.

Up to this time only simple one-step equations have been discussed. The solving of many equations involves two or more axioms.

Example 12. The solving of the equation $2x + 4 = 20$ requires both the subtraction and the division axioms. (The procedure is usually simpler if additions and subtractions are performed first.)

Solution. $2x + 4 = 20.$

Subtract 4, $2x = 16.$

Divide by 2, $x = 8.$

Check. $2x + 4 = 20.$

$2(8) + 4 \stackrel{?}{=} 20,$

$16 + 4 \stackrel{?}{=} 20,$

$20 = 20.$

Example 13. $\frac{x}{2} - 4 = 20.$

Solution.

Add 4, $\frac{x}{2} = 24.$

Multiply by 2 $x = 48.$

Check. $\frac{48}{2} - 4 \stackrel{?}{=} 20,$

$24 - 4 \stackrel{?}{=} 20,$

$20 = 20.$

Example 14. $\frac{2}{3}x - 4 = 20.$ In solving it is better to use the addition axiom first.

Solution. Method 1.

Add 4, $\frac{2}{3}x = 24.$

Divide by 2, $\frac{x}{3} = 12.$

Multiply by 3, $x = 36.$

Check: $\frac{2}{3}x - 4 = 20.$

$\frac{2}{\cancel{3}_1}(\cancel{36}^{12}) - 4 \stackrel{?}{=} 20.$

$24 - 4 \stackrel{?}{=} 20.$

$20 = 20.$

Method 2: $\frac{2}{3}x - 4 = 20.$

Add 4, $\frac{2}{3}x = 24.$

Multiply by 3, $2x = 72.$

Divide by 2, $x = 36.$

Check. See Method 1.

Example 15. $3x + 6 + 3 = 47 - 2.$

Solution. Simplify each member:

$$3x + 9 = 45.$$

Subtract 9, $3x = 36.$

Divide by 3, $x = 12.$

Check: $3x + 6 + 3 = 47 - 2.$

$$3(12) + 9 \stackrel{?}{=} 45,$$
$$36 + 9 \stackrel{?}{=} 45,$$
$$45 = 45.$$

Example 16. $5x + 7 - 3 = 18 - 2x.$

Solution.

$$5x + 4 = 18 - 2x.$$
$$7x + 4 = 18.$$
$$7x = 14.$$
$$x = 2.$$

Check. $5(2) + 7 - 3 \stackrel{?}{=} 18 - 2(2).$

$$14 = 14.$$

The reader should decide which axiom was used in solving the equation in each example.

EXERCISE 3

Solve and check these equations (simplify first if necessary).

1. $2x = 18.$

2. $\frac{1}{2}x = 18.$

3. $x + 45 = 25 + 3x.$

4. $x - 3 = 12 - 4x.$

5. $\frac{2}{3}x = 48.$

6. $\frac{1}{10}x = 50.$

7. $2x + 0.2 = 3.4.$

8. $3x + 0.6 = 4.2 + x.$

9. $72 = 3x.$

10. $50x = 10.$

11. $3x + 4 = 40.$

12. $5x - 4 = 36.$

13. $7x + 5 = 47 + x.$

14. $\frac{3}{4}x - 6 = 30 + \frac{1}{4}x.$

15. $\frac{2}{5}x + 12 = 28.$

16. $32 = 4 + 7x - 7.$

17. $111 = 11x - 10.$

18. $3x + 9 = 36 - 3.$

19. $3 + 4x - 2 = 23.$

20. $8 + \frac{2}{5}x - 3 = 25 - 10.$

Write an equation for each of the following problems. Solve the equation and check.

21. If five is added to three times a number, the result is equal to three less than seven times the number. Find the number.

22. Tom has twice as much money as John. If Tom gives John seven dollars, the boys will have equal amounts. How many dollars will each boy have?

23. A steel pole stands vertically in a pond of water, with one fourth of its length in mud and rock, one third of its length in water, and 35 feet of its length extending upward into the air. How long is the pole?

24. Find the value in cents of three nickels, five dimes and seven quarters. If a collection of nickels and dimes is worth 195 cents and has three more dimes than nickels, how many coins of each kind are there?

25. A collection of dimes and quarters is worth 220 cents. If there are three times as many dimes as quarters, how many coins of each kind are there?

26. A man's salary has been increased by 10 per cent. If he now receives $6380, what was his original salary?

27. Eighty-five per cent of the students in a class took the final examination. If 34 students took the final examination, how many students were in the class?

19.4 SIGNED NUMBERS—OPERATIONS

We discussed the real numbers and the operation of addition for the set of real numbers at the end of Chapter 3. The real numbers can be used to describe the distances to points on a line, from a fixed initial point, in terms of a fixed unit of measure for distances to the right or to the left of the initial point. It is assumed that *there is a one-to-one correspondence between the set of all real numbers and the set of all points on a line.* The fixed initial point on the line is called the *origin*; the origin is assigned to correspond to the number zero (0). The point one unit to the right of the origin corresponds to the natural number one; successive natural numbers are assigned to points at successive unit distances to the right. Units of measure to the left of the origin are called *negative* units. The points at successive units of measure to the left of the origin correspond to the negative numbers $-1, -2, -3, \cdots$. These negative numbers are the *additive inverses* of the positive numbers, where addition of signed numbers corresponds to the addition of distances, where distances measured to the right are positive, and where distances measured to the left are negative. The additive identity for this system is the distance zero, which when added to any distance leaves it unchanged.

Addition of signed numbers can be illustrated on the number line (Fig. 1).

Example 1. Add each pair of signed numbers by using distances on the number line: (*a*) 3 and 2, (*b*) 4 and -3, (*c*) -2 and -5, (*d*) 3 and -6, (*e*) -4 and 4.

Notes. (1) When no sign is shown before a numeral, the numeral is assumed to represent a positive number. (2) The sign for the operation of addition is $+$. (3) As already mentioned, positive numbers are measured to the right and negative numbers are measured to the left. The first measurement begins at zero, and successive measurements begin where the preceding one terminated.

Solution. (*a*) $(3) + (2)$ means (measure) 3 units to the right plus 2 units to the right, which terminates at the point 5 units to the right of the origin. Thus $3 + 2 = 5$. Is the answer different for $2 + 3$?

(*b*) $(4) + (-3)$ means 4 units to the right plus 3 units to the left, which terminates at the point 1 unit to the right of the origin. Thus $4 + (-3) = 1$. Is the answer different for $(-3) + (4)$?

(*c*) $(-2) + (-5)$ means 2 units to the left plus 5 units to the left, which terminates at the point 7 units to the left of the origin. Thus $(-2) + (-5) = -7$. What is the sum of (-5) and (-2)?

(*d*) $(3) + (-6)$ means 3 units to the right plus 6 units to the left, which terminates at the point 3 units to the left of the origin. Thus $3 + (-6) = -3$. What is the sum of (-6) and (3)?

(*e*) $(-4) + (4)$ means 4 units to the left plus 4 units to the right, which terminates at the origin. Thus $(-4) + 4 = 0$. Similarly, $4 + (-4)$ means 4 units to

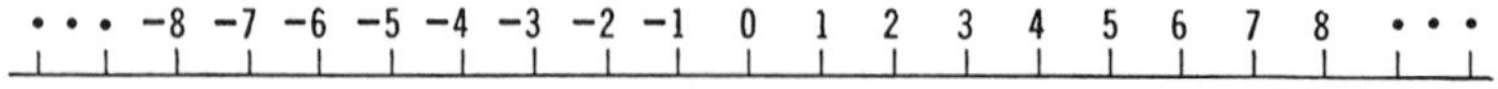

• • • −8 −7 −6 −5 −4 −3 −2 −1 0 1 2 3 4 5 6 7 8 • • •

Fig. 1

the right plus 4 units to the left, which terminates at 0. Thus $4 + (-4) = 0$. What would be the sum of any natural number and the negative of that natural number?

The number of units' distance corresponding to a signed number, without regard to the direction in which the distance is measured, is called the *absolute value* of the number. Absolute value is indicated by inclosing a numeral between vertical bars. Thus

$$|2| = 2 \qquad |-3| = 3 \qquad |0| = 0.$$

Algebraic addition of signed numbers can now be described in terms of adding or subtracting the absoute values of the numbers. The illustrations in Example 1 indicate the basis for the following generalizations.

RULE 1

To add algebraically two signed numbers having the same signs (both positive or both negative), find the sum of their absolute values, obtaining a number with the same sign as that of the two addends.

RULE 2

To add algebraically two numbers having opposite signs (one positive and the other negative) find the difference of their absolute values, obtaining a number with the sign of the addend which has the greater absolute value. If the difference of the absolute values is zero, the answer is 0, which is a number having no sign.

Example 2. Find the sums of the following:

$$\begin{array}{r} 2 \\ \underline{-3} \end{array} \qquad \begin{array}{r} -5 \\ \underline{7} \end{array} \qquad \begin{array}{r} 6 \\ \underline{-6} \end{array} \qquad \begin{array}{r} 0 \\ \underline{-3} \end{array} \qquad \begin{array}{r} 5 \\ \underline{2} \end{array} \qquad \begin{array}{r} -4 \\ \underline{-5} \end{array} \qquad \begin{array}{r} -8 \\ \underline{2} \end{array}$$

Solution.

$$\begin{array}{r} 2 \\ \underline{-3} \\ -1 \end{array} \qquad \begin{array}{r} -5 \\ \underline{7} \\ 2 \end{array} \qquad \begin{array}{r} 6 \\ \underline{-6} \\ 0 \end{array} \qquad \begin{array}{r} 0 \\ \underline{-3} \\ -3 \end{array} \qquad \begin{array}{r} 5 \\ \underline{2} \\ 7 \end{array} \qquad \begin{array}{r} -4 \\ \underline{-5} \\ -9 \end{array} \qquad \begin{array}{r} -8 \\ \underline{2} \\ -6 \end{array}$$

The difference of $|-3|$ and $|2|$ is 1, and $|-3|$ is greater than $|2|$, hence the answer is negative. The difference of $|7|$ and $|-5|$ is 2, and $|7|$ is greater than $|-5|$, hence the answer is positive. The difference of $|6|$ and $|-6|$ is 0. Since 0 is the additive identity, $0 + (-3) = -3$, which can also be verified by using distances or absolute values. The sum of $|5|$ and $|2|$ is 7, and 5 and 2 are positive. The sum of $|-4|$ and $|-5|$ is 9, and -4 and -5 are negative. The difference of $|-8|$ and $|2|$ is 6, and $|-8|$ is greater than $|2|$.

It is assumed that these rules apply not only to the set of positive and negative integers and zero but also to the set of positive and negative fractions, mixed numbers and zero (rational numbers), as well as the set of all real numbers, the latter being the set that corresponds one-to-one with the set of all points of the line. It should be noted that the set of integers is a subset of the set of rational numbers, which is a subset of the set of all real numbers. It is assumed that addition as defined thus far, for numbers in any one of the three sets, is *closed* (for numbers within the set), *associative*, and *commutative*.

Algebraic subtraction is the inverse of the operation of algebraic addition. Thus

$$3 - (2) = ? \quad \text{means} \quad 3 = ? + (2).$$

In these equations the minus sign (−) indicates the operation of subtraction, and the plus sign indicates the operation of addition. The subtraction problem is solved by algebraic addition as follows.

$$3 = ? + (2).$$
$$3 + (-2) = ? + (2) + (-2).$$
$$3 + (-2) = ? + [2 + (-2)].$$
$$1 = ? + 0, \text{ hence } ? = 1.$$

Thus $3 - (2) = 1$.

Add (−2), which is the additive inverse of 2, to both members of the equation. Use the associative law and algebraic addition, plus the fact that 0 is the additive identity.

The procedure used in this example is quite general;

$$a - (b) = x \quad \text{means} \quad a = x + (b).$$

By adding $(-b)$ to both members of the equation in the second form, obtain.

$$a + (-b) = x + b + (-b) = x.$$

Thus $a - (b) = a + (-b)$, which leads to the rule for algebraic subtraction:

RULE 3

To subtract algebraically one signed number (subtrahend) from a second number (minuend), add the negative of the subtrahend to the minuend.

Example 3. Perform the following subtractions:

$(a)\ 3 - (5)$, $(b)\ -3 - (2)$, $(c)\ 5 - (-7)$, $(d)\ -6 - (-4)$.

Solutions. (*a*) $3 - (5) = 3 + (-5) = -2.$

(*b*) $-3 - (2) = -3 + (-2) = -5.$

(*c*) $5 - (-7) = 5 + (7) = 12.$

(*d*) $-6 - (-4) = -6 + (4) = -2.$

Note that when we find the negative of a negative number, it is the positive number with the same absolute value. This follows from the definition of the negative of a number as its additive inverse. Thus $(-5) + ? = 0$ means 5 units measured to the left plus "what" equals zero. Since 5 units to the left plus "5 units to the right" yield 0, it follows that (5) is the negative of (−5).

In the algebra of simple equations and formulas, as well as in general work with algebraic expressions, the concept of "similar terms" will occur. The *terms* of an algebraic expression are the parts of the expression separated from one another by addition and subtraction signs of operation. Thus the expressions

$$3x - 2y + 4a^2, \qquad 5 - 2x + 7 - 3x$$

have, respectively, three terms and four terms. *Similar terms* are terms in an expression which have the same literal part but not necessarily the same numerical coefficient. Thus 5 and 7 in the second expression are similar terms, and $-2x$ and $-3x$ are similar terms. Similar terms may be added algebraically by using the associative and commutative laws to place the similar terms together and then the fact that the coefficients in the similar terms count objects of the same kind, which can be added.

Example 4. Combine the similar terms in each expression.

(*a*) $3x - 2 + 4x - 7$; (*b*) $x^2 - 2x + 3 + 4x - x^2 - 5$.

Solutions. (*a*) $3x - 2 + 4x - 7 = 3x + 4x - 2 - 7 = 7x - 9$.

(*b*) $x^2 - 2x + 3 + 4x - x^2 - 5 = x^2 - x^2 - 2x + 4x + 3 - 5$
$= 2x - 2$.

Example 5. Subtract the second expression from the first.

(*a*) $3x + 2,\quad 5x - 3$ (*b*) $4x + y - 8,\quad 2x + y - 11$.

Solutions. (*a*) $3x + 2 - (5x - 3) = 3x + 2 - 5x + 3 = -2x + 5$.

(*b*) $4x + y - 8 - (2x + y - 11) = 4x + y - 8 - 2x - y + 11$
$= 2x + 3$.

EXERCISE 4

1. Add algebraically

3	5	−2	−3	−6	−8	7
2	−3	4	−5	2	8	6

2. Use a number line with an origin (0) and positive and negative integers on it to verify the answers for problem 1.

3. Subtract algebraically the lower number from the upper number in each part of problem 1.

4. Verify the answers to the subtractions in problem 3 by adding algebraically the negative of each subtrahend to the given minuend.

5. Combine similar terms.

(*a*) $3x - 2y - 4$
$\underline{7x + 2y - 3}$

(*b*) $-5x + y - 11$
$\underline{5x - 2y - 7}$

(*c*) $3z - 5w$
$\underline{-4z - 5w - 7x}$

6. Simplify each of the following expressions:

(*a*) $3x - 2 + 5x - 3 + 7$ (*b*) $-x + y + 2x - 2y - 3x$ (*c*) $3 - 2 - x - x$.

7. Simplify each member of the following equations and solve.

(*a*) $3x - 2 + x = 4 - x + 4$ (*b*) $5 - x + 3 = 2x - 1$.

8. Subtract the second expression from the first.

(*a*) $2x + 3,\quad 3x - 2$ (*b*) $4x - 5 - x,\quad 3x - 2 + 5$.

9. Add algebraically the following mixed numbers:

$3\frac{1}{2}$	$-2\frac{1}{3}$	$6\frac{1}{5}$	$-7\frac{1}{2}$	$11\frac{5}{8}$	$-21\frac{3}{5}$	$8\frac{5}{8}$
$-2\frac{1}{4}$	$-4\frac{1}{3}$	$-8\frac{2}{3}$	$3\frac{3}{8}$	$-25\frac{3}{4}$	$2\frac{1}{4}$	$-16\frac{2}{3}$

19.5 RATIONAL NUMBERS—OPERATIONS

Multiplication of signed numbers is defined in such a way that it satisfies the *closure law*, the *associative law*, and the *commutative law*. Also it is assumed that there exists the identity element for multiplication (the unit 1, such that $1 \times a = a \times 1 = a$ for all a in the set) and that inverses exist with respect to the identity element for all elements except zero. Thus for every signed number a, except zero, there exists a^* such that $a \times a^* = 1$. These requirements are met by the set of all positive and negative rational numbers, including zero in the set, and they are also satisfied by the set of all real numbers. One further law that is satisfied for the two operations on these sets is the *distributive law*. Thus

$$a(b + c) = ab + ac, \quad \text{for all numbers in the set.}$$

It is evident that for the rational numbers, or fractions, in the form a/b (a and b being positive or negative integers, with b not equal to zero), the inverse* of the number a/b is b/a. Thus

$$\frac{a}{b} \times \frac{b}{a} = \frac{ab}{ba} = \frac{ab}{ab} = 1.$$

By using the distributive law and the definition of the additive identity zero, additive inverses, and other properties of the operations, we can show the following three important properties of multiplication for signed numbers:

1. $0(a) = (a)0 = 0$ 2. $(-a)b = -(ab) = a(-b)$ 3. $(-a)(-b) = ab$ for all a and b of the set of rational or of real numbers. Proof of these follow:

1. Since $a = a + 0$ for all a in the set of rational numbers, $0 = 0 + 0$. Hence $a(0) = a(0 + 0) = a0 + a0$ by the distributive law. Adding $-(a0)$ to both members, we have $0 = a0$. Similarly, $0a = 0$.

2. Consider $(-a)b + ab$. By the distributive law we have $(-a)b + ab = [(-a) + a]b = 0b = 0$; hence $(-a)b + ab = 0$. Adding $-(ab)$ to both members of $(-a)b + ab = 0$, we have $(-a)b + ab + [-(ab)] = -(ab)$, or $(-a)b + 0 = -(ab)$; hence $(-a)b = -(ab)$.

3. Note that $(-a)(-b) + (-a)b = (-a)[(-b) + b] = -a(0) = 0$. Substituting $-(ab)$ for $(-a)b$, we have $(-a)(-b) + [-(ab)] = 0$, and, adding ab to both members, we have $(-a)(-b) + 0 = ab$, which proves 3 above.

A second proof that $(-a)(-b) = ab$, using ordered pairs, is given in section 19.8.2.

* The multiplicative inverse of a rational number (or a real number) is sometimes called its *reciprocal*.

The following rule for the product of signed numbers is obtained from the properties discussed:

RULE 4

The product of two signed numbers is a positive number if both factors have the same sign. The product of two signed numbers is a negative number if the two factors have opposite signs.

Illustrations. $(-2)(-3) = 6$; $(-2)(3) = -6$; $(5)(-3) = -15$; $(4)(3) = 12$.

Division is the inverse of multiplication. Thus the statement that $-10/2 = -5$ is equivalent to the statement that $-10 = (-5)(2)$ or that $-10 = 2(-5)$. More generally,

$$\frac{a}{b} = q \quad \text{is equivalent to} \quad a = q(b), \quad \text{where, of course, } b \neq 0.$$

If a and b are of the same sign, then q must be a positive number, and if a and b are of opposite sign then q must be a negative number. These conditions can be checked by putting in a and b, first with the same sign, then with opposite signs, in the statement $a = q(b)$. We summarize these results in the following rule.

RULE 5

The quotient of two signed numbers is positive if both numbers have the same sign. It is negative if the two numbers have opposite signs.

Example 1. Write the product and the quotient of each pair of signed numbers:

(*a*) 8, 5 (*b*) 3, -2 (*c*) -6, 3 (*d*) -3, -7.

Solutions, (*a*) $(8)(5) = 40$, $8 \div 5 = \frac{8}{5}$ or $1\frac{3}{5}$.

(*b*) $3(-2) = -6$, $3 \div (-2) = -\frac{3}{2} = -1\frac{1}{2}$.

(*c*) $(-6)(3) = -18$, $(-6) \div 3 = -2$.

(*d*) $(-3)(-7) = 21$, $(-3) \div (-7) = \frac{3}{7}$.

Example 2. In the rational number field (set of positive and negative fractions and 0) find the multiplicative inverse for 3, -2, $\frac{1}{4}$, $-\frac{3}{5}$, a, b/a ($a \neq 0$, a, and b, integers).

Solution. The inverse of any rational number except zero exists as another rational number. It is such that the product with the given number equals 1. Thus $\frac{1}{3}$ is the inverse of 3, since $(\frac{1}{3})(3) = 1$; $-1/2$ is the inverse of -2, since $(-1/2)(-2) = 1$; 4 is the inverse of $\frac{1}{4}$, since $(4)(\frac{1}{4}) = 1$; $-5/3$ is the inverse of $-3/5$, since $(-5/3)(-3/5) = \frac{15}{15} = 1$; $1/a$ is the inverse of a, since $(1/a)(a) = a/a = 1$; and $-a/b$ is the inverse of $b/-a$, since $(-a/b)(b/-a) = -ab/-ba = ab/ab = 1$.

Example 3. Using the distributive law and the rules for signed numbers, expand and simplify each of the following:

(*a*) $3(2x - 3y)$ (*b*) $2x(3 - 2x)$ (*c*) $-4(5 - x + 2y)$ (*d*) $(6x - 9y) \div (-3)$ (*e*) $-2(5 - 3)$.

Solutions. (*a*) $3(2x - 3y) = 3(2x) + 3(-3y) = 6x - 9y$.

(*b*) $2x(3 - 2x) = 2x(3) + 2x(-2x) = 6x - 4x^2$.

(*c*) $-4(5 - x + 2y) = -4(5) + (-4)(-x) + (-4)(2y) = -20 + 4x - 8y$.

(*d*) $(6x - 9y) \div (-3) = (6x) \div (-3) + (-9y) \div (-3) = -2x + 3y$.

(*e*) $-2(5 - 3) = -10 + 6 = -4$, or $-2(2) = -4$ (note two ways of solving).

EXERCISE 5

Simplify each of the following:

1. $(-3)(-2)$; $(-5)(7)$; $3(-4 + 5)$(two ways); $-5(3 - 8)$(two ways).
2. $(-3)(x - 2y)$; $6(4 - 3x)$; $-7(-2x + 3y)$; $(-5x)(-3 + 4y)$.
3. $12 \div (-4)$; $-7 \div 7$; $-10 \div (-2)$; $-10 \div 20$; $-30a \div (-6a)$.
4. $(8x - 4y) \div 4$; $(6x + 12y) \div (-3)$; $(x - 2y + 3) \div 2$.
5. $5x(-x + 3)$; $-2(3x - 2y)$; $7(-2x + 4y)$; $-5y(-4y - 3x)$.
6. $-x(x + y + z)$; $2x(4 - 5)$(two ways); $-4(-x - y)$; $5a(x + 1 - a)$.

19.6 EQUATIONS AND APPLICATIONS

Any equation involving only the first power of an unknown, with rational coefficients and rational numbers, will now have a solution set when the unknown is in the set of rational numbers.

Example 1. Solve each equation, assuming that x is in the set of rational numbers.

(*a*) $3x + 2x - 5 = x - 11$ (*b*) $-2x + 3 = 7 + 2x$.

Solutions. (*a*)

$$\begin{aligned} 3x + 2x - 5 &= x - 11 \\ 5x - 5 &= x - 11 \\ \underline{-x + 5} &= \underline{-x + 5} \\ 4x &= -6 \end{aligned}$$

Add the negatives of x and of -5 to both members of the equation.

Multiply both members by the inverse of 4. $\frac{1}{4}(4x) = \frac{1}{4}(-6)$.

$$x = -\frac{6}{4} = -\frac{3}{2}.$$

Check.

$$3\left(-\frac{3}{2}\right) + 2\left(-\frac{3}{2}\right) - 5 \stackrel{?}{=} \left(-\frac{3}{2}\right) - 11$$

$$-\frac{9}{2} - 3 - 5 \stackrel{?}{=} \frac{-3 - 22}{2}$$

$$-\frac{25}{2} = -\frac{25}{2}.$$

(*b*)
$$\begin{aligned} -2x + 3 &= 7 + 2x \\ -2x - 3 &= -3 - 2x \\ \hline -4x &= 4 \end{aligned}$$

$$\left(-\frac{1}{4}\right)(-4)x = \left(-\frac{1}{4}\right)(4)$$

$$x = -1.$$

Check.
$$\begin{aligned} -2(-1) + 3 &\stackrel{?}{=} 7 + 2(-1) \\ 2 + 3 &\stackrel{?}{=} 7 - 2 \\ 5 &= 5. \end{aligned}$$

Example 2. Solve, assuming that x is in the set of rational numbers.

$$3(x - 3) + 5(x + 2) = 7(2x + 1).$$

Solution. Using the distributive law we find that

$$3(x - 3) + 5(x + 2) = 7(2x + 1)$$

becomes
$$3x - 9 + 5x + 10 = 14x + 7$$

or
$$\begin{aligned} 8x + 1 &= 14x + 7 \\ -14x - 1 &= -14x - 1 \qquad \text{(adding inverses)} \\ \hline -6x &= 6 \\ x &= -1. \end{aligned}$$

Check.
$$\begin{aligned} 3(-1 - 3) + 5(-1 + 2) &\stackrel{?}{=} 7[2(-1) + 1] \\ 3(-4) + 5(1) &\stackrel{?}{=} 7(-1) \\ -12 + 5 &= -7. \end{aligned}$$

EXERCISE 6

Solve each of the following equations for x in the set of rational numbers:

1. $5x - 3 = x + 7 - 2.$

2. $-3x + x - 5 = 7x + 2 - 11x.$

3. $\frac{x}{2} + 5 = \frac{x}{3}.$

4. $-\frac{4x}{3} + \frac{7}{3} = 11.$

5. $\frac{x}{3} + \frac{2x}{5} = 11.$

6. $3x - 2 + \frac{7x}{2} = 5x - 1.$

7. $3(x - 2) = x + 12.$

8. $4(x + 3) = 5(2x + 1) + 3.$

9. $\frac{x + 1}{3} = \frac{x - 2}{5} + 3.$

10. $7(3 - x) = 4(5 - 2x).$

11. $\frac{2x}{3} + 4 = \frac{5}{7}(x + 4).$

12. $5x + 15 = 10(x - 2).$

Work out each of the following problems by first representing the unknown quantities by a letter symbol, second writing an equation for the statement involving the number, and third solving the equation.

13. How many dimes added to three nickels makes a sum of 85 cents?

14. How many nickels added to three dimes makes a sum of 85 cents?

15. If $\frac{2}{3}$ of a number plus $\frac{3}{4}$ of the same number makes a total of 34, find the number.

16. Two numbers added together make a total of twenty units. If one number is x, what quantity represents the other? If the first number is three times the second, find the two numbers.

17. Two numbers have a sum of 33. The larger number is four more than the other. Find the two numbers.

18. The difference of two numbers is 28, and the larger number is three times the smaller. Find both numbers.

19. There are eighteen coins in a collection; some are quarters and the rest are dimes. If the value of the collection is $2.85, how many coins of each kind are there?

20. One third of the total height of a building is made up of the basement floors, one half of the total height is made up of office floors, and the remaining height of 36 feet is the penthouse tower. What is the total height of the building?

21. The length of a rectangle is three feet more than twice its width. If the perimeter of the rectangle is 78 feet, find the dimensions of the rectangle.

22. The width of a rectangle is one quarter its length, and the perimeter of the rectangle is 60 feet. Find the dimensions of the rectangle.

19.7 PROPORTION

A special kind of equation is obtained when two ratios are set equal to each other. A *ratio* is a fraction or an indicated division. We speak of a ratio of 3 to 2, written $3 : 2$, $\frac{3}{2}$, or $3 \div 2$. An equation indicating that two ratios are equal is called a *proportion*. Thus $\frac{3}{2} = \frac{24}{16}$ is a proportion. Similarly $4x/25 = \frac{2}{5}$ is a proportion. Proportions are statements of equality between fractions. A general proportion can be written in the form

$$\frac{a}{b} = \frac{c}{d},$$

where a, b, c, and d may be taken from the set of rational numbers or the set of real numbers, in which $b \neq 0$ and $d \neq 0$. The elements a, b, c, and d of a proportion are called the *first*, *second*, *third*, and *fourth terms*, respectively. The first and fourth terms are called the *extremes*, and the second and third terms are called the *means*. An important principle used in solving a proportion is that *the product of the means in any proportion equals the product of the extremes of the proportion.* This result is obtained by multiplying both members of the equation for the proportion by bd.

Thus

$$bd\left(\frac{a}{b}\right) = bd\left(\frac{c}{d}\right),$$

$$\frac{bda}{b} = \frac{bdc}{d}$$

$$da = bc \quad \text{or} \quad ad = bc.$$

Example 1. Solve each proportion, assuming that x is in the set of rational numbers.

$$(a)\ \frac{3x}{7} = \frac{12}{35} \qquad (b)\ \frac{x-2}{3} = \frac{7}{9}.$$

Solution.

$$(a)\ (3x)(35) = 7(12), \qquad 105x = 84, \qquad x = \frac{84}{105} = \frac{4}{5}.$$

$$(b)\ 9(x-2) = 3(7), \qquad 9x - 18 = 21, \qquad 9x = 39,$$

$$x = \frac{39}{9} = \frac{13}{3} = 4\tfrac{1}{3}.$$

Proportions have many applications. In geometry many applications follow from the fact that *corresponding sides of similar figures are proportional.* In elementary physics and chemistry many scientific laws are stated as proportions. Thus distance is proportional to elapsed time if the rate is constant, and force is proportional to acceleration if the mass is constant.

Example 2. Assuming that taxes are proportional to assessed valuation, find the taxes on property valued at $5200 if the taxes on property valued at $3900 amount to $270.

Solution. Let t represent the tax in dollars on property valued at $5200; then

$$\frac{t}{5200} = \frac{270}{3900} = \frac{9}{130} \qquad \text{(reducing the second ratio to lowest terms).}$$

Hence $130(t) = 9(5200)$; $\quad t = \dfrac{9(5200)}{130} = 9(40) = 360.$ The tax is $360.

Note that 130 is a common divisor of 130 and 5200.

EXERCISE 7

Solve each proportion, assuming that x is in the set of rational numbers.

1. $\dfrac{3x}{35} = \dfrac{6}{7}.$
2. $\dfrac{x-3}{5} = \dfrac{7}{10}.$
3. $\dfrac{12}{x} = \dfrac{6}{5}.$
4. $\dfrac{7}{13} = \dfrac{x}{65}.$
5. $\dfrac{6}{x-2} = \dfrac{5}{x+2}.$
6. $\dfrac{7}{10} = \dfrac{14}{x}.$

7. $\dfrac{2x+3}{8} = \dfrac{11}{4}$. 8. $\dfrac{6}{5x} = \dfrac{12}{x+9}$. 9. $\dfrac{7-x}{10} = \dfrac{2}{5}$. 10. $\dfrac{5-x}{2} = \dfrac{11}{4}$.

Set up each problem as a proportion and solve.

11. Taxes are proportional to income on the first \$4000 of net income (gross income less deductions). If taxes on \$2500 net are \$500, what are taxes on a net income of \$2175?

12. Vertical poles and their shadow lengths on level ground are proportional for light coming from a fixed direction. If a yardstick held vertically casts a shadow 46 inches long, how high is a flagpole whose shadow is 92 feet long? (Be careful to compare similar units.)

13. The lamp at the top of a post makes a shadow 10 feet long for a man who is 6 feet tall, and who stands at a point that is 30 feet from the bottom of the post. How high is the post, assuming measurements are correct to the nearest inch?

14. The areas of similar figures are in the same ratio as (are proportional to) the squares of the corresponding sides. What is the ratio of the areas of two similar triangles if a pair of corresponding sides has a ratio of 4:5?

15. Perimeters of similar figures are proportional to their corresponding altitudes. If the altitudes of two similar figures are in a ratio of 5 to 6 and the perimeter of the first figure is 35 inches, what is the perimeter of the second figure?

16. Separate 95 into two parts whose ratio is 2:3. (*Hint.* Let x represent the number of units in one part, then $95 - x$ will represent the number of units in the other part.)

17. Separate 78 into two parts whose ratio is 5:1.

18. Separate 120 into two parts whose ratio is 7:8.

19. Earnings of a certain kind of investment are proportional to the investment. If an investment of \$3500 earns \$85.00, how much would an investment of \$4500 earn?

20. The sides of one triangle are 5, $7\frac{1}{2}$, and $8\frac{1}{2}$ inches. What are the lengths of the sides of a second triangle similar to the first if the shortest side of the second triangle is $7\frac{1}{2}$ inches long?

19.8 THE FIELD POSTULATES OF ALGEBRA

In the preceding chapters of this book various postulates of algebra have been stated as needed in connection with the number system of arithmetic. It seems desirable now to present these postulates in a more formal manner.

Consider a set M of undefined elements $a, b, c, \cdots$, finite or infinite, with at least two elements, and the undefined operations $+$ and $\times$. Thus $M = \{a, b, c, \cdots\}$, and we are considering two operations on these elements. The only restriction to be placed on $+$ and $\times$ is that of uniqueness; that is, $a + b$ yields one and only one result; likewise, for $a \times b$ the result is unique.

(*a*) *Postulates involving the operation* $+$.

1. CLOSURE

If a and b are any two elements of the set M, then $a + b = c$ is an element of the set M.

2. ASSOCIATIVITY

If a, b, c are elements of the set M, then $a + (b + c) = (a + b) + c$.

3. IDENTITY

For any element a of the set M, there exists an element I of the set M such that $a + I = I + a = a$. I is called the *additive identity* element of M.

4. INVERSE

For any element a of the set, there exists an element a' of the set M such that $a + a' = a' + a = I$. a' is called the *additive inverse* of a in M.

5. COMMUTATIVITY

If a and b are any two elements of the set M, then $a + b = b + a$.

(*b*) *Postulates involving the operation* $\times$.

1. CLOSURE

If a and b are any two elements of the set M, then $a \times b = c$ is an element of the set M.

2. ASSOCIATIVITY

If a, b, and c are elements of the set M, then $a \times (b \times c) = (a \times b) \times c$.

3. IDENTITY

For any element a of the set M, there exists an element E of the set M such that $a \times E = E \times a = a$. E is called the *multiplicative identity* element of M.

4. INVERSE

For any element a of the set M, except the additive identity, there exists an element a^* of the set M such that $a \times a^* = a^* \times a = E$.

5. COMMUTATIVITY

If a and b are any two elements of the set M, then $a \times b = b \times a$.

(*c*) *Postulate involving both operations* $+$ *and* $\times$.

1. DISTRIBUTIVITY

If a, b, and c are any three elements of the set M, then $a \times (b + c) = a \times b + a \times c$.

If all eleven of these postulates are satisfied by a set of elements M, then this set M is said to form a *field*.

If a set Q of elements satisfies (*a*) 1, 2, 3, and 4, it is said to form a *group* under $+$. If also this set Q satisfies (*a*) 5, it is said to form an Abelian (or commutative) group under $+$.

If a set R of elements satisfies (*b*) 1, 2, 3, and 4 it is said to form a group under $\times$. It is an Abelian (commutative) group under $\times$ if (*b*) 5 is satisfied.

The first numbers used in arithmetic are the natural numbers 1, 2, 3, 4, $\cdots$. Does this infinite set of numbers form a field or a group under the operations of $+$ and $\times$, in which these operations are defined as they are in ordinary arithmetic?

Since the sum and product of any pair of natural numbers produce natural numbers, the closure postulates (a)1 and (b)1 are satisfied. The reader can easily satisfy himself that the associative postulates (a)2 and (b)2, the commutative postulates (a)5 and (b)5, and the distributive postulate (c)1 hold. What can be said about the identity postulates (a)3 and (b)3? Considering (a)3 first, does a natural number I exist such that when it is added to a, the sum is still a? This is obviously impossible. Hence the set of natural numbers forms neither a field nor a group under $+$.

A new set of numbers consisting of the natural numbers and a number I which satisfies (a)3 may be defined. This is the zero of elementary arithmetic. This new set can be shown to satisfy (a)1, (b)1, (a)2, (b)2, (a)3, (a)5, (b)5, (c)1, and possibly (b)3.

Consider again the set of natural numbers. Does this set satisfy (b)3? That is, does a natural number, E, exist such that $a \times E = E \times a = a$, where a is any natural number of the set? The natural number 1 has this property, hence the multiplicative identity E is 1.

The remaining postulates to be considered are (a)4 and (b)4. Since (a)4 requires the existence of a natural number a' such that $a + a' = a' + a = I$, and since the additive identity under $+$ does not exist in the set of natural numbers, (a)4 is not satisfied. This now means that the set of natural numbers does not form a group under $+$. Using the enlarged set mentioned above by adding zero to the natural numbers still does not help, since no natural number a' can be found such that $a + a' = a' + a = 0$. The (b)4 postulate requires the existence of natural numbers a' such that $a \times a' = a' \times a = 1$ for every a. If $a = 1$, then $a' = 1$, and this condition is satisfied. But it is necessary that there exist an a' for every a. Take $a = 2$. It is obvious that no a' exists, since 2 times 1, the smallest natural number, is greater than 1. Hence the set of natural numbers does not form a group under $\times$.

19.8.1. Finite sets of numbers. A set of numbers, modulo m, is one consisting of a finite set of elements made up of 0 and 1; 0, 1, and 2; or 0, 1, 2, 3, etc. These elements can be added and multiplied in the usual sense unless the resulting number is equal to or greater than the modulus m, in which case it is decreased by a multiple of m. Thus, for a set of numbers, modulo 7, $3 + 4 = 0$, $5 + 6 = 4$, $3 + 5 = 1$. This is a finite set consisting of 0, 1, 2, 3, 4, 5, 6. A few products are $0 \times 4 = 0$, $2 \times 5 = 3$, $2 \times 3 = 6$, and $3 \times 3 = 2$.

Consider now a set of numbers, modulo 5. The numbers of this finite set are 0, 1, 2, 3, and 4. Does this set form a field? The following addition and multiplication tables will be helpful in answering the question proposed:

Addition, modulo 5

+	0	1	2	3	4
0	0	1	2	3	4
1	1	2	3	4	0
2	2	3	4	0	1
3	3	4	0	1	2
4	4	0	1	2	3

Multiplication, modulo 5

×	0	1	2	3	4
0	0	0	0	0	0
1	0	1	2	3	4
2	0	2	4	1	3
3	0	3	1	4	2
4	0	4	3	2	1

An examination of these tables will show that those postulates satisfied by the set of natural numbers will also be satisfied by the modulo 5 numbers. It will be recalled that the postulates (*a*)3, (*a*)4, and (*b*)4 were not satisfied by the infinite set of natural numbers.

The addition table shows that when any number, a, of the finite set is added to 0 the sum is a. Likewise, if 0 is added to a, the sum is a. Thus 0 is the additive inverse, and (*a*) 3 is satisfied by the modulo 5 set of numbers.

An examination of the addition table again shows the following sums: $0 + 0 = 0$, $1 + 4 = 4 + 1 = 0$, $2 + 3 = 3 + 2 = 0$. This means that an additive inverse exists for each number of the finite set, hence (*a*)4 is satisfied.

It has been shown that the finite set of modulo 5 numbers forms a group under + and, since (*a*)5 is also satisfied, that it is an Abelian group.

In order to show that this set of numbers forms a field, it is necessary that the remaining postulate (*b*)4 be satisfied; that is, for every element a in the modulo 5 set, with the exception of zero, an element a^* exists such that $a \times a^* = a^* \times a = 1$. The multiplication table shows that $1 \times 1 = 1$, $2 \times 3 = 3 \times 2 = 1$, $4 \times 4 = 1$. Hence (*b*)4 is satisfied, and the finite set of modulo 5 numbers (except zero) forms a group under ×. Furthermore, since (*b*)5 is satisfied, it is an Abelian group. Now, because this set of modulo 5 numbers satisfies all eleven of the field postulates, the set forms a field.

EXERCISE 8

1. Consider the infinite set of numbers made up of the even natural numbers.
(*a*) Does this set satisfy the closure postulates under + and ×?
(*b*) Has it an identity element under +? Under ×?

2. Consider the infinite set of numbers made up of the odd natural numbers.
(*a*) Does this set satisfy the closure postulates under +? Under ×? Why?
(*b*) Has it an identity element under +? Under ×? Why?

3. Construct addition and multiplication tables for a modulo 2 set of numbers.

4. (*a*) Does the set of numbers in problem 3 form a group under +? Under ×? Why?
(*b*) Does this set form a field? Why?

5. Construct addition and multiplication tables for a modulo 4 set of numbers.

6. (*a*) Does the set of numbers in problem 5 form a group under +? Under ×? Why?
(*b*) Does this set form a field? Why?

7. Given the finite set of elements A, B, C, D, E, F, the + and × tables are as follows:

+	A	B	C	D	E	F
A	A	B	C	D	E	F
B	B	C	D	E	F	A
C	C	D	E	F	A	B
D	D	E	F	A	B	C
E	E	F	A	B	C	D
F	F	A	B	C	D	E

×	A	B	C	D	E	F
A	A	A	A	A	A	A
B	A	B	C	D	E	F
C	A	C	E	A	C	E
D	A	D	A	D	A	D
E	A	E	C	A	E	C
F	A	F	E	D	C	B

(*a*) What element is the identity element under +? Under ×?
(*b*) Does $(B + D) + F = B + (D + F)$?
(*c*) Does $E \times (D \times F) = (E \times D) \times F$?
(*d*) Does the associative postulate hold for both + and × operations?
(*e*) Does an additive inverse exist for each element in the set? What are the additive inverses of E and C?
(*f*) Does a multiplicative inverse exist for C, F, and D?
(*g*) Does this set of elements form a group under + and under ×?
(*h*) Does this set of elements form a field?

19.8.2. The integers. It has been shown that the set of natural numbers had no identity element under +. If the set of natural numbers is augmented by the number zero, it is easily understood that the only number in the augmented set with an additive inverse is zero. In an effort to find an infinite set of numbers for which each element will have an additive inverse, a new set of numbers, called the *integers*, has been developed.

The following definitions are given when the known set of numbers consists of zero and the natural numbers, which are represented by a, b, c, · · · .

POSITIVE INTEGERS AND NEGATIVE INTEGERS

Let a, b, and n be natural numbers, or zero. If $a - b = n$, then the ordered pair of numbers (a, b) is the *positive integer* $+n$. If $b - a = n$, then the ordered pair of numbers (a, b) is the *negative integer* $-n$. If $a - b = 0$, then the ordered pair of numbers $(a, b) = 0$, which is neither positive nor negative.

ADDITION

$$(a, b) + (c, d) = [(a + c), (b + d)].$$

MULTIPLICATION

$$(a, b) \times (c, d) = [(ac + bd), (ad + bc)].$$

EQUALITY

$$(a, b) = (c, d) \text{ if and only if } a + d = b + c.$$

INEQUALITY

$$(a, b) < (c, d) \text{ if and only if } (a + d) < (b + c).$$

Numerical Illustrations. The numeral (7, 2) is a representation of the positive integer +5 because $7 - 2 = 5$. The numeral (12, 10) is another representation. Likewise, (2, 0) is a proper representation of +2.

The numeral (4, 9) is a representation of the negative integer −5. Other representations of this negative integer are (0, 5), (1, 6), and so on.

The additive identity is represented in general by the numerals (k, k), where k is 0 or any natural number. Thus (0, 0), (2, 2), (10, 10) are some of the representations of the additive identity.

One of the stated purposes of expanding the number system from one containing only zero and the natural numbers was to have a new system in which the additive inverse exists. Does an additive inverse exist for each integer? That is, to each integer (a, b) is there a number (c, d), in the set of integers such that $(a, b) + (c, d) = (0, 0)$? If the number (c, d) exists, then by the addition definition $(a, b) + (c, d) = [(a + c), (c + d)] = (0, 0)$. By the definition of the equality of two integers, $a + c + 0 = b + d + 0$ or $a + c = b + d$. Hence, letting c be any natural number, d is determined by the last equation, which proves that an additive inverse exists for each integer.

Example 1. Find the additive inverse of (7, 3).

Solution. Let the additive inverse be (c, d), then $(7, 3) + (c, d) = (7 + c, 3 + d) = (0, 0)$. Hence $7 + c = 3 + d$. Let $c = 1$, then $d = 5$. Thus the additive inverse is (1, 5). If $c = 2$, then $7 + 2 = 3 + d$, or $d = 6$. Another form of the additive inverse is (2, 6). The reader can easily show that (2, 6) = (1,5).

Example 2. Find the following products:

(*a*) (4, 2) × (7, 2) =
(*b*) (4, 2) × (3, 7) =
(*c*) (1, 5) × (10, 8) =
(*d*) (1, 5) × (2, 5) =

Solution. By use of the definition of multiplication,

(*a*) (4, 2) × (7, 2) = [(28 + 4), (8 + 14)] = (32, 22).
(*b*) (4, 2) × (3, 7) = [(12 + 14), (28 + 6)] = (26, 34).
(*c*) (1, 5) × (10, 8) = (50, 58).
(*d*) (1, 5) × (2, 5) = (27, 15).

It is instructive to express the problem in Example 2 in the usual notation for integers, thus

(*a*) $(4, 2) \times (7, 2) = (+2)(+5) = (32, 22) = +10.$
(*b*) $(4, 2) \times (3, 7) = (+2) \times (-4) = (26, 34) = -8.$
(*c*) $(1, 5) \times (10, 8) = (-4) \times (+2) = (50, 58) = -8.$
(*d*) $(1, 5) \times (2, 5) = (-4) \times (-3) = (27, 15) = +12.$

It appears that the new definitions of the integers lead to the following facts:

A positive integer times a positive integer gives a positive product.
A positive integer times a negative integer gives a negative product.
A negative integer times a positive integer gives a negative product.
A negative integer times a negative integer gives a positive product.

Each of these statements can be verified by using general representations of the integers rather than special integers.

As an example it is shown that a negative number times a negative number is always a positive number. Let two general negative numbers be represented by $[a, (a + n_1)]$ and $[b, (b + n_2)]$ where a, b, n_1, n_2 are natural numbers. In the usual representation the first number is $-n_1$; the second is $-n_2$. Multiplication gives $[a, (a + n_1)] \times [b, (b + n_2)] = [(ab + ab + n_2a + n_1b + n_1n_2), (ab + n_2a + ab + n_1b)]$ or $[(2ab + n_2a + n_1b + n_1n_2), (2ab + n_2a + n_1b)]$. Since the first member of this ordered pair is always greater than the second, it is a positive number; in fact, it is the positive integer $+n_1n_2$.

EXERCISE 9

1. Given the integers (5, 2), (2, 8), find
(*a*) $(5, 2) + (2, 8) =$
(*b*) $(5, 2) \times (2, 8) =$
(*c*) Is the answer to (*b*) a positive or negative integer? Why?

2. Order the following integers, placing the smallest first. (1, 0), (2, 3), (4, 1), (7, 9), (4, 4).

3. Express the following in the form (a, b):

$$(2, 4) + (8, 12) \times (1, 3) \times (2, 3) + (4, 0) =$$

4. A representation of the negative integer -1 is (1, 2), another representation is (6, 7). Show the $(-1) \times (-1) = +1$ by finding the product of $(1, 2) \times (6, 7)$.

5. A positive integer may be expressed as $(a, 0)$, where a is a natural number. Likewise a negative integer may be expressed as $(0, b)$, where b is a natural number.

(*a*) Show, using the foregoing representation, that the sum of two positive integers is a positive integer.
(*b*) Show that the sum of two negative integers is a negative integer.

(*c*) Show that the sum of a positive integer and a negative integer may be a positive or negative integer. What is the condition on the addends that the sum be a positive integer? A negative integer?

6. Do (*a*), (*b*), and (*c*) of problem 5 if the operation is times rather than plus.

19.9 THE RATIONAL NUMBERS

In the study of fractions, Chapter 10, section 10.1, rational numbers were defined as being expressible in the form p/q, when p and q are selected from the set of natural numbers and zero with the restriction that q cannot be zero. At that time negative numbers were not defined, but with the usual development of negative numbers, section 19.4, and the ordered-pair development, section 19.8.2, this definition can be changed slightly to include positive and negative (and zero) rational numbers. All that need be done is to change the set from which p and q are selected to the set of integers.

An interesting development in rational numbers may be made by the use of ordered pairs of integers. Let p and q represent numbers selected from the set of integers, with the restriction that 0 is not selected for the value of q; we then have the following definitions:

1. A *rational number* x is defined as the solution of the equation $qx = p$, where x is represented by the ordered pair of integers (p, q), in which $q \neq 0$.

2. *Addition* is defined by the equivalence

$$(p, q) + (r, s) = [(ps + qr), qs].$$

3. *Multiplication* is defined by the equivalence

$$(p, q) \times (r, s) = (pr, qs).$$

4. *Equality* of rational numbers is defined by

$$(p, q) = (r, s) \quad \text{if and only if } ps = qr.$$

5. *Inequality* (order relation) between rational numbers is defined by

$$(p, q) < (r, s) \quad \text{if and only if } pqs^2 < rsq^2.$$

19.9.1. Theorem. $(p, q) = (pk, qk)$ for all p, q, and any k (as integers) except $k = 0$.

Proof. From the definition of equality, $(p, q) = (r, s)$ if and only if $ps = qr$; hence in this theorem $(p, q) = (pk, qk)$ if and only if $p(qk) = q(pk)$. But $q(pk) = (qp)k = (pq)k = p(qk)$ by the application of the associative and commutative postulates for integers, which proves the theorem.

The reader can show that these new numbers satisfy all eleven of the field postulates. Hence the rational numbers form a field. Note also that they form a commutative or Abelian group under + and also under ×.

In the interest of developing a definition of division, one of the suggested tasks for the reader is carried out here. Does the multiplicative inverse exist for the rational numbers? In other words, can a number (p', q') be found such that $(p, q) \times (p', q') = (1, 1)$?

By the definition of a product of rational numbers, if such a number $(p' q')$ exists, then $(pp', qq') = (1, 1)$. From the definition of equality of two rational numbers it follows that $pp'1 = qq'1$ or $pp' = qq'$. One apparent solution is $p' = q$, $q' = p$. If $q' = p$, then p cannot be zero. Hence with the allowable exception $(0, 1)$, every integer has an inverse.

The existence of the multiplicative inverse makes division possible; thus

$$(p, q) \div (r, s) = (ps, qr). \tag{1}$$

Example 1. Find the multiplicative inverse of $(4, -3)$.

Solution. If (p', q') is the multiplicative inverse, then $(4, -3)(p', q') = (4p', -3q') = (1, 1)$. Hence $p' = -3$, $q' = 4$, or the answer is $(-3, 4)$.

Example 2. Perform the indicated division $(2, 3) \div (4, 5)$.

Solution. Using (1), the formula for division $(2, 3) \div (4, 5) = (2 \cdot 5, 4 \cdot 3)$, or $(10, 12)$. By the theorem above, the answer may be written $(5, 6)$.

EXERCISE 10

1. Perform the following operations:
(*a*) $(2, 3) + (4, 5) =$
(*b*) $(2, 3) \times (4, 5) =$
(*c*) $(8, 2) \div (4, 12) =$

2. If $-(2, 3)$ implies $(-1)(2, 3)$, show that $(-1)(2, 3) = (-2, 3)$. *Hint.* Write $-1 = (-1, 1)$.

3. Check each operation in problem 1 by changing the ordered-pair notation (p, q) of the rational number to the usual form p/q.

4. Using the method implied in problem 2, perform the following subtractions:
(*a*) $(4, 5) - (2, 3) =$
(*b*) $(3, -8) - (-4, 2) =$

5. Express the solution of the equation $3x - 9 = 0$ as an ordered pair of numbers.

6. Order the following rational numbers, showing the smallest first.

$$(2, 3), (-1, 5), (0, 8), (4, 5), (4, 1), (1, 4).$$

7. It was found than an integer expressed as an ordered pair of numbers had more than one representation. The same is true for the rational numbers, since the theorem stated in this section gave the equality statement $(p, q) = (pk, qk)$. Thus $(2, 4) = (6, 12) = (1, 2)$, and so on. Find three different representations of the following:
(*a*) $(1, 3)$ (*b*) $(-2, 5)$ (*c*) $(-2, -10)$ (*d*) $(0, 1)$.

8. Write each of the following rational numbers as ordered pairs of numbers:
(*a*) $\frac{2}{3}$ (*b*) $\frac{4}{5}$ (*c*) 2 (*d*) .2 (*e*) 0 (*f*) -1 (*g*) $\frac{2}{-5}$ (*h*) $\frac{-2}{5}$ (*i*) $\frac{1}{5}$.

9. Determine which pairs of rational numbers are equal in problem 8.

10. Express the rational number $\dfrac{4 - \frac{1}{2}}{\frac{1}{3} + \frac{1}{5}}$ as an ordered pair of numbers.

REFERENCES

Brumfiel, C. F., R. E. Eicholz, and M. E. Shanks, *Algebra I*, pp. 42–95, 126–169, 271–286.

Eulenberg, M. D. and T. S. Sunko, *Introductory Algebra, A College Approach*, pp. 1–75, 242–265.

Layton, W. I., *College Arithmetic*, pp. 131–155.

20

Square Root and the Pythagorean Theorem

20.1 SQUARE ROOT

Let N represent a positive number. If a positive number x exists such that $x^2 = N$, then x is said to be the positive square root of N and is represented by the symbol $\sqrt{N}$. Since $9 = 3^2$, then $3 = \sqrt{9}$. Also, since $4 = 2^2$, then $2 = \sqrt{4}$. Hence, if the positive square root of 6 is desired, it would be indicated by $\sqrt{6}$, and, since 6 lies between 4 and 9, $\sqrt{6}$ lies between 2 and 3. A table of squares such as Table 16 is helpful in finding square roots. If the positive square root of 1681 is desired, look in the column, under N^2, for 1681. In the same row and in the first column under N is 41, which is $\sqrt{1681}$.

EXERCISE 1

Find the positive square root of each of the following numbers.

1. 5776 **2.** 29,241
3. 7396 **4.** 676
5. 1225 **6.** 32,041
7. 900 **8.** 9801
9. 5625 **10.** 33,124

20.2 METHODS OF FINDING THE SQUARE ROOTS OF NUMBERS

(*a*) *Interpolation method.* Table 16 lists only certain numbers under N^2 which are the perfect squares of the corresponding numbers under N. An examination of the table will show that many of the numbers under N^2 between 1 and 40,000 are missing. Hence, if $\sqrt{6}$ is desired, it cannot be

Table 16
Table of Squares

N	N^2	N	N^2	N	N^2	N	N^2
0	0	50	2500	100	10000	150	22500
1	1	51	2601	101	10201	151	22801
2	4	52	2704	102	10404	152	23104
3	9	53	2809	103	10609	153	23409
4	16	54	2916	104	10816	154	23716
5	25	55	3025	105	11025	155	24025
6	36	56	3136	106	11236	156	24336
7	49	57	3249	107	11449	157	24649
8	64	58	3364	108	11664	158	24964
9	81	59	3481	109	11881	159	25281
10	100	60	3600	110	12100	160	25600
11	121	61	3721	111	12321	161	25921
12	144	62	3844	112	12544	162	26244
13	169	63	3969	113	12769	163	26569
14	196	64	4096	114	12996	164	26896
15	225	65	4225	115	13225	165	27225
16	256	66	4356	116	13456	166	27556
17	289	67	4489	117	13689	167	27889
18	324	68	4624	118	13924	168	28224
19	361	69	4761	119	14161	169	28561
20	400	70	4900	120	14400	170	28900
21	441	71	5041	121	14641	171	29241
22	484	72	5184	122	14884	172	29584
23	529	73	5329	123	15129	173	29929
24	576	74	5476	124	15376	174	30276
25	625	75	5625	125	15625	175	30625
26	676	76	5776	126	15876	176	30976
27	729	77	5929	127	16129	177	31329
28	784	78	6084	128	16384	178	31684
29	841	79	6241	129	16641	179	32041
30	900	80	6400	130	16900	180	32400
31	961	81	6561	131	17161	181	32761
32	1024	82	6724	132	17424	182	33124
33	1089	83	6889	133	17689	183	33489
34	1156	84	7056	134	17956	184	33856
35	1225	85	7225	135	18225	185	34225
36	1296	86	7396	136	18496	186	34596
37	1369	87	7569	137	18769	187	34969
38	1444	88	7744	138	19044	188	35344
39	1521	89	7921	139	19321	189	35721
40	1600	90	8100	140	19600	190	36100
41	1681	91	8281	141	19881	191	36481
42	1764	92	8464	142	20164	192	36864
43	1849	93	8649	143	20449	193	37249
44	1936	94	8836	144	20736	194	37636
45	2025	95	9025	145	21025	195	38025
46	2116	96	9216	146	21316	196	38416
47	2209	97	9409	147	21609	197	38809
48	2304	98	9604	148	21904	198	39204
49	2401	99	9801	149	22201	199	39601

found directly from the table. However, as indicated above, the table does show that $\sqrt{6}$ is greater than 2 and less than 3.

It can be shown that the square root of 6 is an irrational number. However, a rational approximation may be made to it as follows:

Consider the table

$$\left\{\begin{matrix} \left\{\begin{matrix} 2^2 = 4 \\ N^2 = 6 \end{matrix}\right\} \\ 3^2 = 9 \end{matrix}\right\}$$

Since 6 is nearer to 4 than to 9, the square root of 6, represented by N, should be nearer to 2. A method of making an intelligent guess is to set up a proportion indicated by the braces shown above.

$$\frac{N-2}{3-2} = \frac{6-4}{9-4},$$

$$N - 2 = \frac{2}{5},$$

$$N = 2.4.$$

This procedure is called interpolation. It can be assumed that 2.4 is the square root of 6 accurate to $\pm .05$. To test its accuracy, the following table is set up. Since $(2.4)^2$ is less than 6, $(2.5)^2$, which is greater than 6, is also computed. Thus $\sqrt{6}$ lies between 2.4 and 2.5.

$$(2.4)^2 = 5.76,$$
$$N^2 = 6,$$
$$(2.5)^2 = 6.25.$$

The values of $(2.4)^2$ and $(2.5)^2$ may be computed by actual squaring, or, better still, these values can be found in Table 16. Since $(10N)^2 = 100N^2$, it is possible to determine the appropriate values of $(2.4)^2$ and $(2.5)^2$ by checking the rows occupied by 24 and 25. Since N^2 is 100 times the number wanted, all that must be done is to divide by 100. The reader should compare the values given in the table above with Table 16. In order to obtain a better approximation, another interpolation is carried out. Thus

$$\frac{N - 2.4}{2.5 - 2.4} = \frac{6 - 5.76}{6.25 - 5.76}, \quad \text{or } N - 2.4 = .1\left(\frac{.24}{.49}\right).$$

$N = 2.4 + .049 = 2.449.$

$$(2.449)^2 = 5.997601,$$
$$N^2 = 6,$$
$$(2.450)^2 = 6.002500.$$

Since $(2.449)^2$ is nearer than $(2.450)^2$ to 6, it would appear that $\sqrt{6} = 2.449$, correct to four significant figures.

(*b*) *Newton's method.* This method makes use of an algorithm credited to Newton. Let A_1 represent the first approximation to the square root of N. The second approximation, A_2, may be obtained from $A_2 = \frac{1}{2}[A_1 + (N/A_1)]$. To illustrate, find $\sqrt{6}$ by this method, accurate to four significant figures. First, by the use of a table or by actual squaring, it could be determined that $2.4 = A_1$ is a usable approximation to $\sqrt{6}$; $6 \div 2.4 = 2.5$, hence, $A_2 = \frac{1}{2}(2.4 + 2.5)$, or 2.45. $A_3 = \frac{1}{2}[2.45 + (6/2.45)] = 2.449$, which is probably the answer to four significant figures. To be certain, compute $A_4 = \frac{1}{2}[2.449 + (6/2.449)] = 2.44949$.

The reader may note that Newton's formula for the square root gives a better approximation at each step, since it is always an average between a number that is larger than the square root and a number that is smaller than the square root, unless an exact square root has been obtained.

(*c*) *The general method.* The usual proof of this method requires algebra, hence it is not given here. In order to illustrate the method, the same example in the two preceding methods is used, namely, find $\sqrt{6}$ accurate to four significant places.

Add decimal places to the number 6. Now separate 6.00000000 into periods of two digits, counting from the decimal point, as shown in the illustrative example. It will be seen in this example that the period farthest to the left has only one digit, 6. One digit in our square root answer will correspond to each of the periods of our number, and the decimal point in the answer will be directly above the decimal point in the given number.

Step 1. The largest square in the extreme left period is 4. Take the square root of 4, which is 2, and write it as the first digit in the root. Subtract the square 4 from 6. Bring down the next period to form the remainder 200.

```
   2
 √6.0 0'0 0'0 0'0 0
  4
  2 0 0
```

Step 2. Double the partial root 2 and put this product to the left of 200. Estimate the next digit in the root by dividing 200 by 10 × 4, or 40. The quotient of 5 may be the desired next place in our answer. Tentatively, try 5 in the root and attach 5 to the divisor to make 45. Now multiply 5 × 45 = 225. Since this is larger than the remainder 200, we replace 5 by 4 as the second digit in the root and also in the divisor. The product 44 × 4 = 176. Subtract 176 from 200 and bring down the next period.

```
     2. 5
   √6.0 0'0 0'0 0'0 0
    4
45| 2 0 0
    2 2 5

     2. 4
   √6.0 0'0 0'0 0'0 0
    4
44| 2 0 0
    1 7 6
      2 4 0 0
```

Step 3. Now double the partial root 24 and estimate the next digit in the root by dividing 2400 by 480. Since $4 \times 484 = 1936$, 4 is the next digit in the root. Subtract 1936 from 2400 and bring down the next period.

```
     2. 4  4
   √6.0 0'0 0'0 0'0 0
    4
44 | 2 0 0
     1 7 6
484 | 2 4 0 0
      1 9 3 6
        4 6 4
```

Step 4. Additional places in the square root may be found by continuing this process. Five places should be obtained and the answer rounded to four significant figures. Thus $\sqrt{6}$ to four significant places is 2.449.

```
     2. 4  4  9 4
   √6.0 0'0 0'0 0'0 0
    4
44 | 2 0 0
     1 7 6
484 | 2 4 0 0
      1 9 3 6
4889 | 4 6 4 0 0
       4 4 0 0 1
48984 | 2 3 9 9 0 0
        1 9 5 9 3 6
          4 3 9 6 4
```

In order to give the reader a second opportunity to examine the steps in finding the square root, we shall use the different methods in determining $\sqrt{9208}$ to three significant places. Little or no explanation is given.

(*a*) *Using the interpolation method.* From Table 16

$$95^2 = 9025$$

$$N^2 = 9208$$

$$96^2 = 9216$$

$$\frac{N-95}{96-95} = \frac{9208-9025}{9216-9025}$$

$$N - 95 = \frac{183}{191}, \quad \text{hence } N = 95.96.$$

Since Table 16 does not give the squares of four-digit numbers, a table must be constructed.

$$(95.95)^2 = 9206.4$$

$$N^2 = 9208$$

$$(95.96)^2 = 9208.3$$

$$\frac{N - 95.95}{95.96 - 95.95} = \frac{1.6}{1.9} = .8$$

$$N = 95.95 + .8 \times .01 = 95.958.$$

Hence, $\sqrt{9208}$ is 95.96 accurate to four significant figures.

(*b*) *Using Newton's method.* Table 16 indicates that $N_1 = 96$ is an approximation. Hence

$$N_2 = \frac{1}{2}\left(96 + \frac{9208}{96}\right) = \tfrac{1}{2}(96 + 95.916) = 95.958$$

or 95.96 to four significant places. Similarly,

$$N_3 = \frac{1}{2}\left(95.96 + \frac{9208}{95.96}\right) = 95.9583,$$

which verifies the four-place accuracy of N_2.

(*c*) *Using the general method.*

```
               9  5. 9  5  8
            √9 2'0 8.0 0'0 0'0 0
             8 1
        185 | 1 1 0 8
                9 2 5
       1909 |  1 8 3 0 0
               1 7 1 8 1
      19185 | 1 1 1 9 0 0
                  9 5 9 2 5
     191908 | 1 5 9 7 5 0 0
                1 5 3 5 2 6 4
                    6 2 2 3 6
```

Hence $\sqrt{9208} = 95.96$ to four significant places.

EXERCISE 2

1. Find the exact square root, or an approximation to four significant places, of the following numbers, using the general method:

(*a*) 625 (*b*) 5329
(*c*) 6192 (*d*) 850

2. Use Newton's method to find the square roots of the following numbers:

(*a*) 750 (*b*) 375
(*c*) 1955 (*d*) 36335

3. Use the interpolation method to find the square root of each of the following numbers:

(*a*) 42 (*b*) 310
(*c*) 1584 (*d*) 39142

4. (*a*) In extracting the square root of 783 by the general method, the first steps are

```
        2 7
      √7'8 3
        4
  4 7 | 3 8 3
        3 2 9
        -----
          5 4
```

Note the last indicated remainder is 54, which is larger than 47. Should 48 have been used instead of 47? Find an approximation to this square root to four significant places.

(*b*) Find another number for which the general process of determining a square root leads to a situation similar to that in (*a*).

20.3 THE PYTHAGOREAN THEOREM

The theorem in geometry which states that the square on the hypotenuse is equal to the sum of the squares on the legs of the right triangle is known as the Pythagorean theorem, in honor of a famous Greek mathematician who lived in the period following 580 B.C. Many proofs exist for this theorem, the most famous of which appeared in Euclid's *Elements*. This proof is based upon the comparison of the sum of the areas of the two squares constructed on the legs of the right triangle to the area of the square constructed on the hypotenuse.*

An easy algebraic proof follows:

In the right triangle ABC, draw the altitude from the right angle vertex C to the side AB. Indicate the sides of the various triangles formed as indicated in Fig. 1. Since the altitude to the hypotenuse of a right triangle

* See V. S. Mallory, *New Plane Geometry*, pages 360–361, for this proof.

Fig. 1

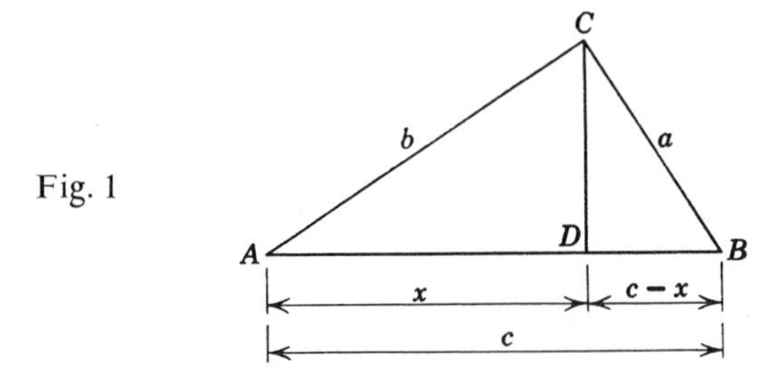

divides the triangle into two similar triangles (see Chapter 21, section 21.5), each similar to the original, it follows that

$$\frac{x}{b} = \frac{b}{c}, \quad \text{or } x = \frac{b^2}{c}, \tag{1}$$

and

$$\frac{c - x}{a} = \frac{a}{c}, \quad \text{or } c^2 - cx = a^2. \tag{2}$$

Substituting the value of x from (1) in (2), we obtain

$$c^2 - c\left(\frac{b^2}{c}\right) = a^2$$

or

$$c^2 = a^2 + b^2, \tag{3}$$

which is the algebraic statement of the Pythagorean theorem.

To illustrate the use of this theorem, let $a = 3$, $b = 4$; then from (3) $c^2 = 3^2 + 4^2 = 9 + 16 = 25$, or $c = 5$. When three such numbers are sides of a right triangle, they are called *Pythagorean numbers*.* In general, if two sides of a right triangle are natural numbers, the third side may be irrational. Thus take $a = 2$, $b = 3$, then $c^2 = 2^2 + 3^2$, or $c = \sqrt{13}$. Likewise, if $a = 5$, $c = 11$, then $5^2 + b^2 = 11^2$. Hence $b^2 = 96$, or $b = 4\sqrt{6}$.

It is interesting to note that if $a = m^2 - n^2$, $b = 2mn$, $c = m^2 + n^2$, where m and n are natural numbers, $m > n$, then the Pythagorean theorem as stated by (3) is satisfied. The reader may easily verify this statement. Hence $m^2 - n^2$, $2mn$, and $m^2 + n^2$ form a set of Pythagorean numbers.

If a right triangle has sides that are rational numbers rather than natural numbers, these rational numbers form a generalized set of Pythagorean numbers. It is easy to see that $(m^2 - n^2)/p$, $2mn/p$, $(m^2 + n^2)/p$, where $m > n$ and m, n, p are natural numbers, will generate a set of generalized Pythagorean numbers.

* These numbers are also called *Pythagorean triples*.

EXERCISE 3

1. Given the right triangle ABC with sides a, b, c, opposite, respectively, the angles A, B, C ($\angle C = 90°$).

(*a*) Given $a = 23.4$, $b = 15.7$, find c accurate to three significant places.

(*b*) Given $a = 132.72$, $c = 832.83$, find b accurate to four significant places.

2. A baseball diamond is a square with home base opposite second base. If each side of the square is 90 feet, find the distance from home to second base, expressing the answer to four significant figures.

3. A straight path is to be constructed diagonally across a rectangular park whose sides are 132.5 and 831.0 rods. Find the length of the path to the nearest tenth of a rod.

4. Show that 12, 5, 13 form a set of Pythagorean numbers.

(*a*) Show that $12k$, $5k$, $13k$, where k is a rational number, will in general form a set of Pythagorean numbers.

5. An equilateral triangle has three sides, each having a length of 18 centimeters. An altitude from any vertex bisects the opposite side. Find the length of the altitude accurate to three significant places.

6. Another method of finding Pythagorean numbers is by adding the reciprocals of any two nonzero natural numbers that differ by two. The numerator and denominator of the fraction representing the sum are the legs of a right triangle, for which the hypotenuse is a natural number. Thus $\frac{1}{5} + \frac{1}{7} = \frac{12}{35}$ and $12^2 + 35^2 = 37^2$, which means that 12, 35, 37 form a Pythagorean set of numbers.

Prove this theorem. *Hint.* Let m and $m + 2$ represent the two natural numbers which differ by two.

7. A ladder 12 feet long is placed against a vertical wall, with the foot 5 feet from the base of the wall. How high does the top of the ladder reach up on the wall? Answer to the nearest .1 foot.

8. A room has dimensions of 20 by 30 by 12 feet. If a string is stretched from one corner of the ceiling to a diagonally opposite corner of the floor, what is the minimum length of the string?

9. An isosceles triangle has sides of length 17, 17, and 16 inches. Find the length of the altitude drawn to the 16-inch side and also find the area of the triangle.

10. Suppose that twenty pennants having the shape of the isosceles triangle in problem 9—dimensions 17, 17, and 16 inches—were made of felt, how many square feet of material would be required, assuming no waste?

11. Express the altitude as well as the number of square units of area of an equilateral triangle with sides of length s, in terms of s.

12. Express the length of a diagonal of a square whose sides are s units long, in terms of s.

13. Use the results found in problem 11 to determine the altitude and the number of square inches of area for an equilateral triangle whose sides are 10 inches long.

14. A steel pole 80 feet high is to be supported by wires attached to its top point and to hooks in the ground 50 feet from the base of the pole. How long should these wires be if 2 feet of wire are used at each end to fasten them?

15. A lodgepole pine 130 feet tall snaps at a point 30 feet above the ground during a heavy storm. If the top of the tree remains attached to the base of the tree at the point where it snaps, how far from the foot of the tree will the tip strike the ground?

16. Look up at least two geometric proofs of the Pythagorean theorem in a geometry text and write an outline of each proof. If it seems feasible to present one of the proofs in terms of cut-out parts of a diagram, prepare the cut-out parts for such proof.

REFERENCES

Brumfiel, C. F., R. E. Eicholz, and M. E. Shanks, *Geometry*, pp. 171–190.

Layton, W. I., *College Arithmetic*, pp. 155–164.

Taylor, E. H., and C. N. Mills, *Arithmetic for Teacher-Training Classes*, fourth edition, pp. 382–393.

21

An Introduction to Geometry

21.1 INTRODUCTION—PRELIMINARY NOTIONS

Since geometrical figures are everywhere about us, it seems reasonable that some topics in intuitive geometry should be taught in elementary schools. Certainly, considerable coverage of this material should be given in junior high schools. Recent curriculum studies indicate a trend toward the presentation of formal geometry in the ninth grade, following algebra in the eighth grade. However, no attempt is made to discuss formal geometry in this book; a purely informal and intuitive approach is used.*

It is assumed that the reader has an intuitive notion of a point as a position in a plane or in three-dimensional space, which may be pictured as a dot of chalk on a blackboard or a dot of ink or graphite on a sheet of paper. Likewise, the reader probably has a clear picture of what is commonly called a straight line. In a strict sense these concepts of *point*, *line*, and *plane* are considered as undefined elements whose interrelations are studied and developed in geometry. For example, it is assumed (or postulated) in formal geometry that two intersecting straight lines determine a single point and two distinct points determine a single line. A line, in general, extends indefinitely in both directions. Figure 1 shows a line

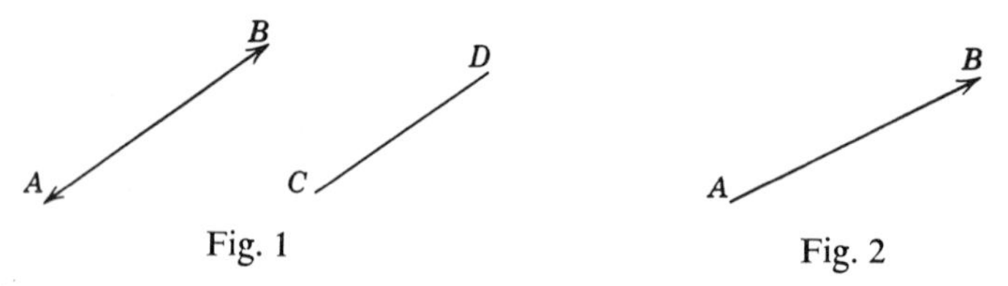

Fig. 1

Fig. 2

* As examples of the newer programs in mathematics, consult the following: Ball State Program, Ball State Teachers College, Muncie, Indiana. School Mathematics Study Group, Yale University, New Haven, Connecticut. University of Illinois Program, University of Illinois, Urbana, Illinois.

Fig. 3 Fig. 4

with points A and B marked. The arrows indicate that the line designated AB extends infinitely in both directions. A *line segment* is a finite portion of a line. Thus $\overline{CD}$ is a line segment, which may be considered as a set of points, with C and D the end points, as members of the set.

Another part of a line is shown in Fig. 2. This is part of a complete line which starts at point A and extends indefinitely in one direction but not in the opposite direction. This portion of a line, appropriately called a *half-line*, is, more generally, known as a *ray*. Figure 2 shows ray $\overrightarrow{AB}$.

Two rays originating at the same point form an *angle*. Thus in Fig. 3 the common point is O and the rays are $\overrightarrow{OA}$ and $\overrightarrow{OB}$. The arrows on the rays indicate that the rays extend indefinitely in one direction. Ordinarily, these arrows may be omitted. When no confusion arises, the bars and arrows over letter pairs for rays and segments may also be omitted.

Suppose a model of an angle is made by soldering the ends of two straight pieces of wire in such a way that the rays reach out from the soldered point in two different directions, with the restriction that neither direction is the opposite of the other. This model would be a concrete representation of the angle pictured in Fig. 3. Would it lie on a table or desk top so that the two rays would touch the flat surface at all points along the rays? A little consideration should convince the reader, intuitively, that this is true. It is possible to visualize a flat surface passing through the two rays of an angle, whether or not the angle rests on a flat surface; this surface is called a *plane*, and it can be said that two rays originating in a point such that they do not lie on a common line determine a plane; in fact, it is assumed (postulated) in geometry that two intersecting noncoincident straight lines determine a plane.

The angle shown in Fig. 4 lies in the plane of this page. It may be said that the angle determines the plane represented by this sheet of paper. For convenience, the common point C (belonging to both half-lines) is called the *vertex* of the angle. Points A and B taken on the rays or *sides* may be used to designate the angle. Thus the angle is read $\angle ACB$ (or $\angle BCA$). The important thing in these designations is that the vertex letter must fall between the other two letters. Suppose now that A and B

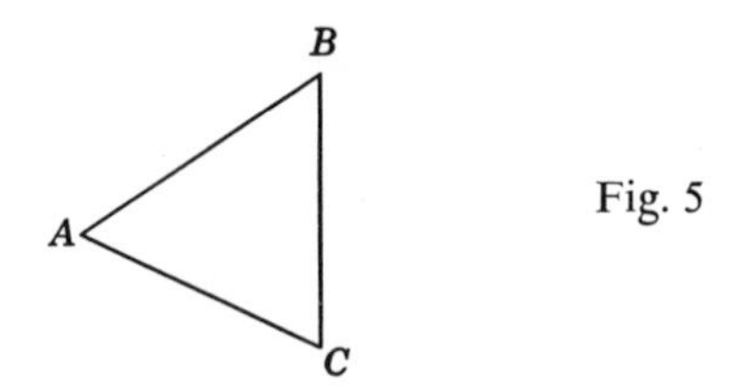

Fig. 5

are joined as shown in Fig. 5. It seems intuitively true that the line segment AB* lies in the plane determined by CA and CB. The geometrical figure consisting of three line segments CA, AB, BC and the three angles $\angle ACB$, $\angle CBA$, and $\angle BAC$ is called a *triangle.* Literally, this means three angles. It could also be called a trilateral (three sides) and is so described in some situations. The triangle is designated by its vertices. Thus $\triangle ABC$ is the designation of the triangle in Fig. 5.

In the above paragraph we spoke, for example, of angle ACB as being part of the triangle. Actually only that part of ACB which is coincident with the sides CA and CB is a part of the triangle. The complete angle is formed by the rays CA and CB. Nevertheless, we refer to such angles as angles of the triangle.

21.2 LINE AND ANGLE MEASURE

The reader is no doubt familiar with line segment measurement, in which any convenient unit, such as the centimeter or the inch, may be used to determine the length of a line. Angle measurement might not be so familiar; hence a brief review is in order.

In the measurement of angles the rotation of one half-line OB from a coincident position with another half-line OA is used to set up a unit of measurement (see Fig. 6). Let OB be rotated from the initial position OA in a counterclockwise direction until it reaches OA again. This rotation is called a positive direction, and the angle generated is called a *perigon* or

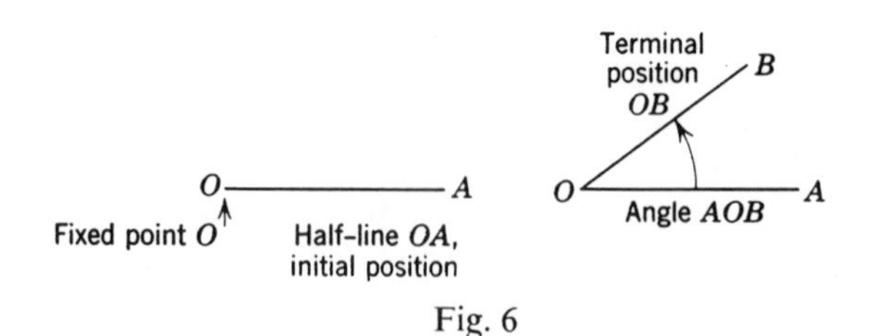

Fig. 6

* The bar, as in $\overline{AB}$, is omitted in the notation for segments in the remainder of this chapter.

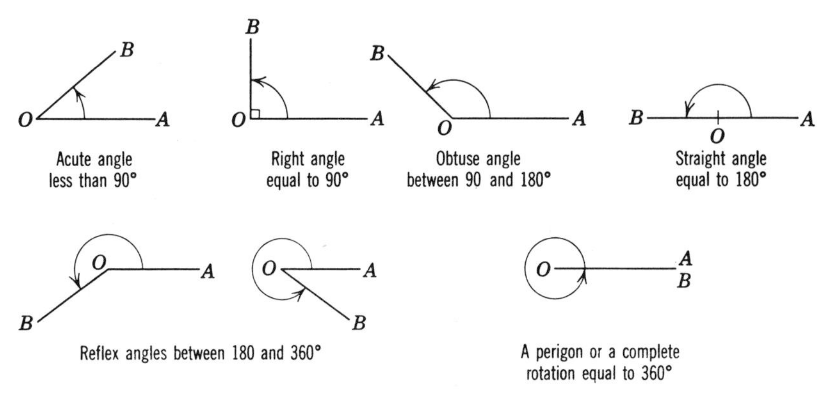

Fig. 7

simply a *complete rotation.* This perigon is divided (arbitrarily or by convention) into 360 equal parts, each of which has a measure of 1. The size of this small angle is 1° (one degree)*. Angles are classified as shown in Fig. 7.

Angles are measured (for purposes of approximation) by using an instrument called a *protractor*, or half a circular disk bounded by a diameter of the circle marked at the center and a semicircular arc graduated in degrees. See Fig. 8.

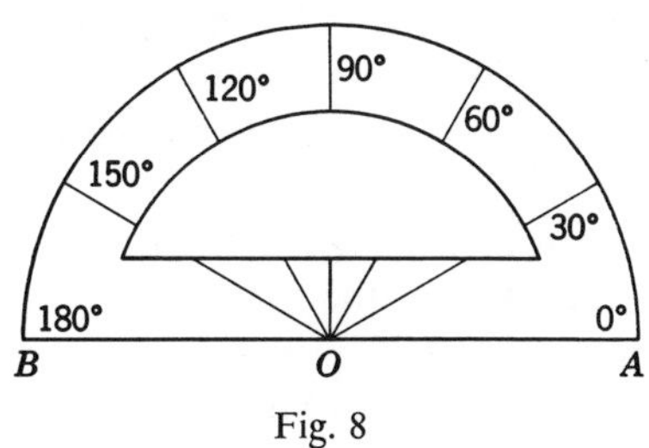

Fig. 8

EXERCISE 1

1. Obtain a protractor and use it to measure each of the angles in Fig. 9.

2. Draw at least three triangles: (*a*) measure each of the angles, then add the three angles of each triangle; (*b*) what relation, if any, seems to hold for the sum of the angles of any triangle?

3. (*a*) Measure the sides of each triangle drawn in problem 2, using a centimeter scale. (*b*) For each triangle, determine if any relation (equality or inequality) exists between the sum of any two sides and the length of the third side.

4. Use a protractor to draw these angles: (*a*) 90°, 180°, 270°; (*b*) 30°, 60°, 45°, 135°; (*c*) 102°, 185°, 285°.

* In general we will follow the more common practice of writing $\angle ACB = 30°$ in place of the size of $\angle ACB$ is 30°.

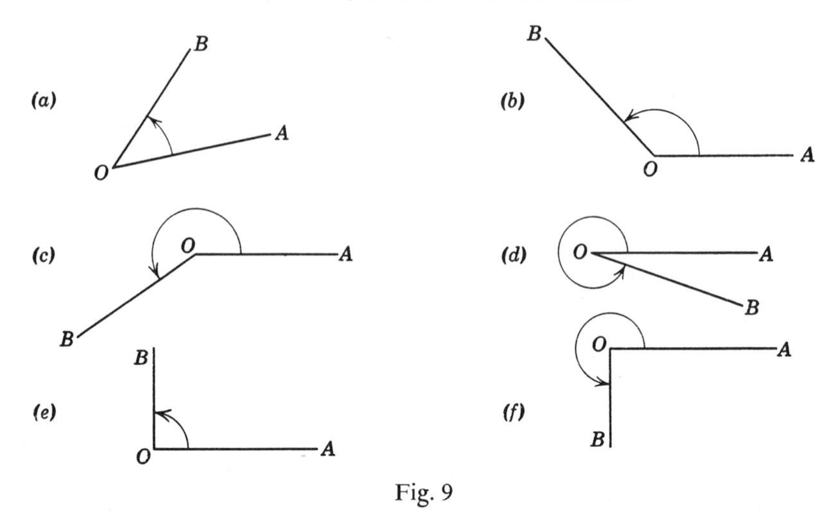

Fig. 9

21.3 MORE ABOUT TRIANGLES

In section 21.1 it was pointed out that a triangle is designated by its vertices. Thus in Fig. 10 the triangle is designated as $\triangle ABC$, usually reading from one vertex to the next in a positive direction (counterclockwise). The angles may be read as indicated previously, $\angle ABC$, $\angle BCA$, and $\angle CAB$. When there is no confusion, these designations may be shortened. Thus, in place of $\angle ABC$, $\angle B$ may be written. If the side BC is extended to the left, as in Fig. 11, the use of $\angle B$ as a designation of $\angle ABC$ would lead to confusion, since it might refer to $\angle ABD$ as well as $\angle ABC$. In this case the angle of the triangle at B must be given a three-letter designation such as $\angle ABC$. It is sometimes convenient to use a simpler form, such as $\angle \alpha$, shown in Fig. 12, in which a single letter, often from the Greek alphabet, is selected. Numerals are also employed in the same way. A small arc of a circle indicates the angle in question.

Triangles may be classified by the nature of their sides, by their angles, or by both. Using sides for classification, we obtain the following definitions:

Equilateral triangle—one for which all three sides are equal.
Isosceles triangle—one for which at least two sides are equal.
Scalene triangle—one for which all sides are unequal.

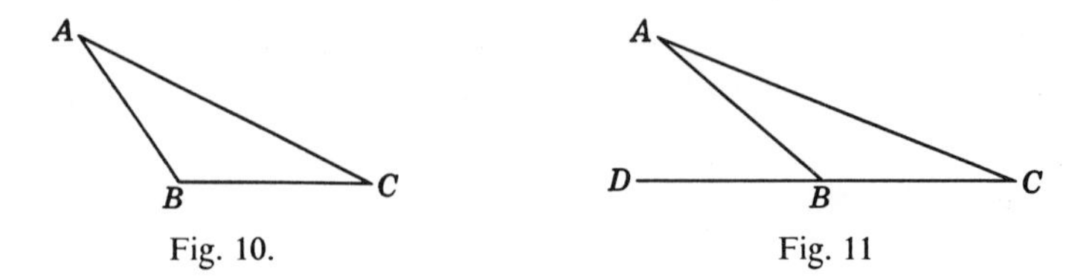

Fig. 10. Fig. 11

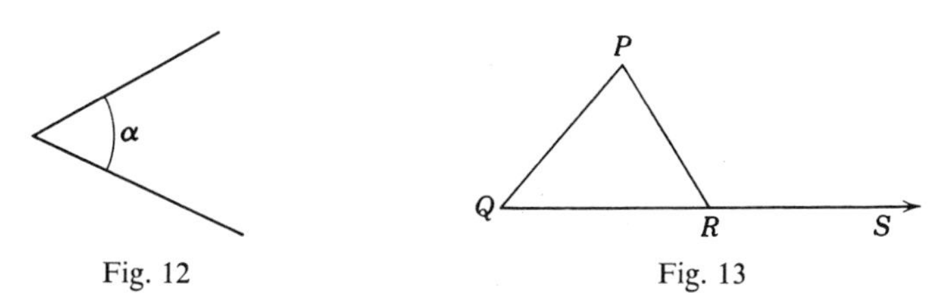

Fig. 12

Fig. 13

Using angles for classification, we obtain the following definitions:

Acute triangle—one for which all angles are acute or smaller than right angles.

Right triangle—one for which one of the angles is a right angle, or 90°.

Obtuse triangle—one for which one of the angles is obtuse or greater than a right angle but less than a straight angle.

Equiangular triangle—a special acute triangle for which all of the angles are equal. (An equiangular triangle is equilateral: the converse statement is also true.)

To construct a triangle, not all of the sides and angles need be given. Thus a triangle is determined and can be constructed under the following sets of conditions:

1. If two sides and the included angle are given.
2. If two angles and the included side are given and if the sum of the two angles is less than 180°. (*Note.* Since it can be proven that the sum of the three angles of a triangle is 180°, the construction just discussed can be carried out if the side that is given is opposite either of the given angles.)
3. If three sides are given and if the sum of any two sides is greater than the third side.

EXERCISE 2

In this and subsequent exercises the reader may wish to refer to a high school geometry text for methods of doing geometrical constructions. Some constructions will be discussed in the next section of this chapter.

1. In the triangle $\triangle PQR$ (Fig. 13), which is shown with one side extended, list some of the ways in which the angles of the figure may be designated.

2. Use a protractor to draw an equiangular triangle. Measure the sides with a compass. Are the sides equal?

3. Construct an equilateral triangle for which each side is equal in length to 5 centimeters. *Note:* Draw a line 5 centimeters in length; then use compass and straightedge to complete the construction.

4. Draw the following triangles:

(*a*) An acute scalene triangle.
(*b*) A right isosceles triangle.
(*c*) A right scalene triangle.
(*d*) An obtuse scalene triangle.

5. Answer the following questions concerning the angles of a triangle:

(*a*) How many obtuse angles may a triangle have?
(*b*) How many right angles may a triangle have?
(*c*) How many acute angles may a triangle have?
(*d*) How many acute angles may an obtuse triangle have?
(*e*) How many acute angles may a right triangle have?

6. Develop your own technique for constructing a triangle when the lengths of its three sides are given (any two sides greater than the third).

(*a*) Construct a triangle with sides of length 6, 7, and 8 centimeters.
(*b*) Construct a triangle with sides of length 3, 4, and 5 centimeters.
(*c*) Construct a triangle with sides of length 5, 7, and 10 centimeters.

21.4 CONSTRUCTIONS

Constructions in geometry are made with a straightedge and compass. If a ruler is substituted for a straightedge, only the edge and not the graduated scale is used. Line segments are copied with a compass, and circular arcs and circles are drawn with a compass. Seven of the fundamental geometric constructions and their applications are to be considered.

1. Bisecting a line segment.
2. Bisecting an angle.
3. Constructing a perpendicular to a line from a point outside the line.
4. Constructing a perpendicular to a line through a point on the line.
5. Constructing a line segment equal to a given line segment.
6. Constructing an angle equal to a given angle.
7. Constructing a line parallel to a given line, through a given point.

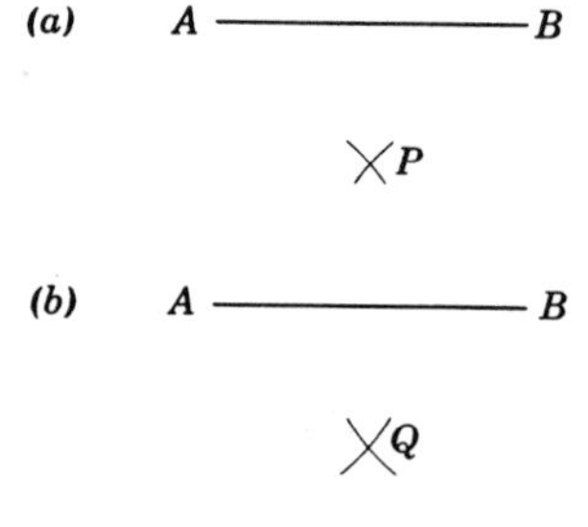

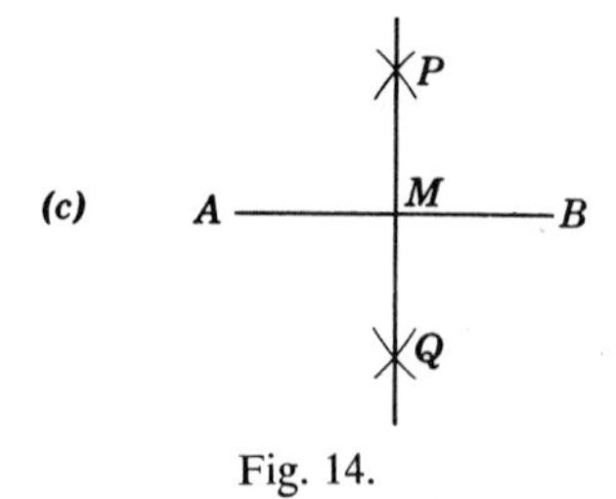

Fig. 14.

To bisect line segment AB (Fig. 14). Given segment AB (*a*).

With points A and B as centers, and with a convenient radius greater than one half AB, describe arcs above and below the line segment AB, which intersect at points P and Q as shown in (*b*).

With a straightedge, draw a line through points P and Q, as shown in (*c*). Point M, where PQ intersects AB, is the mid-point of AB. Thus $AM = BM$.

Comment. This method may be used to construct the perpendicular bisector of a line segment since it can be shown that the line PMQ is the perpendicular bisector of AB.

To bisect $\angle ABC$ (Fig. 15). Given $\angle ABC$ (*a*)

With B as center, and a convenient radius, describe arcs intersecting the sides of $\angle ABC$ at points A and C (*b*).

With points A and C as centers, and the same radius or a more convenient one, describe arcs intersecting within the angle at point O. With a straightedge, draw the line through B and O. Then BO bisects $\angle ABC$ or $\angle ABO$ equals $\angle OBC$ (*c*).

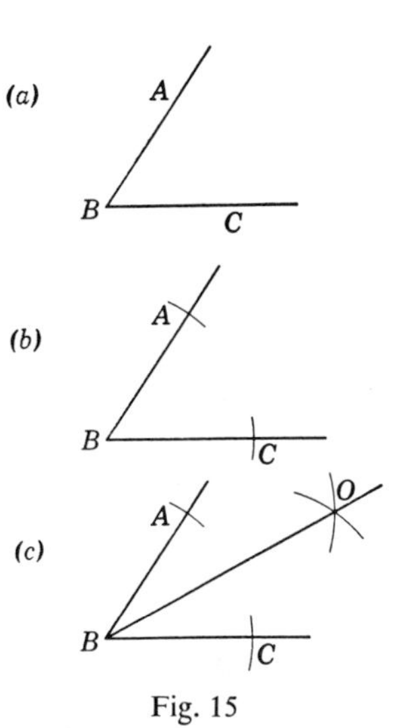

Fig. 15

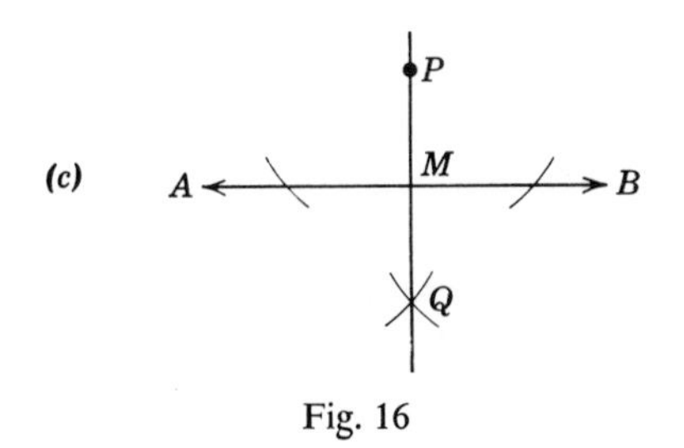

Fig. 16

To construct a perpendicular to line AB through point P above the line AB (Fig. 16). Given a line AB with point P above it (*a*).

With point P as a center, and a convenient radius (greater than the distance from P to AB), describe arcs intersecting the line AB in two places, X and Y (*b*).

With X and Y as centers, and the same radius or a more convenient one, describe arcs intersecting below AB at point Q (*c*).

Let points P and Q determine the line PQ, which is perpendicular to AB at M and passes through point P.

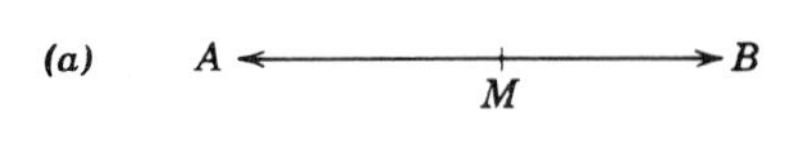

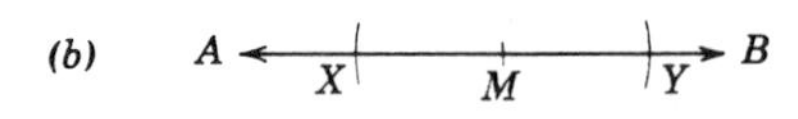

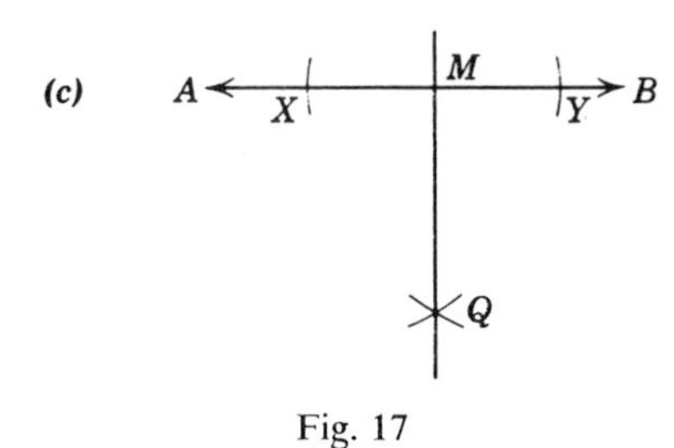

Fig. 17

To construct a perpendicular to line AB through point M on line AB (Fig. 17). Given line AB with point M on it (*a*).

With point M as a center, and a convenient radius, describe arcs intersecting line AB in two places, points X and Y (*b*).

With X and Y as centers, and a larger radius, describe arcs intersecting either above or below line AB, at point Q (*c*).

The line through points M and Q will be the required perpendicular. QM is perpendicular to AB at M.

To construct a line segment $\overline{CD}$ equal to the given line segment $\overline{AB}$ (Fig. 18). Given line segment $\overline{AB}$.

Using a compass, and with A as a center, determine a radius equal to the length of $\overline{AB}$. On a ray $\overrightarrow{CD}$, with C as center, mark off an arc of radius equal to length $\overline{AB}$. Line segment $\overline{CD}$ equals line segment $\overline{AB}$.

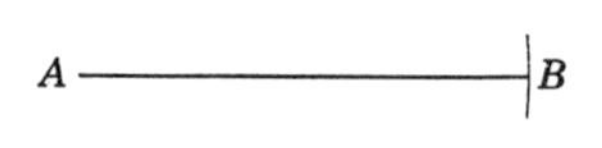

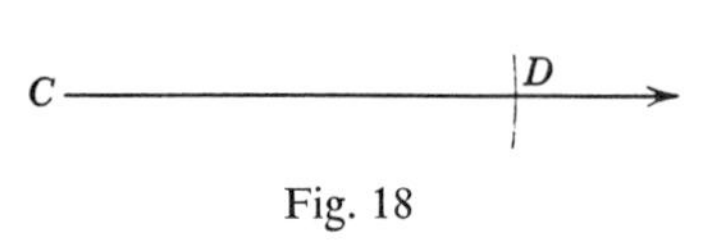

Fig. 18

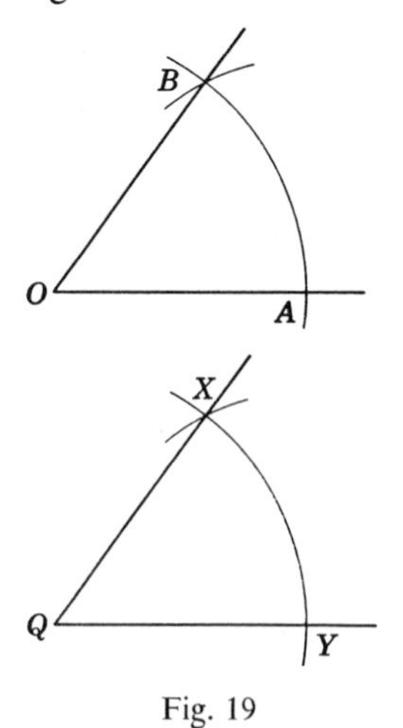

Fig. 19

To construct $\angle XQY$ equal to a given angle $\angle BOA$ (Fig. 19). Given $\angle BOA$.

On a working line QY, select point Q for the vertex of the new angle. With O as center, and a convenient radius, describe arcs intersecting both sides, BO and AO, of the $\angle BOA$. Then, with Q as a center, and the same radius, describe an arc XY in the same relative position intersecting QY at Y. With A as a center, determine the length across arc AB by using a compass. With Y as a center and the radius equal to AB, describe an arc intersecting the arc XY at point X. Pass a line through points X and Q. $\angle XQY$ is the required angle. $\angle XQY$ equals $\angle BOA$.

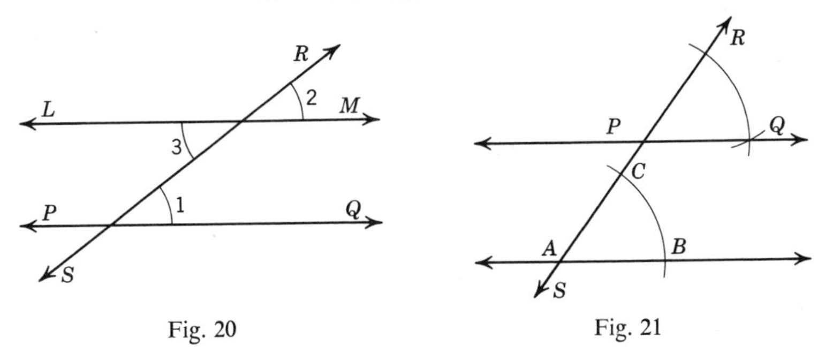

Fig. 20 Fig. 21

Two lines in the same plane which do not meet (intersect), however far extended, are said to be *parallel*. The lines in Fig. 20, LM and PQ, are parallel; this fact is indicated by the expression $LM \parallel PQ$. The line RS is a *transversal*, and two angles, such as $\angle 1$ and $\angle 2$, which are in corresponding positions, are called *corresponding angles*. Angles such as 1 and 3 are called *alternate interior angles*. It can be proved that when a transversal cuts two parallel lines the corresponding angles are equal and, likewise, the alternate interior angles are equal.

With these definitions and properties of parallels as a basis of procedure, we can construct pairs of parallel lines. Three methods are considered.

To construct a line parallel to a given line through a given point. Given line AB and an external point P. To construct $PQ \parallel AB$ (Fig. 21).

Method 1. Constructing equal corresponding angles with a transversal through point P. Through point P draw any line (to become a transversal) such as PA to form an angle PAB with line AB. At vertex P construct $\angle RPQ$ equal to angle PAB. The line that joins P and Q is the parallel to AB.

Method 2. Constructing equal alternate interior angles with a transversal through point P (Fig. 22). Through point P draw any line such as PB, making $\angle PBA$ with line AB. With P as a vertex, construct an alternate interior angle BPQ equal to $\angle PBA$. PQ is the required line parallel to AB.

Method 3. Constructing equal arcs on a semicircle through point P (Fig. 23). Take point O on line AB so that O is on one side of P. With O

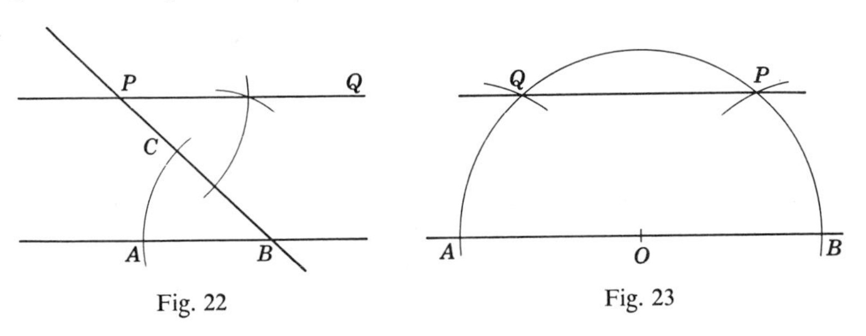

Fig. 22 Fig. 23

as a center and OP as a radius, describe a semicircle with the line segment AB as a diameter. Take the length of arc BP. With A as a center and that length as a radius, describe an arc intersecting the semicircle at Q. A line through P and Q will be parallel to line AB.

EXERCISE 3

1. Draw any triangle. Construct the perpendicular bisectors of the sides. (If these three perpendiculars meet in a point, your construction is assumed to be correctly done.)

2. Draw a triangle. From each vertex construct the perpendicular line to the opposite side. This line segment from the vertex to the opposite side is called the *altitude* from the vertex. (If these three altitudes or the extended altitudes meet in a point, your construction is assumed correct.)

3. (*a*) From the mid-point of each side of a given triangle draw a line to the opposite vertex. These segments are called the *medians*. (If the three medians of a triangle meet in a point, your construction is assumed correct.) (*b*) What relation does the common point of intersection of the medians have to the length of each median?

4. Draw a triangle. Bisect each angle. (If these bisectors meet in a point, your construction is assumed correct.)

5. Draw a triangle ABC. Through the vertices A, B, C, draw parallels to the sides BC, AC, AB, respectively. Label the intersection of the parallels through the points B and C by the letter A'. Label the intersection of the parallels through A and C by B' and the intersection of those through A and B by C'. $\angle A'$ should be equal to $\angle A$, $\angle B' = \angle B$, and $\angle C' = \angle C$ if your construction is correctly done. Check these angles with your compass.

6. Construct a triangle if its three sides are known (Fig. 24). Given the sides of a triangle, construct a triangle whose sides are a, b, and c.

Using three sides of different lengths, carry through this construction.

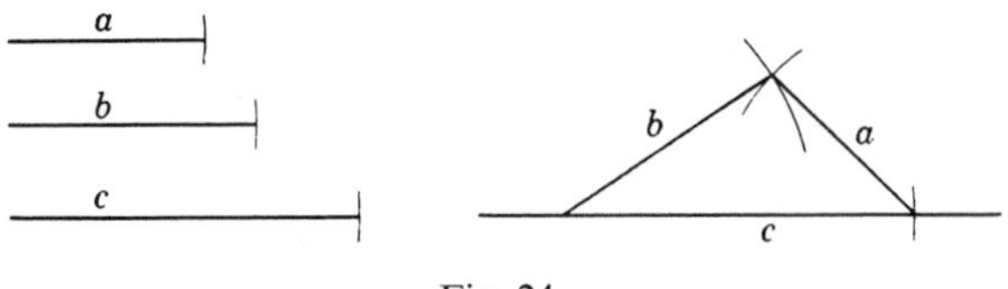

Fig. 24.

7. Construct a triangle if two sides and the included angle are known (Fig. 25). Given two sides and the included angle, construct a triangle whose sides are b, and c, and whose included angle is $\angle A$.

Carry through this construction, using included angle and sides of different sizes.

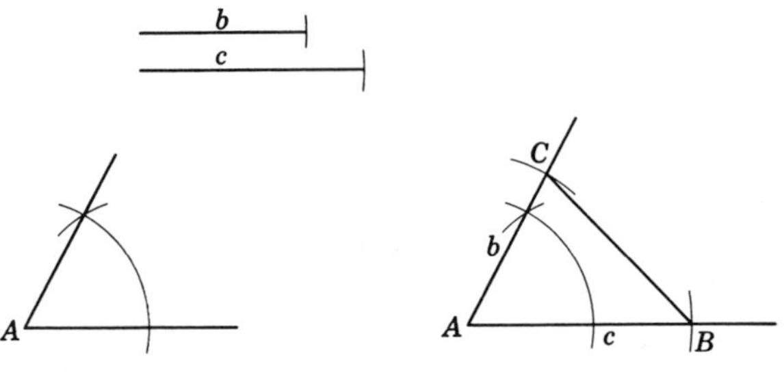

Fig. 25.

8. Construct a triangle if two angles and the included sides are known (Fig. 26). Given two angles and the included side, construct a triangle having angles A and B and included side c.

Carry through this construction, using included side and angles of different sizes.

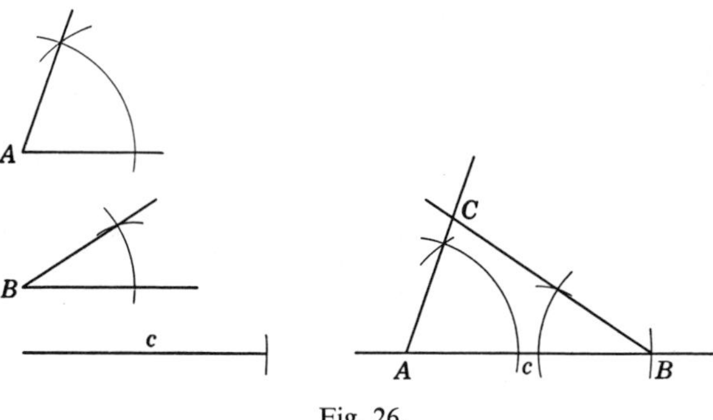

Fig. 26.

21.5 CONGRUENT, SIMILAR, AND EQUAL TRIANGLES

Two triangles are *congruent* if they can be made to coincide, that is, if the corresponding angles and the corresponding sides are equal. Two triangles are *similar* if the lengths in each pair of corresponding sides of the two triangles are proportional and the corresponding angles of the triangles are equal. Two triangles are *equal in area* if the product of the altitude and base of one triangle is equal to the product of the altitude and base of the other. These concepts are illustrated in the diagram of Fig. 27.

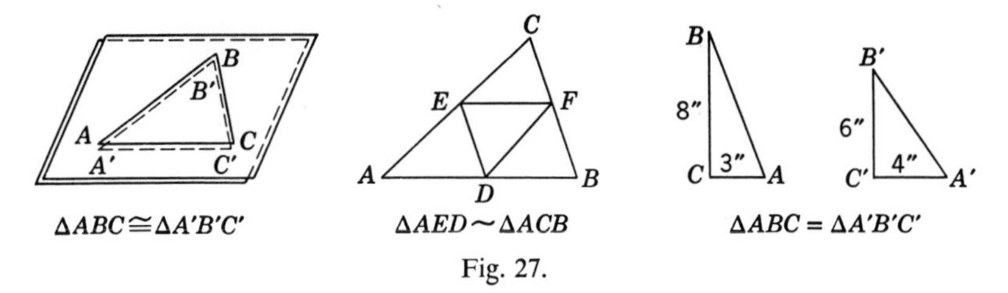

Fig. 27.

In the first case we can obtain examples of congruent triangles by drawing a triangle on one sheet of paper, placing a second sheet of paper under it, and then cutting through the two sheets of paper on top of a cardboard, using a razor blade or sharp knife. The two triangles cut out are congruent. In the second case we can obtain similar triangles by drawing a given triangle and then connecting the mid-points of the sides. In this case four small congruent triangles are obtained, and all are similar to the large triangle. In the third case two triangles whose altitudes and bases are legs of right triangles in which the product of each base and altitude is the same are examples of triangles having equal area.

If two triangles are equal in area, they are said to have the same *size*. If two triangles are similar they are said to have the same *shape*. It should be observed that two congruent triangles have the same size and the same shape; they are indeed equal in area and similar.

The definitions of congruent triangles and of similar triangles lead to the following theorems, which are stated without proof:

1. Two triangles in which two sides and the included angle of one are equal, respectively, to two sides and the included angle of the other are congruent.
2. Two triangles in which two angles and the included side of one are equal, respectively, to two angles and the included side of the other are congruent.
3. Two triangles in which three sides of one are equal, respectively, to the three sides of the other are congruent.
4. Two triangles that are mutually equiangular are similar.
5. If two triangles are similar, then they are mutually equiangular.
6. Two triangles are similar if an angle of one is equal to an angle of the other and if the including sides are proportional.

Example 1. In Fig. 28, $BC = CD$, $AB = DE$, and AE and DB are straight lines. Prove that $\triangle ABC$ is congruent to $\triangle ECD$.

Solution. By the use of theorem 1 above and a postulate about vertical angles at C, it can be determined that triangle CAB is congruent to triangle CDE, which is written in the form $\triangle CAB \cong \triangle CDE$. Two angles such as $\angle ACB$ and $\angle DCE$

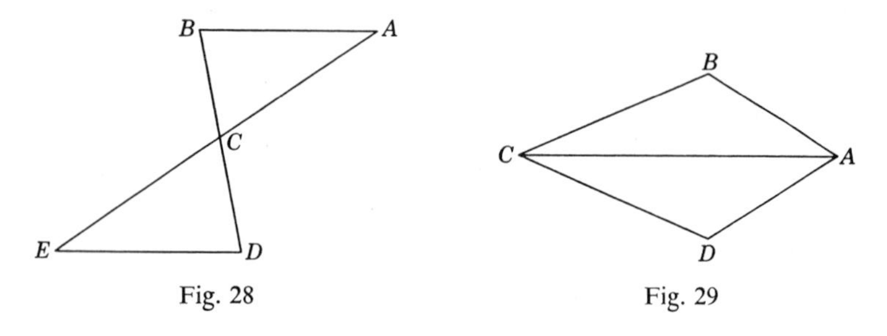

Fig. 28

Fig. 29

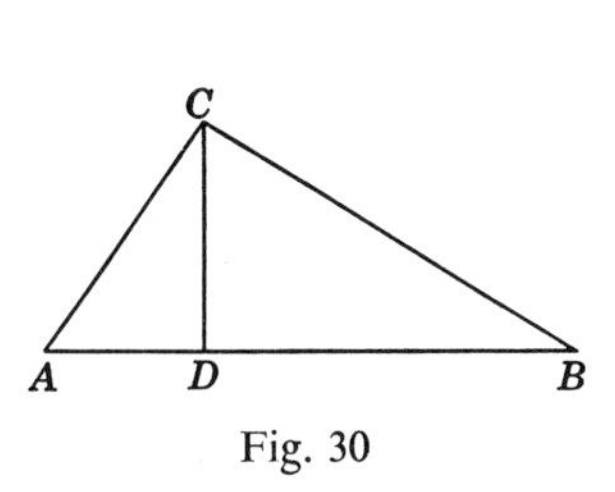

Fig. 30

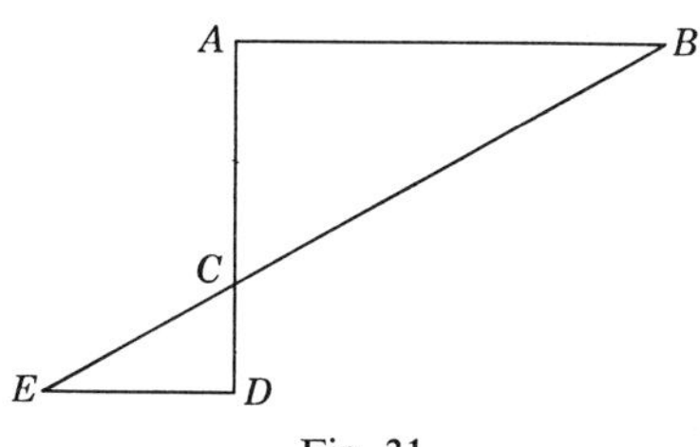

Fig. 31

are called *vertical angles*; they are opposite angles formed by intersecting straight lines. It is postulated that two such vertical angles are equal. Thus in this example, since $BC = CD$, $AC = CE$, and $\angle ACB = \angle DCE$, the conditions of theorem 1 are fulfilled, hence $\triangle CAB \cong \triangle CDE$.

Example 2. In Fig. 29 $\angle ACB = \angle ACD$, $\angle BAC = \angle DAC$. Show that $\triangle ABC \cong \triangle ADC$.

Solution. Since CA is a common side for both triangles, it is seen that the conditions for congruence required in theorem 2 are fulfilled. These conditions are $\angle ACB = \angle ACD$, $\angle BAC = \angle DAC$, $AC = AC$. Hence $\triangle ABC \cong \triangle ADC$.

Example 3. The perpendicular segment from the vertex of the right angle of a right triangle is dropped to the opposite side (Fig. 30). This segment is an altitude of the right triangle. Show that the two new right triangles so formed are similar to the original triangle and to each other.

Solution. In the diagram $\angle ADC$ and $\angle BDC$ are both right angles since CD is drawn perpendicular to AB. Using the assumption made previously that the sum of the angles of a triangle is 180°, it follows that $\angle ACD$ is complementary to $\angle A$.

Note. Two angles whose sum is 90° or a right angle are said to be *complementary*, and each is called the *complement* of the other. In the example it is shown that $\angle B$ is also the complement of $\angle A$. Hence $\angle ACD = \angle B$, since complements of the same or of equal angles are equal, and it follows that $\triangle ADC$ and $\triangle ABC$ are mutually equiangular. Therefore by theorem 4 the two triangles are similar. This is indicated by $\triangle ACD \sim \triangle ABC$. In like manner it can be shown that $\triangle BCD \sim \triangle ABC$, and $\triangle BCD \sim \triangle ACD$.

Example 4. In Fig. 31 AD is perpendicular to AB and to ED. Show that $\triangle ABC \sim \triangle DEC$.

Solution. Since $\angle ACB$ and $\angle DCE$ are vertical angles, they are equal. But $\angle A = \angle D$, since AD is perpendicular to AB and to DE. Since the sum of the angles of a triangle is 180°, $\angle B = \angle E$, and by theorem 4 the two triangles are similar.

Example 5. Given $\triangle ABC$ and $\triangle A'B'C'$, for which $\angle A = \angle A'$, $\angle B = \angle B'$, and necessarily, $\angle C = \angle C'$, and $AB = 6$, $BC = 12$, $AC = 10$, $A'B' = 20$, find the lengths of $B'C'$ and $A'C'$ (Fig. 32).

Solution. Since two angles of one triangle are equal to the corresponding angles of the other, the triangles are similar. Their corresponding sides are proportional. Thus

$$\frac{AB}{BC} = \frac{A'B'}{B'C'}$$

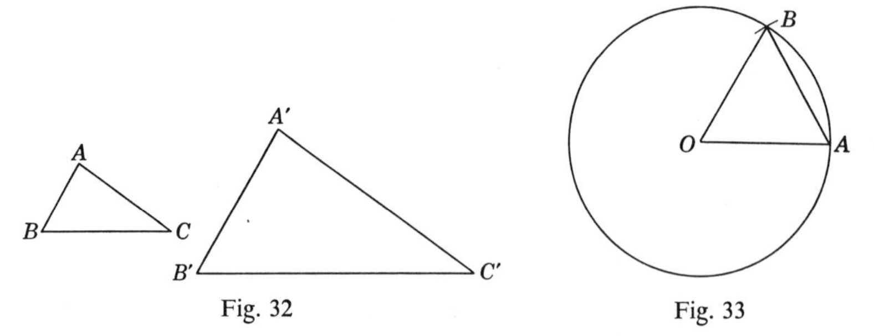

Fig. 32

Fig. 33

or

$$\frac{6}{12} = \frac{20}{B'C'}, \quad \text{and} \quad B'C' = 40.$$

Likewise,

$$\frac{AB}{AC} = \frac{A'B'}{A'C'}, \quad \text{or} \quad \frac{6}{10} = \frac{20}{A'C'}, \quad \text{and} \quad A'C' = 33\tfrac{1}{3}.$$

EXERCISE 4

1. Show that two right triangles in which two legs of one equal, respectively, two corresponding legs of the other, are congruent.

Note. In this problem and in others similar the sides of the right triangle adjacent to the right angle are called the *legs*. The third side, opposite the right angle, is called the *hypotenuse*.

2. Show that two right triangles are congruent if an acute angle of one and its adjacent leg are equal, respectively, to an acute angle and the adjacent leg of the other.

3. Show that the angles opposite the equal sides of an isosceles triangle are equal. (*Hint.* Draw the bisector of the vertex angle in the triangle.)

4. Show that a triangle that is equilateral is also equiangular.

5. Draw any circle of convenient size with a compass (Fig. 33). At any point on the circle lay off a chord AB of the circle, equal in length to a radius of the circle. Call the center of the circle O. Draw lines AO and BO.

(*a*) What kind of triangle is $\triangle OAB$?

(*b*) How many degrees are in $\angle AOB$?

(*c*) If one complete rotation is an angle of 360°, how many triangles such as ΔOAB can be drawn in the circle without overlapping?

(*d*) Draw all of the triangles mentioned in (*c*).

6. The figure formed by the chords in problem 5 is called a *regular hexagon*, which is inscribed in a circle. (All vertices are on the circle.) Show how you would inscribe a regular three-sided figure in a circle. Do the same for a regular four-sided figure and for a twelve-sided figure.

7. A tree casts a shadow 80 feet long. At the same time a nine-foot post casts a shadow twelve feet long. How tall is the tree?

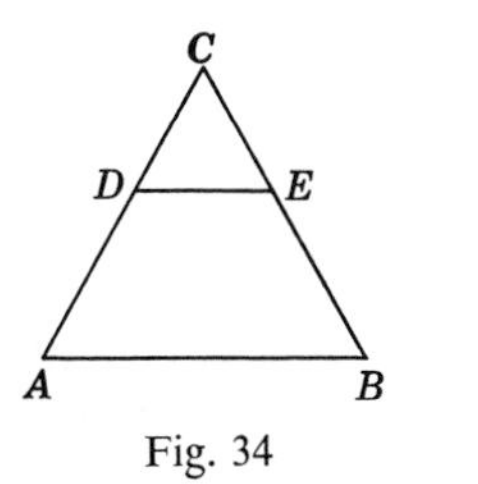

Fig. 34

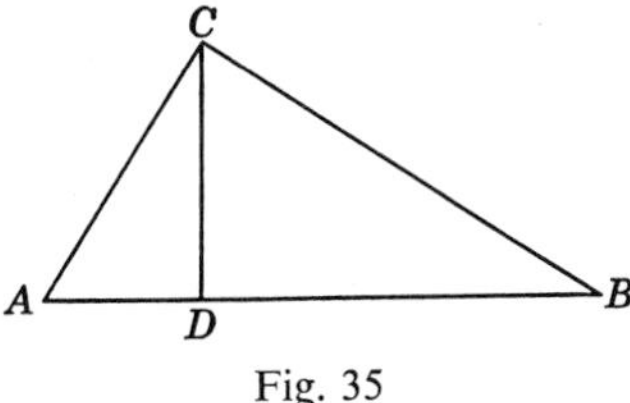

Fig. 35

8. In Fig. 34 $DE \parallel AB$, and $AD = 32$, $DC = 20$, $DE = 18$. Find the length of AB. If $CE = 24$, find the length of EB.

9. The altitude from the right-angle vertex is drawn to the hypotenuse. The triangle is lettered as shown in Fig. 35 with the right angle at C. If $AD = 9$, $DB = 25$, find the length of DC, the altitude.

10. An equilateral triangle has a side which is 30 centimeters long. How long would a side of another equilateral triangle be if its altitude were one half as long as the altitude of the given triangle?

11. A parallelogram is defined as a plane figure having four sides, with the opposite sides parallel. Thus, in parallelogram $ABCD$ (Fig. 36), $AB \parallel DC$ and $BC \parallel AD$. DB is called a *diagonal.* Show that DB divides the parallelogram into two congruent triangles.

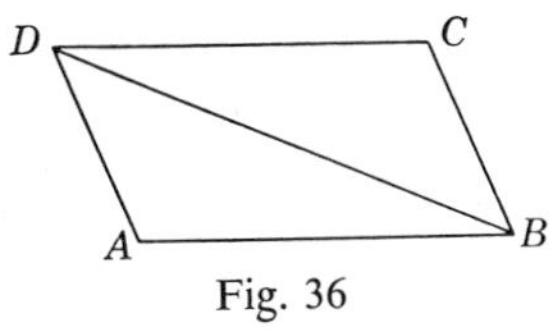

Fig. 36

12. The sides of a given triangle are 7, $9\frac{1}{2}$, and $11\frac{2}{3}$ inches long. How long are the sides of a similar triangle if its shortest side is 42 inches long?

21.6 AREAS OF PLANE GEOMETRICAL FIGURES

A plane geometrical figure bounded by four straight line segments is called a *quadrilateral* (Fig. 37). The bounding lines are called the *sides.*

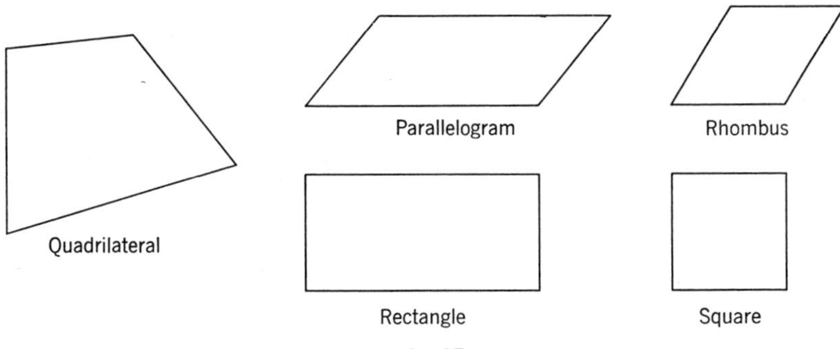

Fig. 37

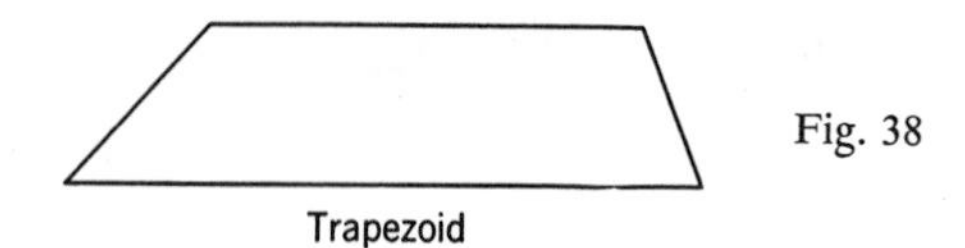

Fig. 38

A quadrilateral for which the pairs of opposite sides are parallel is called a *parallelogram*. Special cases of parallelograms are the following:

A *rhombus* is a parallelogram in which all sides are equal. (It can be proved that this condition holds—all four sides are equal—if two consecutive sides of the parallelogram are given equal.)

A *square* is a rhombus each of whose angles is a right angle or has measure equal to 90°. (It can be proved that the four angles of a parallelogram are right angles if one of them is given as a right angle.)

A *rectangle* is a parallelogram each of whose angles is a right angle or has measure equal to 90°. (Again, one right angle is sufficient to prove that all angles of the parallelogram are right angles.) It should be noted that a square could have been defined as a rectangle with all sides equal.

A *trapezoid* is a quadrilateral in which one pair of opposite sides is parallel and the other pair is not (Fig. 38).

For completeness the triangle and the circle, previously defined, should be mentioned here. They are considered in the work with areas.

A five-sided plane geometrical figure is called a *pentagon*, a six-sided figure is a *hexagon*, and, in general, these and others having more than six sides are called *polygons*. We may distinguish among polygons by calling them 3-sided, 4-sided, 5-sided, · · · , or n-sided polygons, n being a natural number greater than or equal to three.

To determine the areas of plane figures, it is best to start with the rectangle, since its area has already been determined as the product of the length of the base times the length of the altitude. If AB, in Fig. 39, is called the base, then the altitude is the perpendicular distance between the parallel sides AB and DC. If the length of the base is b units and the length of the altitude is a units, then the area is $b \times a$ square units. This same formula applies to the square, in which $a = b$, and the area is $a \times a$, or a^2, square units.

The area of the parallelogram is determined in Fig. 40. From D drop

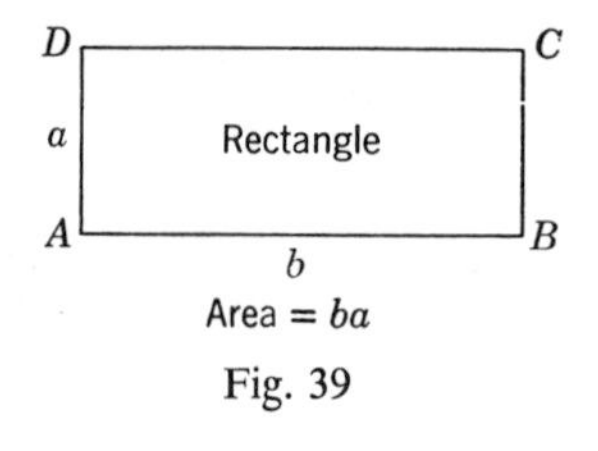

Fig. 39

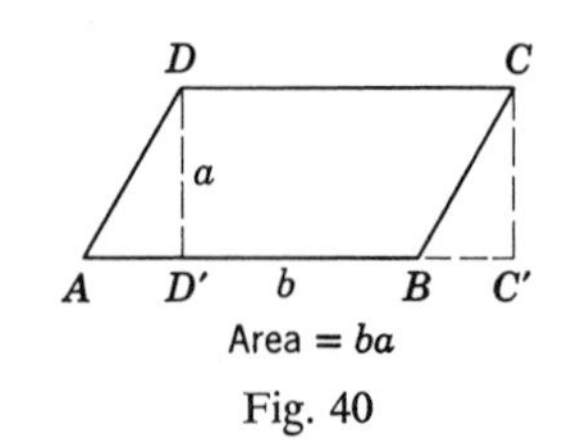

Fig. 40

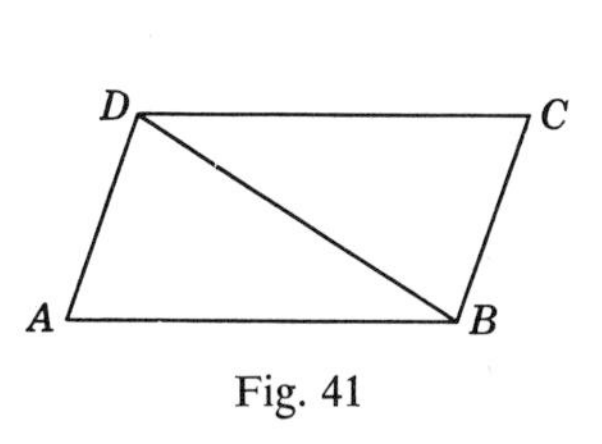

Fig. 41

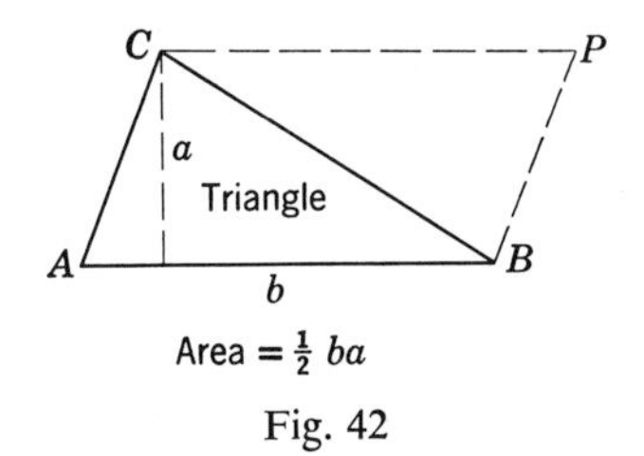

Fig. 42

a perpendicular to AB, cutting AB in D'. Drop a perpendicular from C to AB extended, meeting it in C'. It can be shown that $\triangle AD'D \cong \triangle BC'C$, hence their areas are equal. It follows that the area of parallelogram $ABCD$ is equal to that of the rectangle $DD'C'C$. If the length of the base is b units and the length of the altitude is a units, then the area of the parallelogram is $a \times b$ square units. This formula also applies to the area of a rhombus.

The parallelogram has been defined as a quadrilateral whose opposite sides are parallel. With the proper development of the postulates and theorems of geometry, it can be proved that the opposite sides of a parallelogram are equal.

In Fig. 41, as shown, draw diagonal BD of the parallelogram $ABCD$. Since the opposite sides of a parallelogram are equal, $AD = BC$ and $AB = DC$. But BD is a common side of $\triangle ABD$ and $\triangle CDB$. Hence $\triangle ABD \cong \triangle CDB$. (Three sides of one triangle are equal, respectively, to three sides of the other.) This means that the area of $\triangle ABD$ is one half that of the parallelogram $ABCD$.

Consider now the triangle ABC shown in Fig. 42. Through B draw a line parallel to AC, and through C draw a line parallel to AB. Let these lines meet in point P. The quadrilateral $ABPC$ thus formed is a parallelogram, since the pairs of opposite sides are parallel. Hence the area of the triangle is $\frac{1}{2} \times b \times a$.

The area of a trapezoid may now be derived (Fig. 43). Divide the trapezoid into two triangles by means of a diagonal. By adding the areas of the triangles, we obtain the formula for the area of the trapezoid. The development of the formula is left as an exercise for the reader. Sometimes it is stated as follows: the area of a trapezoid is the product of the altitude times the average of the lengths of the parallel sides (or bases).

Fig. 43

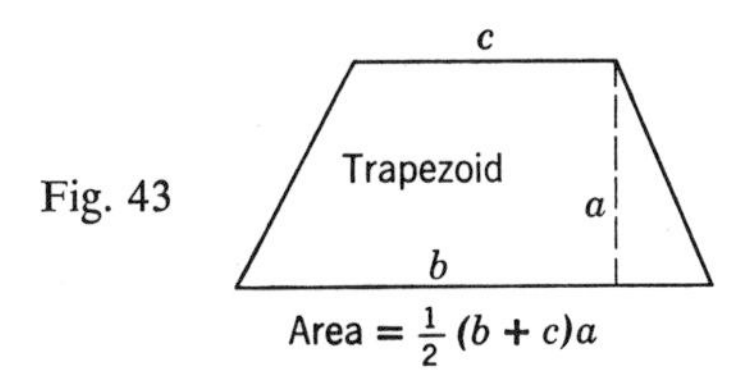

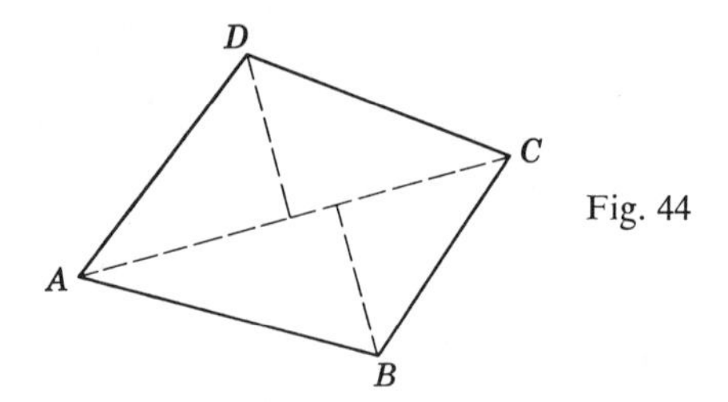

Fig. 44

It should be noted that the area of the general quadrilateral may be found by dividing it into two triangles by means of a diagonal. The lengths of the altitudes drawn to this diagonal and the length of the diagonal give sufficient data to compute the area. An example is given in Fig. 44. In quadrilateral $ABCD$ the diagonal AC is drawn to divide the quadrilateral into two triangles ABC and CDA. AC is measured and found to be 3.8 centimeters long. The altitude from B to AC has length 1.3 centimeters. Hence the area of $\triangle ABC = \frac{1}{2}(3.8 \times 1.3) = 2.47$ square centimeters. The altitude of $\triangle CDA$ is 1.4 centimeters; hence the area of $\triangle CDA$ is $\frac{1}{2}(3.8 \times 1.4) = 2.66$ square centimeters. The area of the quadrilateral $ABCD$ is $2.47 + 2.66 = 5.13$, or 5.1 square centimeters.

This method may also be used to find the area of any polygon. The pentagon shown in Fig. 45 may be divided into three triangles as shown. The hexagon may be divided into four triangles. It would appear that a polygon of n sides may be divided into $n - 2$ triangles by drawing all possible diagonals from one vertex. Referring to Fig. 46, consider the hexagon. $\triangle ABC$ contains two sides of the hexagon and $\triangle AEF$ also contains two sides. Each of the other triangles contains only one side of the hexagon. Thus the total number of triangles is $6 - 2$, or 4, which agrees with the formula stated above.

The *circle* is defined as the locus of all points equidistant from a fixed point called the *center*. In Fig. 47 the center is designated by O. Any line segment passing through the center and terminating on the circle is called a *diameter*. Half of the diameter (or the distance from the center to the points of the circle) is called a *radius*. The length of the circle, or its perimeter is called the *circumference*. If the circumference is divided by the

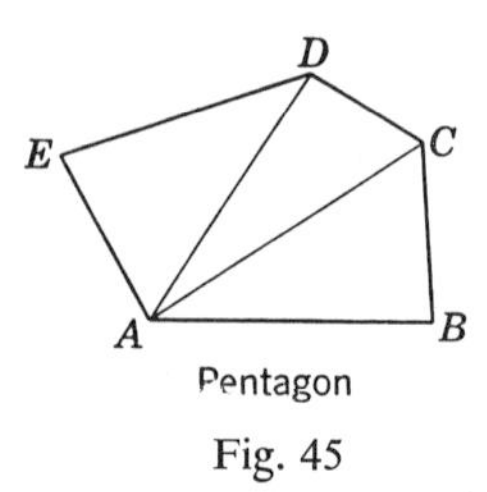

Pentagon

Fig. 45

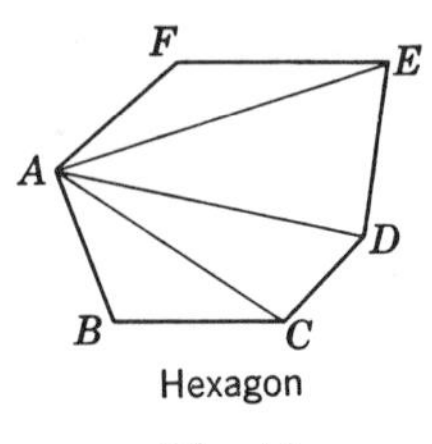

Hexagon

Fig. 46

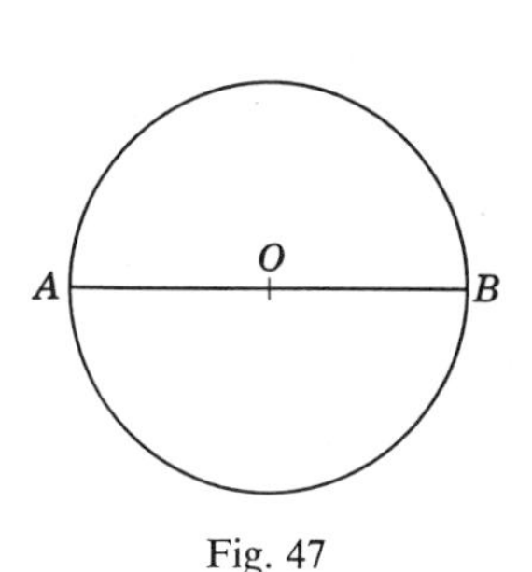

Fig. 47

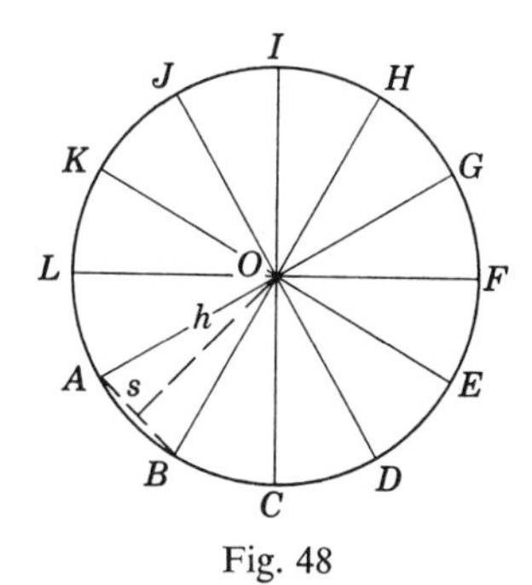

Fig. 48

diameter, a constant number is obtained for all possible circles. This constant ratio is designated by the Greek letter π.

In problems involving the circumference and the area of a circle a rational approximation is used for π. The particular rational approximation selected depends upon the accuracy desired. Thus there are $3\frac{1}{7}$, 3.14, 3.142, 3.1416, or other more accurate values. Modern digital computing machines make it possible to compute π to as many decimal places as desired.

Let c and r represent the circumference and the radius of the circle in Fig. 47. If the diameter is represented by d, then by definition we have

$$\frac{c}{d} = \pi, \quad \text{hence} \quad c = \pi d.$$

From Fig. 47 it is noted that AO and OB are radii of the circle and furthermore AB is the diameter. Thus $2r = d$. Substituting in the formula above for the circumference, we obtain the usual formula for the circumference in terms of the radius,

$$c = 2\pi r.$$

A number of methods may be used to find the area of a circle. All involve the idea of a limit, which would not be readily understood by the elementary student. The following method, although not rigorous from a mathematical point of view, may be helpful to an understanding of the formula. Consider Fig. 48, in which the circle is divided into, say, n sectors, as indicated. (A *sector* is a part of a circular disk contained between two radii and an arc of the circle.) Each sector differs but little from a triangle. Actually, the sector AOB differs very little from the triangle AOB if the arc AB is a sufficiently small part of the circumference of the circle. In fact, if the number of sectors is increased in such a way that the arcs for the sectors become and remain as small as desired, then the area of the circle is the limit of $n \times \frac{1}{2} \times (c/n) \times h$, where $\frac{1}{2} \times (c/n) \times h$ is taken as the area of one of the sectors and the arc segment c/n is used in place of the chord s. (The ratio $(c/n) \div s$ tends to the value 1 as n becomes large.) Since h tends to r as the number of sectors increases, the area of the circle should be given by $\frac{1}{2} \times c \times r$. The usual formula, $A = \pi r^2$, is now obtained by substituting $2\pi r$ for c.

EXERCISE 5

1. Find the area of the following plane figures:

(*a*) Parallelogram, base $= 6$, altitude $= 5$
(*b*) Rectangle, base $= 9$, altitude $= 5$
(*c*) Triangle, base $= 7$, altitude $= 4$
(*d*) Trapezoid, parallel sides are 14 and 18, altitude $= 10$
(*e*) Square, side $= 6$
(*f*) Rhombus, base $= 5$, altitude $= 4$
(*g*) Circle, radius $= 14$ (Use $\pi = 3\frac{1}{7}$)
(*h*) Circle, radius $= 3.125$ (Use $\pi = 3.142$)

2. Find the area of the shaded portion of Fig. 49. The outer corners are quarter circles. Use 3.14 for the value of π.

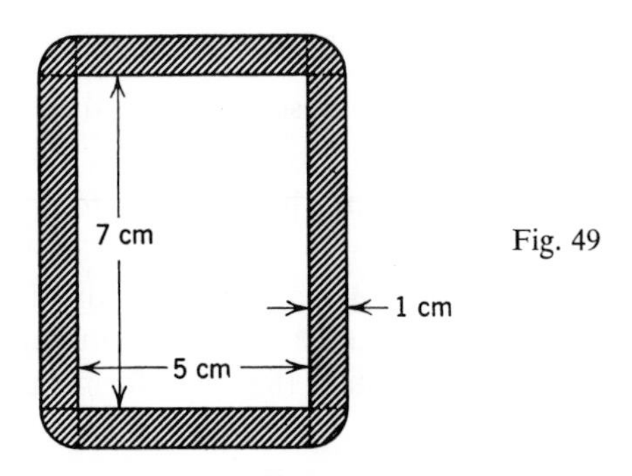

Fig. 49

3. How much larger would the area in problem 2 be if all corners were right angles?

4. The base and altitude of a triangle are 8 and 4. By what is the area multiplied if both the base and altitude are doubled?

5. A circle has a radius of 5 units. By how much is the area multiplied if the radius is doubled?

6. Consider a square with side 10 inches long. Find the perimeter of the square and use it in the following exercises.

(*a*) Use the perimeter of the square as the circumference of a circle. Find the radius and then the area of the circle. How does this area compare with that of the square?
(*b*) Construct a rectangle with two sides 4 inches long and the other two sides each 16 inches long. Find the area of this rectangle.

(*c*) Construct a number of other rectangles by using the perimeter of the square in this example. Can you draw any conclusion in relation to the rectangle having the greatest area for the given perimeter?

7. A lot is 140 feet wide and 320 feet deep. Does this lot contain as much as one acre or more?

8. In Fig. 50 AD is parallel to CF, and $AB = BD$. What can you say about the areas of triangles ABC, ABF, ADE, and ADC?

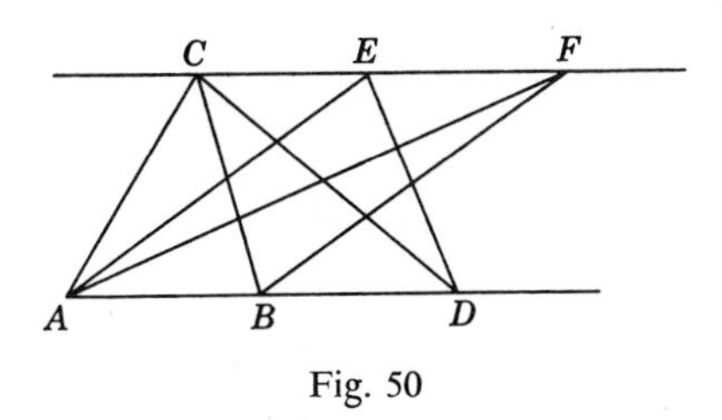

Fig. 50

9. A circular pool 40 feet in diameter is bordered by a paved walk 5 feet wide (Fig. 51). At the cost of 65 cents per square foot, what is the total cost of paving this walk?

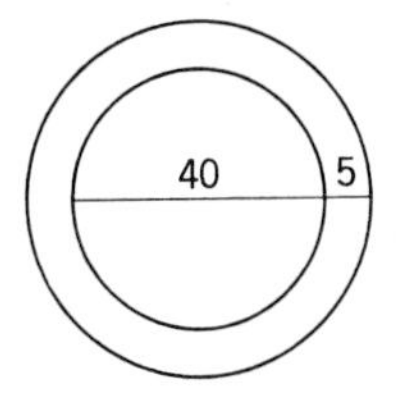

Fig. 51

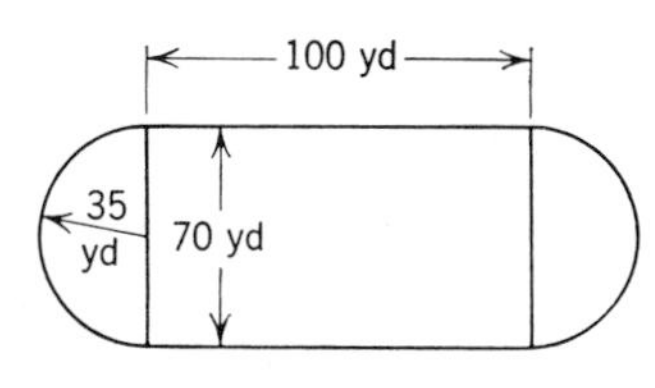

Fig. 52

10. The measured value of the diameter of a circle is 82.4 centimeters. Compute the length of the circumference to as many significant places as the data will allow. *Note.* Use care in selecting the most desirable value of π for this calculation.

11. Describe an experimental way of determining an approximation to π which would be understandable to arithmetic pupils.

12. Find the area of a football field if the ends are semicircles and the dimensions are 100 yards and 70 yards as shown in Fig. 52.

21.7 THE ARITHMETIC OF COMMON SOLIDS

Volumes and surface areas for some of the more common solids are considered in this section. A solid bounded by portions of planes is called a *polyhedron*. The portions of planes that form the boundary are called the *faces* of the polyhedron. The faces intesect in lines called the *edges* of the polyhedron, and the edges meet in points that are called the *vertices*.

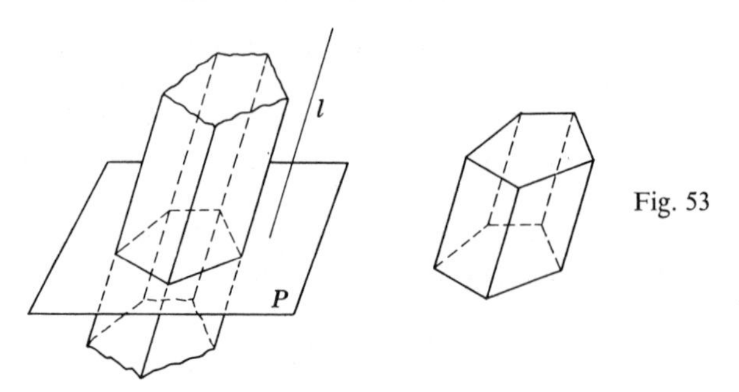

Fig. 53

The number of edges, vertices, and faces are related by a formula developed by the famous Swiss mathematician Euler:

$$e + 2 = v + f,$$

where e, v, f represent the number of edges, vertices, and faces, respectively.

The solids with which arithmetic is generally concerned are called prisms. A *prismatic surface* is formed by a line passing through a plane polygon if the line moves parallel to a fixed line, not parallel to the plane, or maintains a fixed direction in space. See Fig. 53. A *prism* is the three-dimensional figure formed between two parallel planes which cut through a prismatic surface. Two congruent polygons are formed in the parallel planes when they intersect the prismatic surface; these two polygons are called the *bases* of the prism. The *lateral edges* and *lateral faces* of the prism are the portions of the prismatic surface cut off between the bases of the prism; the lateral faces are parallelograms, since the lateral edges of the prism are parallel to a fixed line in space. If the lateral edges of a prism are perpendicular to the bases, the prism is called a *right prism*. A prism whose bases are parallelograms is called a *parallelepiped*. If the prism is a right prism and the bases are rectangles, the prism is called a *rectangular parallelepiped*, which is illustrated by the usual rectangular box (Fig. 54).

As assumed in Chapter 8, the volume of a rectangular solid (Fig. 54) is the product of the edges that meet at one vertex. Let the area of the base of this solid be represented by B. Then $B = bc$, and the volume, V is

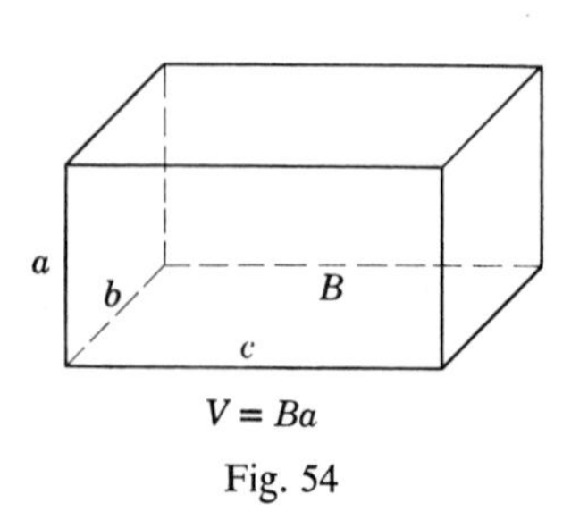

Fig. 54

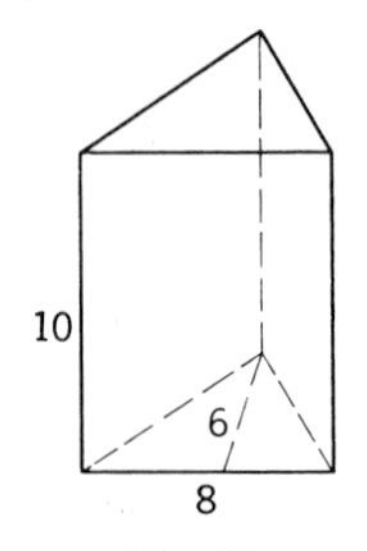

Fig. 55

$B \times a$. Thus $V = bca$. The formula $V = B \times a$ holds for the general parallelepiped if a now represents the length of the *altitude*, which is the distance between the parallel bases. In fact, the volume of any prism is given by $B \times a$, where B is the area of the base and a is the length of the altitude. The number a counts the number of layers of cubic units which can be placed on the base having area B square units, and the product of B and a gives the number of cubic units of volume in the solid.

Example 1. Find the volume of a triangular prism (Fig. 55) of altitude 10 if the base is a triangle with a side 8 and an altitude to that side equal to 6.

Solution. The area of the base of the prism is $B = \frac{1}{2}(8)(6) = 24$ square units; hence the volume of the prism is $V = (24)(10) = 240$ cubic units.

The *area of the lateral surface* of a prism is the sum of the areas of the parallelograms making up the surface. The *total area* of the prism is the area of the lateral surface plus the area of the two bases.

Example 2. Find the lateral and total area of a right prism 10 inches high if the base is a square whose side is 8 inches long.

Solution. The area of the lateral suface is $4(8 \times 10) = 320$ square inches. Each base has area $8 \times 8 = 64$ square inches. Hence the total area is $320 + 2 \times 64 = 448$ square inches.

A *pyramidal surface* is formed by a line that passes through a fixed point in space and moves along the sides of a polygon in a given plane. Usually only the half-lines, or rays issuing from the fixed point, are taken to generate the pyramidal surface. See Fig. 56. If a plane cuts across the pyramidal surface, then the portion of the surface between the plane and the fixed point or *vertex* of the pyramidal surface and the polygon in the plane form a *pyramid*. The polygon formed in the cutting plane is called the *base* of the pyramid. The *altitude* of the pyramid is the distance from its base to its vertex. The *lateral faces* of a pyramid are triangles with a common vertex at the vertex of the pyramid. In Fig. 56 the base of the pyramid is a hexagon and the faces are triangles meeting at the vertex P. If B is the area of the hexagonal base and a is the altitude, it can be shown that $V = \frac{1}{3}B \times a$ or the volume is one third of the volume of a prism having the same base and altitude.

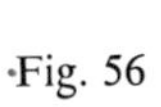
Fig. 56

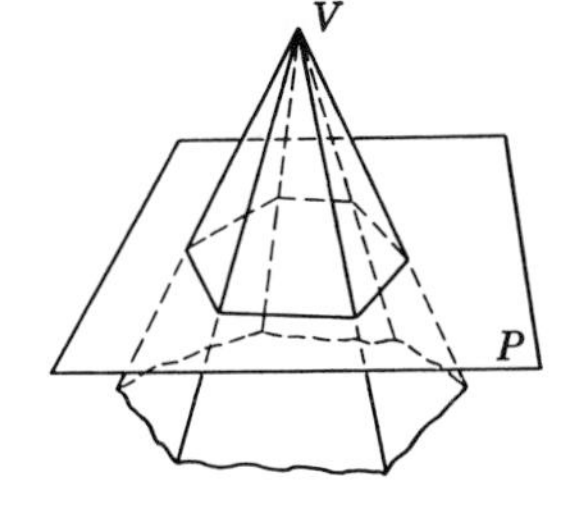

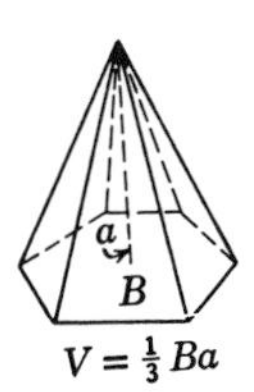

Project. An experimental method of showing the correctness of the formula for the volume of a pyramid consists in constructing a plastic prism open at the top and marked on its lateral faces at the one-third level and the two-thirds level. Next, construct a pyramid of plastic having the same base and altitude as the prism. These solids should, of course, be hollow and of thin watertight material. The pyramid should have a corked opening in the base for filling purposes. To check the formula for the volume of a pyramid, fill the pyramid with water and then pour it into the prism. If the construction has been done properly and if the formula for the volume of the pyramid is correct, the level of the water in the prism should just reach the one-third mark.

Example 3. Find the volume of a pyramid of altitude 10 feet having a square base of side 6 feet.

Solution. The area of the base is $6 \times 6 = 36$ square feet; hence the volume is $\frac{1}{3}(36)(10) = 120$ cubic feet.

The *area of the lateral surface* of a pyramid is that part which includes the areas of the lateral triangles. If the pyramid is a *right pyramid*, with the vertex directly over the center of a regular polygon as the base (the vertex is on a line perpendicular to the base at its center), then the lateral faces are congruent triangles and their altitudes from the vertex of the pyramid to the mid-points of their bases are equal. The length of one of these altitudes is called the *slant height* of the regular pyramid and is designated by s. The area of the lateral surface is then one half the sum of the bases of the triangles times the slant height. Let b = the sum of the bases; then S, the area of the lateral surface, is given by $S = \frac{1}{2}bs$.

Example 4. Find the area of the lateral surface of the pyramid in Example 3, assuming that it is a right pyramid.

Solution. The base is a square; hence the perpendicular dropped from the vertex of the pyramid will cut the base at a point three feet from the side of the pyramid. It is necessary to find the length of the hypotenuse of the right triangle shown in Fig. 57 in order to determine the slant height of the pyramid. Thus $s^2 = 10^2 + 3^2 = 109$, and s, the slant height, is $\sqrt{109}$. The area of the lateral surface of the pyramid is

$$S = \tfrac{1}{2} \times 4 \times 6 \times \sqrt{109} \quad \text{or} \quad 12\sqrt{109} \text{ square feet.}$$

The area of the base is $6 \times 6 = 36$ square feet; hence the total area is

$$36 + 12\sqrt{109} \text{ square feet} \quad \text{or} \quad \text{about } 161 \text{ square feet.}$$

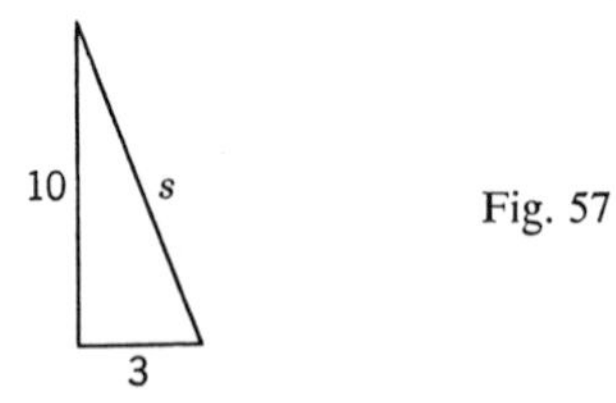

Fig. 57

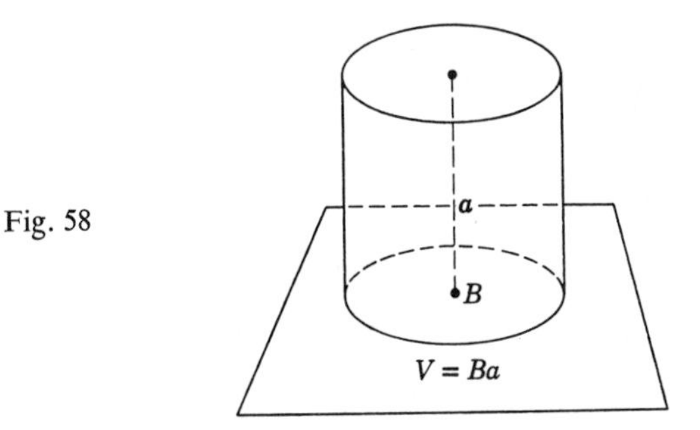

Fig. 58

Consider a closed curve lying in a plane (Fig. 58). Allow a line to touch this curve in such a way that it does not lie in the plane of the curve. Now allow the line to move and to remain parallel to its original direction, traveling completely around the curve. A *cylindrical surface* is generated. Cut this cylindrical surface by a plane parallel to the first plane. The solid bounded by the two planes and the cylindrical surface between them is usually called a *cylinder*. Intuitively, it is seen that the two curves in the parallel planes are congruent. The portions of curves bounded by these planes are called the *bases* of the cylinder.

The cylinder may be considered as the limiting case of a prism as the number of lateral faces becomes infinite and the width of each side tends to zero. Thus the same volume formula as that used for prisms should be the volume formula for the cylinder, that is, the area of the base times the altitude.

Example 5. Find the altitude of a cylinder of volume 80π cubic inches if the base is a circle of radius 4 inches.

Solution. Since $V = B \times a$, $80\pi = \pi(4^2)(a)$. Hence $a = 5$ inches, or the altitude of the cylinder is 5 inches.

The cylinder shown in Fig. 58 is a right circular cylinder, in which the bases are circles. The perpendicular dropped from the center of one base to the other will pass through the center of the latter. The lateral wall of the cylinder is perpendicular to the bases of the cylinder. The formula for the area of the lateral surface of a right circular cylinder may be developed easily by cutting the lateral surface along a line perpendicular to the base. The lateral surface may then be rolled out flat as a rectangle with an altitude equal to the altitude of the cylinder and a base equal to the length of the base curve. Hence the area of the lateral surface is given by

$$S = l \times a,$$

where l represents the length of the base curve. If this curve is a circle then $l = c$, the circumference of the circle. The total area of a cylinder includes the areas of the bases as well as the lateral surface area.

Example 6. A right circular cylinder has an altitude of 9 centimeters and a base whose radius is 5 centimeters. Find the area of the lateral surface and the total area.

Solution. The circumference of the base is $2\pi(5) = 10\pi$ centimeters. Hence the lateral surface area is $S = (10\pi)(9) = 90\pi$ square centimeters. The total area is

$(90\pi + 2\pi \times 5^2)$ or 140π square centimeters.

(Using $\pi = 3\frac{1}{7}$, this is 440 square centimeters)

If the top base of a cylinder is replaced by a point, and a line is allowed to pass through this point and to move along the lower base curve, the surface generated is called a *cone*. The cone would appear to be a limiting case of a pyramid, which indeed it is. Thus the formula for the volume of a cone should be the same as that of the pyramid, which is $V = \frac{1}{3}B \times a$. See Fig. 59.

Example 7. The volume of a cone is 120π cubic centimeters. Its altitude is 8 centimeters. Find the area of the base of the cone.

Solution. Substituting in the formula for the volume, we have

$$120\pi = \frac{1}{3} B(8); \quad \text{thus} \quad B = 45\pi \text{ square centimeters.}$$

Example 8. If the cone in Example 7 has a circular base, find the radius of this base.

Solution. Call the length of the radius, r; $45\pi = \pi r^2$; hence

$$r^2 = 45 \quad \text{or} \quad r = \sqrt{45} = 3\sqrt{5} \text{ centimeters.}$$

A *right circular cone* is one for which the perpendicular from the vertex to the base passes through the center of the base, which is a circle. The area of the lateral surface of a right circular cone may be developed by cutting the cone from a point on its base curve along a straight line to the vertex of the cone. When the base curve is a circle the lateral surface may be flattened out, as shown in Fig. 60. Thus it appears, as in the case of a pyramid, that the lateral surface area is $S = \frac{1}{2}cs$, where s is the slant height of the cone, and c is the circumference (or perimeter) of the base curve.

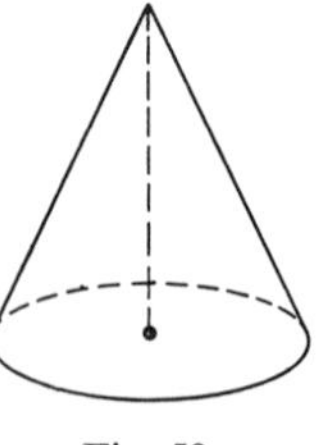

Fig. 59

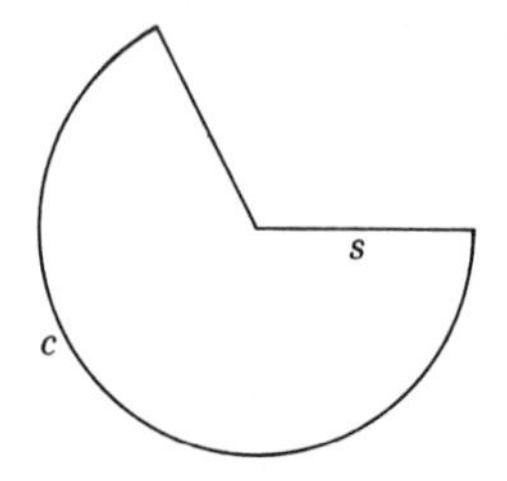

Fig. 60

Example 9. Find the slant height of a right circular cone whose lateral area is 20π square units and whose base is a circle of radius 4.

Solution. Since $S = \frac{1}{2}cs$, $20\pi = \frac{1}{2}(2\pi)(4)s$, or $s = 5$, which is the required slant height.

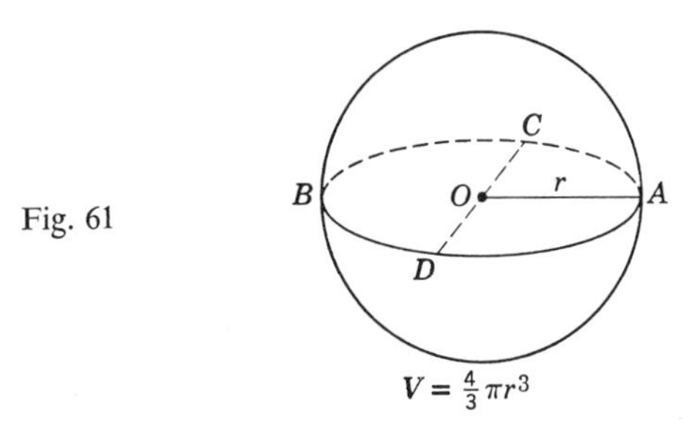

Fig. 61

$V = \frac{4}{3}\pi r^3$

A *sphere* is defined as the locus of a point moving in three-dimensional space in such a way that its distance from a fixed point, O, called the *center*, is constant. In Fig. 61, OA is the *radius* or constant distance for the sphere with center at O. The circle through A, C, B, D is cut from the sphere by a plane passing through the center of the sphere. This circle and all other circles formed by planes passing through the center of the sphere are called *great circles* of the sphere. Any circle cut from the sphere by a plane that does not pass through the center of the sphere is called a small circle of the sphere. Examples of great circles may be observed by looking at a globe of the world. The equator and the meridians on the globe are great circles. The parallels of latitude (not including the equator) are small circles of the sphere of the earth.

It can be shown that the area of the sphere is equal to four times the area of a great circle. Thus $S = 4\pi r^2$ square units.

One method of developing the volume of a sphere, although not rigorous, is to use pyramids as the elements of the volume of the sphere. For this purpose divide the surface of the sphere into n equal polygons. Join the vertices of all the polygons to the center of the sphere. One then has n solids that look much like pyramids, with base approximately equal to S/n and altitude equal to r. The volume of each of these pyramid-type elements is approximately $\frac{1}{3}(S/n)r$, and the volume of the sphere is approximately equal to $(Sr)/3$, since there are n of these elements. The so-called pyramids become more nearly equivalent to pyramids in their volume as n becomes large, whereas each nth part of S, S/n, becomes small. Hence it is reasonable to assume that the volume of the sphere is given by

$$V = \frac{Sr}{3} = \frac{4\pi r^2 r}{3} = \frac{4\pi r^3}{3} \quad \text{or} \quad \frac{4}{3}\pi r^3.$$

Example 10. Determine how many gallons a spherical tank of radius 2 feet will hold.

Solution. The volume of the tank is $4\pi/3 \times 2^3 = 32\pi/3$ cubic feet. Since the number of cubic inches in one gallon is 231, the number of gallons content of the sphere is

$$\frac{(32/3)\pi \times 12^3}{231} = 251 \text{ gallons}$$

using 3.142 for π and rounding to the nearest gallon.

Example 11. Find the area of the sphere in Example 10 in square inches.

Solution. By use of the formula given, $S = 4\pi 2^2$, or 16π square feet. Since each square foot contains 12×12, or 144 square inches, the area in square inches is 2304π. This would be about 6925 square inches.

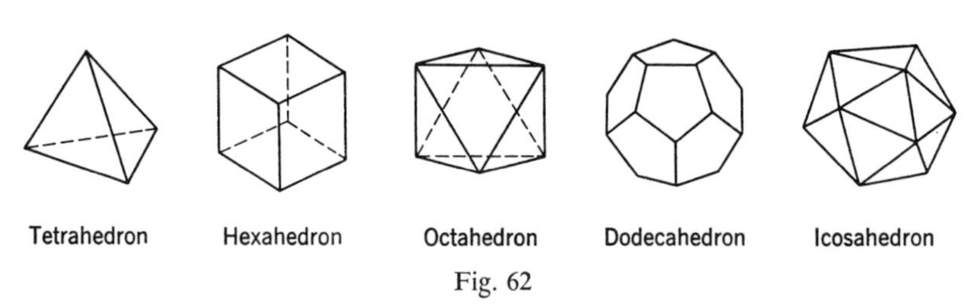

Fig. 62

21.8 THE REGULAR POLYHEDRONS

An interesting group of solids is the set of five regular polyhedrons. A *regular polyhedron* is one whose faces are congruent polygons and whose polyhedral angles are congruent. It can be proved that only five such regular solids exist. These five solids are called the regular tetrahedron, hexahedron, octahedron, dodecahedron, and icosahedron. The prefixes tetra, hexa, octa, dodeca, and icosa stand for 4, 6, 8, 12, and 20, respectively. The faces of the 4-, 8-, and 20-faced solids are equilateral triangles. The faces of the 6-faced solid are squares, and those of the 12-faced solid are pentagons. The five regular solids are shown in Fig. 62.

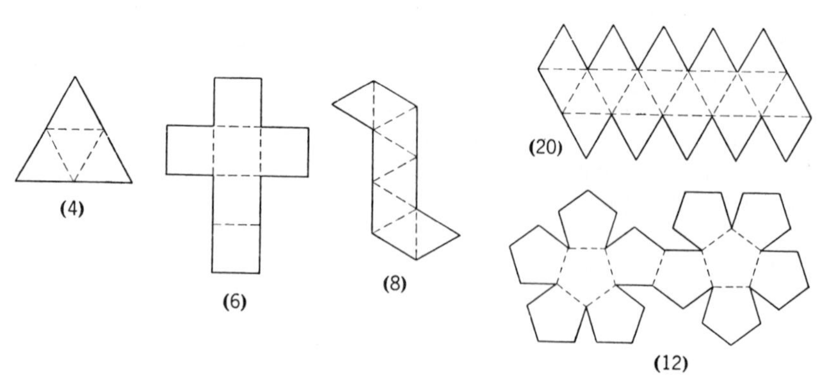

Fig. 63

The sketches in Fig. 63 indicate how models of each regular polyhedron may be constructed. On light cardboard, construct figures similar to those shown in the sketches, making the edges at least twice as large as the edges shown. Cut along the solid lines and fold on the dotted lines. Fasten the edges together with scotch tape. It will be instructive for the reader to make models of several of these regular polyhedrons.

EXERCISE 6

1. Make a sketch of each of the following solids and check Euler's formula for each:

(*a*) A triangular prism.
(*b*) A triangular pyramid. (Note that this solid is sometimes called a tetrahedron because it has four faces.)
(*c*) A pentagonal prism.
(*d*) A hexagonal pyramid.
(*e*) A cube.

2. Find the volume of each of the following solids:

Solid	Base area	Altitude
(*a*) Prism	16 square inches	6 inches
(*b*) Pyramid	16 square inches	6 inches
(*c*) Cylinder	16 square inches	6 inches
(*d*) Cone	16 square inches	6 inches

3. What is the area of the base of a triangular prism of height 4 inches if it is to have the same volume as a cube, each edge of which is 3 inches?

4. A triangular prism has a base that is a regular triangle (equilateral) and an altitude of 3 centimeters. What is the length of the side of the triangle if the volume of the prism is 81 cubic centimeters?

5. The volume of a rectangular parallelepiped is 11,250 cubic inches. Find the lengths of the edges if they are in the ratio of 3:5:6. (*Hint:* Let the sides be represented by $3k$, $5k$, and $6k$.)

6. A regular pyramid has been defined as one whose base is a regular polygon and whose vertex lies in a perpendicular erected at the center of the base. (*a*) Find the total area of the lateral faces of a regular hexagonal pyramid of side 4 centimeters long and for which the altitude of each triangular face is 8 centimeters. This altitude is also known as the slant height. (*b*) Find the area of the base of this pyramid. Find also the total area of the pyramid, which is the sum of the lateral area and the area of the base. (*c*) Find the volume of this pyramid.

7. A right circular cylinder has an altitude of 5 inches and a base area of 25 square inches. Find the altitude of a cone having the same volume if the area of its base is the same as that of the cylinder.

8. A one-gallon measuring can is to be made in the form of a right circular cylinder. If the radius of the base is to be 3 inches, what is the altitude? Indicate the levels at which the one-quart, two-quart, and three-quart marks should be made. Note that one gallon equals 231 cubic inches.

9. Find the volume and also the area of the surface of a sphere of radius 9 centimeters.

10. A tank has a square base of side 6 inches and a height of 10 inches. The tank is filled with water to a height of 8 inches. A solid sphere is immersed in the tank until completely covered. If the water level in the tank is raised $1\frac{1}{2}$ inches, what is the volume of the sphere?

11. If the method in problem 10 is used, could the volume of any shaped non-absorptive solid be found?

12. A cylindrical bar of lead 2 inches in diameter and 25 inches long is melted to form drops which fall through the air and cool in the shape of small spheres of diameter $\frac{1}{8}$ inch. Approximately how many such spheres will there be if the entire cylinder is reduced to spheres?

13. A volley ball 9 inches in diameter is packed in a box that measures 9 inches on each edge. What per cent of the box is filled by the inflated ball? Would this ratio change for a larger ball fitted into a cubical box?

14. How many 5-ounce glasses would a hemispherical punch bowl fill if the bowl had a diameter of 20 inches and was filled originally to the brim? Note that 32 ounces equal one quart, and one gallon equals 231 cubic inches.

15. A conical paper cup is 3 inches deep and 2 inches in diameter. How many cubic inches will the cup hold if it is level full?

16. How deep, to the nearest .1 inch, should a half-gallon carton with a square base 4 inches on a side be made if one gallon equals 231 cubic inches?

REFERENCES

Brumfiel, C. F., R. E. Eicholz and M. E. Shanks, *Geometry*, pp. 43–105, 180–208.

Eves, H., *An Introduction to the History of Mathematics*, pp. 111–128.

Gould, S. H., "Origin and Development of Concepts of Geometry," National Council of Teachers of Mathematics, *Twenty-third Yearbook*, *Insights into Modern Mathematics*, pp. 273–305.

Hemmerling, E. M., *College Plane Geometry*, pp. 3–42.

Kasner, E., and J. R. Newman, *Mathematics and the Imagination*, pp. 112–155.

Larsen, H. D., *Arithmetic for Colleges*, pp. 185–198.

Lieber, L. R., *The Education of T. C. Mits*, pp. 123–128.

Mallory, V. S., *New Plane Geometry*, pp. 360–361.

Marks, J. L., C. R. Purdy, and L. B. Kinney, *Teaching Arithmetic for Understanding*, pp. 288–308.

McSwain and Cooke, *Understanding and Teaching Arithmetic in the Elementary School*, pp. 256–262.

Wheat, H. G., *How to Teach Arithmetic*, pp. 290–314.

appendix A

Instructional Materials Visual Aids

A.1 INTRODUCTION AND PURPOSE

Recent developments in basic procedures for arithmetic instruction have included the use of visual aids. As the engineer Fred Morris has stated,* "Good instruction is the handrail of learning that helps the student in his climb toward professional competence." Well-planned and coordinated materials help to achieve good instruction; they should appeal to the senses of sight, hearing, and touch. Such materials tend to make arithmetic concepts meaningful; with proper treatment, they can simplify the work, but they should not be considered as ends within themselves. Although instructional materials include many forms and kinds, only a limited number is presented in this appendix. Class visitation is considered an aid and is discussed. Visual aids and instructional materials may be classified by the grade level, by the subject-matter content, such as addition, or by the kinds of materials, such as flash cards. The classification by kinds of materials is used in an attempt to avoid unnecessary duplication.

Illustrative materials and diagrams have been suggested in various chapters, and some are given here in more detail. Commercial materials are abundant, but some schools do not budget money for this purpose. The enterprising teacher will sometimes want to make her own, develop others as class projects, or have the pupils make their own as the need and occasion arise. The projects suggested here are quite simple and of a general nature. For some of the construction details, consult references 2 and 3 at the end of this appendix.

* Morris, Fred C., *A Manual for Engineering Instructors*, page 4, McGraw-Hill, 1950.

A.2 CLASS VISITATION

Students training to become teachers gain much from a visit to a school in which they can observe an arithmetic class in action. Before the visit the students should be briefed by their professor on its purpose, which is one of observation for learning and not for criticism or faultfinding. The following are points to observe:

(*a*) *Class environment.* Is there a suitable learning atmosphere, in pleasant surroundings with appropriate posters and other displays?

(*b*) *Learning situation.* Are methods used which stimulate interest, and is there variety in methods of presentation?

(*c*) *Individual differences.* Are provisions made for the varying abilities and levels of achievement of the pupils?

(*d*) *Cooperation and participation.* Do the activities of the class promote alertness and a cooperative spirit on the part of individual members and of the class as a whole? Are opportunities provided for individual and group participation?

(*e*) *Question periods.* Are the students given the opportunity to ask questions and to express reactions?

(*f*) *Applications and assignments.* Are suitable applications made for the material being presented? Are the students given further work along the lines of the topics being considered?

(*g*) *Instructional materials.* What supplementary materials are being used and how effective are they?

(*h*) *Class attitudes and control.* Do the procedures in the classroom contribute to mature attitudes of behavior and citizenship?

A.3 GENERAL REQUIREMENTS FOR VISUAL AIDS AND INSTRUCTIONAL MATERIALS

There are some general requirements to be considered when selecting visual aids and instructional materials for use in class. In planning the arithmetic lesson in which visual and other aids are to be presented, the following considerations should be kept in mind:

1. The need for visual aids or instructional materials must be within the experience of the students.
2. These materials should be readily manipulated and, preferably, easily transported.
3. Class materials must be large enough to be visible and legible from all parts of the room.
4. The materials must be organized in proper sequence in advance so that no time will be lost in presenting them.

5. Some situations, particularly when films or film strips are to be shown, will be more beneficial to the students if they are briefed in advance on what items to expect or what questions will be dealt with and answered.

6. Proper use of visual aids and instructional materials should help to make the transition from the concrete to the semiconcrete to the abstract in easy stages.

7. A follow-up is desirable. A general discussion period after the use of the materials provides an opportunity for their evaluation.

A.4 FILMS AND FILMSTRIPS

Films and filmstrips dealing with arithmetic operations may be used to introduce a topic, to summarize or review a topic, or for enrichment purposes. Students usually get more from the films if they are shown for comparison or summary when some familiarity with the content already exists. The following are typical of many excellent films available for sale or rental:

Coronet Films. *Per Cent in Every Day Life* (10 minutes).
Johnson-Hunt Productions (each film 10 minutes).
Introduction to Fractions
How to Add Fractions
How to Subtract Fractions
How to Multiply Fractions
How to Divide Fractions
How to Change Fractions
Decimal Fractions
Knowledge Builders (each film 10 minutes).
Areas
Pythagorean Theorem
Net Film Service, Indiana University (each film 30 minutes).
The Earliest Numbers
Base and Place
Big Numbers
Fundamental Operations
United World. *The Origin of Mathematics* (10 minutes).

A.5 KITS, CARDS, CHARTS, AND BOARDS

There are many kinds of visual aids classifiable under the general headings of kits, charts, and markers. Such uniform objects as coins, coffee-stirring sticks, jacks, and large buttons, which can be used to illustrate number relations, come under the general heading of *markers*.

Markers are not discussed specifically beyond this brief mention, but a number of charts, boards, and kits are covered in the remaining paragraphs of this section.

A.5.1. Flannel boards. A flannel board has many and varied uses in kindergarten and throughout the grades. Its construction is rather simple. A large piece of cardboard or thin plywood at least 18 by 20 inches or larger, preferably about 24 by 30, is needed. Cotton outing flannel of a solid color is stretched tightly across the board and fastened to the back. If plywood or masonite is used, the flannel can be tacked or taped. Suede-finished cardboard may be purchased in art stores and mounted on heavier cardboard. This material is sometimes referred to as velour paper. For most class uses, the flannel board may be rested in the chalk tray with its bottom edge as far away from the board as is possible. All materials used on the flannel board should be made of felt or be backed with a strip of flannel, a piece of velour paper, or a strip of sandpaper, so that they will adhere to the board when pressed against it. Some kinds of construction paper stick to the flannel board without any special backing. Only a few of the many uses of the flannel board are discussed here.

(*a*) *Counting.* Materials needed: ten or more animal pictures cut out of felt or other material, all of the same size, kind, and color. These animal pictures may be cut from a color book and stripped with flannel. If animals are not suitable, use ten or more squares of the same size, ten or more circles, or other objects. The animals, squares, or circles are placed on the board and the pupils count the objects. The same materials can illustrate addition and subtraction. For example, two dogs and three dogs make five dogs, or five circles take away three circles leave two circles. Later the children may make up their own stories and illustrate the addition and subtraction facts involved. When not in use, the flannel board should be kept flat so that it will not warp.

(*b*) *Other Uses.* Besides being used for counting, cutouts can identify the proper number symbols or numerals with groups of objects. The operations of addition, multiplication, subtraction, and division can be illustrated with small disks. Circles, squares, and rectangles can be cut up and the parts can be used to give the meanings of fractions and of operations with fractions. Most of the uses described for the pocket chart also apply to the flannel board if the materials mentioned are properly backed for adhering to the flannel.

A.5.2. Pocket chart board. Materials: heavy construction paper such as shelf lining. A pocket chart board is made by pleating the paper uniformly in pleats two, three, or four inches wide, taping the ends, and backing the paper with a piece of stiff cardboard. The pleats are arranged horizontally so that they become pockets which open upward. See reference 3 at the end of this appendix. Care must be taken to allow sufficient depth in the pockets so that whatever is inserted will be firmly held. If the pockets are two inches deep, the inserts should be four inches high, with two inches hidden in the pocket; this portion should contain no writing. If the pockets are three inches deep, the inserts should be six inches high, with no writing on the lower half. This assumes that the pleats do not overlap.

Some suggested uses for the pocket chart board are the following:

(*a*) *Place value chart.* If insert headings of *hundreds*, *tens*, and *ones* are made for the top pocket, the chart can be used as a place value chart to illustrate the composition of numbers as well as their addition and subtraction. As an example, it can be shown how to take 28 away from 75, where regrouping becomes necessary.

(*b*) *Vocabulary.* Emphasis can be placed on essential vocabulary. The pupils may state the meanings or check the spellings as words are inserted in the pockets.

(*c*) *Figures and formulas.* One set of inserts can consist of the names of figures, such as triangle, square, circle, rectangle, parallelogram, and trapezoid. The students can be asked to sketch each of the figures as the name is placed in the pocket and to write the formulas associated with each figure.

(*d*) *Matching columns.* If the chart has two to ten pockets, then two columns of items can be set up and the students can be asked to match them.

(*e*) *Topics, Key Words, Outlines, Summaries.* These are some of the other uses for the inserts of the pocket chart board. Example: the key words of pound, quart, and dozen are inserted in the top pocket, and the pupils are asked to place the names of items to be bought under the headings, according to the way they are sold.

A.5.3. Flash cards. Flash cards are sets of cards containing simple examples that have been prepared in advance to be "flashed" before the pupils for an answer that can be obtained mentally. The flash cards discussed here are classified according to their purpose or content:

1. Number and its representation.
2. Number family cards.
3. Basic facts: addition, subtraction, multiplication, division.
4. Combined operations.
5. Fractions—six sets.
6. Areas and perimeters.

(*a*) *Number and its representation.* Materials: a series of 8 by 10 cards with a picture on the upper half of each card representing a number, and with the numerals and words from one to ten written underneath; also a series of ten blank cards, 5 by 8 inches.

SUGGESTED USES AND ACTIVITIES

1. As flash cards—holding up the cards, one at a time, and showing the upper half, for the class to call out in unison or individually the number of birds, chickens, or dogs shown on each card.

2. As a series placed in mixed order in the chalk tray with the blank cards as covers. The blank cards are removed and the teacher and pupils review the number symbols and the ways in which the numerals are formed.

3. Pupils can rearrange the cards so that the numbers are in consecutive order.

(*b*) *Number family cards.* Materials: a series of number cards, $8\frac{1}{2}$ by 11 inches or larger, with one number, 1 to 10, on one side and the combinations making up that number on the other. (The use of the symbol 0 for zero can be delayed until the end of the second grade. If that is done, the 0 would be omitted here.) On the back of the card showing number 1 would be 1 and 0, also 0 and 1; on the back of the card with number 2 would be 2 and 0, also 0 and 2, and 1 and 1; on the back of the card with number 3 would be 3 and 0, also 0 and 3, 1 and 2, and 2 and 1; on the back of the card with number 4 would be 4 and 0, 0 and 4, 1 and 3, 3 and 1, 2 and 2, and so on. Continue up to 10 and later up to 20.

SUGGESTED USES AND ACTIVITIES

1. Four or five pupils at a time are lined up in front of the room and each is given a card to hold behind him. When it is his turn, each will hold up his card with the single number turned toward the class and will call on another pupil to name the members of that number family. At first the families should go up to 10 only.

2. The teacher shows the cards to the class and calls for individual or rows of pupils to answer.

Another form of number-family cards is a set of folded pages on which the basic addition and subtraction facts appear as one part and the basic multiplication and division facts as another. Materials: sheets of heavy paper, $8\frac{1}{2}$ by 11 inches, folded horizontally to divide the paper into four equal sections. On one section is written $4 + 3 = 7$ and on the next, $3 + 4 = 7$; on the third section $7 - 4 = 3$ appears, and on the last section, $7 - 3 = 4$. Each sheet represents a different basic addition and subtraction fact. Another set is prepared for the multiplication and division facts. Example, on the first section, $4 \times 7 = 28$, on the second, $7 \times 4 = 28$, on the third, $28 \div 4 = 7$, and on the last section, $28 \div 7 = 4$. The cards, or sheets of paper, are folded to show only one of the four relations; the students are

Front	Back				
2 +8	10 −8	4 +2	6 −2	6 +3	9 −3

Fig. 1

to give the other three. If each student makes his own sets, he will have them for future reference and study. Pupils enjoy making up story problems to accompany each relation.

(*c*) *Flash cards, basic facts. Addition and subtraction.* Materials: at least 100 cards 4 by 8 for class use, 3 by 5 for individual use. Use one side for an addition fact and the other side for the corresponding subtraction fact. In making the cards, it is convenient for self-checking purposes to have the top number on one side as the answer to the problem on the opposite side. Make one card for each basic fact (Fig. 1).

USES

Group or individual responses can be requested when the teacher holds a card in front of the room. Cards can also be placed along the chalk tray, and each child, in turn, may answer four cards at a time. Alternatively, the pupils can be asked to write the answers down, and to make their own cards for any combinations missed. Another procedure requires the pupils to give as many answers as they can in ten seconds.

Multiplication and division. Materials: 91 flash cards. Cards, 4 by 8, are acceptable for class work, as are 3 by 5 cards for individual work. On one side the multiplication fact is given as a problem, and on the other side the answer to the multiplication fact becomes the dividend in the division problem. Prepare one card for each basic multiplication fact and the corresponding division fact (Fig. 2).

For suggested uses and activities, read the discussion of basic facts in the preceding paragraph.

Some teachers prefer to set up each division fact in three different ways, with the single answer on the back of the card. Make one card for each basic division fact (Fig. 3).

(*d*) *Flash cards. Combined operations.* Materials: a series of flash cards, $8\frac{1}{2}$ by 11, 8 by 10, or 6 by 8. One set of cards could contain three

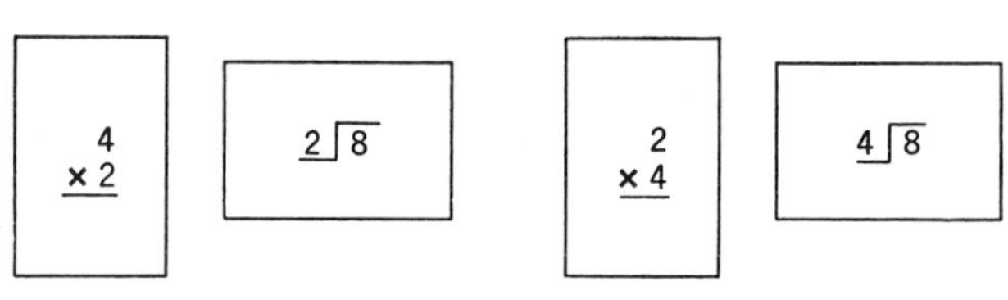

Fig. 2

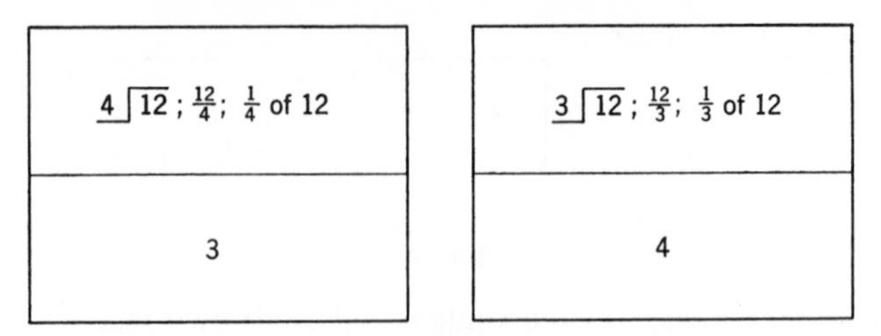

Fig. 3

numbers for vertical additions; another set, three numbers for horizontal addition; and still others for multiplication with addition, multiplication with subtraction, and so on (Fig. 4).

The number of cards needed could be cut in half if the sides were marked *A* and *B*, with side *A* containing problems of one set and side *B* containing problems of another. The answer to the problem on side *A* could be written in small numerals in the corner of side *B*, and the answer to side *B*, in the corner on side *A*. The problems for the flash cards could be taken from errors made by the pupils or from facts that have not been mastered. A few suggested uses are the following: for review, for drill, for timed tests, to develop speed and accuracy, for contests during the class period, and for individual study.

(*e*) *Flash cards for fractions.* Flash cards to develop skill in working with fractions could be prepared for practice with the following procedures:

1. Reduction of fractions.
2. Changing improper fractions to mixed numbers and vice versa.
3. Changing fractions to per cents; changing per cents to fractions.
4. Changing fractions to decimal fractions; changing decimal fractions to fractions.
5. Changing per cents to decimal fractions; changing decimal fractions to per cents.

Suggestion. The problem on side *A* can be the answer to the problem on side *B* and vice versa, as shown in the following examples:

1. Reduction of fractions (changing fractions to lower order and to higher order) (Fig. 5).
2. Changing improper fractions to mixed numbers and mixed numbers to improper fractions (Fig. 6).

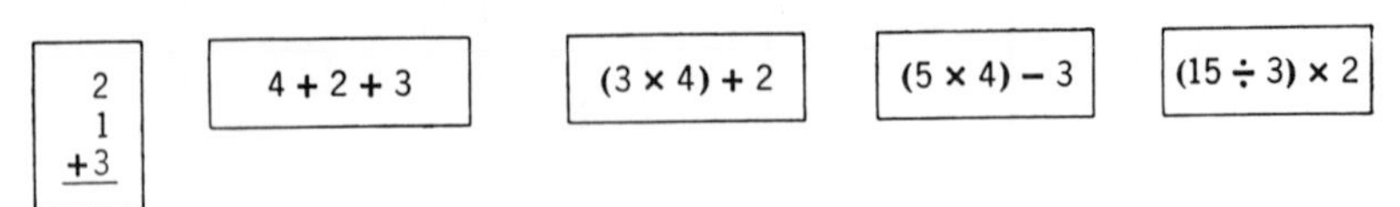

Fig. 4

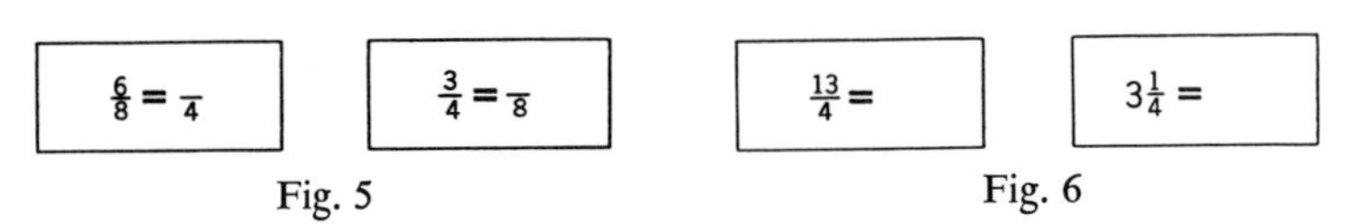

Fig. 5 Fig. 6

3. Changing fractions to per cents; per cents to fractions (Fig. 7).
4. Changing fractions to decimal fractions; decimal fractions to fractions (Fig. 8).

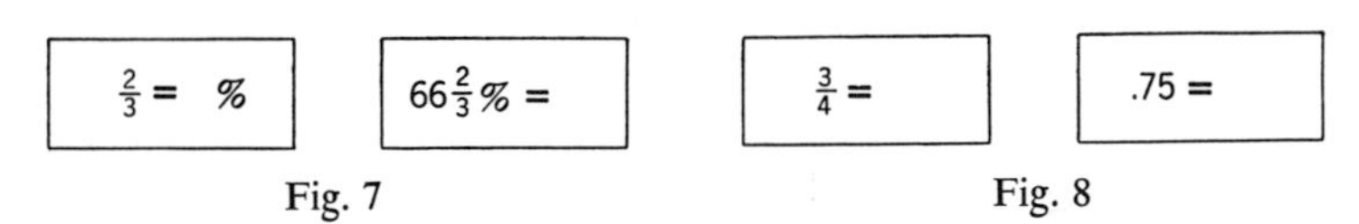

Fig. 7 Fig. 8

5. Changing per cents to decimal fractions; decimal fractions to per cents (Fig. 9).

75% =	.75 = %

Fig. 9

(*f*) *Flash cards, areas and perimeters.* Materials: Prepare a series of cards with figure diagrams on which dimensions are shown. One set is to be used for finding the perimeters, the other for finding the areas. Another set could show both the perimeter and the area. Samples:

Find the perimeters (Fig. 10).

Find the areas (Fig. 11).

Find the perimeter and the area (Fig. 12).

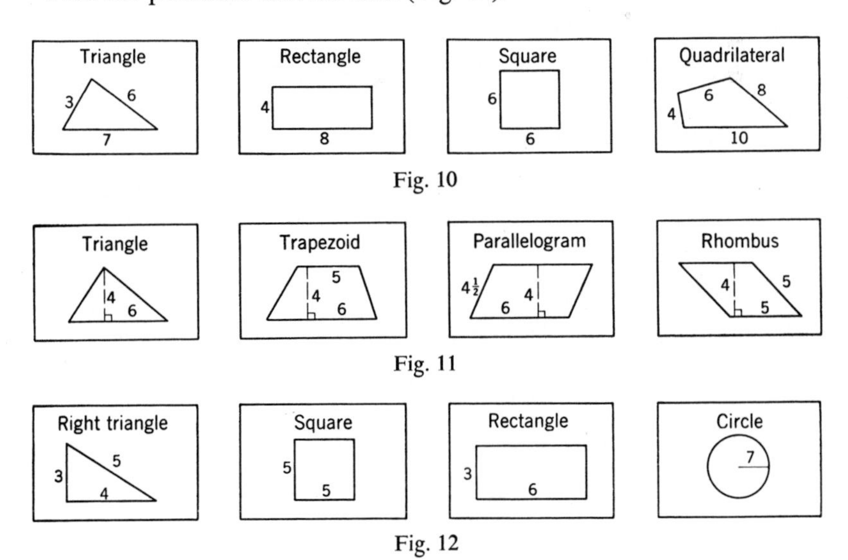

Fig. 12

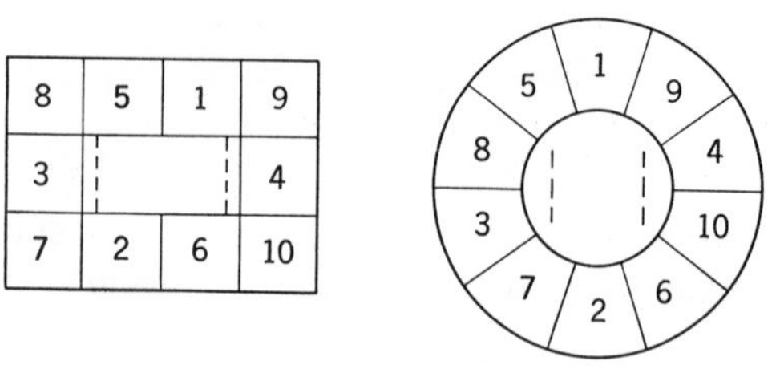

Fig. 13

USES

These cards can be used as a class exercise, as an oral exercise, for individual work, or for work between partners, oral or written.

A.5.4. Charts, graphs, and tables. These instructional materials may be large for class display or notepaper size for individual work. From the suggestions given here the teacher should be able to prepare materials to meet the needs of her class or her individual pupils.

(*a*) *Addition charts and wheels.* Materials: Cut a large card from heavy cardboard at least 12 by 16 inches and mark it with 4 by 4 squares all around the outside, leaving a blank space 4 by 8 in the center (Fig. 13). Enter the numbers 1 to 10 around the outside in mixed order. About $1\frac{1}{2}$ inches inside the blank center space make vertical slits about 4 inches long. These slits provide a holder for a center number which can be changed as desired. Prepare a series of cards about $3\frac{1}{2}$ by 7 inches on material that is not quite so heavy as the original chart for insertion in the blank space in the center. Place a number, 1 to 10, on each card. This number in the center is to be added in turn to each of the numbers around the outside. If preferred, the numbers may be placed on a large circular chart. Similar charts can be prepared for practice with higher-decade addition. See the chart in Fig. 14.

SUGGESTED USES AND ACTIVITIES

1. The number chart or wheel with a number placed in the center is hung in front of the room. This number is to be added to the numbers

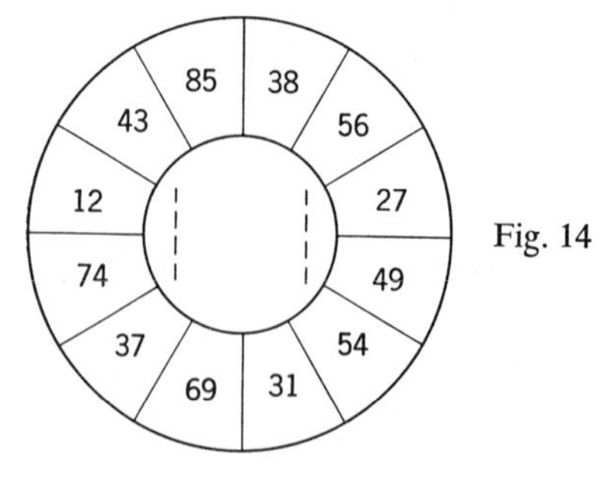

Fig. 14

around the outside of the chart. For example, if a 3 were placed in the center, the pupil called on would give 8 and 3 are 11, 5 and 3 are 8, 1 and 3 are 4, 9 and 3 are 12, and so on. In more advanced work, only the sums need to be stated, not the numbers making the sums. When practice is completed, the number 3 is removed from the center and another number is put in its place.

2. When more advanced work is needed, a chart with two-digit numbers may be prepared (Fig. 14). In the beginning only one-digit numbers are inserted in the center slits. Later, the two-digit numbers may be added. Oral or written answers may be given.

(*b*) *Addition facts chart.* Materials: Dittoed or mimeographed sheets with eleven columns across and eleven rows down (Fig. 15). The numbers 1 to 10 in irregular order are placed across the top, leaving the first place blank, and in the same order down the first column, leaving the first space blank. Each pupil is given a prepared sheet.

SUGGESTED USES AND ACTIVITIES

1. To discover any lack of mastery of the number facts.
2. To improve the response time when confronted with number combinations.
3. To keep the child's mind alert to number combinations.

Method. The first number in the left column is to be added to each number across the top row. When that is completed, the second number in the left column is added to each number across the top. After two or three rows have been done orally, without pencil work, instruct the pupils to write the sums in the spaces provided.

Add	3	10	8	6	9	2	7	5	1	4
3										
10										
8										
6										
9										
2										
7										
5										
1										
4										

Fig. 15

10	17	14	11
19			18
16	12	15	13

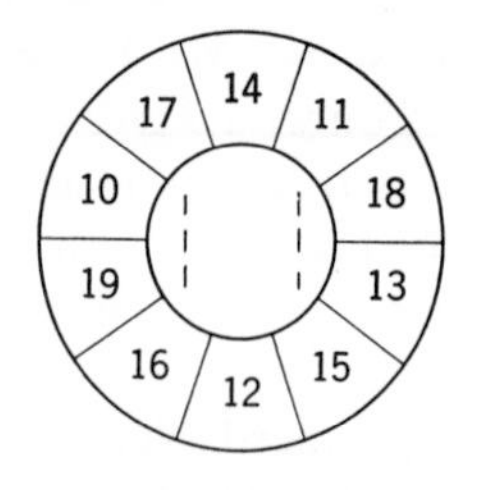

Fig. 16

(*c*) *Subtraction charts and wheels.* Prepare materials similar to those used for addition charts and wheels but substitute numbers for subtrahends on the cards at the center (Fig. 16).

USES

The uses parallel those for addition charts except that the process now is subtraction. For example, if a 4 were placed in the center, the pupil called on would say 10 take away 4 is 6, 17 take away 4 is 13, 14 take away 4 is 10, and so on.

(*d*) *Multiplication charts and wheels.* The charts prepared for addition can be adapted for the multiplication operation. For multiplication-facts review, the dittoed sheets described for the addition-facts review will also serve.

(*e*) *Multiplication tables.* Prepare a large chart of the multiplication tables. Have different members of the class show how to find the product of two numbers each not greater than 9. A second form for a multiplication table is suggested in Chapter 4, section 4.3.

Multiplication Table

	1	2	3	4	5	6	7	8	9
1	1	2	3	4	5	6	7	8	9
2	2	4	6	8	10	12	14	16	18
3	3	6	9	12	15	18	21	24	27
4	4	8	12	16	20	24	28	32	36
5	5	10	15	20	25	30	35	40	45
6	6	12	18	24	30	36	42	48	54
7	7	14	21	28	35	42	49	56	63
8	8	16	24	32	40	48	56	64	72
9	9	18	27	36	45	54	63	72	81

USES

For reference when mastering the basic multiplication facts and for review.

(*f*) *Division charts.* Materials: Prepare a chart for analyzing division.

$$\begin{aligned} 528 \div 2 &= (500 + 20 + 8) \div 2 \\ &= 250 + 10 + 4 \\ &= 264 \end{aligned}$$

$$\begin{aligned} 13.8 \div 2 &= (12 + 1.8) \div 2 \\ &= 6 + .9 \\ &= 6.9 \end{aligned}$$

$$\begin{aligned} 92 \div 4 &= (80 + 12) \div 4 \\ &= 20 + 3 \\ &= 23 \end{aligned}$$

USES

To make meaningful the usual procedures followed in division and to give a pattern for students to follow in writing original division problems for analysis.

(*g*) *Number scale division.* Materials: Prepare a chart to show different methods of illustrating division.

Example. To divide 24 into six equal parts.

Method 1. Using a scale, four parts in each group.

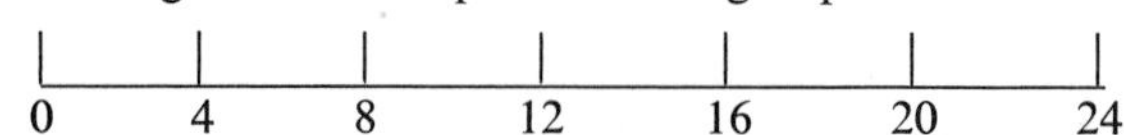

Method 2. Using grouping, four in each group.

• • • •   • • • •   • • • •   • • • •   • • • •   • • • •

Method 3. By continuous subtraction; 6 could be subtracted four times (Fig. 17).

Fig. 17

$$\begin{array}{r} 24 \\ -6 \\ \hline 18 \\ -6 \\ \hline 12 \end{array} \qquad \begin{array}{r} 12 \\ -6 \\ \hline 6 \\ -6 \\ \hline 0 \end{array}$$

USES

To help the pupils into understanding the procedures in division.

(*h*) *Division charts and wheels.* Materials: Charts and wheels similar to those made for addition, multiplication, and subtraction (Fig. 18). However, care must be exercised in selecting the numbers and the divisors if the quotient is to be exact. It is recommended that the division charts

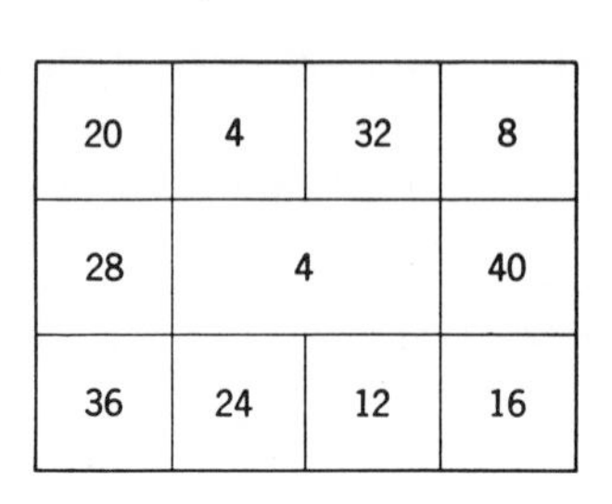

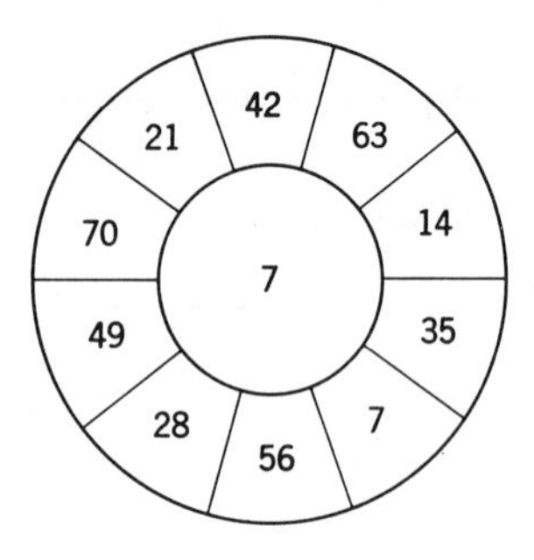

Fig. 18

be made with a fixed number at the center that is not exchangeable. This, however, will require more charts and more wheels.

USES

The numbers around the outside are to be divided by the number at the center. The class may give answers in unison, pupils may be called on individually, or the chart may be used for a written exercise.

(*i*) *Fraction charts and wheels.* Prepare large charts or wheels as shown (Fig. 19).

The number in the center is to be expressed as a fractional part, in simplest form, of each number around the outside.

Another form is the following (Fig. 20): the numbers across the top are what fractional part of the number in front? Later these fractions may be expressed as per cents.

(*j*) *Fraction chart.* Prepare a chart showing some of the different ways in which a whole can be divided (Fig. 21).

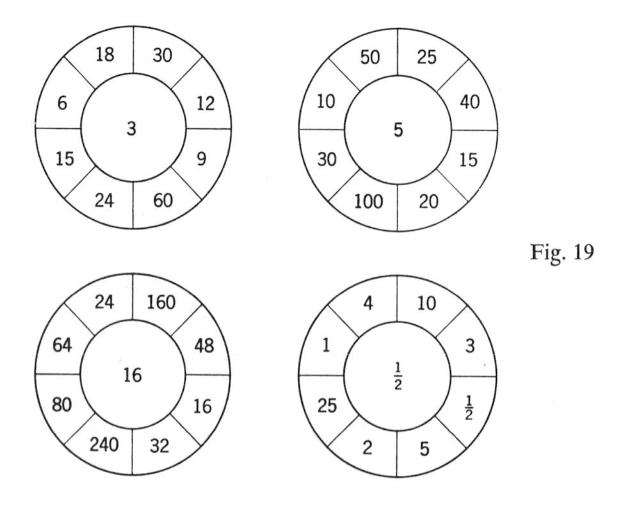

Fig. 19

24	2	6	12	24	48

Fig. 20

50	5	15	25	75	100

USES

To show the number of halves, the number of fourths, the number of thirds, the number of sixths, and the number of eighths in a unit (Fig. 21). Also to show equal fractions such as

$$\frac{1}{2} = \frac{2}{4} = \frac{3}{6} = \frac{4}{8}; \quad \frac{1}{3} = \frac{2}{6}.$$

(*k*) *Denominate number charts.* Prepare tables of measurement in chart form, similar to the one which follows. Separate charts can show linear measure, square measure, cubic measure, weights, formulas, or comparison of the metric system with the English.

Linear Measure

12 inches = 1 foot

3 feet = 1 yard

$16\frac{1}{2}$ feet = $5\frac{1}{2}$ yards = 1 rod

5280 feet = 1760 yards = 320 rods = 1 mile

USES

To place on the bulletin board or in front of the room when denominate numbers are being studied. To have for ready reference in working problems dealing with measurement.

Fig. 21

1							
$\frac{1}{2}$				$\frac{1}{2}$			
$\frac{1}{4}$		$\frac{1}{4}$		$\frac{1}{4}$		$\frac{1}{4}$	
$\frac{1}{3}$			$\frac{1}{3}$			$\frac{1}{3}$	
$\frac{1}{6}$	$\frac{1}{6}$	$\frac{1}{6}$	$\frac{1}{6}$	$\frac{1}{6}$	$\frac{1}{6}$		
$\frac{1}{8}$	$\frac{1}{8}$	$\frac{1}{8}$	$\frac{1}{8}$	$\frac{1}{8}$	$\frac{1}{8}$	$\frac{1}{8}$	$\frac{1}{8}$

(*l*) *Per cent and areas*

100 Square Unit Board

	1	2	3	4	5	6	7	8	9	10
1										
2										
3										
4										
5										
6										
7										
8										
9										
10										

Using a convenient unit, construct a 10 by 10 square as shown above. This could be painted on a board or heavy cardboard. On light cardboard prepare other squares of exactly the same size as the heavier one. These can be cut along vertical and horizontal lines to form any desired smaller rectangles.

SUGGESTED USES

1. To introduce 100 per cent as representing the whole; also to show that 1 per cent $= \frac{1}{100} = .01$ of the whole.

2. To show $\frac{1}{10} = 10$ per cent, and so on.

3. Color or cover up certain parts for discussion and have the pupils determine the fractional part covered or colored and also the per cent represented.

4. To introduce the meaning of area and the way it is determined.

5. To differentiate between perimeter and area. For example, cut one of the 10 by 10 squares into two equal parts along a horizontal line. Place these two 5 by 10 rectangles side by side so that two of the 5-unit sides are coincident, forming a 20 by 5 rectangle. This new rectangle has the same area as the original square. However the perimeter of the new rectangle is larger.

(*m*) *Area relationships.* Materials: One square yard of a suitable plane surface. Mark off one square yard on the floor or cut a piece of cardboard to size. Add cross markings at one-foot intervals.

USES

To help visualize 3 feet = 1 yard, and 9 square feet = 1 square yard. One square foot could be marked off into 144 square inches.

(*n*) *Number line.* Prepare a large number line, showing the numbers at equal intervals, to be used for counting, grouping, and measuring. One variation of the number line is a magnified ruler with the inch marks of equal length, the half marks, a shorter length, and the quarter marks still shorter. Some teachers find it desirable to include the eighth divisions. Others prefer color to designate the divisions. This enlargement can be used to illustrate the meaning of fractions, the way to measure with a ruler, the addition of some simple fractions, and so on.

If the line is divided into one hundred equal parts, then its parts can be used to represent per cents.

A.5.5. Individual envelope kits. Each child has his own envelope of materials to manipulate at his desk. Four illustrations are discussed.

(*a*) *Number kit.* Each pupil should have in his envelope the numbers 1 to 10 and zero on separate cards. When the pupils are more advanced the numbers could be 1 to 20, instead of 1 to 10, or a duplicate set of 1 to 10 might be supplied from which the pupil could make his own numbers 11 to 20 by putting two cards side by side.

SUGGESTED USES AND ACTIVITIES

1. The teacher tells a story about animals, birds, and so on, and the pupils take turns supplying the number of objects mentioned.

2. The teacher or a pupil calls out numbers and each child selects the appropriate card to show. A quick glance by the teacher checks the numbers shown.

3. In more advanced work the numbers can be used for a number-flash system whereby the answer to a problem is held up when the student has completed the work.

4. Just placing the cards in consecutive order on the top of the desk is a good exercise for the beginner.

(*b*) *Stick kit.* Each envelope contains thirty or more sticks or toothpicks, which can be grouped or tied in groups of ten.

USE

These sticks can be used to illustrate all of the basic addition and subtraction facts. For example, the pupil would find the sum of 9 and 7 by counting one group of nine sticks and another of seven. These two groups are combined. The sum is obtained by counting the sticks in the combined group. The teacher should guide the pupil in making short cuts which would lead to an understanding of place value.

(*c*) *Bottle-top kit.* In each envelope place twenty-four milk bottle tops.

If bottle tops are not available cut out paper circles which will serve for the same purpose.

USE

Each pupil can manipulate these objects to determine for himself the answers to problems similar to this: if six is divided into two equal groups, how many are there in each group? If six is divided into three equal groups, how many would there be in each group? The numbers can be increased from six to twelve, to twenty-four, and the groups from two to three, to four, to six, to eight, to twelve or whatever number is appropriate for division without a remainder.

(*d*) *Fraction kit.* In this envelope are circles and fractions of circles (circular sectors). Consult the second reference at the end of this appendix for detailed instructions and suggested uses.

A.6 MISCELLANEOUS INSTRUCTIONAL MATERIALS

There are numerous materials suitable for use in the primary grades. Only a few of the more common types are considered in this section. The teacher can often take ideas and modify them to meet his needs. Some materials can be developed as projects by the pupils in their class work.

(*a*) *Number peg board.* Materials: A square board with ten rows of ten pegs, hooks, or nails, and a series of small cards of uniform size, with numerals 0 to 99, one number symbol to each card; leave the reverse side blank. These cards are punched with a hole near the center of the top so that they can be hung on the pegs without overlapping.

SUGGESTED USES AND ACTIVITIES

1. All cards with the numerals showing are placed on the peg board, which rests in the chalk tray or hangs on the wall so that it can be seen by all. The board could be used in consecutive counting aloud individually or in unison. Pupils could take turns pointing to different numbers, and individual pupils or the class could respond by naming the designated number.

2. Turn over two or three cards in each row. Individual pupils or the class in unison can name the missing numbers orally. Pupils can write down the missing numbers. A check could be made either by turning the card back or by writing the numbers on the backboard.

3. Arrange the numbers on the board with the numbers in each row in random order but keep all numbers in their correct rows. The pupils may then take turns replacing the numbers in their correct consecutive order.

(*b*) *Counting blocks.* Materials: A chart of squares or a set of 55 blocks to help in counting 1 to 10 (Fig. 22).

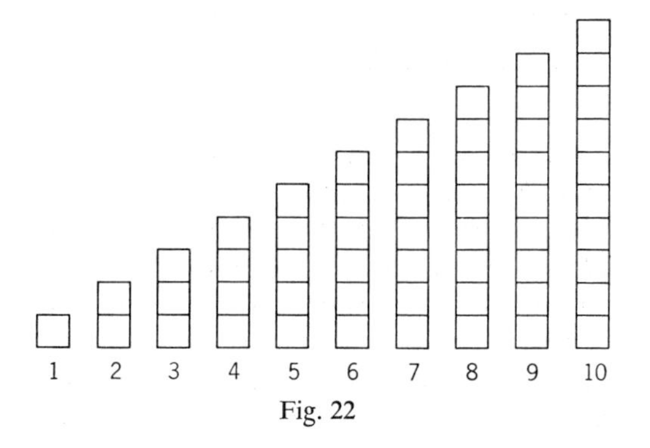

Fig. 22

(*c*) *Counting frame.* Materials: Two pegs mounted on a flat board about 12 by 2 inches (Fig. 23). The pegs should be 3 or 4 inches high. The upper end of the peg should have a hole in it or a deep notch in the top. Through the hole or in the notch place a heavy wire (a wire coat hanger will serve). Before bending back the ends of the wire to make it secure, string it with twelve or more large wooden beads of uniform size.

USES

The string of beads could be used by beginners in learning to count. It could also illustrate division, in particular the relation between the divisor and the quotient with a constant dividend. If the set of beads is taken as one group, there are twelve beads. If the set is divided equally into two groups, there are six beads in each. If the set is divided equally into three groups, there are four beads in each. If the set is divided equally into four groups, there are three beads in each, and so on.

(*d*) *Number sponge.* Materials: A small sponge for each pupil or one large sponge for the teacher's use, depending on whether this is to be an individual or a class project; also a supply of small sticks or toothpicks.

USES

The teacher or a pupil calls out numbers and the pupils place the corresponding number of sticks in the sponge. The sticks may be removed after checking. A sponge could also be used to illustrate addition and subtraction.

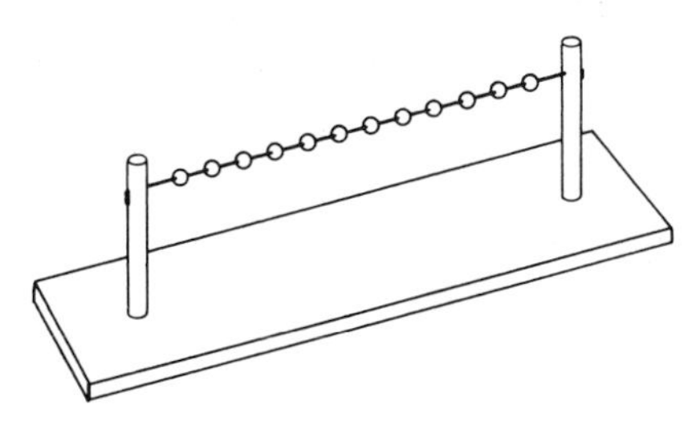

Fig. 23

2,0.9.4,7.0.0,6.1.5.

Fig. 24

(*e*) *Reading form for numerals.* Place a series of numerals on a stiff cardboard, with holes for pegs between each pair of numerals (Fig. 24). In these peg holes pegs with tails attached for commas are inserted at the appropriate places. A peg without a tail may be used for the decimal point. At first the teacher might use only the commas to separate the periods in natural numbers. For more advanced work, the decimal point could be added. By covering up some of the numerals, numbers of two, three, or four digits can be formed, and the numbers may be read orally.

(*f*) *Dominoes.* A set of dominoes is a very desirable asset in the elementary classroom. It has many uses:

1. In counting—count the number of dots.
2. In addition—4 dots on one portion and 3 on the other make a total of 7.
3. In subtracting—7 dots are on the block; cover up the part with 3 dots; 4 dots remain.
4. In multiplying or dividing—the double dominoes can be used as an introduction to multiplication and division: 3 and 3 are 6; two 3's are 6; $\frac{1}{2}$ of 6 is 3; 6 divided by 2 is 3.

(*g*) *Egg cartons.* Materials: egg cartons of at least two types, one with two rows of six places and one with three rows of four places, can be used to illustrate division and in discussing fractions.

A.7 GAMES CENTERING AROUND ARITHMETIC

Various games involving number combinations can be played in the classroom. Descriptions of some of these games are given in the references listed at the end of this appendix. In this section some uses of magic squares are discussed.

MAGIC SQUARES

The magic square has several purposes. Four examples are given. A nine-division square is drawn on cardboard as shown (Fig. 25).

1. Pupils are given sets of small cards with numbers 1 to 9. These cards are to be placed on the squares to make a sum of 15, whether added

One solution

8	3	4
1	5	9
6	7	2

Fig. 25

Fig. 26

	3	
	5	
		2

horizontally, vertically, or diagonally. A hint can be given that there are even numbers in the corners. One solution is shown on the right of the figure.

2. Another is a game for two (Fig. 26): separate the cards into sets of odd and even numbers. Place the cards face down in front of the two players, the set of odd-numbered cards in front of one player and the even numbers in front of the other. Each player takes a turn drawing a card, turning it over, and placing it on one of the blank squares. The player who draws a card that will complete a sum of 15 either vertically, horizontally or diagonally wins a point. The cards are then turned over, the odds and evens are exchanged, and the game is started again. A score of 5 or 10 can be set to win the game.

3. The magic square may be used to review addition and subtraction facts. The pupil is given a square with three of the subsquares filled in and is asked to determine what the numbers on the other squares should be if the sum is to be 15 in each direction.

4. For more difficult work use a magic square of sixteen squares with some of the squares filled. The pupil may be told the required sum or he may be given a completed row from which to find the sum. He is to fill in the remaining squares.

Example.* Use the numbers 1 to 16 to fill the squares (Fig. 27). If the sum of each row, column, and diagonal is 34, find the missing number.

Hint. One method could be to start with the third row, continue with the second column, then the first row, third column, and so on.

Fig. 27

1			4
	6	7	
8		11	5
	3		

* W. W. R. Ball, *A Short History of Mathematics*, page 119, The Macmillan Co., New York, 1908.

A.8 BULLETIN BOARD

The bulletin board in the classroom is the source of another opportunity to display supplementary instructional materials. Problems related to the work being discussed can be illustrated. Important or key vocabulary items may be posted; the students may be asked to illustrate them. Mathematical themes, such as learning to tell time, may be worked out: illustrate the time a child goes to bed, the time he gets up, the time he goes to school, and so on. Another theme is measurement in cooking or clothing. Comparison of addition in Roman numerals with addition in Hindu-Arabic numerals is an interesting topic.

Arrangement of the bulletin board provides activity for the pupils as well as information in the form of enrichment materials. The issues of the *Arithmetic Teacher* and the publications of the National Council of Teachers of Mathematics offer many worthwhile ideas for work with the classroom bulletin board.

DISCUSSION ITEMS AND PROJECTS

1. Discuss briefly some of the general requirements for materials to be used in the improvement of instruction.

2. Select one visual aid. Give some advantages and some disadvantages of its being purchased commercially, made by the teacher, made as a class project, or made by an individual pupil.

3. Demonstrate with diagrams or with the materials themselves how bundles of sticks can be used to show the meaning of two-digit numbers and how to add and subtract numbers.

4. Prepare a chart or diagram to distinguish between the fact that three 4's are twelve and four 3's are also twelve.

5. Prepare a report on "Five Ways of Showing What Six 4's Equal" from the *51st Yearbook of the National Society for the Study of Education, Part II, Teaching Arithmetic.* Be able to illustrate each method before the class and to describe its advantages or disadvantages.

6. Visit an arithmetic class and give a report covering the items listed under "briefing."

7. Select one or more visual aids that are of particular interest to you and prepare the materials for them.

8. Prepare a denominate number chart for comparing units of weight in the metric system with those in the English system, making it similar to the chart suggested in the text for comparing units of length.

REFERENCES

Bradley Company, Milton, *Arithmetic Aids.* A four-page catalogue, with twenty-four illustrations of arithmetic aids that are meaningful and practical.

Bruckner, L. J., E. L. Merton, and F. E. Grossnickle, *The New Exploring Numbers, Grade 5, Teachers' Edition*, 1956, John C. Winston Company. The section on "Additional Teaching Aids," pp. 377–392, describes place-value charts, fraction kits, and flash cards and gives detailed instructions.

Ceccarini, F., and W. H. Dutton, *Making Instructional Aids and Independent Seat Work in Arithmetic*, 1955. Available at Box 25342, Los Angeles 25, California. This 74-page booklet gives detailed instructions and directions for making teacher-directed aids and describes materials and gives instructions for many types of mathematical games.

Compton, E. E. and Company, *Arithmetic Problems Have Answers*, 1954. E. E. Compton Co., 1000 North Dearborn Street, Chicago 10, Illinois. This is an 18-page reprint from the 1954 Edition of *Compton's Pictured Encyclopedia*, with articles on arithmetic, number systems, addition, subtraction, multiplication, fractions, etc.

DeMay, Amy J., *Guiding Beginners in Arithmetic*, 1957. Row, Peterson and Company, White Plains, New York. This 178-page book gives an outline for directed activities in mathematics for the first two grades of school.

Drewes, R. H., A. L. Mermer, and W. P. von Boenigk, *Practical Plans for Teaching Arithmetic*, 1954. William C. Brown Co., Dubuque, Iowa, 132 pages. The chapter on teaching aids has 19 pages of illustrations, directions, and uses.

Fox, Marion W., "Manipulative Materials in Intermediate Grades," *The Arithmetic Teacher*, Vol. V, No. 3, April 1958, 140–142. This article lists 35 items of equipment for experimentation in computing and measuring.

Ginn and Company, *Ginn Games for Arithmetic, Grades* 3–8, 1957. Ginn and Company, Boston, 20 pages. This booklet describes and illustrates games for understanding numbers, the number system, and other concepts of arithmetic.

Houghland, Amy, *My Fraction Book*, 1948. Kenworthy Educational Service, Inc., Buffalo, New York, 50 pages. A workbook designed to teach fractions by having the pupil work with parts of whole figures.

Ideal School Supply Company, *Ideal Visual Aids*, 8312 Birkhoff Avenue, Chicago 20, Illinois. A four-page brochure illustrating visual aids.

National Council of Teachers of Mathematics, *Eighteenth Yearbook*, 1945. "Multisensory Aids in Teaching Arithmetic." N.C.T.M., Washington 16, D.C.

National Council of Teachers of Mathematics, *Twenty-Fifth Yearbook*, 1960. "Instruction in Arithmetic," Chapter 10. Instructional materials are discussed on pp. 224–247. Film and filmstrip titles and sources are given.

School Service Company, *Tools of Teaching*, 4223 Crenshaw Boulevard, Los Angeles 8, California. This catalogue gives illustrations and prices of visual aids.

appendix B

Notes on Number Theory

B.1 PROOF OF EUCLID'S THEOREM ON PERFECT NUMBERS

Euclid's theorem on perfect numbers states that any natural number N, of the form $N = 2^{p-1}(2^p - 1)$, is a perfect number if $2^p - 1$ is a prime number.

We must show that the sum of the divisors of $2^{p-1}(2^p - 1)$, with $2^p - 1$ a prime, will be equal to the number itself. Let the number $2^{p-1}(2^p - 1)$ be represented by N. The divisors of N are either divisors of 2^{p-1} or of $2^p - 1$ or they are products of such divisors. Since $2^p - 1$ is prime, the complete list of divisors is the following set:

$$\begin{Bmatrix} 1, & 2, & 2^2, \cdots, & 2^{p-2}, 2^{p-1} \\ 2^p - 1, & 2(2^p - 1), & 2^2(2^p - 1), \cdots, & 2^{p-2}(2^p - 1) \end{Bmatrix}$$

The sum of the divisors of N is S, where

$$(1) \quad S = (1 + 2 + 2^2 + \cdots + 2^{p-2} + 2^{p-1}) + (2^p - 1)(1 + 2 + 2^2 + \cdots + 2^{p-2}).$$

But this sum can be condensed to $S = (2^p - 1) + (2^p - 1)(2^{p-1} - 1)$, or $S = (2^p - 1)(1 + 2^{p-1} - 1) = 2^{p-1}(2^p - 1)$, hence $S = N$.

Thus the sum of the divisors of N is equal to N, and N is a perfect number. The two sums in (1) were computed by the formula for the sum of the terms in a geometric series. However, the sums can be computed directly as follows: let

$$U = 1 + 2 + 2^2 + \cdots + 2^{p-2} + 2^{p-1}.$$

Then

$$2U = \quad 2 + 2^2 + \cdots + 2^{p-2} + 2^{p-1} + 2^p.$$

(Every term moves one place to the right when multiplied by 2. Try interpreting this problem by means of numerals in base two!).

Now $2U - U = U$, on the left, and all terms except 2^p and 1 (subtracted) drop out, on the right. Hence $U = 2^p - 1$, when the upper line U is subtracted from $2U$.

In exactly the same way it can be shown that $V = 2^{p-1} - 1$, if

$$V = 1 + 2 + 2^2 + \cdots + 2^{p-3} + 2^{p-2}.$$

B.2 A PROOF THAT $\sqrt{2}$ IS IRRATIONAL

We shall assume the truth of Euclid's first theorem in number theory: *if a product of two integers a and b is divisible (exactly) by c and c is relatively prime to b, then c is a divisor of a.* An important corollary of this theorem is known as the *fundamental theorem of arithmetic*: *the factoring of any natural number into prime factors is unique, except for the order of arrangement of the factors.* An immediate consequence of both theorems is the fact that if a prime number p divides the square of a natural number n^2, then p divides n.

Suppose now that the number $\sqrt{2}$ is a rational number and has the form $\sqrt{2} = p/q$, where p and q are relatively prime natural numbers (p/q is in lowest terms). We shall show that this assumption leads to a contradiction, hence that $\sqrt{2}$ cannot be rational.

By squaring both sides of the equation $\sqrt{2} = p/q$, we obtain the equation $2 = p^2/q^2$, which is equivalent to $p^2 = 2q^2$.

Let N be the natural number represented by p^2 and by $2q^2$, the two expressions being equal. Since $N = 2q^2$, 2 is a divisor of N, or N is even, which means that p^2 is even. If p^2 is even, 2 is a divisor of p^2, and by the fundamental theorem of arithmetic 2 is a divisor of p. This means that p is even, or $p = 2r$, with r a natural number. Now $N = (2r)^2 = 4r^2$, hence $4r^2 = 2q^2$. Thus $q^2 = 2r^2$, q^2 is even, and consequently q is even. The conclusion that p and q are both even contradicts the assumption that integers p and q relatively prime represent the number $\sqrt{2}$. Hence the number $\sqrt{2}$ cannot be rational.

B.3 A PROOF OF EUCLID'S ALGORITHM

Euclid's algorithm for finding the greatest common divisor of two natural numbers is proved as follows:

Consider two natural numbers b_0 and b_1 such that $0 < b_1 < b_0$. We begin to construct the greatest common divisor by dividing b_0 by b_1. The number b_1 is contained in b_0 at least once, with a remainder less than b_1 and greater than or equal to zero. If the remainder is zero the process stops, with b_1 as the greatest common divisor. The algebra of this step is given in (0).

(0) $$b_0 = b_1q_1 + b_2 \qquad 0 \leqq b_2 < b_1.$$

If b_2 is not zero, we continue, dividing b_1 by b_2, obtaining

(1) $$b_1 = b_2q_2 + b_3 \qquad 0 \leqq b_3 < b_2.$$

If b_3 is zero, we stop. Otherwise we continue:

(2) $$b_2 = b_3q_3 + b_4 \qquad 0 \leqq b_4 < b_3.$$

. . . .

$(k-1)$ $$b_{k-1} = b_kq_k + b_{k+1} \qquad 0 \leqq b_{k+1} < b_k.$$

This procedure must stop at some finite step k, with

(k) $$b_k = b_{k+1}q_{k+1},$$

since the decreasing sequence of natural numbers,

$$b_0 > b_1 > b_2 > \cdots > b_{k-1} > b_k > b_{k+1} \geqq 0,$$

must terminate. There are at most b_0 natural numbers less than b_0 and greater than or equal to zero.

The number b_{k+1} obtained at step (k) is a common divisor of b_0 and b_1, as is seen by working upward through the system of equations (0), (1), (2), $\cdots$, $(k-1)$, (k). For, b_{k+1} divides b_k, as seen in (k). Since b_{k+1} divides b_{k+1} and b_k, it divides b_{k-1}, as seen in equation $(k-1)$. Similarly b_{k+1} divides $b_{k-2} \cdots$ up to b_4 and b_3. Since b_{k+1} divides b_4 and b_3, it divides b_2, as seen in (2). Since b_{k+1} divides b_3 and b_2, it divides b_1, as seen in (1). Finally, since b_{k+1} divides b_1 and b_2, it divides b_0 in (0).

Suppose now that c is any common divisor of b_0 and b_1. To test the divisor c, rewrite (0) to $(k-1)$ as follows:

(0′) $$b_0 - b_1q_1 = b_2$$

(1′) $$b_1 - b_2q_2 = b_3$$

(2′) $$b_2 - b_3q_3 = b_4$$

. . . .

$(\overline{k-1}')$ $$b_{k-1} - b_kq_k = b_{k+1}.$$

(0′) shows that c divides b_2 as well as b_0 and b_1; (1′) shows that c divides b_3 as well as b_1 and b_2; $(\overline{k-1}')$ shows that c divides b_{k+1} as well as b_{k-1} and b_k. Thus any common divisor of b_0 and b_1 divides b_{k+1}, hence b_{k+1} is the greatest common divisor of b_0 and b_1.

The reader will understand the proof better if he carries out its steps with a particular example, such as that of finding the greatest common divisor of 112 and 42. A further aid to understanding the proof would be to assume that $b_4 = 0$ in (2) and work back through (1) and (0).

appendix C

Bibliography

Adler, Irving, *Mathematics: The Story of Numbers, Symbols and Space*, Golden Press, New York, 1958.

———, *The New Mathematics*, John Day, New York, 1958.

Apostle, H. G., *A Survey of Basic Mathematics*, Little, Brown, Boston, 1960.

Bakst, Aaron, *Arithmetic for the Modern Age*, Van Nostrand, Princeton, N.J., 1960.

———, *Mathematical Puzzles and Pastimes*, Van Nostrand, Princeton, N.J., 1948.

———, *Mathematics, Its Magic and Mastery*, Van Nostrand, Princeton, N.J., 1952.

Banks, J. Houston, *Elements of Mathematics*, Second Edition, Allyn and Bacon, Boston, 1961.

———, *Learning and Teaching Arithmetic*, Allyn and Bacon, Boston, 1959.

Bell, E. T., *Men of Mathematics*, Simon and Schuster, New York, 1937.

———, *The Development of Mathematics*, McGraw-Hill, New York, 1940.

———, *The Magic of Numbers*, McGraw-Hill, New York, 1946.

Bendick, Jeanne, *How Much and How Many?*, McGraw-Hill, New York, 1947.

Bowman, M. E., *Romance in Arithmetic: Currency, Weights and Measures*, London University Press, London, 1950.

Boyer, L. E., *Introduction to Mathematics for Teachers*, Henry Holt, New York, 1945.

Brueckner, L. J., and F. E. Grossnickle, *How to Make Arithmetic Meaningful*, J. C. Winston, Philadelphia, 1947.

———, *Making Arithmetic Meaningful*, J. C. Winston, Philadelphia, 1953.

Brumfiel, C. F., R. E. Eicholz, and M. E. Shanks, *Algebra I*, Addison-Wesley, New York, 1961.

Buckingham, B. R., *Elementary Arithmetic: Its Meaning and Practice*, Ginn, Boston, 1947.

Cajori, F., *A History of Elementary Mathematics*, Macmillan, New York, 1916.

Dantzig, Tobias, *Number, The Language of Science*, Fourth Edition, Macmillan, New York, 1954.

DeMay, Amy J., *Guiding Beginners in Arithmetic*, Row, Peterson, Evanston, Ill., 1957.

Drewes, R. H., A. S. Mermer, W. P. Von Boenigk, *Practical Plans for Teaching Arithmetic*, William C. Brown, Dubuque, Iowa, 1954.

Dubisch, Roy, *The Nature of Number*, Ronald, New York, 1952.

Eulenberg, M. D., and T. S. Sunko, *Introductory Algebra, A College Approach*, Wiley, New York, 1961.

Eves, Howard, *An Introduction to the History of Mathematics*, Rinehart, New York, 1958.

Friend, J. N., *Numbers*, Scribner's, New York, 1954.

Hardgrove, C. E., *The Elementary and Junior High School Mathematics Library*, National Council of Teachers of Mathematics, Washington, D.C., 1960.

Hemmerling, E. M., *College Plane Geometry*, Wiley, New York, 1958.

Hogben, Lancelot, *The Wonderful World of Mathematics*, Garden City, New York, 1955.

Hooper, A., *An Arithmetic Refresher*, Holt, New York, 1944.

Huberich, P. G., *Short Method Arithmetic*, Max Stein, Chicago, 1951.

Kasner, Edward, and James Newman, *Mathematics and the Imagination*, Simon and Schuster, New York, 1940.

Kraitchik, Maurice, *Mathematical Recreations*, Dover, New York, 1953.

Larsen, H. D., *Arithmetic for Colleges*, Macmillan, New York, 1958.

Lay, L. C., *Arithmetic: An Introduction to Mathematics*, Macmillan, New York, 1961.

Layton, W. I., *College Arithmetic*, Wiley, New York, 1959.

Marer, Fred, Samuel Skolnik, and Orda Lewis, *Arithmetic*, Little, Brown, Boston, 1960.

Maria, May H., *The Structure of Arithmetic and Algebra*, Wiley, New York, 1958.

Marks, J. L., C. R. Purdy, and L. B. Kinney, *Teaching Arithmetic for Understanding*, McGraw-Hill, New York, 1958.

McSwain, E. T., and R. J. Cooke, *Understanding and Teaching Arithmetic in the Elementary School*, Holt, New York, 1958.

Morton, R. L., *Teaching Arithmetic in the Elementary School*, Vol. II, Silver Burdette, New York, 1938.

———, *Teaching Children Arithmetic*, Silver Burdette, New York, 1953.

Mott-Smith, G., *Mathematical Puzzles*, Dover, New York, 1954.

Mueller, Francis J., *Arithmetic, Its Structure and Concepts*, Prentice-Hall, Englewood Cliffs, N.J., 1956.

National Council of Teachers of Mathematics, *Sixteenth Yearbook, Arithmetic in General Education*, NCTM, Washington, D.C., 1941.

———, *Eighteenth Yearbook, Multi-Sensory Aids in Teaching Arithmetic*, NCTM, Washington, D.C., 1945.

———, *Twentieth Yearbook, The Metric System*, NCTM, Washington, D.C., 1948.

———, *Twenty-third Yearbook, Insights into Modern Mathematics*, NCTM, Washington, D.C., 1957.

Polya, G., *How to Solve It*, Princeton University Press, Princeton, N.J., 1948.

Price, H. V., and L. A. Knowler, *Basic Skills in Mathematics*, Ginn, Boston, 1952.

Richardson, Moses, *Fundamentals of Mathematics*, Macmillan, New York, 1941.

Rosenbaum, R. A. and L. J. Rosenbaum, *Bibliography of Mathematics for Secondary School Libraries*, Third Edition, Wesleyan University, Middletown, Conn., 1959.

Sanford, Vera, *A Short History of Mathematics*, Houghton Mifflin, New York, 1930.

Schaaf, W. L., *Mathematics our Great Heritage*, Harper, New York, 1948.

———, *Recreational Mathematics: A Guide to the Literature*, National Council of Teachers of Mathematics, Washington, D.C., 1955.

School Mathematics Study Group, *Studies in Mathematics* (texts and teacher guides in elementary algebra, geometry, sets and functions), Yale University Press, New Haven, Conn., and Stanford University, Stanford, Calif., 1960.

Smith, D. E., *History of Mathematics*, Vol. II, Ginn, Boston, 1925. (Also paperback edition, Dover, New York, 1958.)

———, *Number Stories of Long Ago*, National Council of Teachers of Mathematics, Washington, D.C., 1958.

———, and Jekuthiel Ginsberg, *Numbers and Numerals*, National Council of Teachers of Mathematics, Washington, D.C., 1958.

Spencer, P. L., and M. Brydegaard, *Building Mathematical Concepts in the Elementary School*, Holt, New York, 1952.

Spitzer, H. F., *Teaching Arithmetic*, Houghton Mifflin, Boston, 1948.

Stabler, E. R., *An Introduction to Mathematical Thought*, Addison-Wesley, New York, 1953.

Stern, Catherine, *Children Discover Arithmetic*, Appleton-Century-Crofts, New York, 1951.

Studebaker, J. W., W. C. Findley, and F. B. Knight, *Number Stories, Book 2*, Scott, Foresman, New York, 1947.

Swain, R. L., *Understanding Arithmetic*, Rinehart, New York, 1957.

Taylor, E. H., and C. N. Mills, *Arithmetic for Teacher-Training Classes*, Fourth Edition, Holt, New York, 1958.

Titchmarsh, E. C., *Mathematics and the General Reader*, Hutchinson, London, England, 1948.

Wheat, H. G., *How to Teach Arithmetic*, Row, Peterson, Evanston, Ill., 1956.

Answers to Odd-Numbered Exercises

CHAPTER 1 (*Answers for all exercises*)

Exercise 1, p. 13. **1.** See chart, p. 7. **2.** Measurement and partition. **3.** See section 1.4. **4.** Drill theory, incidental-learning theory, meaning theory. **5.** Repetition and addition. **6.** 111_2 means 1 of 2^2 plus 1 of 2 plus 1 of 1, therefore $4 + 2 + 1$, or 7.

7.

+	1	10	11	100
1	10	11	100	101
10	11	100	101	110
11	100	101	110	111
100	101	110	111	1000

8.

Base ten:	9,	10,	11,	12,	15,	16,	31,	32
Base two:	1001,	1010,	1011,	1100,	1111,	10,000,	11,111,	100,000

9. Addition, with subtraction as its inverse; multiplication, with division as its inverse. **10.** See section 1.5. **11.** Metric and English. **12.** More in each case. **13.** 4419 meters, 17,056 feet, 2561 feet. **14.** 1.61 kilometers equals 1 mile, approximately. **15.** 0.019, 0.081, 0.09, 0.129, 0.35, 0.4, 0.567, 0.73, 0.8.

16. 46 inches. **17.**

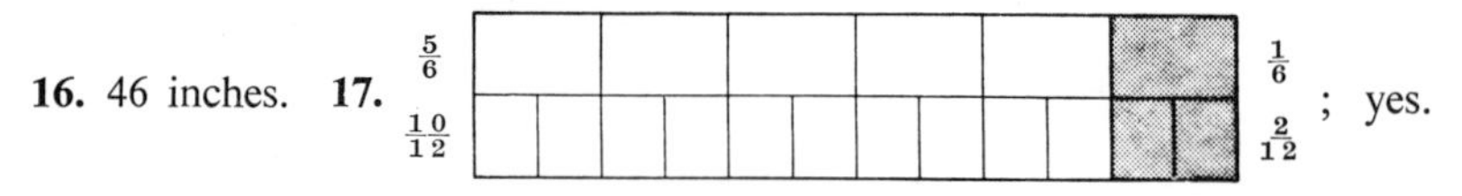

; yes.

18. 4 gallons = 16 quarts, 15 liters = 15.9 quarts; hence 4 gallons > 15 liters, 5 gallons = 20 quarts; hence 5 gallons < 19 liters.

CHAPTER 2

Exercise 1, p. 18. **1.** Yes. **3.** The fingers of one hand correspond to the five camels. **5.** 10,000. **7.** 84. **9.** There are at most 80,000 different numbers of hairs, hence at the latest point in checking person number 80,001 would have exactly as many hairs as some person in the first 80,000; person number 160,001 would have exactly as many hairs as two other persons in the first 160,000, and so on; there would have to be at least one group with four or more persons having the same number of hairs per head; there need not be a group of five persons having the same number of hairs per head.

Exercise 2, p. 19. **1.** Cardinal: *b*, *e*, *g*, *i*; ordinal: *a*, *c*, *d*, *f*, *h*, *j*. **3.** The boxing match lasted 7 rounds; the champion won in the 7th round. A sprinter made 3 attempts to run 100 yards in 9 seconds; he was successful in the 3rd attempt, crossing the 100th yard marker during the 9th second. **5.** The number of objects in a collection is given by its cardinal number. **7.** "Cardinal" principles consist of a fixed collection of basic principles: the "ten" Commandments; Newton's "three" laws of motion; the "four" cardinal points of the mariner's compass.
9. Ordinal: 1, 2, 3, 4, 5, 6, 7, 8, 9, 10, 11, 12
Cardinal: 1, 3, 6, 10, 15, 21, 28, 36, 45, 55, 66, 78.
11. (*a*) 1, 2, 3, 4, (*b*) 2, 3, 4, 5, (*c*) 7 and 8, for the 7th diagonal, 10 and 11, for the 10th diagonal.

Exercise 3, p. 23. **1.** $\ddot{\equiv}$, ∩IIIIIII, $i\zeta$, XVII. **3.** 99999∩∩∩I, $\phi\lambda\alpha$, DXXXI.
5. 𓆼𓆼 9999999 ∩∩∩∩∩∩∩∩ IIIIIII, $\beta'\psi\pi\zeta$, MMDCCLXXXVII. **7.** (*a*) 79, (*b*) 1850, (*c*) 18, (*d*) 75. **9.** (*a*) 222, (*b*) 5529, (*c*) 43,998, (*d*) 1,651,761.

Exercise 4, p. 25. **1.** Addition. **3.** (*a*) 443, (*b*) 403. **5.** MMMML, MMMMV, CCCCV or CDV.

Exercise 5, p. 32. **1.** (*a*) $3(10)^3 + 7(10)^2 + 6(10) + 2$, (*b*) $5(10)^3 + 6(10)$, (*c*) $2(10)^3 + 3(10)^2 + 4(10) + 5$. **3.** (*a*) 45, (*b*) 118, (*c*) 15,982, (*d*) 4595, (*e*) 23. **5.** 40_7, 132_7, 100_7, 151_7, 201_7, 234_7, 1000_7, 2626_7. **7.** 10_{12}, 26_{12}, 59_{12}, ee_{12}, 300_{12}, $6e4_{12}$. **9.** 1040_{12}, 3360_8, $24{,}101_5$, $11{,}011{,}110{,}000_2$. **11.** 9, 11, 12, 5.

Exercise 6, p. 35. **1.** See paragraphs 1, 4 and 5 of section 2.7. **3.** (*a*) 803,024, (*b*) 6,280,056, (*c*) 283,318, (*d*) 4,068,000,005,000, (*e*) 70,008,000,403, (*f*) 1,000,000,000,000, (*g*) 1,000,000,000,000,000. **5.** (*a*) Twenty-eight thousand, six hundred, three, (*b*) sixteen thousand, seventy-five, (*c*) one hundred eighty-six thousand, three hundred, (*d*) ninety-two million, nine hundred thousand, (*e*) eight hundred twenty-one million, six hundred thirty-nine thousand, seven hundred, forty-eight, (*f*) eleven billion, eleven million, sixty thousand, fifty-three, (*g*) seven trillion, eight hundred forty-six billion, seven hundred eighty-three million, fifty-six thousand, twelve. **11.** 879, 6647. **13.** Yes, $300,000,000,000 more.

Exercise 7, p. 36. **1.** 35. **5.** 6005. **9.** 15,010,008,007. **4.** Six hundred, nine. **8.** Five hundred three thousand, one. **11.** Write out I, II, III, · · · , XXV. **15.** CCCXLVII. **19.** MDCCCCLXIV. **14.** 94. **18.** 147,000. **21.** 44. **23.** 223. **25.** 3167. **27.** 250,536. **29.** 236. **31.** 16,458. **33.** 317. **35.** 95,166. **37.** 54,321, 25,679, 32,755, 36,238, 33,107, 8830, 24,188, 11,128. **3.** 504. **7.** 40,803. **13.** LXXXIV.

CHAPTER 3

Exercise 1, p. 43. **5.** (*a*) hundreds 3, 5, 4, 0, 0; tens 7, 6, 0, 2, 1; ones 4, 4, 2, 0, 7, (*b*) 3, 8, 5, (*c*) 8, (*d*) 7 hundreds, 8 tens, 2 ones; 1 thousand, 3 hundreds, 5 tens, 4 ones, (*e*) to show no ones and one ten. **7.** 2775.

Exercise 2, p. 46. **1.** 32, 54, 62, 27, 53, 55, 47, 44, 87, 91, 61, 21, 32, 51, 52, 61, 24, 68, 98, 74. **3.** 15, 38, 71, 77, 49, 62, 28, 84, 46, 90, 18, 41, 74, 80, 52, 65, 31, 87, 49, 93, 20, 43, 76, 82, 54, 67, 33, 89, 51, 95.

Exercise 3, p. 48. **1.** 27, 27, 20, 20, 30, 29, 24, 30, 30, 25. **3.** 83, 107, 121, 124, 130, 106, 147, 82, 81, 131. **5.** 1730, 2094, 800, 1740, 4336, 7039, 4438, 19,342.

Exercise 4, p. 51. **1.** 260, 306, 284, 295, 273, 328. **3.** (*a*) 7, (*b*) 7. **5.** (*a*) eleven, (*b*) seven.

Exercise 5, p. 52. **1.** See section 3.9.

Exercise 6, p. 53. **1.** 9 gross 3 ones; 9 gallons and 2 quarts. **3.** (*a*) twenty (*b*) 14 score 1, or 281, (*c*) 7 tens, 8 tens 7, 12 tens 4, 28 tens 1, or 281. **5.** Sums: 84, 332, 633, 127, 748, all base ten. **7.** Average, $79\frac{1}{7}$, median, 78.

Exercise 7, p. 57. **1.** (*a*) \$3.50, (*b*) \$5.60, (*c*) \$4.50. **3.** 230, 300, 1404, 6327, 1720, 2325, 44,895, 27,090, 62,484, 204,960. **5.** (*a*) 450 miles, (*b*) 720 miles, (*c*) 840 miles, (*d*) 945 miles. **7.** 71,760, 337,246, 390,336, 280,263, 365,328, 2,441,201. **9.** 105. **11.** 503. **13.** 1002. **15.** 200. **17.** 502. **19.** 15 cents. **21.** \$4690.

CHAPTER 4

Exercise 1, p. 64. Discussion.

Exercise 2, p. 69. **7.** 4, 9, 7 × 5, 8, 2.

Exercise 3, p. 71. **1.** 700, 7000, 70,000; 130, 1300, 13,000; 2030, 20,300, 2,030,000; 6800, 680,000, 6,800,000.

Exercise 4, p. 72. **1.** (*a*) (1) yes, (2) yes, (3) yes, (4) no; see next entry; (*b*) correct answer for (4) is 182,077; (*c*) 574,704, compensating errors; this is the correct answer for (3).

Exercise 5, p. 73. **1.**

```
              . . . .
. . . . . .   . . . .
. . . . . .   . . . .
. . . . . .   . . . .
. . . . . .   . . . .
              . . . .
```

commutative law.

7. (*a*) 54, multiplicand; 6, multiplier; 324, product, (*b*) 54, 6, (*c*) 27, 12; 9, 36; 3, 3, 3, 3, 2, 2. **9.** $\begin{array}{c}4\\\underline{3}\end{array}$ $\begin{array}{c}8\\\underline{9}\end{array}$ $\begin{array}{c}32\\\underline{3}\end{array}$ $\begin{array}{c}62\\\underline{3}\end{array}$ $\begin{array}{c}46\\\underline{2}\end{array}$ $\begin{array}{c}68\\\underline{4}\end{array}$ $\begin{array}{c}437\\\underline{2}\end{array}$ $\begin{array}{c}301\\\underline{2}\end{array}$ $\begin{array}{c}203\\\underline{3}\end{array}$ $\begin{array}{c}402\\\underline{5}\end{array}$. See section 4.6.

11. (*a*) product, (*b*) 20 is composed of 2 tens and 0 ones, (*c*) 3 means 3 tens, hence the 7 is placed in the tens' column, (*d*) 4100, 100, (*e*) 8 + 8 + 8 + 8 + 8.

Exercise 6, p. 76. **1.** 4502_8, $32{,}075_8$, $663e8_{12}$, $237et_{12}$. **3.** Products: 2370, 13,373, 135,356, 47,806. **5.** Base 6: 13, 13, 40, 40, 20, 140, 22, 22. **7.** Base 8: 11, 14, 30, 43.

CHAPTER 5

Exercise 1, p. 78. **1.** Driving from school to home. **3.** Boiling an egg, cutting a pie, growing a year older.

Exercise 2, p. 79. **1.** Take away. **3.** Addition. **5.** Take away. **7.** 3 + 4 = 7.

Exercise 3, p. 82. **1.** 5 − 0 = 5, 6 − 1 = 5, 7 − 2 = 5, 8 − 3 = 5, 9 − 4 = 5, 10 − 5 = 5, 11 − 6 = 5, 12 − 7 = 5, 13 − 8 = 5, 14 − 9 = 5. **3.** There are 64 facts, including the zero facts, and 54 facts when the zero facts are excluded; do not include either 10 − 0 or 10 − 10. **5.**

$$\begin{array}{rcr} 12 & = & 10 + 2 \\ -8 & = & -8 \\ \hline 4 & = & 2 + 2. \end{array}$$

Exercise 4, p. 84. **1.** Higher decade type: (*a*), (*b*), (*e*), (*i*); basic subtraction facts: (*d*), (*g*), (*h*); neither: (*c*), (*f*), (*j*). **3.** 31 − 30, 19 − 15, 42 − 40, 20 − 20.

Exercise 5, p. 88. **1.** 2875. **3.** 4544.

Exercise 6, p. 89. **1.** Yes; yes (but not correct); 4 and 5 are interchanged; yes. **3.** (*b*), (*e*), (*f*). **5.** 1638, 26,147, 3344, 72,782, 3874. **7.** Base twelve: 653*u*, 3189, 1233, 21,429, 2299. **9.** Base nine: 2564, 20,125, 71,230, 1,734,344.

CHAPTER 6

Exercise 1, p. 93. **1.** (*a*) 6, dividend; 2, divisor; 3, quotient; (*f*) 72, dividend; 9, divisor; 8, quotient. **3.** (*a*) $36 \div 9 = 4$, $36 \div 4 = 9$, (*b*) $45 \div 3 = 15$, (*c*) $64 \div 8 = 8$, (*d*) $49 \div 7 = 7$, (*e*) $42 \div 6 = 7$, $42 \div 7 = 6$, (*f*) $28 \div 4 = 7$, $28 \div 7 = 4$.

Exercise 2, p. 94. **1.** Partition: eight may be partitioned into two equal parts. Measurement: there are four 2's in eight. **3.** (*a*) 5 bows, (*b*) measurement. **5.** (*a*) A sum of 35 cents is to be distributed among 7 boys. How much money does each boy receive? If one candy bar costs 7 cents, how many can be purchased for 35 cents? **7.** $40. **9.** 5, 5.

Exercise 3, p. 96. **1.** Yes. **3.** (*a*) 5 *R* 2, (*b*) 8 *R* 1, (*c*) 5 *R* 6, (*d*) 7 *R* 2, (*e*) 5 *R* 7, (*f*) 8 *R* 8, (*g*) 7 *R* 1, (*h*) 4 *R* 1, (*i*) 5 *R* 5, (*j*) 9 *R* 3. **5.** (*a*) $85 = 9 \times 9 + 4$, (*b*) $107 = 12 \times 8 + 11$, (*c*) $59 = 7 \times 8 + 3$, (*d*) $49 = 7 \times 7 + 0$, (*e*) $31 = 4 \times 7 + 3$.
7. (*c*)

$$\begin{array}{l} 5 \times 7 + 0 = 35 \\ 5 \times 7 + 1 = 36 \\ 5 \times 7 + 2 = 37 \\ 5 \times 7 + 3 = 38 \\ 5 \times 7 + 4 = 39 \end{array}$$

(*e*)

$$\begin{array}{l} 3 \times 7 + 0 = 21 \\ 3 \times 7 + 1 = 22 \\ 3 \times 7 + 2 = 23 \end{array}$$

Exercise 4, p. 98. **1.** (*a*) 34, (*b*) 25, (*c*) 38 *R* 3, (*d*) 40 *R* 4. **3.** 903, 677 *R* 1, 541 *R* 4, 301.

Exercise 5, p. 103. **1.** (*a*) 130 *R* 16, (*b*) 204 *R* 16. **5.** (*a*) 637 *R* 19, (*b*) 705 *R* 24.

Exercise 6, p. 104. **1.** (*a*) 1423, (*b*) 189, (*c*) 993, (*d*) 430 *R* 3, (*e*) 11,302, (*f*) 91 *R* 7, (*g*) 618 *R* 1, (*h*) 1175*R* 6, (*i*) 1179, (*j*). 3477 *R* 1.

Exercise 7, p. 104. **1.** (*a*) Yes, (*b*) no, (*c*) yes, (*d*) yes, (*e*) no. **5.** (*a*) 565 *R* 31, (*b*) 1249 *R* 50, (*c*) 1261 *R* 10, (*d*) 2184 *R* 24. **7.** (*a*) 0, 1, 2, 3, (*b*) 7, 8, 9. **9.** 124 cubic feet, remainder 770 cubic inches. **11.** $0.38. **13.** $2060. **15.** 134 cubic feet.

Cumulative Review. **(a) 1.** Addition, subtraction, multiplication, division. **3.** Subtraction. **5.** Quotient, divisor, and dividend. **7.** Numeration. **9.** Decimal. **(b) 1.** *T.* **3.** *T.* **5.** *F.* **7.** *F.* **9.** *F.* **11.** *T.* **13.** *F.* **15.** *T.* **(c) 1.** 42, 18, 211, 34. **3.** 230. **5.** 1031_5. **7.** 4.208×10^3. **9.** 1000_7. **11.** 177_9. **13.** 619 years, $36\frac{7}{17}$ years. **15.** $47\frac{1}{9}$ miles per hour, $7.44, $17\frac{2}{3}$ miles per gallon. **(d) 1.** $\frac{2}{3}$, $\frac{5}{4}$, $3\frac{2}{5}$. **3.** 21, 42, 1, 40. **5.** (*a*) $\frac{21}{8}$, (*b*) $\frac{7}{4}$, (*c*) $\frac{101}{12}$, (*d*) $\frac{75}{2}$. **7.** (*a*) $\frac{5}{8}$, (*b*) 2. **9.** (*a*) $\frac{9}{32}$, (*b*) $\frac{18}{35}$. **11.** (*a*) $10\frac{7}{8}$, (*b*) $18\frac{11}{20}$, (*c*) $29\frac{1}{18}$. **13.** (*a*) $3\frac{1}{3}$, (*b*) $4\frac{7}{8}$, (*c*) $5\frac{3}{5}$, (*d*) $7\frac{3}{5}$.

CHAPTER 7

Exercise 1, p. 117. **1.** Cross out multiples of the prime numbers up to and including 13

3.

Number	8338	54	1384	12,345	13,560	495
Divisible by 2	yes	yes	yes	no	yes	no
Divisible by 4	no	no	yes	no	yes	no
Divisible by 3	no	yes	no	yes	yes	yes
Divisible by 5	no	no	no	yes	yes	yes
Divisible by 9	no	yes	no	no	no	yes
Divisible by 11	yes	no	no	no	no	yes

5. (*a*), (*c*). **7.** (*a*) 8975, (*b*) 8783, (*c*) 1331, (*d*) 5232, (*e*) 43,210. **9.** (*a*) 3, 5, 19, (*b*) 17, 17, (*c*) 2, 2, 2, 3, 3, 5, (*d*) 2, 2, 2, 2, 2 ,2, 2, (*e*) 11, 11, 11.

Exercise 2, p. 121. **1.** (*a*) 2, 2, 2, 2, 3, 3, (*b*) 2, 2, 3, 5, (*c*) 2, 2, 3, 3, 3, (*d*) 3, 3, 7, (*e*) 2, 2, 2, 2, 2, 3. **3.** (*a*) 12. **5.** 14, 18. **7.** 19, 19.

Exercise 3, p. 124. **3.** $12 = 2^2 \times 3$, $18 = 2 \times 3^2$, $25 = 5^2$, $34 = 2 \times 17$, $42 = 2 \times 3 \times 7$, $51 = 3 \times 17$, $56 = 2^3 \times 7$, $66 = 2 \times 3 \times 11$, $72 = 2^3 \times 3^2$, $87 = 3 \times 29$, $91 = 7 \times 13$, $93 = 3 \times 31$, **5.** 17, 67, 73, 97, 103, 179, 229, 641. **7.** (*a*) $2^3 \times 3^2 \times 5$, (*b*) $2 \times 3^3 \times 5^2$, (*c*) $7^2 \times 11 \times 13$, (*d*) $2^3 \times 5^2 \times 7^2$, (*e*) $2 \times 3^3 \times 5 \times 7^2$. **9.** (*a*) 96, (*b*) 80, (*c*) 60, (*d*) 42, (*e*) 108, (*f*) 630, (*g*) 24, (*h*) 50, (*i*) 48.

Exercise 4, p. 125. **1.** 9. **3.** 1. **5.** $\frac{4}{3}$. **7.** \$88.20. **9.** \$70.40.

Exercise 5, p. 129. **1.** 2, 3, 4, $\cdots$, 19, 20; 1, 3, 6, 10, 15, 21, 28, 36, 45, 55, 66, 78, 91, 105, 120, 136, 153, 171, 190, 210. **3.** 3, 5, 7, $\cdots$, 37, 39; 1, 4, 9, 16, 25, 36, 49, 64, 81, 100, 121, 144, 169, 196, 225, 256, 289, 324, 361, 400. **5.** 31, 211. **7.** 3160, 3240, 6400.

Exercise 6, p. 130. **1.** 496: $1 + 2 + 4 + 8 + 16 + 31 + 62 + 124 + 248 = 496$; 8128: $1 + 2 + 4 + 8 + 16 + 32 + 64 + 127 + 254 + 508 + 1016 + 2032 + 4064 = 8128$. **3.** 1, 5, 12, 22 (See J. V. Uspensky and M. A. Heaslet, *Elementary Number Theory*, McGraw-Hill, New York, 1939, page 10).

CHAPTER 8

Exercise 1, p. 133. **1.** 12 inches, 11 feet, 2 inches. **3.** 4 feet. **5.** 25 yards. **7.** 168 feet. **9.** Circumferences: 14π feet, 7π yards, 2π feet; areas: 49π square feet, $49\pi/4$ square yards, π square feet. **11.** 4 units.

Exercise 2, p. 134. **1.** 8 square inches, 6 square inches, 12 square inches, 4 square inches, 9 square inches, $11\frac{1}{2}$ square inches. **3.** Figures 2 and 6. **5.** An inch square means a square with sides of length 1 inch. A square inch means an area of 1 square inch, regardless of the shape of the area. A 2-foot square has an area of 4 square feet.

Exercise 3, p. 136. **1.** 144 square inches. **3.** 1200 square feet. **5.** 6500 square feet. **7.** 11 yards. **9.** Two times larger; two times larger; four times larger. **11.** 40 feet, 100 square feet, 80 feet, 400 square feet. **13.** 103 feet. **15.** 5000 square yards.

Exercise 4, p. 137. **1.** 3 rows of 5 squares each and 5 rows of 3 squares each.

Exercise 5, p. 139. **3.** 60 cubic feet. **5.** About $9\frac{1}{4}$ inches.

Exercise 6, p. 139. **1.** (*a*) $7\frac{7}{8}$, (*b*) $8\frac{1}{12}$, (*c*) $13\frac{31}{40}$, (*d*) $18\frac{3}{40}$. **3.** (*a*) $\frac{9}{5}$, (*b*) 20, (*c*) $10\frac{2}{5}$, (*d*) $35\frac{1}{16}$, (*e*) 2, (*f*) $\frac{2}{15}$, (*g*) $5\frac{1}{4}$, (*h*) $\frac{3}{2}$. **5.** 80 cents. **7.** $\frac{2}{3}$ pound. **9.** $8\frac{1}{3}$ pounds.

CHAPTER 9

Exercise 1, p. 143. **1.** (*a*) 2, (*b*) 5, (*c*) 2, (*d*) fifths, (*e*) 5, (*f*) dividend, (*g*) 5. **3.** $\frac{1}{4}$, $\frac{1}{2}$, $\frac{1}{8}$, $\frac{7}{8}$, $\frac{3}{8}$, $\frac{1}{2}$, $\frac{1}{2}$, $\frac{1}{8}$.

Exercise 2, p. 146. **1.** $\frac{1}{4}$. **3.** $\frac{1}{4}$. **5.** $\frac{9}{5}$. **7.** $\frac{1}{20}$. **9.** $\frac{1}{12}$. **11.** $\frac{8}{24}$ or $\frac{1}{3}$. **13.** 6 feet, 3 inches. **15.** \$4.32. **17.** 18 feet. **19.** $\frac{5}{7}$.

Exercise 3, p, 147. **1.** (*a*) 25 cents, (*b*) 15 minutes, (*c*) 1 cup, (*d*) 9 inches, (*e*) 4 ounces; (*a′*) 20 cents, (*b′*) 12 minutes, (*c′*) 400 pounds, (*d′*) 73 days, (*e′*) 3 hours·

Exercise 4, p. 150. **1.** Proper: $\frac{3}{8}$, $\frac{7}{23}$, $\frac{7}{8}$, $\frac{1}{3}$; improper: $\frac{7}{4}$, $\frac{6}{2}$, $\frac{5}{3}$, $\frac{3}{2}$, $\frac{7}{2}$, $\frac{21}{4}$. **3.** $\frac{6}{9}$, $\frac{2}{3}/1$, $\frac{10}{15}$, $\frac{16}{24}$, $1/1\frac{1}{2}$, $\frac{15}{20}$, $1/\frac{4}{3}$, $\frac{27}{36}$, $\frac{3}{2}/2$, $\frac{36}{48}$. **5.** (*a*) $\frac{2}{3}$, $\frac{7}{3}$; $\frac{1}{2}$, $\frac{7}{2}$; $\frac{7}{8}$, $\frac{4}{8}$, $\frac{3}{8}$; (*b*) $\frac{1}{2} = \frac{5}{10} = \frac{4}{8}$; $\frac{2}{3} = \frac{4}{6}$; $\frac{7}{8} = \frac{21}{24}$. **7.** (*a*) 48, (*b*) 16, (*c*) 20, (*d*) 7, (*e*) 63, (*f*) 1, (*g*) 7, (*h*) 2, (*i*) $\frac{7}{4}$, (*j*) 3. **9.** $\frac{1}{6}$, $\frac{1}{4}$, $\frac{3}{8}$, $\frac{2}{5}$, $\frac{1}{2}$, $\frac{5}{8}$, $\frac{2}{3}$, $\frac{3}{4}$, $\frac{4}{5}$, $\frac{5}{6}$.

Exercise 5, p. 152. **1.** *F*, $\frac{3}{3}$, **3.** *F*. **5.** *T*. **7.** *T*. **9.** *T*. **11.** *T*. **13.** *F*. **15.** *F*. **17.** *T*. **19.** *T*. **21.** *T*.

CHAPTER 10

Exercise 1, p. 158. **1.** $\frac{5}{7}$. **3.** $2\frac{1}{3}$. **5.** $\frac{13}{16}$. **7.** $1\frac{7}{12}$. **9.** $\frac{9}{20}$. **11.** $1\frac{19}{40}$. **13.** $1\frac{2}{3}$. **15.** $2\frac{1}{4}$. **17.** $1\frac{3}{8}$. **19.** $7/x$. **21.** $1\frac{19}{24}$. **23.** $\frac{143}{180}$.

Exercise 2, p. 160. **1.** $\frac{3}{7}$. **3.** $\frac{1}{2}$. **5.** $\frac{2}{5}$. **7.** $\frac{1}{8}$. **9.** $\frac{7}{12}$. **11.** $\frac{1}{6}$. **13.** $3/x$. **15.** $(ay - bx)/(by)$. **17.** $\frac{79}{240}$.

Exercise 3, p. 161. **1.** $4\frac{1}{12}$. **3.** $12\frac{11}{12}$. **5.** $78\frac{1}{2}$. **7.** $5\frac{5}{12}$. **9.** $11\frac{1}{3}$. **11.** $\frac{1}{2}$. **13.** $4\frac{7}{12}$.

Exercise 4, p. 162. **3.** $8\frac{5}{8}$. **5.** $10\frac{17}{60}$. **7.** $16\frac{17}{24}$. **9.** $2\frac{13}{60}$. **11.** $\frac{1}{6}$. **13.** $2\frac{7}{8}$. **15.** $2\frac{9}{16}$. **17.** $8\frac{5}{6}$.

Exercise 5, p. 167. (*d*) **1.** 93,840. **3.** $871{,}645\frac{1}{4}$. **5.** $411{,}713\frac{1}{6}$.

Exercise 6, p. 171. (*c*) **1.** $5\frac{1}{7}$. **3.** $\frac{13}{15}$. **5.** $21\frac{1}{3}$. **7.** 21. **9.** $3\frac{1}{9}$. **11.** 2. **13.** 21 **15.** 4.

Exercise 7, p. 172. **1.** 25 cents. **3.** 14 cents (to the nearest cent). **5.** \$2.17. (to the nearest cent). **7.** 75 cents. **9.** \$1. **11.** $7\frac{1}{2}$ cups of flour, 4 cups of shortening, $2\frac{1}{4}$ cups of sugar, $4\frac{1}{2}$ teaspoons of salt, $4\frac{1}{2}$ teaspoons of baking powder, 3 cups of milk. **15.** $\frac{1}{240}$ inch. **17.** $58\frac{5}{6}$ feet, $212\frac{1}{2}$ square feet. **19.** 30 miles per hour.

Exercise 8, p. 176. **1.** Multiply by 100, divide by 6. **3.** Multiply by 200, divide by 3. **5.** Multiply by 700, divide by 8. **7.** 1600. **9.** 8600. **11.** 25,500. **13.** 174. **15.** 63,700. **17.** (*a*) $\frac{1}{3}$, (*b*) $\frac{1}{2}$, (*c*) 2, (*d*) $\frac{1}{5}$, (*e*) $\frac{20}{9}$, (*f*) 2, (*g*) $\frac{1}{4}$, (*h*) $\frac{1}{2}$, (*i*) $\frac{1}{3}$. **19.** $16\frac{7}{12}$. **21.** (*a*) $\frac{4}{21}$, (*b*) $1803\frac{3}{4}$, (*c*) $9143\frac{3}{4}$, (*d*) $8875\frac{1}{6}$. **23.** (*a*) $\frac{9}{10}$, (*b*) $1\frac{28}{47}$, (*c*) $\frac{27}{40}$, (*d*) 4.

Exercise 9, p. 177. **1.** (*c*) (*a′*) 2, 2, 2, 2, 19, (*b′*) 2, 5, 29, (*d*) 61, 67, 71, 73, 79, 83, 89. **3.** (*a*) 240, (*b*) See discussion in the text. **5.** Examples: $\frac{2}{3}$, $\frac{5}{4}$, $3\frac{1}{2}$, $(2\frac{1}{2} + \frac{1}{3})/7$. **7.** $\frac{5}{9}$, $\frac{7}{8}$, $\frac{4}{7}$, $\frac{2}{7}$, $\frac{3}{4}$, $\frac{3}{7}$. **9.** (*a*) 300, (*b*) $8\frac{1}{3}$. **11.** (*a*) 10, (*b*) 300. **13.** \$5000. **15.** \$2.20. **17.** 20.

CHAPTER 11

Exercise 1, p. 180. **1.** (*a*) $\frac{3}{10}$, (*b*) $\frac{13}{5}$, (*c*) $\frac{1}{25}$, (*d*) $\frac{23}{100}$, (*e*) $\frac{1}{2500}$. **3.** (*a*) 1, (*b*) $2\frac{3}{10}$, (*c*) $5\frac{47}{200}$, (*d*) $28\frac{1}{10}$, (*e*) 100.

Exercise 2, p. 181. **1.** (*a*) .3, (*b*) .16, (*c*) .06, (*g*) 3.7, (*h*) .3, (*d*) 1.471, (*e*) .004, (*f*) .042, (*i*) .0472, (*j*) .6891. **3.** Each problem may have many correct answers. The following is a set of proper answers: (*a*) $\frac{4}{5}$, (*b*) $\frac{1}{25}$, (*c*) $\frac{42}{200}$, (*d*) $\frac{21}{50}$, (*e*) $\frac{3}{50}$, (*f*) $\frac{14}{200}$, (*g*) $\frac{58}{250}$, (*h*) $\frac{9}{200}$, (*i*) $\frac{222}{2000}$, (*j*) $\frac{274}{2000}$. **5.** Simple decimal fractions, (*b*), (*c*), (*d*), (*e*), (*f*); complex decimal fractions, (*a*), (*g*).

Exercise 3, p. 185. **1.** (*a*) Twenty-three hundredths, (*b*) sixty-four thousandths, (*c*) two and one hundred seven thousandths, (*d*) twelve thousand three hundred forty-five hundred-thousandths, (*e*) twenty-three and four hundred ninety-two ten-thousandths. **3.** (*a*) .58, (*b*) .304, (*c*) 300.004, (*d*) .4321. **5.** (*a*) .02306, (*b*) 700.405. **7.** (*a*) .022, (*b*) 237.0587, (*c*) 500.002, (*d*) $6261.49\frac{1}{3}$. **9.** (*a*) $4(10^1) + 2(10^0) + 3(10^{-1}) + 2(10^{-2}) + 5(10^{-3})$, (*b*) $2(10^2) + 0(10^1) + 6(10^0) + 0(10^{-1}) + 4(10^{-2}) + 2(10^{-3})$, (*c*) $3(10^2) + 3(10^1) + 0(10^0) + 3(10^{-1}) + 3(10^{-2}) + 3(10^{-3})$. **11.** Hundredths, thousandths, ten-thousandths, hundred-thousandths, millionths. **13.** (*a*) $\frac{11}{36}$, (*b*) $3\frac{19}{36}$. **15.** (*a*) $.5_8$, (*b*) $.2_8$, (*c*) $.06_8$, (*d*) $.34_8$ (*e*) $.022_8$.

Exercise 4, p. 186. **1.** (*a*) 2.100, 73,820, 9.002, (*b*) yes, after having obtained one set, another can be obtained by multiplying preceding set by any negative power of 10. **3.** .75, .6, .567, .403, .37, .2, .195, .09, .078.

Exercise 5, p. 190. **1.** (*a*) 29.74, (*b*) 82.269, (*c*) 75602.645, (*d*) 7.4, (*e*) .061. **3.** (*b*) .04, partition. **5.** 30, measurement. **7.** Measurement for parts (*a*) and (*c*); partition for parts (*b*) and (*d*). **9.** (*a*) 6.586, (*b*) 63.005, (*c*) 1.711. **11.** .92, 1, 5.92, .00008 **15.** (*a*) .15, (*b*) 5, (*c*) .08, (*d*) 175. **17.** (*a*) .375, (*b*) .0625, (*c*) .28, (*d*) .46.

Exercise 6, p. 194. **1.** (*a*) .166 · · · , (*b*) .230769230769 · · · , (*c*) .375, (*d*) .066 · · · , (*e*) .2142857142857 · · · , (*f*) .5625, (*g*) .8, (*h*) .08, (*i*) .875, (*j*) .1219512195 · · ·.

Exercise 7, p. 196. **1.** (*a*) $1.86(10^5)$, (*b*) $1.0(10^{-6})$, (*c*) $3.2(10^{13})$, (*d*) $9.003(10^{-2})$. **3.** (*a*) 606,000,000,000,000,000,000,000, (*b*) .00000001, (*c*) 6,240,000,000,000, (*d*) .0000000000000000000000016. **5.** (*a*) 10^{12}, (*b*) 10^5, (*c*) 10^{-9}, (*d*) 10^{-5}. **7.** 602,500,000,000,000,000,000,000. **9.** 5×10^7, or 50,000,000.

CHAPTER 12

Exercise 1, p. 200. **1.** (*a*) .20, (*b*) .32, (*c*) .02, (*d*) .045, (*e*) .875, (*f*) .40, (*g*) .015, (*h*) 1.30, (*i*) 2.05, (*j*) $.16\frac{2}{3}$. **3.** (*a*) 30%, (*b*) 112%, (*c*) 23.4%, (*d*) $8\frac{1}{3}$%, (*e*) 1.1%, (*f*) $4\frac{1}{2}$%, (*g*) 125%, (*h*) $87\frac{1}{2}$%, (*i*) 5.5%, (*j*) .45%.

Exercise 2, p. 202. **1.** (*a*) 9.45, (*b*) 35.55, (*c*) .22, (*d*) 15.6, (*e*) .792, (*f*) 11. **3.** (*a*) 500, (*b*) $133\frac{1}{3}$, (*c*) $66\frac{2}{3}$, (*d*) 180, (*e*) 4800, (*f*) 5. **5.** 72. **7.** 300 pounds. **9.** $102.44. **11.** $828.64 loss.

Exercise 3, p. 203. **1.** (*a*) $8\frac{1}{3}$% increase, (*b*) 17.2% decrease, (*c*) 15.4% increase, (*d*) 14% decrease. **3.** (*a*) $140, (*b*) $80.75, (*c*) 20 cents, (*d*) 55 cents. **5.** $500. **7.** $70 per month. **9.** 150. **11.** 92. **13.** 32%. **15.** $36.92.

Exercise 4, p. 205. **1.** Fourths: 25%, 50%, 75%, 100%; sixths: $16\frac{2}{3}$%, $33\frac{1}{3}$%, 50%, $66\frac{2}{3}$%, $83\frac{1}{3}$%, 100%. **3.** Twelfths: $8\frac{1}{3}$%, $16\frac{2}{3}$%, 25%, $33\frac{1}{3}$%, $41\frac{2}{3}$%, 50%, $58\frac{1}{3}$%, $66\frac{2}{3}$%, 75%, $83\frac{1}{3}$%, $91\frac{2}{3}$, 100%; fifteenths: $6\frac{2}{3}$%, $13\frac{1}{3}$%, 20%, $26\frac{2}{3}$%, $33\frac{1}{3}$%, 40%, $46\frac{2}{3}$%, $53\frac{1}{3}$%, 60%, $66\frac{2}{3}$%, $73\frac{1}{3}$%, 80%, $86\frac{2}{3}$%, $93\frac{1}{3}$%, 100%. **5.** (*a*) $\frac{3}{8}$, (*b*) $\frac{5}{6}$, (*c*) $\frac{1}{12}$, (*d*) $\frac{1}{16}$.

Exercise 5, p. 206. **1.** (*a*) 325%, (*b*) 350%, (*c*) 800%, (*d*) 150%, (*e*) $66\frac{2}{3}$%, (*f*) $62\frac{1}{2}$%, (*g*) 160%, (*h*) $66\frac{2}{3}$%, (*i*) $.66\frac{2}{3}$%, (*j*) .4%, (*k*) $.37\frac{1}{2}$%, (*l*) .1%. **3.** (*a*) $3\frac{4}{5}$, (*b*) $1\frac{3}{4}$, (*c*) 20, (*d*) $\frac{22}{25}$, (*e*) $\frac{1}{200}$, (*f*) $\frac{13}{200}$, (*g*) $\frac{7}{2000}$, (*h*) $\frac{1}{2500}$.

Exercise 6, p. 207. **1.** *b.* **3.** *d.* **5.** *b.* **7.** *b.* **9.** *d.*

Exercise 7, p. 208. **1.** Type 1; 3750. **3.** Type 1; 75 pounds. **5.** Type 2; $11\frac{1}{9}$% cement, $33\frac{1}{3}$% sand, $55\frac{5}{9}$% gravel. **7.** Type 2; 7.1%. **9.** 25. **11.** 1579 eggs. **13.** $16.88. **15.** 230 pounds.

CHAPTER 13

Exercise 1, p. 211. **1.** $23.32. **3.** $633.50. **5.** $128.37. **7.** Both are the same.

Exercise 2, p. 212. **1.** $3.60, 90 cents. **3.** $50.00, $7.50, $57.50. **5.** $390.

Exercise 3, p. 213. **1.** Overhead $15; margin $20. **3.** Margin $25; cost $55. **5.** Margin $33; profit $11. **7.** Profit $15.75. **9.** Selling price $12.88. **11.** Selling price $420; margin per cent $33\frac{1}{3}$%.

Exercise 4, p. 215. **1.** (*a*) 40%, (*b*) 71.4%, (*c*) 29.4%, (*d*) 185.7%, (*e*) 36.4%, (*f*) 150%. **3.** (*a*) 28.6%, (*b*) 41.7%, (*c*) 22.7%, (*d*) 65%, (*e*) $26\frac{2}{3}$%, (*f*) 60%. **5.** (*a*) $16\frac{2}{3}$%, (*b*) 44.4%, (*c*) 28.6%, (*d*) 40%, (*e*) 25.9%, (*f*) $33\frac{1}{3}$%, (*g*) 50%. **7.** (*a*) $57\frac{1}{7}$%, 75%, (*b*) $54\frac{1}{6}$%, $84\frac{8}{13}$%, (*c*) 40%, 150%, (*d*) 78%, $28\frac{8}{39}$%.

Exercise 5, p. 218. **1.** $595.76. **3.** $100,000,000.

Exercise 6, p. 219. **1.** $3.38 **3.** (*a*) 5%, (*a*) 5%, $21\frac{2}{3}$%, 45%, (*b*) 10%, 24%, 36%. **5.** 8.2%. **7.** 38.8%. **9.** 3125 bulbs. **11.** 2000 eggs.

CHAPTER 14

Exercise 1, p. 224. **3.** (*a*) 21, (*b*) 26, (*c*) 23, (*d*) 35, (*e*) 65, (*f*) 128, (*g*) 34, (*h*) 994, (*i*) 890, (*j*) 106, (*k*) 140. **5.** (*a*) 792, (*b*) 9984, (*c*) 39,975, (*d*) 2574, (*e*) 7557, (*f*) 50,237.

Exercise 2, p. 228. **1.** (*d*). **3.** (*b*). **5.** (*a*). **7.** (*b*). **9.** (*a*). **11.** 1.850%. **13.** 37,100 feet. **15.** $5\frac{65}{132}$. **17.** 630 gallons. **19.** 12.8 miles per gallon. **21.** 56.1%, 128%.

CHAPTER 15

Exercise 1, p. 232. **1.** 4. **3.** 5. **5.** 3. **7.** 2. **9.** 3. **11.** 8.25. **13.** .0050. **15.** 3.142. **17.** 10. **19.** 1.7×10^3. **23.** 1.860×10^5. **25.** 1.234×10^{-2}. **27.** 8.000×10^4. **29.** 5.756×10^7.

Exercise 2, p. 236. **1.** 522.94. **3.** 43.41. **5.** 37.74. **7.** 19.4. **9.** 7.05. **11.** .7545. **13.** 8.43×10^4. **15.** 4.84 seconds. **17.** 8.6400×10^4, 11.6 days. **19.** 5.0×10^2 seconds. **23.** 3.141593.

CHAPTER 16

Exercise 2, p. 242. **1.** (*a*) 12 yards, 8 inches, (*b*) 12 hours, 10 minutes, 5 seconds, (*c*) 10 years, 2 months, 20 days, (*d*) 13 tons, 1250 pounds, (*e*) 16 gallons, 3 quarts, (*f*) 24 pounds, 14 ounces.

Exercise 3, p. 243. **1.** (*a*) 15 yards, 1 foot, 4 inches, (*b*) 22 pounds, 3 ounces, (*c*) 55 hours, 12 minutes, (*d*) 31 quarts, 1 pint. **3.** (*a*) 1 foot, 5 inches, (*b*) 3 yards, 2 feet, (*c*) $113\frac{1}{2}$ feet, (*d*) 1280 rods, (*e*) 15,840 feet, (*f*) 29 pints, (*g*) 90 ounces, (*h*) 4 pounds, 14 ounces, (*i*) 4 tons, 400 pounds, (*j*) 922 days (counting 30 days per month) (*k*) 10 yards, 2 feet, 9 inches, (*l*) 3 pounds, 15 ounces, (*m*) 61 gallons, (*n*) 14 minutes, 24 seconds, (*o*) 54 rods, 5 yards, 0 feet, 6 inches, (*p*) 11 rods, 4 yards, 2 feet, 6 inches.

Exercise 4, p. 246. **1.** (*a*) .35 meters, (*b*) .02835 kilogram, (*c*) 160,900 centimeters, (*d*) 100 liters (*e*) 7.5 centimeters, (*f*) .1 liter, (*g*) 25 centimeters, (*h*) 10,000 cubic centimeters. **3.** 929 square centimeters. **5.** 299,274 kilometers. **7.** 8842 meters or 8.842 kilometers. **9.** $617.25. **11.** (*a*) 920 grams, (*b*) 1033 grams, (*c*) 1.360×10^4 grams. **13.** 17.1 pounds. **15.** 1.078 pounds.

CHAPTER 17

Exercise 1, p. 250. **1.** $730.25, $95.25. **3.** (*a*) $7.84, (*b*) $12.20, (*c*) $14.97, (*d*) $2.91, (*e*) $2.17.

Exercise 2, p. 251. **1.** $2.67. **3.** $56. **5.** $3.18.

Exercise 3, p. 253. **1.** $637. **3.** 50 years; no. **5.** November 11.

Exercise 4, p. 254. **1.** $283.02; $16.98. **3.** $4809.52.

Exercise 5, p. 258. **1.** $670.05, $170.05. **3.** $2721.03, $1221.03. **5.** $1442.94, $547.94 **7.** $5499.76. **9.** $43.45; $57.04.

Exercise 6, p. 259. **1.** $394.70. **3.** $217.09. **5.** $217.09, **7.** The first; $4.89.

CHAPTER 18

Exercise 1, p. 263. **1.** $577.50, proceeds, $22.50. **3.** (*a*) $1000.67, (*b*) $30.02, (*c*) $970.65, (*d*) 13.03%, (*e*) 6.19%, (*f*) no. **5.** Interest rate of 4%. **7.** $466.88, $459.88.

Exercise 2, p. 266. **1.** (*a*) $2000, (*b*) $280, (*c*) $95, (*d*) 15.4%. **3.** 13.4%, no. **5.** $i = 24(Rn - B)/[(n + 1)B]$.

Exercise 3, p. 269. **1.** $2437.50, $32, $2469.50. **3.** $7300, $74, $7374. **5.** $3412.50, $36, $3448.50. **7.** $3810, $44.80, $3854.80. **9.** $412.50, $18, $430.50. **11.** $2600, $32, $2568. **13.** $14,625, $132, $14,493. **15.** $2325, $27, $2298. **17.** $4565, $42.90, $4522.10. **19.** $775, $22, $753. **21.** $3149 gain. **23.** $522 loss. **25.** (*a*).

Exercise 4, p. 271. **1.** 4.44%. **3.** 2.94%. **5.** 2.19%. **7.** (*b*).

CHAPTER 19

Exercise 1, p. 275. **1.** 52 inches. **3.** 115 square inches. **5.** 75 cubic inches. **7.** 10,000. **9.** 154.5 feet. **11.** $A = lw$. **13.** $h = 24d$. **15.** $c = p + 5n + 10d$. **17.** $S = 2(LW + WH + LH)$; 432 square inches. **19.** 63, 525. **21.** (*a*) 5°C, (*b*) 15°C, (*c*) $176\frac{1}{3}$°C, (*d*) $426\frac{2}{3}$°C, (*e*) $232\frac{2}{9}$°C, (*f*) 100°C. **23.** (*a*) 283.15°K, (*b*) 200°K, (*c*) 300°K, (*d*) 308.15°K, (*e*) 373.15°K, (*f*) 3.15°K.

Exercise 2, p. 279. **1.** 5. **3.** 150. **5.** 135. **7.** 25. **9.** 60. **11.** 4. **13.** 56. **15.** 450. **17.** Let p = the number of pages, then $p - 72 = 234$; $p = 306$. **19.** Let s = the number of dollars of salary, then $s + 120 = 880$; $s = 760$.

Exercise 3, p. 281. **1.** 9. **3.** 10. **5.** 72. **7.** 1.6. **9.** 24. **11.** 12. **13.** 7. **15.** 40. **17.** 11. **19.** $5\frac{1}{2}$. **21.** $3x + 5 = 7x - 3$; $x = 2$. **23.** Let x = length of the pole in feet, then $x/4 + x/3 + 35 = x$; $x = 84$. **25.** Let x = number of quarters, $3x$ = number of dimes, then $25(x) + 10(3x) = 220$; $x = 4$. Four quarters and twelve dimes. **27.** $0.85N = 34$; $N = 34 \div 0.85 = 40$.

Exercise 4, p. 285. **1.** 5, 2, 2, −8, −4, 0, 13. **3.** 1, 8, −6, 2, −8, −16, 1. **5.** (*a*) $10x - 7$, (*b*) $-y - 18$, (*c*) $-z - 10w - 7x$. **7.** (*a*) $x = 2$, (*b*) $x = 3$. **9.** $1\frac{1}{4}$, $-6\frac{2}{3}$, $-2\frac{7}{15}$, $-4\frac{1}{8}$, $-14\frac{1}{8}$, $-19\frac{7}{20}$, $-8\frac{1}{24}$.

Exercise 5, p. 288. **1.** 6, −35, 3, 25. **3.** −3, −1, 5, $-\frac{1}{2}$, 5. **5.** $-5x^2 + 15x$, $-6x + 4y$, $-14x + 28y$, $20y^2 + 15xy$.

Exercise 6, p. 289. **1.** $x = 2$. **3.** $x = -30$. **5.** $x = 15$. **7.** $x = 9$. **9.** $x = 17$. **11.** $x = 24$. **13.** Seven dimes. **15.** 24. **17.** $14\frac{1}{2}$, $18\frac{1}{2}$. **19.** seven quarters, eleven dimes. **21.** 12 × 27 feet.

Exercise 7, p. 291. **1.** 10. **3.** 10. **5.** −22. **7.** $9\frac{1}{2}$. **9.** 3. **11.** \$435. **13.** 24 feet. **15.** 42 inches. **17.** 65, 13. **19.** \$109.29.

Exercise 8, p. 295. **1.** (*a*) Yes, yes, (*b*) No, no.

3.

+	0	1
0	0	1
1	1	0

×	0	1
0	0	0
1	0	1

5.

+	0	1	2	3
0	0	1	2	3
1	1	2	3	0
2	2	3	0	1
3	3	0	1	2

×	0	1	2	3
0	0	0	0	0
1	0	1	2	3
2	0	2	0	2
3	0	3	2	1

7. (*a*) *A*, *B*, (*b*) yes, (*c*) yes, (*d*) yes, (*e*) yes, *C*, *E*, (*f*) no, yes, no, (*g*) yes, no, (*h*) no.

Exercise 9, p. 298. **1.** (*a*) (7, 10), (*b*) (26, 44), (*c*) negative, since $44 > 26$. **3.** (202, 208) or (0, 6). **5.** (*a*) $(a, 0) + (b, 0) = (a + b, 0) = (c, 0)$, (*b*) $(0, b) + (0, c) = (0, b + c) = (0, d)$, (*c*) if $a > b$, then $(0, a) + (b, 0) = (b, a)$, with (b, a) negative, if $b > a$ then $(0, a) + (b, 0) = (b, a)$, with (b, a) positive.

Exercise 10, p. 300. **1.** (*a*) (22, 15), (*b*) (8, 15), (*c*) (96, 8) or (12, 1). **3.** Check. **5.** x = (3, 1). **7.** (*a*) (3, 9), (−1, −3), (5, 15), (*b*) (2, −5), (−4, 10), (−10, 25), (*c*) (1, 5), (4, 20), (−1, −5), (*d*) (0, 4), (0, −1), (0, 20). **9.** (*d*) and (*i*); (*g*) and (*h*).

CHAPTER 20

Exercise 1, p. 302. **1.** 76. **3.** 86. **5.** 35. **7.** 30. **9.** 75.

Exercise 2, p. 308. **1.** (*a*) 25, (*b*) 73, (*c*) 78.69, (*d*) 29.15. **3.** (*a*) 6.481, (*b*) 17.61, (*c*) 39.80, (*d*) 197.8.

Exercise 3, p. 310. **1.** (*a*) 28.2, (*b*) 822.2. **3.** 841.5 rods. **5.** 15.6 centimeters. **7.** 10.9 feet. **9.** 15 inches, 120 square inches. **11.** $h = s\sqrt{3}/2$, $A = s^2\sqrt{3}/4$. **13.** $h = 5\sqrt{3} = 8.66$ inches, $A = 25\sqrt{3} = 43.3$ square inches. **15.** 95.4 feet.

CHAPTER 21

Exercise 1, p. 315. **1.** (*a*) 45°, (*b*) 135°, (*c*) 213°, (*d*) 341°, (*e*) 90°, (*f*) 270°. **3.** The sum of two sides of a triangle is greater than the third side.

Exercise 2, p. 317. **1.** $\angle Q$, $\angle P$, $\angle PQR$, $\angle QPR$, $\angle PRQ$, $\angle PRS$, $\angle QRS$. **3.** Construction. **5.** (*a*) One, (*b*) one, (*c*) three, (*d*) two, (*e*) two.

Exercise 3, p. 322. **1.** Construction. **3.** (*a*) Construction, (*b*) the medians of a triangle intersect in a point $\frac{2}{3}$ of the distance from a vertex to the mid-point of the opposite side. **5.** Construction. **7.** Construction.

Exercise 4, p. 326. **1.** s.a.s. = s.a.s. **3.** Use s.a.s. = s.a.s. and show that corresponding parts of congruent triangles are equal. **5.** (*a*) Equilateral triangle, (*b*) 60°, (*c*) 6, (*d*) construction. **7.** 60 feet. **9.** 15. **11.** Use a.s.a. = a.s.a.

Exercise 5, p. 332. **1.** (*a*) 30, (*b*) 45, (*c*) 14, (*d*) 160, (*e*) 36, (*f*) 20, (*g*) 616, (*h*) 30.68 (all square units). **3.** 0.86 square centimeter. **5.** By 4. **7.** 1240 square feet more. **9.** $459.46. **11.** Use a tape measure to find the diameter of a large circular disk and use the same tape to measure the circumference of the disk; divide the length of the diameter into the length of the circumference.

Exercise 6, p. 341. **1.** (*a*) $V + F = E + 2$, $5 + 6 = 9 + 2$, (*b*) $4 + 4 = 6 + 2$, (*c*) $10 + 7 = 15 + 2$, (*d*) $7 + 7 = 12 + 2$, (*e*) $8 + 6 = 12 + 2$. **3.** $6\frac{3}{4}$ inches. **5.** 15 inches, 25 inches, 30 inches. **7.** 15 inches. **9.** 3054 cubic centimeters, 1018 square centimeters. **11.** Yes. **13.** 52.4%, no. **15.** 3.14 cubic inches.

Index

TABLES